Engineering

The brightness of the future depends upon the diligence and imagination with which the engineering student pursues his studies today. Opportunities for the engineering graduate are unlimited since the expanding frontiers of knowledge permit investigation of an ever-increasing array of discoveries.

GEORGE C. BEAKLEY
Professor of Engineering
Arizona State University

H. W. LEACH
Instrumentation Engineer
Bell Helicopter Company

Engineering

*an introduction to a
creative profession*

SECOND EDITION

The Macmillan Company *New York*

Collier-Macmillan Limited London

Preface

Today's world is a world of change, challenge, and opportunity. Never before have so many compelling technological problems occupied positions of prominence in man's system of values. The engineer's role in this environment is more important than ever before in history, and the student who chooses engineering as a career should realize that, perhaps more than any other, his profession will shape the destiny of civilizations yet unborn. Challenge and opportunity? Yes . . . but not without a consciousness for and a realization of the accompanying moral and ethical responsibilities that should accompany the emergence of new processes, designs, and systems. Recognizing the importance of an early commitment toward these ends, this work has been prepared as an informational and motivational instrument for the use of those who are interested in preparing themselves today for the solution of tomorrow's problems.

The first edition of this textbook was experimental in the sense that it was multipurpose in scope, rather than singular in purpose, as has been the case traditionally with many other introductory engineering textbooks. Its nine printings over a brief span of time attest to its popularity for use in (*a*) informational courses that introduce the student to the profession of engineering, (*b*) engineering problems and analysis courses that give the student some practice in engineering problem solving, and (*c*) introduction to engineering design courses that give the student a sense of personal involvement in undertaking real engineering tasks. Some teachers have preferred to organize courses that drew material from each of these areas.

Recognizing the enthusiastic adopter response to the first edition, the authors have attempted to retain those qualities of the text most often praised and to update and improve it throughout. They are most appreciative of the suggestions received from the more than 200 schools who used the first edition, and they are very desirous of learning the opinions of those who read this new edition—both students and faculty—concerning its utility and serviceability in meeting the needs for which it has been written. Improvements that are suggested will be incorporated in later editions.

In order to give the student an understanding of the types of problems that are likely to be encountered in the practice of engineering, a large number of varied situations are described in problems throughout the book. Some of the problems are straightforward, and appropriate data are given to permit a unique solution. In other problems, data are given in general terms, sometimes with insufficient data so that the student must add information, and sometimes with an overabundance of data from which the student must select what he needs. In all cases, the problems are designed to introduce the student to the realm of engineering study, to offer him work with engineering concepts, and to confront him with situations in which decisions must be made where a number of choices exist.

The problem-solving method introduced in the authors' previous textbooks has been expanded to include more of the creative phases of engineering. It is not enough just to manipulate numbers in engineering work; the engineer must be able to see applications of scientific principles, to develop designs that are based upon abstract principles, and to assume the lead in formulating innovative solutions to unfamiliar problems. Every effort is made here to motivate the student to think imaginatively and constructively, and also to present material that will provide the best introduction to a career in engineering or technology.

The format of this text is such that the student can record points of emphasis and certain class notes and questions directly as they occur without the use of extra notepaper. Marking pens may be used for highlighting sentences or phrases, and the use of colored ink for underlining is recommended. For the student to get the most out of the text he should "live in it." If he does, the book will have a "lived-in" appearance.

For additional classroom material, a workbook of problems is available (on request directly from the authors) to supplement the problems given in the text. These problems require a minimum of layout work so that more time is available to the student for practice in problem analysis and computation.

In preparing this book the authors have been aided not only by reviews and criticisms of previous editions but also by comments and suggestions from numerous engineering professors and practicing engineers and technologists in industry throughout the United States. The professional colleagues of the authors have been most influential in giving this book a unique blend of the academic and the industrial viewpoints. In particular, the authors wish to thank Professors Roy W. Dike, Michael J. Nielsen, and Ernest G. Chilton for their assistance in the preparation of Chapters 14, 15, 16, 17, and 18. William J. Martins prepared much of the material in Chapter 13, and George C. Beakley III prepared the material in Chapter 15 relating to the planning of engineering projects. The authors gratefully acknowledge these contributions as well as those of the many organizations who have supplied illustrative materials for inclusion in the text.

The cover design, an electronic-computer-produced artform, was used originally for the first edition. It is the work of Donald Robbins and Leigh Hendricks of the Sandia Corporation, Albuquerque, New Mexico, who have made it available again for this specific use. The typing and proofreading of the manuscript were masterfully accomplished by Esther F. Taylor, and the art work was most ably drawn by David C. Gironda. To each we express our appreciation.

To the many others who have given the authors the benefit of their experience by making recommendations as to format and content of this new second edition, we wish to express our sincere gratitude.

G. C. B.
H. W. L.

Acknowledgments

Frontispiece   National Aeronautics and Space Administration
Part I headpiece   *The Journal of Industrial Engineering*
Illustration 1-1   Maddox and Hopkins
Illustration 1-2   W. S. Dickey Clay Manufacturing Company
Illustration 1-3   Maddox and Hopkins
Illustration 1-4   Ewing Galloway
Illustration 1-5   Maddox and Hopkins
Illustration 1-6   Maddox and Hopkins
Illustration 1-7   Southern Pacific Company
Illustration 1-8   General Electric *Forum*
Illustration 1-9   Lockheed Missiles and Space Company
Illustration 2-1   H. Armstrong Roberts
Illustration 2-2   Floyd A. Craig, Christian Life Commission, Southern Baptist Convention
Illustration 2-3   Planned Parenthood–World Population
Illustration 2-4   Monsanto Company
Illustration 2-5   Ambassador College
Illustration 2-6   Republic Steel Corporation
Illustration 2-7   Pennsylvania State Department of Health
Illustration 2-8   Union Electric Company
Illustration 2-9   U. S. Department of Housing and Urban Development
Illustration 2-10   Merrill, Lynch, Pierce, Fenner & Smith, Inc.
Illustration 2-11   Bethlehem Steel Corporation
Illustration 2-12   U. S. Department of Housing and Urban Development

Illustration 2-13   U. S. Department of Agriculture
Illustration 2-14   Floyd A. Craig, Christian Life Commission, Southern Baptist Convention
Illustration 2-15   Bethlehem Steel Corporation
Illustration 2-16   Shell Oil Company
Illustration 2-17   The Mitre Corporation
Illustration 2-18   Hewlett-Packard
Illustration 2-19   Hewlett-Packard
Figure 2-3   L. P. Gaucher
Illustration 2-20   General Electric Company
Figure 2-4   Institute of Traffic Engineers
Illustration 2-21   Shell Oil Company
Illustration 2-22   Planned Parenthood–World Population
Illustration 2-23   General Electric Company
Illustration 2-24   Parsons, Brinckerhoff, Quade & Douglas; Bay Area Rapid Transit District; The American Society of Civil Engineers
Illustration 2-25   Institute of Traffic Engineers
Illustration 2-26   Sylvania Electric Products, Inc.
Illustration 2-27   Thomson-CSF
Illustration 2-28   *Time* Publishing Services
Illustration 3-1   National Aeronautics and Space Administration
Illustration 3-2   Eastman Kodak Company
Illustration 3-3   Eastman Kodak Company
Illustration 3-4   Bell Telephone Laboratories
Illustration 4-1   E. I. du Pont de Nemours & Co., Inc.
Illustration 4-2   General Dynamics, Convair Division
Illustration 4-3   Sperry Gyroscope Company
Illustration 4-4   E. I. du Pont de Nemours & Co., Inc.

Contents

Engineering

Part One

Engineering —a creative profession

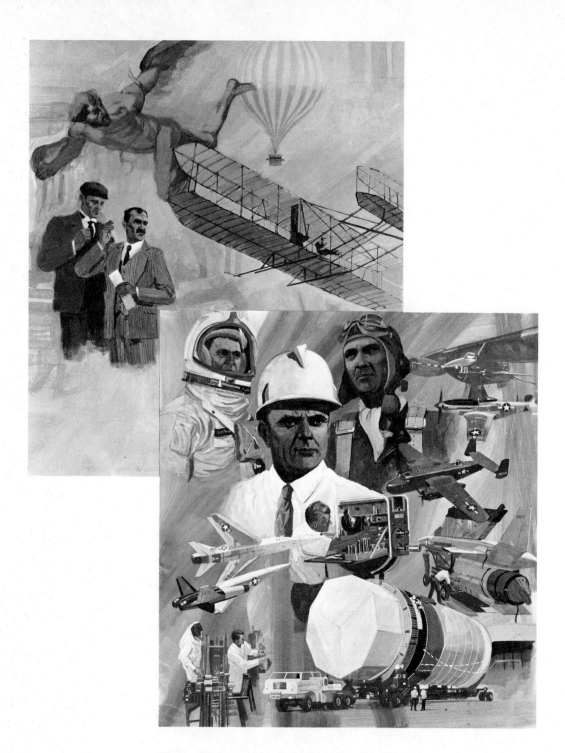

The engineer of tomorrow must rise to challenges in the future with the same degree of competence as the engineer of today has done in meeting the challenge of space exploration.

1

Engineering— the story of man's developing civilization

When did engineering begin? Who were the first engineers? What were the objectives of work by the early engineers? Answers to these questions and others concerning the beginning of engineering appear in the fragments of historical information available to us. In fact the beginnings of civilization and the beginnings of engineering are coincident. As early man emerged from caves to make homes in communities, he adapted rocks and sticks as tools to aid him. Simple as these items may seem to us today, their useful employment suggests that the creative ideas which emerged in the minds of early man were developed into useful products to serve the recognized needs of the day. Some served as tools in the struggle for existence of an individual or group, and others were used for protection against wild animals or warlike neighbors. Early engineering was therefore principally either civil or military.

Down through the ages, the engineer has been in the forefront as a maker of history. His material accomplishments have had as much impact on world history as any political, economic, or social development. Sometimes his accomplishments have stemmed from the pressures of need from evolving civilizations. At other times his abilities to produce and meet needs have led the way for civilizations to advance. In general, engineers do the things required to serve the needs of the people and their culture.

Basically, the role of the engineer has not changed through the centuries. His job is to take knowledge and make practical use of it. He converts scientific theory into useful application, and in so doing, he provides for man's material needs and well being. From era to era, only the objectives that he has pursued, the techniques of solution that he has used, and the tools of analysis at his disposal have changed.

It is helpful to review the past to gain insight to the driving forces of science and to learn of the men who developed and applied these principles. A review also will reveal certain facts concerning the discovery and use of fundamental scientific principles. Primarily, science builds its store of knowledge on facts which, once determined, are available from then on for further discovery. This principle is in contrast to the arts, since, for example, the ability of one person to produce a beautiful painting does not make available to others his skills in producing paintings.

Outstanding characteristics of engineers through the centuries have been a willingness to work and an intellectual curiosity about the behavior of things. Their queries about "Why?," "How?," "With what?," and "At what cost?" have all served to stimulate an effort to find desirable answers to many types of technological problems.

Another characteristic associated with engineers is the ability to "see ahead." The engineer must have a fertile imagination, must be creative, and must be ready to accept new ideas. Whether an engineer lived at the time of construction of the pyramids or has only recently graduated in nuclear engineering, these characteristics have been an important part of his intellectual makeup.

The following sections present a brief picture of the development of engineering since the dawn of history and outline the place that the engineer has held in various civilizations.

The beginnings of engineering: 6000 B.C.—3000 B.C.

The beginning of engineering probably occurred in Asia Minor or Africa some 8000 years ago. About this time, man began to cultivate plants, domesticate animals, and build permanent houses in community groups. With the change from a nomadic life came requirements for increased food production. Among the first major engineering projects were irrigation systems to promote crop growing. Increased food production permitted time for men to engage in other activities. Some became rulers, some priests, and many became artisans, whom we may call the first engineers.

Early achievements in this era included methods of producing fire at will, melting certain rocklike materials to produce copper and bronze tools, invention of the wheel and axle, development of a system of symbols for written communication, origination of a system of mathematics, and construction of irrigation works.

Early records are so fragmentary that only approximate dates can be given for any specific discovery, but evidence of the impact of early engineering achievements is readily discernible. For example, in setting up stable community life in which land was owned, men had to provide both for irrigation and for accurate location and maintenance of boundaries. This necessity stimulated the development of surveying and of mathematics. The moving of earth to make canals and dams required computations, and to complete the work the efforts of many men had to be organized and directed. As a result, a system of supervisors, foremen, and workers was established that formed the beginnings of a class society.

In this society, craftsmen became a distinct group producing useful items such as pottery, tools, and ornaments that were desired by others. As a result, trade and commerce were stimulated and roads were improved. Some 5000 years ago man first used the wheel and axle to make two-wheeled carts drawn by animals.

In order to record the growing accumulation of knowledge about mathematics and engineering, the early engineer needed a system of writing and some type of writing material. In the Mesopotamian region, soft clay was used on which cuneiform characters were incised. When baked, the clay tile material was used for permanent documents, some of which are legible even today (see Illustration 1-1). In the Nile Valley, a paperlike material called *papyrus* was made from the inner fibers of a reed. In other parts of Asia Minor, treated skins of animals were used to form parchment. Occasionally, slabs of stone or wood were used as writing materials. The type of

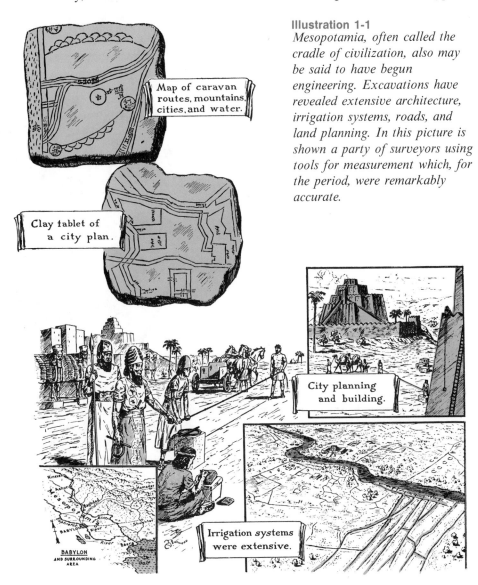

Illustration 1-1
Mesopotamia, often called the cradle of civilization, also may be said to have begun engineering. Excavations have revealed extensive architecture, irrigation systems, roads, and land planning. In this picture is shown a party of surveyors using tools for measurement which, for the period, were remarkably accurate.

Map of caravan routes, mountains, cities, and water.

Clay tablet of a city plan.

City planning and building.

Irrigation systems were extensive.

Mesopotamia, often called the "Cradle of civilization," could also be said to have nurtured engineering in its infancy. Clay tablets, such as the ones shown on this page, have been unearthed which show city plans, irrigation, water supply systems, and what appear to be road maps. Although no engineering tools have been discovered among the remains of ancient Mesopotamia, the evidence unearthed of their remarkable architectural construction indicates that they used measuring tools, which, even though primitive, aided in producing engineering of a high degree for this period. Their cities, with their water supply, irrigation systems, and road networks, were among the wonders of the ancient world.

Many outstanding contributions of mathematics were made by the Mesopotamians. It has been proven that they had knowledge of the sexagesimal system, in which they divided the circle into 360 degrees, the hour into 60 minutes and the minute into 60 seconds.

Illustration 1-2

Ancient builders employed engineering principles in the construction of their structures. Clay plumb bobs, such as the one pictured here being used by Babylonian builders, have been unearthed recently by archeologists.

writing that developed was strongly influenced by the writing material available. For example, the incised characters in soft clay differed significantly from the brush strokes used in writing on papyrus.

In engineering work, a source of energy is necessary. This requirement led to the enslavement and use of numbers of humans as primary sources of energy. The construction of all early engineering works, whether Oriental, Mediterranean, or American Indian, were accomplished principally by human labor. It was not until near the end of the period of history known as the Middle Ages that mechanical sources of power were developed.

Engineering in early civilizations: 3000 B.C.—600 B.C.

After about 3000 B.C., enough records were made on clay tablets, on papyrus and parchment, on pottery, and as inscriptions on monuments and temples to provide us with information about ancient civilization. These records show that urban civilizations existed in Egypt, Mesopotamia, and the Indus Valley and that a class society of craftsmen, merchants, soldiers, and government officials was a definite part of that civilization.

In Mesopotamia, clay tablets have been uncovered which show that Babylonian engineers were familiar with basic arithmetic and algebra. From these writings we know that they routinely computed areas and volumes of land excavations. Their number system, based on 60 instead of 10, has been handed down through the centuries to us in our measures of time and angle. Their buildings were constructed principally of baked brick. Primitive arches were used in some of their early hydraulic works. Bridges were built with stone piers carrying wooden stringers for the roadway. Some roads were surfaced with a naturally occurring asphalt, a construction method not used again until the nineteenth century.

It was in Egypt that some of the world's most remarkable engineering was performed (see Illustration 1-3). Beginning about 3000 B.C. and lasting for about 100 years, the Pyramid Age flourished in Egypt. The first pyramids were mounds covered with stone, but the techniques progressed rapidly until the Great Pyramid was begun about 2900 B.C. Stones for the structures were cut by workmen laboriously chipping channels in the native rock, using a ball made of a harder rock as a tool. By this method, blocks weighing 15 tons or more were cut for use in building. The Egyptian engineers apparently used only the lever, the inclined plane, the wedge, and the wheel in their construction efforts (see Illustration 1-4).

Although early construction tools were primitive, the actual structures, even by today's standards, are outstanding examples of engineering skill in measurement and layout. For example, the base of the Great Pyramid is square within about 1 inch in a distance of 756 feet, and its angles are in error by only a few minutes despite the fact that the structure was built on a sloping rocky ledge.

The Egyptian engineers and architects held a high place in the Pharaoh's court. Imhotep, a designer of one of the large pyramids, was so revered for his wisdom and ability that he was included as one of the Egyptian gods after his death. Not only were the Egyptian engineers skilled builders, they were also skilled in land measurement. Annual overflows of the Nile River obliterated many property lines and a resurvey of the valley was frequently necessary. Using geometry and primitive measuring equipment, they restored markers for land boundaries after the floods receded.

The Egyptians also were skilled in irrigation work. Using a system of dikes and canals, they reclaimed a considerable area of desert. An ancient engineering contract to build a system of dikes about 50 miles long has recently been discovered.

Although the skill and ingenuity of the Egyptian engineers were outstanding, the culture lasted only a relatively short time. Reasons which may account for the failure to maintain leadership are many, but most important was the lack of pressure to continue development. Once the engineers formed the ruling class, little influence could be brought to bear to cause them to continue their creative efforts. Since living conditions were favorable after an agricultural system was established, little additional engineering was required. The lack of urgency to do better finally stifled most of the creativity of the engineers and the civilization fell into decay.

Science of the Greeks and Romans: 600 B.C.—A.D. 400

The history of engineering in Greece had its origins in Egypt and the East. With the decline of the Egyptian civilization, the center of learning shifted to the island of Crete and then about 1400 B.C. to the ancient city of Mycenae in Greece.

Illustration 1-3

In Egypt the science of measurement and construction developed rapidly. The pyramids are engineering marvels both in design and construction. Papyrus scrolls show that the Egyptians had knowledge of the triangle and were able to compute areas and volumes.

Resetting boundaries after the Nile floods.

Early geometric application.

In ancient Egypt warfare and strife delayed the development of engineering; however, with the unification of Upper and Lower Egypt, the science of measurement and construction made rapid progress. Buildings, city planning, and irrigation systems show evidence of this development. Good judgment and reasonable engineering design resulted in sound and durable structures. The Pyramids are engineering marvels both in design and construction.

That the Egyptians advanced mathematics is attested to by papyrus scrolls, dating back to 1500 B.C., which show that the Egyptians had knowledge of the triangle and were able to compute areas and volumes. They also had a device to obtain the azimuth from the stars.

The annual floods of the Nile afforded ample practice in measurement surveying. This may well have been the first example of the importance of resurveys. The rope used as a measure was first soaked in water, dried, and then coated heavily with wax to ensure constant length. Probably some crude surveying instruments were devised, but none have been found.

Illustration 1-4
*The pyramids of Egypt exemplify man's desire to create and build enduring
monuments.*

To the engineers of Mycenae were passed not only the scientific discoveries of
the Egyptians but also a knowledge of structural building materials and a language
that formed the basis of the early Greek language. These engineers subsequently
developed the corbeled arch and made wide use of irrigation systems.

From the Mycenaean engineers, the Greeks of Athens and Sparta borrowed many
of their developments. In fact, the engineers of this period were better known for
the intensive development of borrowed ideas than for creativity and invention. Their
water system, for example, modeled after Egyptian irrigation systems, showed
outstanding skill in the use of labor and materials, and these Greeks established
technical procedures that have endured for centuries (see Illustration 1-5).

Greece was famous for its outstanding philosophers. Significant contributions
were made by men such as Plato, Aristotle, and Archimedes. In the realm of abstract
thought, they perhaps have never been equaled, but at that time extensive use of
their ideas was retarded because of the belief that verification and experimentation,
which required manual labor, were fit only for slaves. Of all the contributions of
the Greeks to the realm of science, perhaps the greatest was the discovery that nature
has general laws of behavior which can be described with words.

The best engineers of antiquity were the Romans. Within a century after the
death of Alexander, Rome had conquered many of the eastern Mediterranean
countries, including Greece. Within two more centuries Rome had dominion over

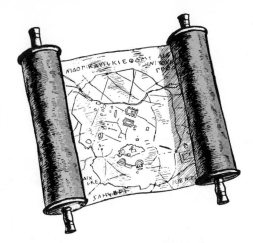

The Greeks constructed many buildings of unusual beauty which show a high degree of engineering skill and architectural design. Their cities had municipal water supplies that required dams and aqueducts to bring water from the mountains. This picture shows a builder laying out a building foundation, using a divided circle, a plumb bob, and a knotted rope.

Hydraulics provide public water

Aqueducts, tunnels and highways

The outstanding progress made by the Ancient Grecians in architecture and mathematics and their contribution to the advancement of engineering demand our admiration.

Aristotle contended that the world was a spheroid. He stated that observations of the various stars showed the circumference of the earth to be about 400,000 *stadia* (4600 miles).

Erathosthenes of Cyrene observed that the sun's rays, when perpendicular to a well at Alexandria, cast a shadow equal to one fiftieth of a circle at Syene (Aswan) 500 miles away. Thus he established that the circumference of the earth was 50 times 500 miles or 25,000 miles.

The Greeks constructed many buildings and structures of large size, which show engineering skill and excellent architectural design. One tunnel, which was built to bring water to Athens, measured 8 feet by 8 feet and was 4200 feet in length. The construction of such a tunnel necessitated extremely accurate alignment both on the surface and underground.

most of the known civilized areas of Europe, Africa, and the Middle East. Roman engineers liberally borrowed scientific and engineering knowledge from the conquered countries for use in warfare and in their public works. Although in many instances they lacked originality of thought, Roman engineers were superior in the application of techniques (see Illustration 1-6).

From experience Rome had learned the necessity for establishing and maintaining a system of communications to hold together the great empire. Thus Roman roads became models of engineering skills. By first preparing a deep subbase and then a compact base, the Romans advanced the technique of road construction so far that some Roman roads are still in use today. At the peak of Roman sovereignty, the network of roads comprised over 180,000 miles stretching from the Euphrates Valley to Great Britain.

In addition, Roman engineers were famous for the construction of aqueducts and bridges. Using stone blocks in the constructing of arches, they exhibited unusual skill. An outstanding example of this construction is the famous Pont du Gard near Nîmes, France, which is 150 feet high and over 900 feet long. It carries both an aqueduct and a roadway.

By the time of the Christian era, iron refining had developed to the extent that iron was being used for small tools and weapons. However, the smelting process was so inefficient that over half of the metallic iron was lost in the slag. Except in the realm of medicine, no interest was being shown in any phase of chemistry.

Despite their outstanding employment of construction and management techniques, the Roman engineers seemed to lack the creative spark and imagination necessary to provide the improved scientific processes required to keep pace with the expanding demands of a far-flung empire. The Romans excelled in law and civil administration but were never able to bring distant colonies fully into the empire. Finally, discontent and disorganization within the empire led to the fall of Rome to a far less cultured invader.

Engineering in the middle ages: fifth to sixteenth centuries

After the fall of Rome, scientific knowledge was dispersed among small groups, principally under the control of religious orders. In the East, an awakening of technology began among the Arabs but little organized effort was made to carry out any scientific work. Rather, it was a period in which isolated individuals made new discoveries or rediscovered earlier known scientific facts.

It was during this time that the name *engineer* first was used. Historical writings of about A.D. 200 tell of an *ingenium*, an invention, which was a sort of battering ram used in attacks on walled defenses. Some thousand years later, we find that an *ingeniator* was the man who operated such a device of war—the beginning of our modern title, *engineer.*

Several technical advances were made late in this period. One important discovery involved the use of charcoal and a suitable air blast for the efficient smelting of iron. Another advance was made when the Arabs began to trade with China and a process of making paper was secured from the Chinese. Within a few years the Arabs had established a paper mill and were making paper in large quantities. With the advent of paper, communication of ideas began to be reestablished. Also in

Illustration 1-6

The rise of the Roman Empire was attributed to the application of engineering principles to military tactics. This picture shows a construction party as they build a section of the famous Roman highways. Notice the heavy foundations which exist to this day.

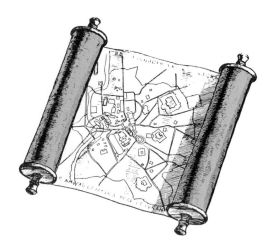

Scientific approach to navigational problems.

Piers and arches, a product of geometry

ROME
AND PART OF THE ROMAN EMPIRE AT ITS HEIGHT

The Romans excelled in the building of aqueducts. Many of these carried water for great distances with perfect grade and alignment. The key design in this type of construction was the arch, which was also used in bridges, tunnels, buildings, and other construction.

Evidence of the Romans' knowledge and understanding of basic geometric principles is further shown by their river and harbor construction and the scientific approach to navigational problems.

Sanitary systems, paved roads, magnificent public buildings, water supply systems, and other public works still in evidence today stand as monuments to the Roman development of engineering as a key to the raising of the standard of living.

The rise of the Roman Empire was attributable to the application of engineering principles applied to military tactics. The invincibility of the Roman legions was the result not only of the valor of the fighting men but also, and perhaps more strongly, to the genius of the Roman military engineers.

Arabia, the sciences of chemistry and optics began to develop. Sugar refining, soap making, and perfume distilling became a part of the culture. The development of a method of making gun powder, probably first learned from China about the fourteenth century, also had rapid and far-reaching results.

After centuries of inaction, the exploration of far-away places began again, aided greatly by the development of a better compass. With the discovery of other cultures and the uniting of ideas, there gradually emerged a reawakening of scientific thought.

With the growth of Christianity, an aversion arose to the widespread use of slaves as primary sources of power. This led to the development of water wheels and wind mills and to a wider use of animals, particularly horses, as power sources.

About 1454, Gutenberg, using movable type, produced the first books printed on paper. This meant that the knowledge of the ages, which previously had been recorded laboriously by hand, now could be disseminated widely and in great quantities. Knowledge which formerly was available only to a few, now was spread to scholars everywhere. Thus the invention of paper and the development of printing served as fitting climaxes to the Middle Ages.

Seldom has the world been blessed with a genius such as that of Leonardo da Vinci (1452–1519). Although still acclaimed today as one of the greatest of all artists, his efforts as an engineer, inventor, and architect are even more impressive. Long after his death his designs of a steam engine, machine guns, a camera, conical shells, a submarine, and a helicopter have been proven to be workable.

Galileo (1564–1642) was also a man of great versatility. He was an excellent writer, artist, and musician, and he is also considered one of the foremost scientists of that period. One of his greatest contributions was his formulation of what he considered to be the scientific method of gaining knowledge.

The revival of science: seventeenth and eighteenth centuries

Following the invention of printing, the self-centered medieval world changed rapidly. At first, the efforts to present discoveries of Nature's laws met with opposition and in some cases even hostility. Slowly, however, freedom of thought was permitted and a new concept of *testing to evaluate a hypothesis* replaced the early method of establishing a principle solely by argument.

Four men in this period made discoveries and formulated laws which have proved to be of great value to engineering. They were Boyle, who formulated a law relating pressures and volumes of gases; Huygens, who investigated the effects of gravitational pull; Hooke, who experimented with the elastic properties of materials; and Newton, who is famous for his three laws of motion. All of the early experimenters were hampered by a lack of a concise vocabulary to express their ideas. Because of this many of the principles were expressed in a maze of wordy statements.

During this period, significant advancements were made in communication and transportation. Canals and locks were built for inland water travel and docks and harbors were improved for ocean commerce. Advances in ship design and improved methods of navigation permitted a wide spreading of knowledge that formerly had been isolated in certain places.

The search for power sources to replace human labor continued. Water power and wind power were prime sources, but animals began to be used more and more. About this time, the first attempts to produce a steam engine were made by Papin and Newcomen. Although these early engines were very inefficient, they did mark the beginning of power from heat engines.

An important industry was made possible in this period by the development of spinning and weaving machinery by such men as Jurgen, Hargreaves, Crampton, and Arkwright. This period also marked a general awakening of science after the Dark Ages. Individual discoveries, although usually isolated, found their way into useful products within a short period of time because of the development of printing and the improvements in communication.

The basic discoveries in this era were made by men who were able to reject old, erroneous concepts and search for principles that were more nearly in accord with Nature's behavior. Engineers in any age must be equally discerning if their civilization is to advance.

Beginnings of modern science: nineteenth century

Early in the nineteenth century, two developments provided an impetus for further technological discoveries. The two developments were the introduction of a method, developed by Henry Cort, of refining iron and the invention of an efficient steam engine by James Watt. These developments provided a source of iron for machinery and power plants to operate the machinery.

As transportation systems began to develop, both by water and by land, a network of railroads and highways was built to tie together the major cities in Europe and in the United States (see Illustration 1-7).

In this period, the awakening of science and engineering truly had begun. Now, although people were slow to accept new ideas, knowledge was not rejected as it had been in earlier centuries. Colleges began to teach more and more courses in science and engineering, and it was here that the fuse was lighted for an explosion of discoveries in the twentieth century.

One of the most important reasons for the significant development of technology in this period was the increasingly close cooperation between science and engineering. It began to become more and more evident that discoveries by research scientists could be used to develop new articles for commerce. Industry soon began to realize that money spent for research and development eventually returned many times its value.

Twentieth century technology

As the twentieth century came into being, a number of inventions emerged that were destined to have far-reaching effects on our civilization. The automobile began to be more widely used as better roads were made available. The inventions of Edison (Illustration 1-8) and DeForest of electrical equipment and electron tubes started

Illustration 1-7

This remarkable picture, taken in 1877 when the high Secrettown trestle in the Sierra Nevada mountains of California was being filled in with dirt by the Central Pacific, now the Southern Pacific Railway, shows the meager tools with which the builders had to work in blasting a trail over and through the rugged mountains for the rails of the first transcontinental railroad. In those days there were none of the power implements that are so common to modern construction. Scrapers were not even used in the grading. Dynamite had been invented but was not in general use during the years the railroad was being built in 1863-69. Chinese "coolies" did the work with pick and shovel, one-horse dump carts, wheel barrows, and back power. At times it was necessary to lower the workmen over cliffs in baskets to ledges where they could level off a grade in the mountainside.

Illustration 1-8

Nations the world over acknowledge their indebtedness to Thomas Alva Edison, inventor, and Charles Proteus Steinmetz, electrical engineer, for their significant inventions relating to electricity.

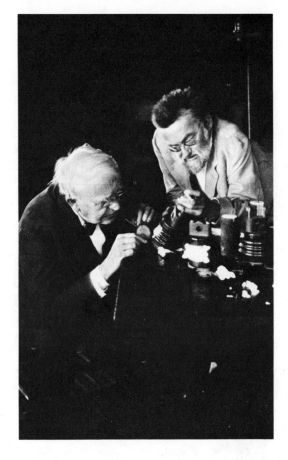

the wide-spread use of power systems and communication networks. Following the demonstrations by the Wright brothers that man could build a machine that would fly, aircraft of many types developed rapidly.

These inventions, typical of many basic discoveries that were made early in the century, exemplify the spirit of progress of this period. So fast has been the pace of discovery, with one coming on the heels of another, that it is difficult to evaluate properly their relative importance, although we certainly can realize their impact on our way of life.

Until late in the nineteenth century, engineering as an applied science was divided into two principal groups, civil and military. Mining and metallurgy was the first group to be recognized as a separate branch and the American Institute of Mining and Metallurgical Engineers was founded in 1871. In 1880 the American Society of Mechanical Engineers was founded, and in 1884 the American Institute of Electrical Engineers (now the Institute of Electrical and Electronics Engineers) was founded. In 1908 the American Institute of Chemical Engineers was founded and since then a number of other branch societies have been founded with objectives peculiar to specialized fields of engineering endeavor.

An outstanding characteristic of this century is the increased use of power. In 1940 it was estimated that the total energy generated in the United States would be the equivalent in "muscle-power energy" of 153 slaves working for every American man, woman, and child in the country. Today a similar calculation would show that about 500 "slaves" are available to serve each person.[1] This is a considerable advance from the days of the Egyptians and Greeks.

Following World War II, the political, economic, and scientific disorganization in the world caused the emigration of many outstanding educators, scientists, and engineers to the United States. Here they have been able to expand their knowledge and skills and to aid generally in advancing our own understanding of the basic natural laws on which the improved techniques of the future will be based.

Engineering today

Broadly speaking, modern engineering had its beginnings about the time of the close of the Civil War. Within the last century, the pace of discovery has been so rapid that it can be classed as a period within itself. In these modern times, engineering endeavor has changed markedly from procedures used in the time of Imhotep, Galileo, or Ampere. Formerly, engineering discovery and development were accomplished principally by individuals. With the increased store of knowledge available and the widening of the field of engineering to include so many diverse branches, it is usual to find groups or teams of engineers and scientists working on a single project. Where formerly an individual could absorb and understand practically all of the scientific knowledge available, now the amount of information available is so vast that an individual can retain and employ at best only a part of it.

Since 1900 the ratio of engineers and scientists in the United States in comparison to the total population has been steadily increasing. Predictions based upon past increases seem to indicate the following:

Year	Ratio of U.S. engineers and scientists to population
1900	1 to 1800
1950	1 to 190
1960	1 to 130
1980	1 to 65
2000	1 to 35

If this is the case there will be an even greater increase in technological advance in the next 20 years than there has been in the past 20 years.

Within the past two decades, three technological developments have produced profound changes in our way of life. These developments are nuclear power, the electronic digital computer, and interplanetary space navigation. These concepts are still in their early stages of development, but historians of the future may well refer to our time as the *nuclear age,* the *computer age,* or the *age of space travel.* The engineer, of course, has been a principal developer of these concepts because of the need for their capabilities. The ocean offers great possibilities for technological exploration and perhaps even greater rewards for civilization than has space exploration (Illustration 1-9).

[1] *The Humble Way,* Third Quarter 1970, p. 10.

Today's engineers have led us into the outer reaches of space. Engineers of tomorrow will also lead us in an exploration of the depths of the seas.

In this age, as in any age, the engineer must be creative and must be able to visualize what may lie ahead. He must possess a fertile imagination and a knowledge of what others have done before him. As Sir Isaac Newton is reputed to have said, "If I have seen farther than other men, it is because I have stood on the shoulders of giants." The giants of science and engineering still exist. All any person must do to increase his field of vision is to climb up on their shoulders.

Problems on history of engineering

1-1. Prepare a chart as a series of columns, showing happenings and their approximate dates in a vertical time scale for various civilizations, beginning about 3000 B.C. and extending to about A.D. 1200.

Chinese	Middle East	Egyptian	Greek	Roman	Western Europe

1-2. Prepare a brief essay on the possible circumstances surrounding the discovery that an iron needle when rubbed on a lodestone and then supported on a bit of wood floating on water will point to the north.

1-3. Determine from historical references the approximate number of years that major civilizations existed as important factors in history.

1-4. What were the principal reasons for the lack of advancement of discovery in Greek science?

1-5. Explain why the development of a successful horsecollar was a major technological advancement.

1-6. Draw to some scale a typical cross section of the "Great Wall" of China, and estimate the volume of rock and dirt required per mile of wall.

1-7. Trace the development of a single letter of our alphabet from its earliest known symbol to the present.

1-8. Describe the details of preparing papyrus from reed-like plants which grew in Egypt.

1-9. Describe the patterns of behavior and accomplishments of ancient engineers that seem to have made successful civilizations, and to have prolonged their existence.

1-10. Prepare lists of prominent persons who contributed outstanding discoveries and developments to civilization during the period from A.D. 1200 to A.D. 1900 in the fields of (*a*) mathematics, (*b*) astronomy, (*c*) electricity, (*d*) mechanics, and (*e*) light.

Person	Date	Major contribution

1-11. List the ten most significant engineering achievements of the twentieth century.

1-12. Beginning with 3000 B.C., list the 25 most significant engineering achievements.

1-13. Based upon your knowledge of world history, describe the probable changes that might have occurred had the airplane not been invented until 1970.

1-14. Describe the precision with which the pyramids of Egypt were constructed. How does this precision compare with that of modern office buildings of more than 50 stories in height?

1-15. Trace the development of the power producing capability of man from 3000 B.C. to the present.

Bibliography

Bell, Daniel (ed.), *Toward the Year 2000,* Houghton Mifflin, Boston (1968).

Bratz, John F. (ed.), *Ocean Engineering: Goals, Environment, Technology,* John Wiley & Sons, Inc., New York (1968).

Briggs, Peter, *Men in the Sea,* Simon and Schuster, New York (1968).

Clarke, Arthur C., *Voices from the Sky,* Pyramid Publications, New York (1967).

DeCamp, L. S., *The Ancient Engineers,* Doubleday, Garden City, N.Y. (1963).

Dobrovolny, Jerry S., *Engineering History and Western Civilization,* McGraw-Hill, New York (1962).

Dugan, James, *et al., World Beneath the Sea,* National Geographic Society, Washington, D.C. (1967).

Dumas, Maurice (ed.), *A History of Technology and Invention,* Crown, New York (1969).

Finch, James Kip, *Engineering and Western Civilization,* McGraw-Hill, New York (1951).

Finch, James Kip, *The Story of Engineering,* Anchor Books, Doubleday, Garden City, N.Y. (1960).

Fleming, A. P., and H. J. Brocklehurst, *A History of Engineering,* Black, London (1925).

Forbes, R. J., *Man the Maker,* Abelard-Schuman, New York (1958).

Jenkins, Rhys, *Links in the History of Engineering and Technology from Tudor Times,* Cambridge U.P., New York (1936).

Kirby, R. S., Sidney Withington, and A. B. Darling, *Engineering in History,* McGraw-Hill, New York (1956).

Klemm, Friedrich, *A History of Western Technology,* M.I.T. Press, Cambridge, Mass. (1964).

Parsons, William Barclay, *Engineers and Engineering in the Renaissance,* Williams & Wilkins, Baltimore (1939).

Sandström, Gösta E., *Man the Builder,* McGraw-Hill, New York (1970).

Sarton, George, *A History of Science: Ancient Science Through the Golden Age of Greece,* Harvard U.P., Cambridge, Mass. (1952).

Walker, Charles R., *Modern Technology and Civilization,* McGraw-Hill, New York (1962).

White, Lynn, "Technology and Invention in the Middle Ages," *Speculum,* Vol. 15 (1940), pp. 141–159.

Wolf, A. A., *A History of Science, Technology and Philosophy in the Eighteenth Century,* Macmillan, New York (1939).

2

The engineer, society, and social responsibility

The earth and its inhabitants form a complex system of constantly changing inter-relationships. From the time of creation until a few thousand years ago the laws of nature programmed the actions of all living things in relation to each other and to their environments. From the beginning, however, change was ever present. For example, as glaciers retreated new forests grew to reclaim the land, ocean levels and coast lines changed, the winding courses of rivers altered, lakes appeared, and fish and animals migrated, as appropriate, to inhabit the new environments. Changes in climate and/or topography always brought about consequential changes in the distribution and ecological relationships of all living things—plants and animals alike. Almost invariably these changes brought about competitive relationships between the existing and migrating species. In this way certain competing forms were forced to adapt to new roles, while others became extinct. As a result of this continual change in the ecological balance of the earth over eons of time, there currently exist some 1,300,000 different kinds of plants and animals that make their homes in rather specific locations. Only a few, such as the cockroach, housefly, body louse, and house mouse, have been successful in invading a diversity of environ-ments—because they chose to follow man in his travels. Presumably even these would be confined to specific regions if man did not exist on the earth.

Primitive man was concerned with every facet of his environment and had to be acutely aware of many of the existing ecological interrelationships. For example, he made it his business to know those places most commonly frequented by animals that he considered to be good to eat or whose skins or pelts were valued for clothing. He distinguished between the trees, plants, and herbs and he knew which would provide him sustenance. Although by today's standards of education men of earlier civilizations might have been classified as "unlearned," they were certainly not ignorant. The Eskimo, for example, knew long ago that his sled dogs were susceptible

"AND ON THE SEVENTH DAY"

In the end,
There was Earth, and it was with form and beauty.
And Man dwelt upon the lands of the Earth, the meadows and trees, and he
   said,
"Let us build our dwelling in this place of beauty."
And he built cities and covered the Earth with concrete and steel.
And the meadows were gone.
And Man said, "It is good."

On the second day, Man looked upon the waters of the Earth.
And Man said, "Let us put our wastes in the waters that the dirt will be washed
   away."
And Man did.
And the waters became polluted and foul in smell.
And Man said, "It is good."

On the third day, Man looked upon the forests of the Earth and saw they were
   beautiful.
And Man said, "Let us cut the timber for our homes and grind the wood for
   our use."
And Man did.
And the lands became barren and the trees were gone.
And Man said, "It is good."

On the fourth day, Man saw that animals were in abundance and ran in the
   fields and played in the sun.
And Man said, "Let us cage these animals for our amusement and kill them for
   our sport."
And Man did.
And there were no more animals on the face of the Earth.
And Man said, "It is good."

On the fifth day, Man breathed the air of the Earth.
And Man said, "Let us dispose of our wastes into the air for the winds shall
   blow them away."
And Man did.
And the air became heavy with dust and all living things choked and burned.
And Man said, "It is good."

On the sixth day, Man saw himself and seeing the many languages and tongues,
   he feared and hated.
And Man said, "Let us build great machines and destroy these lest they destroy
   us."
And Man built great machines and the Earth was fired with the rage of great
   wars.
And Man said, "It is good."

On the seventh day, Man rested from his labors and the Earth was still, for
   Man no longer dwelt upon the Earth.
And it was good.

—New Mexico State Land Office

> The air, the water and the ground are free gifts to man and no one has the power to portion them out in parcels. Man must drink and breathe and walk and therefore each man has a right to his share of each.
> —James Fenimore Cooper, *The Prairie,* 1827

to the diseases of the wild arctic foxes, and the Masai of East Africa have been aware for centuries that malaria is caused by mosquito bites.[1]

For thousands of years after man first inhabited the earth, populations were relatively small and, because man was mobile, the cumulative effect of his existence upon the ecology of the earth was negligible. If, perchance, he did violence to a locality (for example, caused an entire forest to be burned), it was a relatively simple matter for him to move to another area and to allow time and nature to heal the wound. Due to the expanded world population this alternative is no longer available to him.

From century to century man has continued to add to his store of knowledge and understanding of nature. In so doing he has advanced progressively from a crude nomadic civilization, where he used what he could find useful to him in nature, to one that was sustained by domestication and agriculture, where he induced nature to produce more of the things that he wanted, and currently to one in which he is endeavoring to use technologies of his own design to control the forces of nature.

Man's existence is a part of, not independent of, nature—specifically it is most concerned with that part of nature that is closest to the surface of the earth, known as the *biosphere.*[2] This is the wafer-thin skin of air, water, and soil comprising only a thousandth of the planet's diameter and measuring less than 8 miles thick.[3] It might be said to be analogous to the skin of an apple. Within this relatively narrow space, however, it encompasses the entire fabric of life as we know it—from virus to field mouse, man, and whale. Most of the life forms live within a domain extending from the top $\frac{1}{2}$ mile of the ocean to 2 miles above the earth's surface, although some creatures do inhabit the extreme boundaries of the biosphere. A number of processes of nature provide the biosphere with a delicate balance of characteristics that are necessary to sustain life. The life cycles of all living things, both fauna and flora, are interdependent and inextricably interwoven to form a delicately balanced *ecological system* that is as yet not completely understood by man. We do know, however, that not only is every organism affected by the environment of the "world" in which it lives, but it also has some effect on this environment.[4] The energy necessary to operate this system comes almost entirely from the sun, and is utilized primarily through the processes of photosynthesis and heat. Any changes that man exerts on any part of the system will affect its precarious balance and cause internal adjustment of either its individual organisms, its environment, or both. The extent and magnitude of the modifications that man has exerted on this ecological system have increased immeasurably within the past few years, particularly as a consequence of his rapid population growth. Certain of these modifications are of particular concern to the engineer.

[1] Peter Farb, *Ecology,* Time, New York, (1963), p. 164.
[2] *Our Polluted Planet,* Ambassador College Press, Pasadena, Calif. (1968), p. 54.
[3] Robert C. Cook (ed.), "The Thin Slice of Life," *Population Bulletin,* Vol. XXIV, No. 5, p. 101.
[4] Marston Bates, "The Human EcoSystem," *Resources and Man,* W. F. Freeman, San Francisco (1969), p. 25.

Illustration 2-1
There are few areas to be found today that have been spared the ravages of man.

Even during the period of the emergence of agriculture and domestication of animals, man began to alter the ecological balance of his environment. Eventually some species of both plants and animals became extinct, while the growth of others was stimulated artificially. All too often man was not aware of the extent of the consequences of his actions and more particularly of the irreversibility of the alterations and imbalances that he had caused in nature's ecosystem. His concerns have more often been directed toward subduing the earth than replenishing it. Over the period of a few thousand years nature's law of "survival of the fittest" was gradually replaced by man's law of "survival of the most desirable." From man's short-term point of view, this change represented a significant advantage to him. Where once he was forced to gather fruit and nuts and to hunt animals to provide food and clothing for himself and his family—a life filled with uncertainty, at best—now he could simplify his food-gathering processes by increasing the yield of crops such as wheat, corn, rice, and potatoes. In addition certain animals such as cows, sheep, goats, and horses were protected from their natural enemies and, in some instances, their predators were completely annihilated. Such eradication seemed to serve man's immediate interests, but it also eliminated nature's way of maintaining an ecological balance. Man, in turn, was also affected by these changes. At one time only the strongest of his species survived, and the availability or absence of natural food kept his population in balance with the surroundings. With domestication these factors have become less of a problem and "survival of the fittest" no longer governs his increase in numbers. In general, today both strong and weak live and procreate. Because of this condition the world's population growth has begun to mount steadily and *alarmingly* because of the manifold problems that accompany large populations and for which solutions are still to be found.

In many respects the young engineer of today lives in a world that is vastly different from the one known to his grandfather or great grandfather. Without

Illustration 2-2
Man's continued misuse of the world's resources can only lead to a depletion of the essentials for life.

question he enjoys a standard of living that is unsurpassed in the history of mankind; and yet, in spite of the significant agricultural and technological advances that have been made in this generation, over half the world's population still lives in perpetual hunger. Famine, disease, and war continue to run rampant throughout portions of the earth. In addition the residue from his own technology continues to mount steadily. Nevertheless his population growth continues unabated, further compounding these problems.

And God blessed them, and God said unto them, be fruitful, and multiply, and *replenish* the earth, and *subdue* it: and have dominion over the fish of the sea, and over the fowl of the air, and over every living thing that moveth upon the earth.
—Genesis i:28

There is another design that is far better. It is the design that nature has provided. . . It is pointless to superimpose an abstract, man-made design on a region as though the canvas were blank. It isn't. Somebody has been there already. Thousands of years of rain and wind and tides have laid down a design. Here is our form and order. It is inherent in the land itself—in the pattern of the soil, the slopes, the woods—above all, in the patterns of streams and rivers.
—William H. Whyte, *The Last Landscape*

We shape our buildings; and forever afterwards our buildings shape us.
—Sir Winston Churchill; Speech in House of Commons, October 1943

The population explosion
—a race to global famine

Until comparatively recent times the growth of the human race was governed by the laws of nature in a manner similar to that controlling the growth of all other living things. As man's culture changed from nomadic to agrarian to technological however, he began to alter nature's population controls significantly. Through control of disease and pestilence his average life span has been extended over three times. His ability to supply his family consistently with food and clothing has also been improved immeasurably. Combinations of these two factors have caused his population to increase in geometric progression: 2–4–8–16–32–64–128, and so on.[5] Initially it took hundreds of thousands of years for a significant change to occur in the world population. However, as the numbers became larger, and particularly in more recent times as man's life span began to lengthen as a result of his gaining some control over starvation, disease, and violence, the results of geometric growth began to have a profound effect. Where it has taken an estimated 2 million years for the world population to reach slightly over 3 billion persons, it will take only 35 years to add the next 3 billion *if present growth rates remain unchanged.* The significance of this problem is illustrated by Figure 2-1.

As in the case of man's altering his ecological environment, he has not always been wise enough to anticipate all of the various effects of his changes. In the case

[5]T. R. Malthus, 1798. *An Essay on the Principle of Population As It Affects the Future Improvements of Mankind,* Facsimile reprint in 1926 for J. Johnson. Macmillan, London.

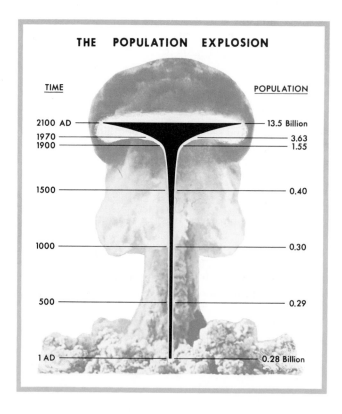

Figure 2-1

Illustration 2-3

Traditionally one person signifies loneliness; two persons—companionship; three persons—a crowd. In more recent times a new concept has been added: multitudes signify pollution and loneliness.

of his own propagation he has managed to introduce "death control," but birth rates have continued to climb, particularly in the underdeveloped countries. It is estimated that the average annual increase in world population in 1650 was only 0.3 per cent.[6] In 1900 this annual growth rate had increased to 0.9 per cent; in 1930, 1.0 per cent; in 1960, 2.0 per cent; and in 1970 over 2.1 per cent. Unless these rates decline significantly, which does not now seem likely, a worldwide crisis is fast approaching.

The earth's land area, only 10 per cent of which appears to be arable, is fixed and unexpandable, and a shortage of food and water is already an accepted fact of life in many countries. Although conditions in some slum areas of the United States are very bad, they bear little resemblance to many areas of the world where people grovel in filth and live little better than animals. Dr. Paul Ehrlich describes a recent visit to India as follows:

> I have understood the population explosion intellectually for a long time. I came to understand it emotionally one stinking hot night in Delhi a couple of years ago. My wife and daughter and I were returning to our hotel in an ancient taxi. The seats were hopping with fleas. The only functional gear was third. As we crawled through the city, we entered a crowded slum area. The temperature was well over 100, and the air was a haze of dust and smoke. The streets seemed alive with people. People eating, people washing, people sleeping. People visiting, arguing, and screaming. People thrusting their hands through the taxi window, begging. People defecating and urinating. People clinging to buses. People herding animals. People, people, people, people. As we moved slowly through the mob, hand horn squawking, the dust, noise, heat, and cooking fires gave the scene a hellish aspect.[7]

[6]Joseph M. Jones, *Does Overpopulation Mean Poverty?*, Center for International Economic Growth, Washington, D.C. (1962), p. 13.
[7]Paul R. Ehrlich, *The Population Bomb*, Ballantine, New York (1968), p. 15.

Illustration 2-4
One half of the people in the world had food to eat this morning . . .

Illustration 2-5
. . . the other one half face starvation.

Over one third of the human beings now living on the earth are starving and another one third are ill fed. The underdeveloped countries of the world are incapable of producing enough food to feed their populations. This deficiency is 16 million tons of food each year and will grow to a staggering 88 million tons of food per year by 1985. For these people to be fed an adequate diet, the current world food production would have to double by 1980, *which appears to be an impossible task.*[8] The quantity of food available is not the only problem; it must also be of the proper quality. For example, in Central Africa every other baby born dies before the age of five *even though food is generally plentiful.* They die from a disease known as *kwashiorkor,* which is caused by a lack of sufficient protein in the diet. The magnitude of the problem continues to grow as the world population increases. More population means more famine. It also means more crowding, more disease, less sanitation, more waste and garbage, more pollution of air, water, and land, and ultimately . . . the untimely death of millions, or possibly, the end of human life on earth.

In the United States, just as in the underdeveloped countries of the world, the population has tended to migrate first to cities and some of the cities have grown to monstrous size, often called megalopolises. These treks have been brought about by the widespread use of mechanized agriculture and the impoverishment of the soil. With these migrations special problems have arisen. No longer is a city dweller self-sufficient in his ability to provide sustenance, shelter, and security for his family. Rather, his food, water, fuel, and power must all be brought to him by others and his wastes of every kind must be taken away. Most frequently his work is located

[8] *Famine! Can We Survive?,* Ambassador College Press, Pasadena, Calif. (1969), p. 14.

Illustration 2-6

Wheat is one of the world's most important food crops because each grain contains a large amount of protein. Even though engineering designs and advances in agricultural science have made possible a substantially increased production, the disparity between food supply and world population continues to increase.

many miles from his home and his reliance upon a transportation system becomes critical. He finds himself vulnerable to every kind of public emergency, and the psychological pressures of city life often lead to mental illness or escape into the use of alcohol and drugs. The incidence of crime increases, and his clustering invites a more rapid spread of disease and pestilence than ever. In general his cities are enormous consumers of electrical and chemical energy and producers of staggering amounts of wastes and pollution. Today 70 per cent of the people in our country live on 1 per cent of the land, and the exodus from the countryside continues.

What are the implications for the engineer of these national and international sociological crises? The engineer is particularly affected because he is the one person whose creative efforts should be directed *to improving* man's physical and economic lot. First, he must learn all he can about the extent and causes of the technological problems that have resulted, and he must direct his energies and abilities to solving them. In general, he must recognize his responsibility to restore the equilibrium to the ecological system of nature in those cases where it has become unbalanced. This requires that he be cognizant of the manifold effects of his designs *prior to their implementation*. The task is not an easy one and the challenge is great, but the consequences are too severe to be disregarded.

Just as the engineer has learned that the physical laws of nature *do* govern the universe, so also must he be aware that nature's laws governing the procession and

For this is the word that the Lord has spoken.
The earth dries up and withers,
The whole world withers and grows sick;
   the earth's high places sicken,
and the earth itself is desecrated by the feet of those who live in it,
because they have broken the laws, disobeyed the statutes
and violated the eternal covenant.
—Isaiah xxiv:3–5 (New English Translation)

diversity of life on this planet are equally valid and unyielding. The remainder of this chapter will consider the severity and complexity of several problems that confront today's society and more particularly to the engineer's social responsibility for their solution.

Our polluted planet

In the last few years the average American has become aware that our "spaceship earth" is undergoing many severe and detrimental ecological changes which may take hundreds of years to restore. Unfortunately he is not always able to distinguish effects that are of a temporary nature from those with long-term consequences. Frequently his most damaging actions to the environment are either of an incremental or visually indistinguishable nature, and for this reason he participates willingly in them. In some measure man's reactions are dulled by the slowness of deterioration. This is somewhat analogous to the actions of a frog that will die rather than jump out, when placed in a bucket of water that is being *slowly* heated. In contrast, if the frog is pitched into a bucket of boiling water, he will immediately jump out and thereby avoid severe injury. The engineer in particular must learn to understand such "cause-and-effect" relationships so that his designs will not become detrimental to the orderly and natural development of life.

The air environment

The atmosphere, which makes up the largest fraction of the biosphere, is a dynamic system that absorbs continuously a wide range of solids, liquids, and gases from both natural and man-made sources. These substances often travel through the air, disperse, and react with one another and with other substances, both chemically and physically. Eventually most of these constituents find their way into a depository, such as the ocean, or to a receptor, such as a man. Some, however, such as helium, escape from the biosphere. Others, such as carbon dioxide, may enter the atmosphere faster than they enter a reservoir and thus gradually accumulate in the air.[9]

Clean, dry air contains 78.09 per cent nitrogen by volume, and 20.94 per cent oxygen. The remaining 0.97 per cent is composed of a gaseous mixture of carbon dioxide, helium, argon, krypton, nitrous oxide, and xenon, as well as very small amounts of some other organic and inorganic gases whose amounts vary with time and place in the atmosphere. Through both natural and man-made processes that exist upon the earth, varying amounts of contaminants continuously enter the atmosphere. That portion of these substances which interacts with the environment to cause toxicity, disease, aesthetic distress, physiological effects, or environmental decay has been labeled by man as a pollutant. In general, the actions of people are the primary cause of pollution and, as population increases, the attendant

[9] *Cleaning our Environment: The Chemical Basis for Action,* American Chemical Society, Washington, D.C. (1969), p. 23.

A recent scientific analysis of New York City's atmosphere concluded that a New Yorker on the street took into his lungs the equivalent in toxic materials of 38 cigarettes a day.
—Robert Rienow and Leona Train Rienow, *Moment in the Sun*

pollution problems also increase proportionally. This is not a newly recognized relationship, however. The first significant change in man's effect on nature came with his deliberate making of a fire. No other creature on earth starts fires. Prehistoric man built a fire in his cave home for cooking, heating, and to provide light for his family. Although the smoke was sometimes annoying, no real problem existed with regard to pollution of the air environment. However, when his friends or neighbors visited him and also built fires in the same cave, even prehistoric man recognized that he then had an *air pollution problem.* Some nineteenth-century cities with their hundreds of thousands of smoldering soft-coal grates coughed amid a thicker and deadlier smog than any modern city can concoct.[10] Today the natural terrain that surrounds large cities is recognized as having a significant bearing on the air pollution problem. However, this is not an altogether new concept either. Historians tell us

[10]Tom Alexander, "Some Burning Questions About Combustion," *Fortune,* February 1970, p. 130.

Illustration 2-7
Complacency leads to industrial pollution.

Illustration 2-8
St. Louis on a smog-free day can be beautiful.

Illustration 2-9
Air pollution often mars a city's attractiveness.

Table 2-1   Sources of air pollutants in the United States*
[millions of tons/year (1969)]

Source	Totals	Per cent of totals	Carbon monoxide	Sulfur oxides	Hydro-carbons	Nitrogen oxides	Particulate matter	Other
Motor vehicles	86	60	66	1	12	6	1	†
Industry	25	17	2	9	4	2	6	2
Power plants	20	14	1	12	†	3	3	
Space heating	8	6	2	3	1	1	1	†
Refuse disposal	4	3	1	†	1	†	1	†
Totals	143	100	72	26	18	12	12	4

* Adapted from *Your Right to Clean Air,* The Conservation Foundation, Washington, D.C. (1970), p. 15.
† Less than 1 per cent.

that the present Los Angeles area, which in recent years has become a national symbol of comparison for excessive smog levels,[11] was known as the "Valley of Smokes" when the Spaniards first arrived.[12] In recent years air pollution has become a problem of world concern.

In the United States the most common air pollutants are carbon monoxide, sulfur oxides, hydrocarbons, nitrogen oxides, and particles (Table 2-1). Their primary sources are motor vehicles, industry, electrical power plants, space heating, and refuse disposal with approximately 60 per cent of the bulk being contributed by motor vehicles and 17 per cent by industry. It seems possible that America's streets will contain twice as many automobiles as the current 100 million by the year 2000. This is certainly a foreboding prospect *unless improved engineering designs are able to alleviate the situation.*[13] Certainly restoring the quality of the atmosphere ranks

[11] The term *Smog* was coined originally to describe a combination of smoke and fog, such as was common in London when coal was widely used for generating power and heating homes. More recently it has come to mean the accumulation of photochemical reaction products which result largely from the action of the radiant energy of the sun on the emissions of internal combustion engines (automobile exhaust).
[12] Henry C. Wohlers, *Air Pollution—The Problem, the Source, and the Effects,* Drexel Institute of Technology, Philadelphia (1969), p. 1.
[13] *Our Polluted Planet,* Ambassador College Press, Pasadena, Calif. (1968), p. 25.

The great question of the seventies is, shall we surrender to our surroundings, or shall we make our peace with nature and begin to make reparations for the damage we have done to our air, to our land, and to our water? . . . Clean air, clean water, open spaces—these should once again be the birthright of every American. If we act now, they can be.
—President Richard M. Nixon, State of the Union Message, January 22, 1970

Environment pollution . . . now affects the whole earth. Smog produced in urban and industrial areas is hovering over the countryside and beginning to spread over the oceans . . . cities will not benefit much longer from the cleansing effects of the winds for the simple reason that the wind itself is contaminated.
—The New York Times, January 6, 1969

as one of the most difficult and challenging tasks of our generation. As with the determined effort of the 1960's to explore the moon, an engineering venture of this magnitude requires a coordinated national effort of great magnitude. With every man, woman, and child in the United States producing an average of 1400 pounds per year of air pollutants, the problem is certainly one of serious proportions. The National Air Quality Standards Act of 1970, which specified that motor vehicle exhaust emissions should be reduced by 90 per cent by January 1, 1975, could provide the impetus for a sincere and necessary national commitment.

It has been found that the significantly increasing volume of particulate matter entering the atmosphere scatters the incoming sunlight. This reduces the amount of heat that reaches the earth and tends to reduce its temperature. The decreasing mean global temperature of recent years has been attributed to the rising concentrations of airborne particles in the atmosphere.[14] A counteracting phenomenon, commonly referred to as the "greenhouse effect," is caused by the increasing amounts of carbon dioxide found in the atmosphere. Although carbon dioxide occurs naturally as a constituent of the atmosphere and is not normally classified as an air pollutant, man does generate an abnormally large amount of it in those combustion processes that utilize coal, oil, and natural gas. The presence of water vapor in the atmosphere, and to a lesser extent carbon dioxide and ozone, acts in a manner similar to the glass in a greenhouse. Light from the sun arrives as short-wavelength radiation (visible and ultraviolet) and is allowed to pass through it to heat the earth, but the relatively long-wavelength infrared radiation (heat radiation) that is emitted by the earth is absorbed—thereby providing an unnatural and additional heating effect to the earth. It has been estimated that if the carbon dioxide content in the atmosphere continues to increase at the present rate, the mean global temperature could rise to 4°C in the next 40 to 50 years. There has been conjecture that this might become a matter of great importance because small temperature increases could cause a partial melting of the ice caps of the earth (causing continental flooding), with consequential and devastating effects to man.[15]

Air pollution can cause death, impair health, reduce visibility, bring about vast economic losses, and contribute to the general deterioration of both our cities and countryside. It is therefore a matter of grave importance that engineers of all disci-

[14] Reginald E. Newell, "The Global Circulation of Atmospheric Pollutants," *Scientific American,* January 1971, p. 40.
[15] Lord Ritchie-Calder, Quoted in *Engineering Opportunities—College Edition,* February 1970, p. 32.

Illustration 2-10
One solution to the air pollution problem. Surely there must be a more desirable alternative!

plines consciously incorporate in their designs sufficient constraints and safeguards to ensure that they do not contribute to the pollution of the atmosphere. In addition, they must apply their ingenuity and problem-solving abilities to eliminating air pollution where it exists and restoring the natural environment.

The quest for water quality

Water is the most abundant compound to be found upon the face of the earth and, next to air, it is the most essential resource for man's survival. The per capita use of water in the United States is 1000 gallons per day and this demand continues to grow. Early man was most concerned with the quality (purity) of his drinking water and even he was aware that certain waters were contaminated and could cause illness or death. In addition modern man has found that he must be concerned also with the quantity of the water available for his use. An abundant supply of relatively pure water is no longer available in most areas. Today water pollution, *the presence of toxic or noxious substances or heat in natural water sources,* is considered to be one of the most pressing social and economic issues of our time. Just how bad water pollution can become was dramatically illustrated when the oily, chocolate-brown Cuyahoga River in Cleveland, Ohio, caught fire and blazed for several days, nearly destroying two railroad bridges that spanned the river. This once-beautiful river was so filled with municipal and industrial wastes that even the leeches and sludge worms normally found only in polluted rivers could not survive, and it was, in effect, nothing more than a flammable sewer.[16] Unfortunately, many other water bodies in the

[16] Gene Bylinsky, "The Limited War on Water Pollution," *The Environment,* Harper & Row, New York (1970), p. 20.

United States are no less polluted, and now approximately one half of the people in the nation "drink their own treated sewage." Reportedly many city water treatment plants merely remove the particulate matter and disinfect the available water with chlorine to kill bacteria, since they were not originally designed to remove pesticides, herbicides, and other organic and inorganic chemicals that may be present.[17] This problem has become acute in a number of areas in recent months as hundreds of new contaminants have been discovered in streams and lakes: bacteria and viruses, detergents, municipal sewage, acid from mine drainage, pesticides and weed killers, radioactive substances, phosphorus from fertilizers, trace amounts of metals and drugs, and other organic and inorganic chemicals. As the population continues to increase, the burden assumed by the engineer to design more comprehensive water treatment plants also mounts. Indeed, the well-being of entire communities may depend upon his design abilities because it is now a recognized condition of population increase that "everyone cannot live upstream."

The processes of nature have long made use of the miraculous ability of rivers and lakes to "purify themselves." After pollutants find their way into a water body they are subject to dilution, or settling, action of the sun, and to being consumed by beneficial bacteria. The difficulty arises when man disturbs the equilibrium of the ecosystem by dumping large amounts of his organic wastes into a particular water body, thereby intensifying the demand for purification. In time the body of water cannot meet the demand, organic debris accumulates, anaerobic areas develop, fish die, and putrification is the result. This process also occurs in nature but it may take many hundreds of years to complete the natural processes of deterioration. Man can alter nature's time scale appreciably.

Lake Erie, the smallest of the Great Lakes, provides a classic example of what can happen when man ignores his responsibility to protect a natural resource.[18]

---

[17] *Ibid.,* p. 25.
[18] Victor W. Wigotsky, "Engineering and the Urban Crisis," *Design News,* December 7, 1970, p. 31.

Illustration 2-11
Contaminated water discharges are responsible for polluting many of the rivers and lakes of America.

Eutrophication, a term used to denote the process of nutrient enrichment by which lakes fill and die, has overtaken the lake prematurely, and because of this it is estimated to have aged over 15,000 natural years since 1925. These consequences, however, should come as no surprise. The lake is fed by a number of heavily polluted rivers, including the Cuyahoga and Buffalo Rivers. In addition, over 9.6 billion gallons of industrial waste and 1.5 billion gallons of sewage are dumped into the lake *each day* from adjoining states.[19] Among the most damaging pollutants in this lake appear to be detergents and fertilizer polyphosphates which serve to stimulate the growth of algae—tiny, green plants—which then multiply until they become large green mats that literally clog and stifle the lake. When the algae die, their decay depletes the water of its life-giving oxygen, choking forms of desirable aquatic life, including fish.[20]

The presence of radioactive wastes and excess heat are relatively new types of pollution to water bodies, but they are of no less importance for the engineer to take into account in his designs. All radioactive materials are biologically injurious. Therefore radioactive substances that are normally emitted by nuclear power plants are suspected of finding their way into the ecological food chain where they could cause serious problems. For this reason all radioactive wastes should be isolated from the biological environment during the "life" of the isotopes (as much as 600 years in some cases). The "heat" problem arises because nuclear electrical power generating plants require great quantities of water for cooling. Although the heated discharge water from a nuclear power plant is approximately the same temperature

[19]"Eat, Drink, and Be Sick," *Medical World News,* September 26, 1969, p. 32.
[20]Senator Gaylord Nelson, *Congressional Record,* February 26, 1970, p. S2444.

If the people of Cleveland only realized that they are drinking their own and their neighbor's purified urine and fecal matter, they might be prompted to take a closer look at what is floating in one of the world's largest open sewers—Lake Erie and the rivers emptying into it.
—*Medical World News,* September 26, 1969

Illustration 2-13
Man's pollution of his sources of water is becoming a commonplace occurrence.

as that from a fossil-fuel power plant, the quantity has been increased by approximately 40 per cent. The warmer water absorbs less oxygen from the atmosphere, and this accelerates the normal rate of decomposition of organic matter. This unnatural heat also unbalances the life cycles of fish who, being cold blooded, cannot regulate their body temperatures correspondingly. With the prospect of the number of nuclear power plants doubling by 1980, this problem will loom larger than ever.

Engineering designs of the future must take into account all of these factors to ensure for all of the nation's inhabitants a water supply that is both sufficient in quantity and unpolluted in quality. This is not only the engineer's challenge, but his responsibility as well.

Solid waste disposal

We are living in a most unusual time—a time where possibly the most valuable tangible asset that a person could own would be a "bottomless hole." Never before in history have so many people had so much garbage, refuse, trash, and other wastes to dispose of, and at the same time never before has there been such a shortage of "dumping space." The proliferation of refuse, however, is only partly attributable to the population explosion. A substantial portion of the blame must be assumed by an affluent society that is careless with its increasing purchasing power and which has demonstrated a decided distaste for secondhand articles.[21] Table 2-2 lists the primary solid waste constituents of the United States.

The most popular method of solid waste disposal has long been "removal from the immediate premises." For centuries man has been aware of the health hazards that accompany the accumulations of garbage. Historians have recorded that a sign at the city limits of ancient Rome warned all persons to transport their refuse outside the city or risk being fined. Also, it has been recognized that in the Middle Ages the custom of dumping garbage in the streets was largely responsible for the proliferation of disease-carrying rats, flies, and insects that made their homes in piles of refuse.[22]

On the average, each person in the United States has established the following record with regard to the generation of solid waste, refuse, and garbage:

1920   2.75 pounds per person per day
1970   5.5   pounds per person per day
1980   8.0   pounds per person per day (estimated)

From New York to Los Angeles cities throughout the nation are rapidly depleting their disposal space, and there is considerable concern that too little attention has been given to what is fast becoming one of man's most distressing problems—solid waste disposal. Why is trash becoming such a problem? The answer seems to lie partially in man's changing value system. Just a generation or two ago thrift and

[21] Alex Hershaft, "Solid Waste Treatment," *Science and Technology,* June 1969, p. 35.
[22] *Ibid.,* p. 34.

Illustration 2-14 (*opposite*)
The character of a nation is revealed by examining its garbage.

Table 2-2   Solid waste of the United States, 1970*

Category	Composition		Percentage distribution	Estimated production in 10^6 tons/year
Refuse				
Garbage	Animal and vegetable kitchen wastes		15	
Rubbish	Dry household, commercial, and industrial waste	Paper	28	230
		Yard waste	14	
		Glass and metal	10	
		Other	10	
Municipal waste	Construction waste and street sweepings		23	
Industrial wastes	Industrial processing scrap and by-products			120
Scrap metal	Automobiles, machinery, and major appliances			20
Sewage residue	Grit, sludge, and other residue from sewage treatment plants			30
Mining displacement	Overburden and gangue			1200
Agriculture waste	Manure, animal carcasses, crop and logging debris			2400

*Drawn from compilation by Alex Hershaft, "Solid Waste Management," Grumman Aerospace Corporation, Bethpage, New York (1970).

economy were considered to be important tenets of American life, and few items with any inherent value were discarded. Today, we live in the era of "the throwaway." More and more containers of all types are being made of nondecomposable plastic or glass, or nonrustable aluminum, and everything from furniture to clothing is being made from disposable paper products which are sold by advertising that challenges purchasers to "discard when disenchanted." In 1970 the American public threw away approximately 50 billion cans, 30 billion bottles, 35 million tons of paper, 5 million tons of plastic, and 100 million automobile tires. The problem of disposing of 7 million junked automobiles each year is also becoming a problem that can no longer be ignored—particularly when this volume is expected to climb to over 10 million

Illustration 2-15
The engineer can design to alter the actions of man. What may be needed more, however, is something to change the lack of concern in man's nature.

Illustration 2-16
Pollution is a personal matter.

per year by 1980.[23] The truth is that most "consumers" in America have instead become "users and discarders," but this fact has not been taken into account.

Unfortunately most current waste disposal practices make no attempt to recover any of the potential values that are in solid wastes. The methods of disposing of refuse in most common use today are dumping and burning in the open, sanitary land fills, burial in abandoned mines or dumping at sea, and grinding in disposal systems followed by flushing into sewers. Some edible waste, such as garbage, is fed to hogs.

Since almost all of the products of the engineer's design ingenuity will eventually be discarded due to wear or obsolescence, it is imperative that consideration for disposal be given to each design *at the time that it is first produced.* In addition,

[23] *U.S. News & World Report,* September 8, 1969, p. 65.

Illustration 2-17
HELP!

the well-being of society as we know it appears to depend in some measure upon the creative design abilities of the engineer to devise new processes of recycling wastes,[24] and either the changing of the physical form of wastes or the manner of their disposal, or both. Such designs must be accomplished within the constraints of economic considerations and without augmenting man's other pollution problems: air, water, and sound. Basically, the solution of waste accumulation is a matter of attitude, ingenuity, and economics—all areas in which the engineer can make significant contributions.

The rising crescendo of unwanted sound

A silent world is not only undesirable but impossible to achieve. Man's very nature is psychologically sensitive to the many sounds that come to his ears. For example, he is pleased to hear the gurgle and murmur of a brook or the soothing whispering wind as it filters through overhead pine trees, but his blood is likely to chill if he recognizes the whirring buzz of a rattlesnake or hears the sudden screech of

[24] *Environmental Science and Technology,* May 1970, p. 384.

Illustration 2-18
Man is affected psychologically by the sounds that he hears.

an automobile tire as it slides on pavement. He may thrill to the sharp bugle of a far-off hunting horn, but his thoughts often tend to lapse into dreams of inaccessible places as a distant train whistle penetrates the night.[25] Yes, sounds have an important bearing on man's sense of well-being. While the average person's ears continue to alert him to impending dangers, their sensitivity is far less acute than in generations past, particularly for those who lived in less densely populated areas. It is said that, even today, aborigines living in the stillness of isolated African villages can easily hear each other talking in low conversational tones at distances as great as 100 yards, and that their hearing acuity diminishes little with age.[26] Even as man's technology has brought hundreds of thousands of desirable and satisfying innovations, it has also provided the means for the retrogression of his sense of hearing—for deafness caused by a deterioration of the microscopic hair cells that transmit sound from the ear to the brain. It has been found that prolonged exposure to intense sound levels will produce permanent hearing loss, and it matters not that such levels may be considered pleasing. (Some people purport to enjoy "rock" music concerts at sound levels exceeding 110 decibels,[27] Figure 2-2). Today noise-induced hearing loss looms as one of America's major health hazards.

Noise is generally considered to be any annoying or unwanted sound.[28] Noise (like sound) has two discernible effects on man. One causes a deterioration of his sensitivity of hearing, and the other affects his "psychological state of mind." The adverse effects of noise have long been recognized as a form of environmental pollution. Julius Caesar was so annoyed by noise that he banned chariot driving at night, and, prior to the Civil War, studies in England reported substantial hearing losses among blacksmiths, boilermakers, and railroad men.[29] It has only been in recent years, however, that noise has been recognized as a health hazard.[30]

It is estimated that the average background noise level throughout the United States has been doubling each ten years. At this rate of increase, living conditions will be intolerable within a few years. Such a crescendo of sound results from the steady increase of population and the concomitant growth of the use of power on every hand—from the disposal in the kitchen, to the motorcycle in the street, to power tools in the factory. Buses, jet airliners, television sets, stereos, dishwashers, tractors, mixers, waste disposers, air conditioners, automobiles, jackhammers, power lawn mowers, vacuum cleaners, and typewriters are but a few examples of noise producers that are deemed desirable to today's high standard of living but which may very well also prevent man from fully enjoying the fruits of his labors, unless the sound levels at which they operate are altered significantly.

Except in the case of minimizing aircraft noise, the United States lags far behind many countries in noise prevention and control. Virtually all man-made noise can be suppressed, and the same engineer who formulates the idea for a new type of kitchen aid or designs an improved family vehicle must also be capable of solving the acoustical problems that are associated with his designs. In this regard he is responsible to generations yet unborn for the consequences of his actions.

[25] *Noise: Sound Without Value,* Committee on Environmental Quality of the Federal Council for Science and Technology, Washington, D.C. (1968), p. 1.

[26] *The Environment,* The Editors of Fortune, Harper & Row, New York (1970), p. 136.

[27] A *decibel* (abbreviated db) is a unit of measure of sound intensity, or pressure change on the ear.

[28] Michael Rodda, *Noise and Society,* Oliver & Boyd, London (1967), p. 2.

[29] Aram Glorig, *Noise As a Public Health Hazard,* W. Dixon Ward and James E. Fricke (eds.), The American Speech and Hearing Association, Washington, D.C. (1969), p. 105.

[30] Andrew D. Hosey and Charles H. Powell, (eds.), *Industrial Noise,* U.S. Department of Health, Education, and Welfare, Washington, D.C. (1967).

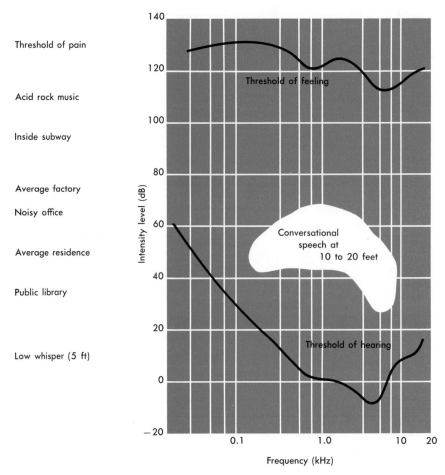

Figure 2-2 Average sound levels.
[Adapted from graphical presentations in Wesley E. Woodson and Donald W. Conover, *Human Engineering Guide for Equipment Designers,* second edition, (Berkley: University of California Press, 1964), p. 4–10.]

Man's insatiable thirst for energy

In man's earliest habitation of the earth he competed for energy with other members of the earth's ecological environment. Initially his energy requirements were primarily satisfied by food—probably in the range of 2000 kilocalories (100 thermal watts) per person per day. However, as he has been able to make and control the use of fire, domesticate the plant and animal kingdoms, and initiate technologies of his own choosing, his per capita consumption of energy has increased appreciably. Today in the United States, man's thirst for energy (or *power,* which is the time rate use of energy) exceeds 10,000 thermal watts per capita per day,[31] which is about 100

[31] M. King Hubbert, *Resources and Man,* W. H. Freeman, San Francisco (1969), p. 237.

Illustration 2-19
If the ear were to shatter or bleed profusely when subjected to abuse from intense or prolonged noise, we might be more careful of its treatment.

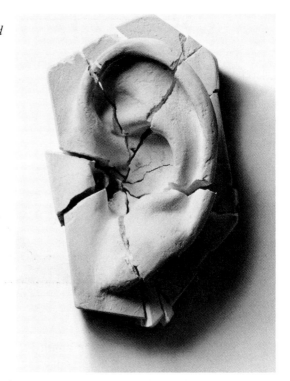

times the average of underdeveloped nations.[32] This demand has followed an exponential pattern of growth similar to the growth of the world population *except that the annual rate of increase for nonnutrient energy utilization is growing at a rate* (approximately 4 per cent per year) *considerably in excess of the world's growth in population* (approximately 2 per cent per year). This is brought about by man's appetite for more gadgets, faster cars and airplanes, heavier machinery, and so on.

The principal sources of the worlds energy prior to about A.D. 1200 were solar energy, wood, wind, and water. At about this time in England it was discovered that certain "black rocks" found along the seashore would burn. From this there

[32]S. Fred Singer, "Human Energy Production as a Process in the Biosphere," *Scientific American,* September 1970, p. 183.

Illustration 2-20
With proper planning industrial installations, such as the nuclear power plant shown here, can perform their functions without polluting the environment.

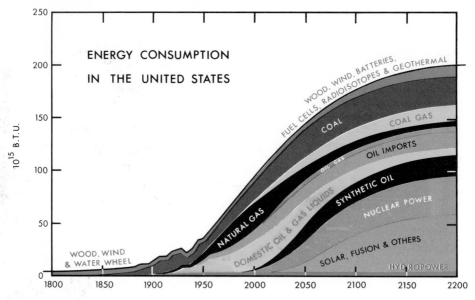

Figure 2-3

followed in succession the mining of coal[33] and the exploration of oil and natural gas reservoirs. More recently nuclear energy has emerged as one of the most promising sources of power yet discovered. The safe management and disposal of radioactive wastes, however, continue to present problems for the engineer.

Figure 2-3 provides a record of the history of energy consumption in the United States since 1800, and represents a prediction of how the continually rising demand might expand in the future.[34] Of course the future is unknown, and such a prediction of our energy sources for the year 2000 and beyond is mere conjecture. It depends to a large extent upon the background and experience of the predictor. External factors may also intervene. It may well be, for example, that although fossil fuels seem to be sufficient in quantity, they might be undesirable for expanded use because of their combustive pollutant effects. On the other hand, the solving of such problems respresents a number of challenges for the engineer, and acceptable solutions might be forthcoming before that time.

In the United States, the use of power is distributed approximately as follows:[35,36,37]

Household	20 per cent
Commercial	10 per cent
Industrial	40 per cent
Transportation	20 per cent
Other	10 per cent

[33] There are evidences that coal was used in China, Syria, Greece, and Wales as early as 1000 to 2000 B.C.

[34] L. P. Gaucher, "Energy Sources in the United States," *Journal of Solar Energy Society*, Vol. 9, No. 3 (1965), p. 122.

[35] Garrett DeBall, "Energy," *The Environmental Handbook*, Ballantine, New York (1970), p. 67.

[36] Chauncey Starr and Craig Smith, "Energy and the World of A.D. 2000," *Engineering for the Benefit of Mankind*, National Academy of Engineering, Washington, D.C. (1970), p. 4.

[37] Alvin M. Weinberg and R. Philip Hammond, "Limits to the Use of Energy," *American Scientist*, August 1970, p. 413.

Considering the fact that currently the five most common air pollutants (carbon monoxide, sulfur oxides, hydrocarbons, nitrogen oxides, and solid particles) are primarily by-products of the combustion of fossil fuels, it behooves the engineer to design and utilize energy sources that are as free from such pollution-causing wastes as possible. It would appear that in the long run the earth can tolerate a significant increase in man's continuous release of energy (perhaps as much as 1000 times the current U.S. daily consumption—or more) without deleterious effect.[38] Such increases would, of course, be necessary to accommodate a constantly increasing population. However, extrapolations and statements of this type concerning the future are meaningless unless the short-range problems—the problems of today—are solved. Our society has invested the engineer with a responsibility for leadership in this regard, and he must not fail.

Go–Go–Go

This year American motorists have travelled over 1 trillion miles on the nation's highways—an equivalent distance of over 2 million round trips to the moon. More than one half of this travel has been in urban areas, Figure 2-4, where for the most part the physical layouts—the planning, the street design, and basic service systems— were created over 100 years ago.[39] As the population of the nation continues to shift to the urban areas, many of the *frustrating* problems of today will become *unbearable* in the future. Since 1896, when Henry Ford built his first car, the mores of the nation have changed gradually from an attitude of "pioneer independence" to a state of

[38] *Ibid.,* p. 418.
[39] *Tomorrow's Transportation,* U.S. Department of Housing and Urban Development, Washington, D.C. (1968), p. 8.

Figure 2-4

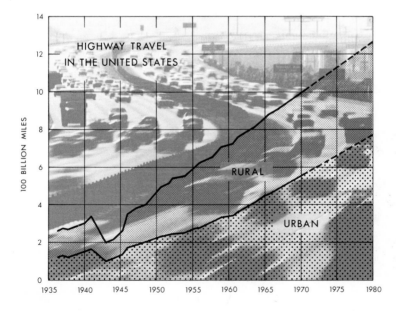

2: *The engineer, society, and social responsibility* **47**

> In the next 40 years, we must completely renew our cities. The alternative is disaster. Gaping needs must be met in health, in education, in job opportunities, in housing. And not a single one of these needs can be fully met until we rebuild our mass transportation systems.
> —Lyndon Baines Johnson, 1968

"apprehensive dependence"—to the point where one's possession of a means of private transportation is now considered to be a *necessity*.

Over three fourths of the families in the United States own at least one automobile, and over one fourth can boast of owning two or more. However, due to inadequate planning this affluence has brought its share of problems for all concerned. Beginning about 3500 B.C. and until recent times roads and highways were used primarily as trade routes for the transport of commerce between villages, towns, and cities. The Old Silk Trade Route that connected ancient Rome and Europe with the Orient, a distance of over 6000 miles, was used ext nsively for the transport of silk, jade, and other valuable commodities. The first really expert road builders, however, were the Romans, who built networks of roads throughout their empire to enable their soldiers to move more quickly from place to place. In this country early settlers first used the rivers, lakes, and oceans for transportation, and the first communities were located at easily accessible points. A few crude roads were constructed, but until 1900 the railroad was generally considered to be the most satisfactory means of travel, particularly where long distances were involved. With the advent of the automobile, individual desires could be accommodated more readily, and many road systems were improvised to connect the railroad stations with frontier settlements. At first these roads existed mainly so farmers could market their produce, but subsequent extensions were the direct result of public demands for an improved highway system. People in the cities wanted to visit the countryside (Illustration 2-21) and people in the outlying areas were eager to "get a look at the big city." Within a few years we became a *mobile* people, but the road and highway system in use today was designed primarily to accommodate the transfer of goods rather than large volumes of people. Because of this, many of these "traffic arteries" are not in the best locations, nor of the most appropriate designs to satisfy *today's* demands. Thus,

Illustration 2-21
Automobile travel and parking problems of yesterday.

Illustration 2-22
Automobile travel today.

attempts to *drive* to work, *drive* downtown to shop, or take a leisurely *drive* through the countryside on a Sunday afternoon are more likely than not apt to be "experiences in frustration", (Illustration 2-22). Vehicle parking is also becoming a critical problem (Illustration 2-23).

Most cities have made only half-hearted attempts to care for the transportation needs of their most populous areas. Although those owning automobiles do experi-

Illustration 2-23
Parking problems today.

Illustration 2-24
Rapid transit systems have proved their usefulness in many major metropolitan areas.

Illustration 2-25
Highway guideway systems would relieve the driver of the tedious and tiring task of maneuvering his vehicle from one destination to another.

ence annoying inconveniences, those without automobiles suffer the most—especially the poor, the handicapped, the secondary worker, the elderly, and the young. Too often the public transit services that do exist are characterized by excessive walking distances to and from stations, poor connections and transfers, infrequent service, unreliability, slow speed and delays, crowding, noise, lack of comfort, and a lack of information for the rider's use. Moreover, passengers are often exposed to dangers to their personal safety while awaiting service.[40] Certainly not to be minimized are the more than 4 million injuries and the 52,000 fatalities that result annually from motor vehicle accidents. (For perspective, since 1963 highway fatalities have exceeded more than ten times the total loss of American lives in the Vietnam War.)[41]

Traditionally people have moved into a locality, built homes, businesses, and schools and then demanded that adequate transportation facilities be brought to them. We may now live in an era where this independence is no longer feasible, but rather people eventually may be required to settle around previously designed transportation systems. Engineers can provide good solutions for all of these problems *if they are allowed to do so by the public.* However, there will be a cost for each improvement—whether it be a better vehicle design, computerized control of traffic flow, redesigned urban bus systems, rapid transit systems (Illustration 2-24), highway guideway systems for vehicles (Illustration 2-25), or some other entirely new concept. In some instances city, state, or federal taxes must be levied; in others, the costs must be borne by each person who owns private transportation. Certainly the quality of urban life depends upon a unified commitment to this end.

---

[40] *Ibid.,* p. 6.
[41] Kenneth P. Cantor, "Warning: The Automobile Is Dangerous to Earth, Air, Fire, Water, Mind, and Body," *The Environmental Handbook,* Ballantine, New York (1970), p. 197.

The challenge of crime

Crime, one form of social pollution, is increasing rapidly in the United States in particular and throughout the world in general. The rate of increase in this country can be attributed variously to the population explosion, the increasing trend to urbanization, the changing composition of the population (particularly with respect to such factors as age, sex, and race), the increasing affluence of the populace, the diminishing influence of the home, and the deterioration of previously accepted value systems, mores, and standards of morality.[42] A recent survey of the National Opinion Research Center of the University of Chicago indicates that the actual amount of crime in the United States is known to be several times that reported. Figure 2-5 provides a comparison of recent increases in the seven forms of crime that are considered to be most serious in this country. A brief examination of these data indicates that the rate of increase of crime is now several times greater than the rate of increase of the population. In fact, crime is becoming such a serious social issue as to challenge the very fabric of our American way of life.

Not all people react in the same way to the threat of crime. Some are inclined to relocate their residences or places of business; some become fearful, withdrawn and antisocial; some are resentful and revengeful; and a large percentage become suspicious of particular ethnic groups whom they believe to be responsible. A number, of course, seize the opportunity to "join in," and they adopt crime as an "easy way" to get ahead in life. The majority, however, merely display moods of frustration and bewilderment. In all cases the consequential results are detrimental to everyone concerned, because a free society cannot long endure such strains on

[42] *The Challenge of Crime in a Free Society,* A Report of the President's Commission on Law Enforcement and Administration of Justice, Washington, D.C. (1967), pp. 17–90.

Figure 2-5 Reported crimes in the United States.

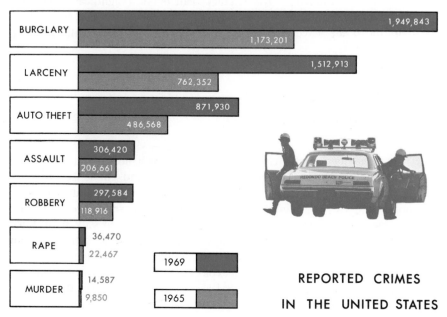

BURGLARY 1,949,843 / 1,173,201
LARCENY 1,512,913 / 762,352
AUTO THEFT 871,930 / 486,568
ASSAULT 306,420 / 206,661
ROBBERY 297,584 / 118,916
RAPE 36,470 / 22,467
MURDER 14,587 / 9,850

1969
1965

REPORTED CRIMES
IN THE UNITED STATES

Illustration 2-26
The low-light-level television is one contribution the engineer has made to aid in the suppression of crime.

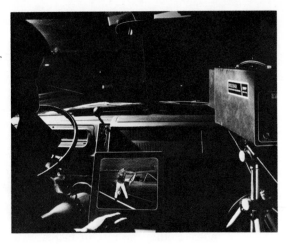

public and private confidences, nor tolerate the continual presence of fear within the populace.

Traditionally the detection, conviction, punishment, and even the prevention of crime have been functions of local, state, or federal agencies. Only in rare instances has private enterprise been called upon to assist in any significant way, and certainly there has been no concentrated effort to bring to bear on these situations the almost revolutionary advances that have been made in recent years in engineering, science, and technology. Rather, a few of the more spectacular developments have been modified or adapted for police operations or surveillance (Illustration 2-26).

What is needed, and needed now, is a delineation of the vast array of problems that relate to the prevention, detection, and punishment of crime, with particular attention being directed toward achieving *general* rather than *specific* solutions. In this way technological efforts can be concentrated in those areas where they are most likely to be productive. The engineer can make a significant contribution in this endeavor, and, in fact, we may have reached the time when such attention will be required if the wave of lawlessness now sweeping the country is to be stemmed.

Other opportunities and challenges

The discussions in this chapter are succinct and not intended to be complete in signalling the manifold and varied problems and challenges that confront the engineer *today*. Rather, an attempt has been made to point out specific areas of opportunity for the engineer and to discuss how these may relate to the well-being of society today and to that of future generations. Of necessity, many very important challenges have not been discussed, such as the mounting congestion caused by the products of communication media and the threatening inundation of existing information-processing systems, ocean exploration with all of its varied technical problems and yet almost unlimited potential as a source of material, the expertise that the engineer can contribute to the entire field of health care and biological and medical advance (Illustration 2-27), and the attendant social problems that are closely related

> . . . As never before, the work of the engineer is basic to the kind of society to which our best efforts are committed. Whether it be city planning, improved health care in modern facilities, safer and more efficient transportation, new techniques of communication or better ways to control pollution and dispose of wastes, the role of the engineer—his initiative, creative ability and hard work—is at the root of social progress in our time . . .
> —President Richard M. Nixon, February, 1971

to urbanization and population growth—such as mass migration, metropolitan planning, improved housing, and unemployment caused by outmoded work assignment.

It is axiomatic that technological advance always causes sociocultural change. In this sense the engineers and technologists who create new and useful designs are also "social revolutionaries."[43] After all it was they who brought about the obsolescence of slave labor, the emergence of transportation machines that allowed redistribution of the population, the radio and television sets that provide "instant commu-

[43] Melvin Kranzberg, "Engineering: A Force for Social Change," *Our Technological Environment: Challenge and Opportunity,* American Society for Engineering Education, Washington, D.C., (1971).

Illustration 2-27
Millions of people are alive today because of the availability of technical support systems that have been made possible by biomedical engineering design.

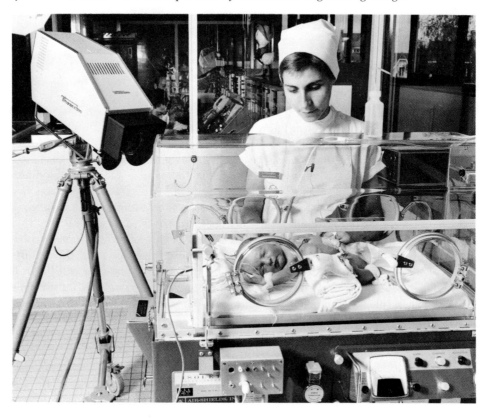

Illustration 2-28
As a professional person carrying great social responsibility for the solving of the manifold problems that have been brought about by the world's increasing population, the engineer cannot afford to be a man with sealed lips.

nication," and every convenience of liberation for the housewife—from mixers, waste disposers, dishwashers, ironers, and dryers to frozen foods. Frequently, society is not prepared to accept such abrupt changes—even though it is generally agreed that they are for the overall betterment of mankind. Because of this the engineer has a dual responsibility to society. He not only must continue to bring about improvements for the benefit of society, but he must exert every possible means to acquaint society with its responsibility for continual change. Without such an active voice in community and governmental affairs, irrational forces and misinformation can prevail (Illustration 2-28).

An environment of change

Man has always lived in an environment of change. As he has been able to add to his store of technical knowledge, he has also been able to change his economic structure and his sociological patterns. For centuries the changes that took place during a lifetime were hardly discernible. Beginning about 1600, the changes became more noticeable; and today technological change is literally exploding at an exponential rate. Although a description of this accelerated expansion by empirical means will suffice for general purposes, it is interesting to contemplate one's future if a growth curve relationship such as $k = a(i)^t$ is followed (Figure 2-6).

In Figure 2-6, engineering and scientific knowledge is assumed to be doubling every 15 to 20 years. Experience with other growth curves of this nature indicates that at some point a threshold will be reached and the rate will begin to decline. However, in considering the expansion of technology, no one can say with certainty when this slowing down is most likely to occur. National and international factors certainly must be taken into account.

We have many ways of measuring the increase in engineering knowledge and in the number of engineers. For example, the world supply of engineering and scientific manpower has been following a consistent growth pattern since the mid-seventeenth century. With this supply doubling approximately every 15 years, it is

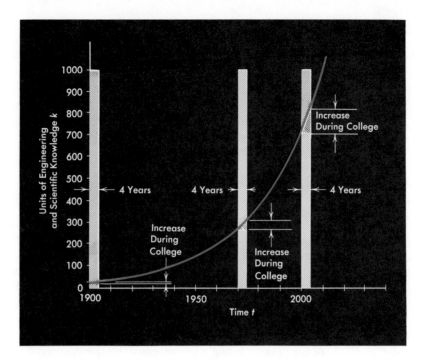

Figure 2-6 Growth of engineering and science.

easy to see that approximately 90 per cent of the engineers and scientists who have ever lived *are alive today.* The total number of scientific journals founded, the number of doctorates granted in engineering, the growth of a tomato vine, the growth of scientific discoveries, the growth of the U.S. population, and many other relationships which vary with time also tend to follow an exponential growth pattern.[44] Of course, they do not all grow at the same rate.

Similar factors are working to provoke changes in educational goals and patterns. In 1900, for example, the engineering student studied for four years to earn his baccalaureate degree, and he saw relatively little change take place in his technological environment during this period. Today, however, due to the accelerated growth pattern of engineering and scientific knowledge, many significant changes will have taken place between his freshman and senior years in college. In fact, complete new industries will be bidding for the services of the young graduate that were not even in existence at the time he began his freshman year of college. This is particularly true of the engineering student who continues his studies for a masters or a doctorate. It is also interesting to contemplate that at the present rate of growth, engineering and scientific knowledge will have doubled within 20 years after graduation. This places a special importance on continuing lifetime studies for all levels of engineering graduates.

These growth patterns, which are promoting change in all phases of society, are also causing educators and leaders in industry to reappraise existing educational practices with a view to increasing their scope and effectiveness. From time to time these changes, while not revolutionary, often provoke a sense of progress that shocks those who received their formal education a scant generation before.

[44]Derek J. De Solla Price, *Little Science, Big Science,* Columbia U. P., New York (1963), p. 11.

The education of the engineer

Engineering students who will be best prepared for a career of change should have better than average abilities in the following areas:

1. An ability to think with imagination and insight.
2. An ability to understand scientific principles and to apply analytical methods to the study of natural phenomena.
3. An ability to conceive, organize, and carry to completion appropriate experimental investigations.
4. An ability to synthesize and to design.[45]

In general, engineering programs in colleges and universities have concentrated upon providing a broad based education that is not closely aligned to a specific state-of-the-art. This has been necessary because for one to acquire even a small part of all the factual knowledge now available, a continuous memorization process would be required. It is, therefore, more appropriate to learn the basic laws of nature and certain essential facts that contribute to an understanding of problem solving. Emphasis must be placed upon developing mature minds and in educating engineers who can *think*. A means of condensing and concentrating the material to be learned is also of paramount importance. A powerful way of doing this is to employ mathematical techniques that can describe technical situations. For this reason mathematics is a most effective tool of the engineer and its mastery early in one's college career will allow for more rapid progress in such subjects as engineering mechanics, physics, and electrical circuit analysis. In a similar way, if a student learns the principles of physics, this knowledge will bind together such diverse engineering developments as magnetic materials, gas discharges, semiconductors, and dielectric and optical properties of materials. Similarly there is no substitute for a mastery of the fundamental principles of other sciences such as chemistry and biology.

Naturally, the education of an engineer must not end upon graduation from college. The pace of discovery is too great to consider any other course of action than to study and keep abreast of the expanding realm of science and technology. Therefore, in addition to learning fundamental principles of science and engineering in college, the student must develop an intellectual and technical curiosity that will encourage him to continue study after graduation.

In his work the engineer is faced constantly with situations in which problems appear where data are incomplete or perhaps where no prior similar experience is known. In such situations the engineer finds that he must make decisions in the face of uncertainty. He will be forced to draw upon his background of fundamental knowledge and frequently to engage himself in research or experimentation to ascertain or verify his conclusions. In obtaining such answers, however, it may be found that a contradictory situation exists to the one previously assumed to be present. It may also be that a specialized knowledge of several complex disciplines is required. In such cases a team effort may be used to advantage. In working with a team, the engineer must have an awareness of the broad relations existing between specialized sections of the team, and he must be able to integrate the in-depth knowledge of specialists into a summary that will clearly define the problem and provide the necessary answers.

[45]Joseph Kestin, Brown University *Engineer,* May 1965, p. 11.

The general objectives toward which an engineer must direct his educational goals are (a) an ability to communicate with his fellow men, (b) a facility for applying the principles of mathematics to his surroundings, (c) an awareness of the social and political implications of his technological achievements, (d) a skill in coordinating the efforts of others, (e) a mastery of the fundamental laws of nature as explained by science, and (f) a capability to recognize and define problems and then apply available knowledge and skills to the economic solution of those problems.

The basic educational needs for an engineer lie in the field of science. They may range from the biological sciences through the whole realm of physical sciences. From the knowledge of fundamental scientific principles, the student can see a pattern of understanding emerge from which he may select the parts needed to make an application of the principles to solve a problem. Since change will be a routine part of the engineer's environment, it is important that the curriculum be designed around a core of engineering sciences such as solid mechanics, energy conversion, electrical science, materials science, fluid mechanics, and mass and energy transfer. However, the process of instructing a student in the integration of a wide mass of knowledge is extremely difficult. One approach frequently used is to confront him with situations in which the data needed for decisions are fragmentary and to encourage him to draw on his own resources to complete the picture. When confronted with such problems the engineering student must realize that in practice the answer is seldom clear-cut and the best that one can hope for is to arrive at a solution which will accomplish the desired result with the fewest unfavorable side effects. Optimization and the evaluation of alternatives guide in the decision process. Here the engineer interrelates and correlates as many factors as possible to provide a good solution while realizing that none of the factors may be the optimum which he would like to have. Since the day, centuries ago, when the first engineers were actively engaged in their work, engineers always have applied their creative abilities to manipulate the materials and forces in nature available to them for the purpose of obtaining designs useful to man. Although technology will continue to change in the years ahead, the role of the engineer will not change.

For the foreseeable future, opportunity for the engineer will continue to expand at an exponential rate. Barring a national catastrophe or world war, available knowledge, productivity, and the living standard will probably continue to increase. For this reason man's resources must also continue to be available in larger and larger quantities, particularly with regard to water, energy, material, information, land, and air. Certainly it is hoped that man's appreciation for moral and esthetic values will continue to deepen and keep pace with this technological explosion.

Problems

2-1. Describe one instance in which the ecological balance of nature has been altered unintentionally by man.

2-2. Plot the rate of population growth for your state since 1900. What is your prediction of its population for the year 2000?

2-3. What can the engineer do that would make possible the improvement of the general "standards of living" in your home town?

2-4. Investigate world conditions and estimate the numbers of people who need some supplement to their diet. How can the engineer help to bring such help about?

2-5. From a technological and economic point of view, what are the fundamental causes of noise in buildings?

2-6. Borrow a sound-level meter and investigate the average sound level in decibels of (*a*) a busy freeway, (*b*) a television "soap opera," (*c*) a college classroom lecture, (*d*) a library reading room, (*e*) a home vacuum cleaner, (*f*) a riverbank at night, (*g*) a "rock" combo, (*h*) a jack hammer, (*i*) a chain saw, and (*j*) a kitchen mixer.

2-7. Which of the air pollutants appear to be most damaging to man's longevity? Why?

2-8. Explain the "greenhouse effect."

2-9. Investigate how the "smog intensity level" has changed over the past ten years for the nearest city of over 100,000 population. With current trends, what level would you expect for 1985?

2-10. Describe some effects that might result from a continually increasing percentage of carbon dioxide in the atmosphere.

2-11. Investigate the methods used in purifying the water supply from which you receive your drinking water. Describe improvements that you believe might be made to improve the quality of the water.

2-12. What are the apparent sources of pollution for the water supply serving your home?

2-13. Seek out three current newspaper accounts where man has caused pollution of the environment. What is your suggestion for remedy of each of these situations?

2-14. Investigate the problems that might be caused by increasing the average water temperature of the nearest river 20°F.

2-15. What means is currently being used to dispose of solid waste in the city where you live? Would you recommend some other procedure or process?

2-16. Estimate the amount of energy consumed by the members of your class in one year.

2-17. Considering the expanding demand for energy throughout the world, list ten challenges that require better engineering solutions.

2-18. What are the five most pressing problems that exist in your state with regard to transportation? Suggest at least one engineering solution for each.

2-19. List five new engineering designs that are needed to help suppress crime.

2-20. In the United States, what are the most pressing communications problems that need solving?

2-21. List five general problems not discussed in this chapter that need engineering solutions.

2-22.[46] The Marginal Chemical Corp. is a small company by Wall Street's standards, but it is one of the biggest employers and taxpayers in the little town in which it has its one and only plant. The company has an erratic earnings record, but production has been trending up at an average of 6 per cent a year—and along with it, so has the pollution from the plant's effluents into the large stream that flows by the plant. This stream feeds a large lake that has become unfit for bathing or fishing.

The number of complaints from town residents about this situation has been rising, and you, as a resident of the community and the plant's senior engineer, also have become increasingly concerned. Although the lake is a gathering place for the youth of the town, the City Fathers have applied only token pressure on the plant to clean up. Your immediate superior, Mr. Jones, the plant manager, has other worries because the plant has been caught in a cost/price squeeze and is barely breaking even.

After a careful study, you propose to Jones that, to have an effective pollution-abatement system, the company must make a capital investment of $1 million. This system will cost another $100,000 per year in operating expenses (e.g., for treatment chemicals, utilities, labor, laboratory support). Jones' reaction is:

"It's out of the question. As you know, we don't have an extra million around gathering dust—we'd have to borrow it at 10 per cent interest per year and, with the direct operating expenses, that means it would acutally cost us $200,000 a year to go through with your idea. The way things have been going, we'll be lucky if this plant

---

[46]Problems 2-22 through 2-25 are reprinted by special permission from *Chemical Engineering*, November 2, 1970, pp. 88–93, Copyright ©, by McGraw-Hill, Inc., New York, N.Y. 10036.

clears $200,000 this year, and we certainly can't raise prices. Even if we had the million handy, I'd prefer to use it to expand production of our new pigment; that way, it would give us a better jump on our competitors and on overseas competition. You can create a lot of new production—and new jobs—for a million dollars. This town needs new jobs more than it needs crystal-clear lakes, unless you want people to fish for a living. Besides, even if we weren't putting anything in the lake, it still wouldn't be crystal clear—there would still be all sorts of garbage in it."

During further discussion, the only concessions you can get from Jones is that you can spend $10,000 so that one highly visible (but otherwise insignificant) pollutant won't be discharged into the stream, and that if you can come up with an overall pollution-control scheme that will pay for itself via product recovery, he will give it serious consideration. You feel that the latter concession does not offer much hope, because not enough products with a ready market appear to be recoverable.

If you were this engineer, what do you think you *should* do? Consider the alternatives below.

    a. Report the firm to your state and other governmental authorities as being a polluter, and complain about the laxness of city officials (even though the possible outcome might be your dismissal, or the company deciding to close up shop).

    b. Go above Jones' head (i.e., to the president of the company). If he fails to overrule Jones, quit your job, and then take step *a.*

    c. Go along with Jones on an interim basis, and try to improve the plant's competitive position via a rigorous cost-reduction program so that a little more money can be spent on pollution control in a year or two. In the meantime, do more studies of product-recovery systems, and keep him aware of your continued concern with pollution control.

    d. Relax, and let Jones tell you when to take the next antipollution step. After all, he has managerial responsibility for the plant. You have not only explained the problem to him, but have suggested a solution, so you have done your part.

    e. Other action (explain).

2-23. *a.* You are the division manager of Sellwell Co.—a firm that has developed an inexpensive household specialty that you hope will find a huge market among housewives. You want to package this produce in 1-gallon and ½-gallon sizes. A number of container materials would appear to be practical—glass, aluminum, treated paper, steel, and various types of plastics. A young engineer whom you hired recently and assigned to the manufacturing department has done a container-disposal study that shows that the disposal cost for 1-gallon containers can vary by a factor of three—depending upon the weight of the container, whether it can be recycled, whether it is easy to incinerate, whether it has good landfill characteristics, and so on.

    Your company's marketing expert believes that the container material with the highest consumer appeal is the one that happens to present the biggest disposal problem and cost to communities. He estimates that the sales potential would be at least 10 per cent less if the easiest-to-dispose-of, salvageable container were used, because this container would be somewhat less distinctive and attractive.

    Assuming that the actual costs of the containers were about the same, to what extent would you let the disposal problem influence your choice? Would you:

    (1) Choose the container strictly on its marketing appeal, on the premise that disposal is the community's problem, not yours (and also that some communities may not be ready to use the recycling approach yet, regardless of which container material you select).

    (2) Choose the easiest-to-dispose-of container, and either accept the sales penalty, or try to overcome it by stressing the "good citizenship" angle (even though the marketing department is skeptical about whether this will work).

    (3) Take the middle road, by accepting a 5 per cent sales penalty to produce a container that is midway on the disposability scale.

(4) Other action (explain).

    b. Do you think the young engineer who made the container-disposal study (but who is not a marketing expert) has any moral obligation to make recommendations as to which container to use? Explain your position.

2-24. Stan Smith, a young engineer with two years of experience, has been hired to assist a senior engineer in the evaluation of air and water pollution problems at a large plant—one that is considering a major expansion that would involve a new product. Local civic groups and labor unions favor this expansion, but conservation groups are opposed to it.

    Smith's specific assignment is to evaluate control techniques for the effluents in accordance with state and federal standards. He concludes that the expanded plant will be able to meet these standards. However, he is not completely happy, because the aerial discharge will include an unusual by-product whose effects are not well known, and whose control is not considered by state and federal officials in the setting of standards.

    In doing further research, he comes across a study that tends to connect respiratory diseases with this type of emission in one of the few instances where such an emission took place over an extended time period. An area downwind of the responsible plant experienced a 15 per cent increase in respiratory diseases. The study also tends to confirm that the pollutant is difficult to control by any known means.

    When Smith reports these new findings to his engineering supervisor, he is told that by now the expansion project is well along, the equipment has been purchased, and it would be very expensive and embarrassing for the company suddenly to halt or change its plans.

    Furthermore, the supervisor points out that the respiratory-disease study involved a different geography of the country and, hence, different climatic conditions, and also that apparently only transitory diseases were increased, rather than really serious ones. This increase might have been caused by some unique combination of contaminants, rather than only the one in question, and might not have occurred at all if the other contaminants had been controlled as closely as they will be in the new facility.

    If Smith still believes that there is a reasonable possibility (but not necessarily certainty) that the aerial discharge would lead to an increase in some types of ailments in the downwind area, should he:

    a. Go above his superior, to an officer of the company (at the risk of his previously good relationship with his superior).

    b. Take it upon himself to talk to the appropriate control officials and to pass their opinions along to his superior (which entails the same risk).

    c. Talk to the conservation groups and (in confidence) give them the type of ammunition they are looking for to halt the expansion.

    d. Accept his superior's reasoning (keeping a copy of pertinent correspondence so as to fix responsibility if trouble develops).

    e. Other action (explain).

2-25. Jerry Williams is a chemical engineer working for a large diversified company on the East Coast. For the past two years, he has been a member—the only technically trained member—of a citizens' pollution-control group working in his city.

    As a chemical engineer, Williams has been able to advise the group about what can reasonably be done about abating various kinds of pollution, and he has even helped some smaller companies to design and buy control equipment. (His own plant has air and water pollution under good control.) As a result of Williams' activity, he has built himself considerable prestige on the pollution-control committee.

    Recently, some other committee members started a drive to pressure the city administration into banning the sale of phosphate-containing detergents. They have been impressed by reports in their newspapers and magazines on the harmfulness of phosphates.

    Williams believes that banning phosphates would be misdirected effort. He tries to explain that although phosphates have been attacked in regard to the eutrophication of the Great Lakes, his city's sewage flows from the sewage-treatment plant directly into the ocean. And he feels that nobody has shown any detrimental effect of phosphate on the ocean. Also, he is aware that there are conflicting theories on the effect of phosphates, even on the Great Lakes (e.g., some theories put the blame on nitrogen or carbon rather than phosphates, and suggest that some phosphate substitutes may do more harm than good).

In addition, he points out that the major quantity of phosphate in the city's sewage comes from human wastes rather than detergent.

Somehow, all of this reasoning makes little impression on the backers of the "ban phosphates" measure. During an increasingly emotional meeting, some of the committee men even accuse Williams of using stalling tactics in order to protect his employer who, they point out, has a subsidiary that makes detergent chemicals.

Williams is in a dilemma. He sincerely believes that his viewpoint makes sense, and that it has nothing to do with his employer's involvement with detergents (which is relatively small, anyway, and does not involve Williams' plant). Which step should he now take?

a. Go along with the "ban phosphates" clique on the grounds that the ban won't do any harm, even if it doesn't do much good. Besides, by giving the group at least passive support, Williams can preserve his influence for future items that really matter more.

b. Fight the phosphate foes to the end, on the grounds that their attitude is unscientific and unfair, and that lending it his support would be unethical. (Possible outcomes: his ouster from the committee or its breakup as an effective body.)

c. Resign from the committee, giving his side of the story to the local press.

d. Other action (explain).

Bibliography

Alexander, Tom, "Some Burning Questions About Combustion," *Fortune,* February 1970.

Bates, Marston, "The Human EcoSystem," *Resources and Man,* W. F. Freeman, San Francisco (1969).

Bylinsky, Gene, "The Limited War on Pollution," *The Environment,* Harper & Row, New York (1970).

Cantor, Kenneth P., "Warning: The Automobile Is Dangerous to Earth, Air, Fire, Water, Mind, and Body," *The Environmental Handbook,* Ballantine, New York (1970).

Cleaning our Environment: The Chemical Basis for Action. American Chemical Society, Washington, D.C. (1969).

Robert C. Cook (ed.), "The Thin Slice of Life," *Population Bulletin,* Vol. XXIV, No. 5.

DeBall, Garrett, "Energy," *The Environmental Handbook,* Ballantine, New York (1970).

"Eat, Drink, and Be Sick," *Medical World News,* September 26, 1969.

Ehrlich, Paul R., *The Population Bomb,* Ballantine, New York (1968).

Environmental Science and Technology, May 1970.

Farb, Peter, *Ecology,* Time, New York (1963).

Ferkiss, Victor C., *Technological Man: The Myth and the Reality,* George Braziller, New York (1969).

Gaucher, L. P., "Energy Sources in the United States," *Journal of Solar Energy,* Vol. 9, No. 3 (1965), p. 122.

Glorig, Aram, *Noise As a Public Health Hazard,* W. Dixon Ward and James E. Fricke (eds.), The American Speech and Hearing Association, Washington, D.C. (1969).

Hershaft, Alex, "Solid Waste Treatment," *Science and Technology,* June 1969.

Andrew D. Hosey and Charles H. Powell, (Eds.), *Indistrial Noise,* U.S. Department of Health, Education, and Welfare, Washington, D.C. (1967).

Hubbert, M. King, *Resources and Man,* W. H. Freeman, San Francisco (1969).

Jones, Joseph M., *Does Overpopulation Mean Poverty?* Center for International Economic Growth, Washington, D.C. (1962).

Kestin, Joseph, Brown University *Engineer,* May 1965.

Kranzberg, Melvin, "Engineering: A Force for Social Change," *Our Technological Environment: Challenge and Opportunity,* American Society for Engineering Education, Washington, D.C. (1971).

Krenkel, Peter A. and Frank L. Parker, (eds.), *Engineering Aspects of Thermal Pollution,* Nashville, Tenn.: (Vanderbilt Univ. Press, 1968).

McLuhan, Marshall, *Understanding Media,* McGraw-Hill, New York (1964).

Malthus, T. R., 1798. *An Essay on the Principles of Population As It Affects the Future Improvements of Mankind,* Facsimile reprint in 1926 for J. Johnson. Macmillan, London.

Malthus, Thomas, Julian Huxley, and Frederick Osborn, *Three Essays on Population.* Mentor Books: The New American Library, New York (1960).

Mock, Jesse (ed.), "The Engineer's Responsibility to Society," American Society of Mechanical Engineers, New York (1969).

Nelson, Senator Gaylord, *Congressional Record,* February 26, 1970.

Newell, Reginald E., "The Global Circulation of Atmospheric Pollutants," *Scientific American,* January 1971.

Noise: Sound Without Value, Committee on Environmental Quality of the Federal Council for Science and Technology, Washington, D.C. (1968).

Price, Derek J. DeSolla, *Little Science, Big Science,* Columbia U. P., New York (1963).

Ritchie-Calder, Lord, Quoted in *Engineering Opportunities—College Edition,* February 1970.

Rodda, Michael, *Noise and Society,* Oliver & Boyd, London (1967).

Singer, S. Fred, "Human Energy Production as a Process in the Biosphere," *Scientific American,* September 1970.

Starr, Chauncey, and Craig Smith, "Energy and The World of A.D. 2000," *Engineering for the Benefit of Mankind,* National Academy of Engineering, Washington, D.C. (1970).

The Challenge of Crime in a Free Society, A Report of the President's Commission on Law Enforcement and Administration of Justice, Washington, D.C. (1967).

The Environment, The Editors of Fortune, Harper & Row, New York (1970).

Tomorrow's Transportation, U.S. Department of Housing and Urban Development, Washington, D.C. (1968).

U.S. News & World Report, September 8, 1969, p. 65.

Weinberg, Alvin M., and R. Philip Hammond, "Limits to the Use of Energy," *American Scientist,* August 1970.

Wigotsky, Victor W., "Engineering and the Urban Crisis," *Design News,* December 7, 1970.

Wohlers, Henry C., *Air Pollution—The Problem, the Source, and the Effects,* Drexel Institute of Technology, Philadelphia (1969).

Your Right to Clean Air, The Conservation Foundation, Washington, D.C. (1970).

3

The role of the scientific team in a technological environment

Some students become interested in a career in engineering at an early age—perhaps even in elementary school. Often the spark of excitement has been provided by some neighbor, friend, or member of the family who is an engineer. Teachers and school counselors also perform a valuable service in providing students with literature pertaining to engineering as a profession; however, it is not uncommon for many freshman or sophomore college students to ask themselves the question, "Do I really want to be an engineer?" This is not surprising since there is a general misunderstanding in the United States today concerning the role played by the engineer in our modern technical society.

The scientific team

In the expanding realm of science and technology, the engineer is a member of a three-part team of technical specialists. These specialists are engineers, scientists, and technicians (Illustration 3-1). Although their spheres of activity overlap, they tend to fit into specific roles appropriate to their interests and areas of work. Since high school graduates sometimes decide to enter one of these fields without understanding the training, qualifications, and type of work each specialist requires, let us consider a brief description of each field.

The engineer

The engineer is concerned primarily with the application of discoveries to benefit mankind. It is his objective to design, plan, develop, and construct usable devices that employ scientific principles. In this role, he must understand the laws and

Illustration 3-1

Engineers, scientists, and technicians worked in concert to overcome almost unsurmountable technical problems in sending a space crew to the moon and returning them safely to earth.

Illustration 3-2

The engineer is responsible for creative and imaginative design. This includes every step in the design process from the origination of the idea to the finished product. Here an engineer is discussing necessary changes in a design with a draftsman in his design group.

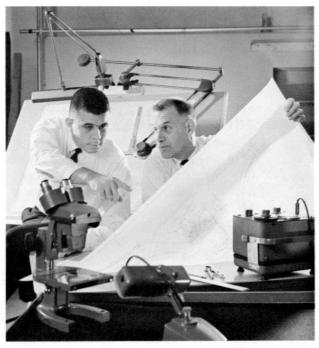

principles of science in order to be able to take new discoveries and to make practical applications of them. For example, recent discoveries in biology have made it possible for engineers, with the assistance of medical doctors, to develop new devices that may add materially to our ability to treat certain diseases and defects of the human heart. Chapters 4 and 5 consider the work of the engineer in more detail.

The scientist

The primary objective of the scientist is to discover, to expand the fields of knowledge, to correlate observations and experimental data into a formulation of laws, to learn new theories and explore their meanings, and to broaden the horizons of science into the unknown. In general, the scientist is less concerned with the practical application of discoveries than with adding to the sum total of human knowledge.

The technician

In many cases, much of the actual fabrication of devices designed by engineers is performed by technicians. These persons are specialists, usually in a specific field, where manual skill is needed. They may be draftsmen, electronic technicians, laboratory technicians, cost estimators, equipment operators, or service and maintenance specialists. Usually, the technician, although he may have studied some courses in

Illustration 3-3
The scientist engages in basic research to discover fundamental facts that form the basis for natural laws.

engineering, has only general training in mathematics and science. The technician frequently performs the manual part of engineering concerned with experimental models, troubleshooting, filling in details of design, recording data while laboratory tests are being conducted, and helping in subprofessional work. The technician's role should not be confused with the work of a craftsman or mechanic. The craftsman or mechanic has specific manual skills, acquired usually over a long period of apprenticeship; he is much less concerned with the scientific, mathematical, or engineering features of a design. Rather, his interest is in using his manual skills to produce a part that will show his competence as a craftsman.

Thus, engineering technology is a part of the engineering field which deals more with applications of established scientific and engineering principles. The engineering technician is the person who is the practitioner in the field of engineering technology.

A report by the Engineers' Council for Professional Development[1] includes a recommendation that the term *engineering technician* be applied to graduates of the more common two-year associate degree programs in engineering technology and the term *engineering technologist* be applied to graduates of four-year baccalaureate programs. At present the term *engineering technician* is most commonly used in industry to denote both levels of training because the four-year programs have, in general, made their appearance in the past few years.

In Figure 3-1 we see pictured the relationship of the engineering technician to others in the realm of science and technology. As is true in a color spectrum, there is no obvious boundary on the extent or limits of the occupational activities. Any given individual might find his interests and work at any place in the spectrum. Education and training for the occupational specialties, however, are divided into the four categories shown in Figure 3-1.

In the relationships pictured, the engineering technician must be practical enough to understand the problems of the craftsman in order to communicate with him and, at the same time, must possess enough technical and theoretical knowledge

[1]Engineers Council for Professional Development, 39th Annual Report, 1970–71.

Figure 3-1 Occupational spectrum.

Craftsman	Engineering technician	Engineer	Scientist
One whose work involves repetitive or manipulative skills.	A trained and skilled person whose work involves the application and execution of designs of an engineering or scientific nature. Practices state-of-the-art. May also supervise the work of skilled labor.	Translates the findings of science into usable forms by his designs. Develops new principles and methods useful to man.	Searches for new knowledge concerning the nature of man and the universe. Infrequently involved in supervisory work.
Skilled labor, individual effort. Seldom supervises the work of others.		Work usually involves a high degree of creativity. Frequently supervises the work of the engineering and scientific team.	

Illustration 3-4

The technician assists the engineer by constructing, testing, and operating equipment that the engineer has designed. Here a technician adjusts voltages on a "breadboard" model of a video telephone system.

to understand the applications of ideas as they are developed by engineers and scientists.

The engineering technician must be able to carry out in a responsible manner proven techniques in various operations and procedures under the direction of engineers and scientists. In general, the work performed by the technician parallels at a different level the work of engineers and scientists. It is of a more practical nature and is usually directed toward the applications of concepts.

Technicians perform work in virtually every phase of engineering and science. They may, for example, work in such functions as research, development, design, experimentation, data processing, or model testing. They may also assist in other activities such as production planning, the making of quality control tests, and in the making of time and motion studies. In addition, they may serve as technical maintenance specialists, technical writers, or as sales representatives.

In order to fit into this part of the scientific team, the technician must have some understanding of scientific and mathematical theory as well as have specialized training in some specific branch of scientific technology. Some mathematical ability is needed to analyze and solve engineering problems and certain additional instruction and training are necessary to provide competence in the operation of complex equipment or, for example, to make technical sketches and drawings for use by others. Frequently, it is also desirable to understand the fundamentals of computer programming to aid in data analysis and problem solving.

The experienced technician is expected to work without close engineering supervision. Frequently his job will require that he supervise the work of craftsmen and of other technicians. In this work, it is necessary that he be able to communicate effectively his ideas and instructions to others, both orally and in writing. Thus an adequate vocabulary is essential, and familiarity with basic rules of grammar is desirable.

From the above we see the technician as an indispensable member of the scientific team because his work forms the bridge between theoretical and abstract concepts and the actual design, construction, fabrication, and production of discrete items.

The role of the engineer

It is generally known that engineering has made possible the many material things that now make our lives more enjoyable and provide extra time for recreation and study. It is also an accepted belief that the engineer will continue to provide innovative and creative designs for the purpose of easing the burdens of man's physical toil and to convert the materials and forces of Nature to the use of all mankind; however, when the time comes to make a choice of careers, each student finds himself groping for an answer to the question, "As an engineer, how would *I* fit into this picture?"

First, we must realize that one does not become an engineer solely by studying a few courses. Engineering education is more than knowing when to manipulate a set of formulas, knowing where to search in an armful of reference books, or knowing how to get accurate answers from a slide rule or computer; it is also a state of mind. Through experience and training the engineer must be able to formulate problem statements and must conceive design solutions that many times involve novel ideas and creative thought processes. He must also exercise judgment and restraint, must design with initiative and reliability, and must be completely honest with himself and with others. These qualities should all mature as the student enginer advances from elementary to graduate-level studies.

What skills does the engineer need?

The public expects all engineers to be competent technically. The profession has through the years built up a record of producing things that work. No one expects a company to produce television tubes that explode spontaneously, or a bridge that falls down, or an irrigation ditch that has the wrong slope. In fact, the technological failures of engineering are so rare that when they do occur, they usually are front page news.

The engineering curriculum followed in college is designed to instill technical competence. The grading system generally used in college rewards acceptable solutions and penalizes inferior or unworkable solutions to practical problems. The subjects studied are not easy, and usually those persons who do not adapt themselves to the discipline of study and who do not accept the ideas of the exactness of Nature's laws will not complete a college engineering course. This discipline has paid handsome dividends. The consistency of quality in the engineering graduate over many years has given the public a confidence that must not be destroyed.

It should also be realized, however, that the completion of a college course is not the end of study for an engineer. The pace of discovery is so rapid today that, even with constant study, the engineer barely can keep abreast of technological improvements. If the engineering graduate should resolve not to continue his technical study, he would be far behind in technology within five years and probably would be completely out of step within ten years.

The engineer, then, must be capable of dealing with technological problems—not only those which he may have been trained to handle in college but also new and unfamiliar situations which arise as a result of new discoveries. Of course, it is obvious that college courses can present problem areas only in general terms. Upon a base of fundamental principles, the engineer is expected to provide solutions to new problem situations.

After college what are the opportunities?

A question that arises frequently in the mind of an engineering student is "What if I start out in engineering and decide to change to another course of study?" Let us examine some of the possibilities. Normally an engineering student will follow engineering as a profession. However, many students change their mind during their college career or after graduation. Many authorities agree that engineering courses are excellent training for a great variety of careers, and records reveal that perhaps as many as 40 per cent of people on a management level have engineering educations. One of the basic and most valuable training concepts of an engineering education is that *engineering students are taught to think logically.* This means that if a career decision is made not to follow engineering as a profession, the training and experience gained in engineering courses still will prepare a person for a wide variety of occupations.

What will the future hold for the serious student who proposes to make engineering his career? *First,* employment possibilities will be good. The rigor of the college courses usually removes those who are unable or unwilling to stick with a problem until they come up with a reasonable answer. Those who graduate in engineering usually are well qualified technically and, in addition, are well rounded in their knowledge of nonengineering courses.

Second, he will enjoy the profession. A sampling of questionnaires sent to engineers in large industrial concerns shows that those with several years experience almost unanimously enjoy their work. They like the opportunities for advancement, the challenges of new and exciting problems to be solved, the friendships gained in contacts with people with diverse backgrounds, and the possibilities of seeing their ideas develop into working realities. The engineer will find that as a profession, the salary scale is among the higher groups, and his individual income usually is determined largely by the quality of his own efforts.

Third, engineering provides unlimited opportunities for creative design. As has been mentioned before, the pace of discovery is so great that the need for the application of discoveries provides countless places where the engineer with initiative and creative ability can spend his time in development. Also, in applications which are old and well known, the clever engineer can devise new, better, and more economical ways of providing the same services. For example, although roads have been built for centuries, the need for faster and more efficient methods of road building offers a continuing challenge to engineers.

Sometimes nontechnical people say that engineers are too dogmatic, that they think of things as being either positive or negative. To a certain extent this is true because of the engineer's training. He is educated to give realistic answers to real problems and to make the answers the most practical ones that he can produce. Within his knowledge of Nature's laws, the engineer usually can obtain a precise solution to a given problem, and he is always willing to defend his solution. To a nontechnical person accustomed to arriving at a solution by surmise, argument, and compromise, the positive approach of the engineer frequently is distressing. Part of the postgraduate training of an engineer is learning to convince nontechnical people of the worth of a design. The ability to reason, to explain by using simple applications, and to have patience in presenting ideas in simple terms that can be understood are essential qualities of the successful engineer.

The engineer does not claim to be a genius. However, by training, he is a leader. Because he has a responsibility to his profession and to his community to exercise that leadership, he should establish a set of technical and moral standards that will provide a wholesome influence upon all levels of his organization and upon his community as a whole.

Problems on the engineer's role

3-1. Interview an engineer and write a 500-word essay concerning his work.
3-2. Survey the job opportunities for engineers, scientists, and technicians. Discuss the differences in opportunity and salary.
3-3. Discuss the role of the engineer in government.
3-4. Frequently technical personnel in industry are given the title "engineer" in lieu of other benefits. Discuss the difficulties that arise as a result of this practice.
3-5. Write an essay on the differences between the work of the engineer, the scientist, and the technician.
3-6. Write an essay on the differences between the education of the engineer, the scientist, and the technician.
3-7. Interview an engineering technician and write a 500-word essay concerning his work.
3-8. Discuss the role of the engineering technician in the aircraft industry.
3-9. Investigate the opportunities for employment of electronic technicians. Write a 500-word essay concerning your findings.
3-10. Investigate the differences in educational requirements of the engineer and the technician. Discuss your conclusions.
3-11. Classify the following items as to the most probable assignment in the Occupational Spectrum:
    a. Detail drawing of a small metal mounting bracket.
    b. Assisting an engineer in determining the pH of a solution.
    c. Boring a hole in an aluminum casting to fit a close tolerance pin.
    d. Determining the behavior of flow of a viscous fluid through a pipe elbow.
    e. Determining the percentage of carbon in a series of steel specimens to be used in fabricating cutter bits.

 f. Designing a device to permit the measurement of the temperature of molten zinc at a location approximately 150 feet from a vat.

 g. Preparation of a laboratory report concerning the results of a series of tests on an assortment of prospective heat-curing bonding adhesives.

 h. Preparing a work schedule for assigning manpower for a 2-day test of a small gasoline engine.

 i. Determining the effects of adding ammonia to the intake air of a gas turbine engine.

 j. Fabrication of 26 identical transistorized circuits using printed circuit boards.

 k. Calculation of the area of an irregular tract of land from a surveyor's field notes.

 l. Preparation of a proposal to study the effect of sunlight on anodized and unanodized aluminum surfaces.

 m. Design and fabrication of a device to indicate the rate of rainfall at a location several hundred feet from the sensing apparatus.

 n. Interpretation of the results of a test on a punch tape controlled milling machine.

 o. Preparing a computer program to determine the location of the center of gravity of an airplane from measured weight data.

3-12. A large office building is to be constructed, and tests of the load-bearing capacity of the underlying soil are to be made. Outline at least one way each of the members of the scientific team, scientists, engineers, technicians, and craftsmen, are involved in the work of determining suitability of the soil for supporting a building.

Bibliography

Engineer's Council for Professional Development, 39th Annual Report, 1970–1971.

Journal of Engineering Education, Vol. 53, No. 9, May 1963.

Journal of Engineering Education, Vol. 57, No. 3, November 1966.

Love, Albert, and James Saxon Childers, *Listen to Leaders in Engineering,* Tupper and Love, Atlanta, Ga. (1965).

Love, Albert, and James Saxon Childers, *Listen to Leaders in Science,* Tupper and Love, Atlanta, Ga. (1965).

O'Dea, William T., *The Meaning of Engineering,* Museum Press, London (1961).

Rapport, Samuel, and Helen Wright, *Engineering,* New York U. P., New York (1963).

Taylor, Lloyd W., *Physics, The Pioneer Science,* Houghton Mifflin, Boston (1941).

Whinnery, John R., *The World of Engineering,* McGraw-Hill, New York (1965).

4

The work of
the engineer

During the years that he is in college, an engineering student will study courses in many subject areas. He will study language courses to better prepare himself in organizing and presenting ideas effectively, mathematics courses to learn the manipulation of symbols as an aid in problem solving, social science courses to help him better find his place in society as an informed citizen, and various technical courses to gain an understanding of natural laws. In his study of technical courses, he will become familiar with a store of factual information that will form the basis for his engineering decisions. The nature of these technical courses, in general, determines the major field of interest of the student. For example, he may decide to concentrate his major interest in some particular field such as civil, chemical, industrial, or mechanical engineering.

The college courses also provide training in learning facts and in developing powers of reasoning. Since it is impossible to predict what kind of work a practicing engineer will be doing after graduation, the objective of an engineering education is to provide a broad base of facts and skills upon which the engineer can practice his profession.

It usually is not sufficient to say that an engineer is working as a *civil engineer*. His work may vary over a wide spectrum. As a civil engineer, for example, he may be performing research on materials for surfacing highways, or he may be employed in government service and be responsible for the budget preparation of a missile launch project. In fact, there are many things that a practicing engineer will be called upon to do which are not described by his major course of study. The *type* of work that the engineer may do, as differentiated from his major field of specialization, can be called "engineering function." Some of these functions are research, development, design, production, construction, operations, sales, and management.

It has been found that in some engineering functions, such as in the management of a manufacturing plant, specialization is of lesser importance, whereas in other functions, such as research in transistor theory, specialization may be extremely important. In order to understand more fully the activities of a practicing engineer, let us examine some of these functions.

Research

Today research is one of the more glamorous functions of engineering. In this type of work the engineer delves into the nature of matter, exploring processes to use engineering materials and searching for reasons for the behavior of the things that make up our world. In many instances the work of the scientist and the engineer who are engaged in research will overlap. The work of scientists usually is closely allied with research. The objective of the research scientist is to *discover truths*. The objective of the research engineer, on the other hand, usually is directed toward the practical side of the problem: not only to discover but also *to find a use for the discovery.*

Illustration 4-1
Research is an important type of work performed by the engineer. In this work he employs basic scientific principles in the discovery and application of new knowledge. This engineer is experimenting with a model in a wind tunnel to determine the effect of pollutants upon the surrounding environment.

The research engineer must be especially perceptive and clever. He must be able to work patiently at tasks never before accomplished and must be able to recognize and identify phenomena previously unnoticed. As an aid to training an engineer to do research work, some colleges give courses in research techniques. However, the life of a research engineer can be quite disheartening. Since he is probing and exploring in new areas, much of his work is trial and error, and outstanding results of investigation usually occur only after long hours of painstaking and often discouraging work.

Until within the last few decades, almost all research was solo work by individuals. However, with the rapid expansion of the fields of knowledge of chemistry, physics, and biology, it became apparent that groups or "research teams" of scientists and engineers could accomplish better the aims of research by pooling their efforts and knowledge. Within the teams, the enthusiasm and competition provide added incentive to push the work forward, and since each person is able to contribute from his specialty, discovery is accelerated.

As has been indicated, a thorough training in the basic sciences and mathematics is essential for a research engineer. In addition, an inquiring mind and a great curiosity about the behavior of things is desirable. Most successful research engineers have a fertile and uninhibited imagination and a knack of observing and questioning phenomena that the majority of people overlook. For example, one successful research engineer has worked on such diverse projects as an automatic lawnmower, an electronic biological eye to replace natural eyes, and the use of small animals as electrical power sources.

Most research engineers secure advanced degrees because they need additional training in basic sciences and mathematics, and in addition, this study usually gives them an opportunity to acquire useful skills in research procedures.

Development

After a basic discovery in natural phenomena is made, the next step in its utilization involves the development of processes or machines that employ the principles involved in the discovery. In the research and development fields, as in many other functions, the areas of activity overlap. In many organizations the functions of research and development are so interrelated that the department performing this work is designated simply as a research and development (R and D) department.

The engineering features of development are concerned principally with the actual construction, fabrication, assembly, layout, and testing of scale models, pilot models, and experimental models for pilot processes or procedures. Where the research engineer is concerned more with making a discovery that will have commercial or economic value, the development engineer will be interested primarily in producing a process, an assembly, or a system *that will work.*

The development engineer does not deal exclusively with new discoveries. Actually the major part of his work will involve using well-known principles and employing existing processes or machines to perform a new or unusual function. It is in this region that many patents are granted. In times past, the utilization of basic machines, such as a wheel and axle, and fundamental principles including Ohm's Law and Lenz' Law, have eventually led to patentable articles, such as the electric

Illustration 4-2

Development engineers use the results of basic research and convert them into models and prototypes for full-scale testing and evaluation. In this picture a team of engineers and technicians are shown engaged in the development of a super cryogenic design.

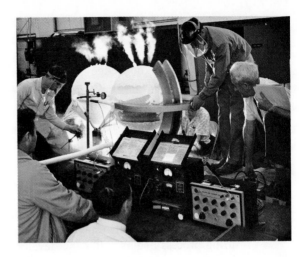

dynamo. On the other hand, within a very short time after the announcement of the discovery of the laser in 1960, a number of patents were issued on devices employing this new principle. Thus the lag between the discovery of new knowledge and the use of that knowledge has been steadily decreasing through the years.

In most instances the tasks of the development engineer are dictated by immediate requirements. For example, a new type of device may be needed to determine at all times the position in space of an airplane. Let us suppose that the development engineer does not know of any existing device that can perform the task to the desired specifications. Should he immediately attempt to invent such a device? The answer, of course, is, "usually not." First, he should explore the files of available literature for information pertaining to existing designs. Such information may come from two principal sources. The first source is library material on processes, principles, and methods of accomplishing the task or related tasks. The second source is manufacturers' literature. It has been said humorously that there is no need to reinvent the wheel. A literature search may reveal a device that can accomplish the task with little or no modification. If no device is available that will do the work, a system of existing subassemblies may be set up and joined to accomplish the desired result. Lacking these items, the development engineer must go further into basic literature, and using results from experiments throughout the world, formulate plans to construct a model for testing. Previous research points a way to go, or perhaps a mathematical analysis will provide clues as to possible methods.

The development engineer usually works out his ideas on a trial or "breadboard" basis, whether it be a machine or a computer process. Having the parts or systems somewhat separated facilitates changes, modifications, and testing. In this process, improved methods may become apparent and can be incorporated. When the system or machine is in a workable state, the development engineer must then refine it and package it for use by others. Here again ingenuity and a knowledge of human nature is important. A device that works satisfactorily in a laboratory when manipulated by skilled technicians may be hopelessly complex and unsuited for field use. The development engineer is the important man behind every push button.

The training of an engineer for development work is similar to the training that the research engineer will expect to receive. However, creativity and innovation are perhaps of more importance, since the development engineer is standing between the scientist or the research engineer and the members of management who provide money for the research effort. He must be able to recognize the economic value of certain processes over others in achieving a desired result, and he must be able to convince others that his conclusions are the ones that should be accepted. A comprehensive knowledge of basic principles of science and an inherent cleverness in making things work are essential skills for the development engineer.

Design

In our modern way of life, mass production has given us cheaper products and has made more articles available than ever before in history. In the process of producing these articles, the design engineer enters the scene just before the actual manufacturing process begins. After the development engineer has assembled and tested a device or a process and it has proved to be one that it is desirable to produce for a mass market, the final details of making it adaptable for production will be handled by a design engineer.

In his role of bridging the gap between the laboratory and the production line, the design engineer must be a versatile individual. He should be well grounded in basic engineering principles and in mathematics, and he must not only understand the capabilities of machines but also the temperament of the men who operate them. He must be conscious also of the relative costs of producing items, for it will be his design that will determine how long the product will survive in the open market. Not only must the device or process work, it must also be made in a style and at a price that will attract customers.

As an example, let us take a clock, a simple device widely used to indicate time. It includes a power source, a drive train, hands, and a face. Using these basic parts, engineers have designed spring-driven clocks, weight-driven clocks, and electrically driven clocks with all variations of drive trains. The basic hands and face have been modified in some models to give a digital display. The case has been made in many shapes and, perhaps in keeping with the slogan "time flies," it has even been streamlined! In the design of each modification the design engineer has determined the physical structure of the assembly, its esthetic features, and the economics of producing it.

Of course the work of the design engineer is not limited solely to performing engineering on mass produced items. Design engineers may work on items such as bridges or buildings in which only one of a kind is to be made. However, in such work he still is fulfilling the design process of adapting basic ideas to provide for making a completed product for the use of others. In this type of design the engineer must be able to use his training, in some cases almost intuitively, to arrive at a design solution which will provide for adequate safety without excessive redundancy. The more we learn about the behavior of structural materials, the better we can design without having to add additional materials to cover the "ignorance factor" area. Particularly in the aircraft industry, design engineers have attempted to use structural materials with minimum excess being allowable as a safety factor. Each part must perform without failure, and every ounce of weight must be saved. Of course to do this, fabricated parts of the design must be tested and retested for resistance to failure due either to static loads or to vibratory fatiguing loads. Also, since surface

Illustration 4-3
The design engineer coordinates the activities of many people as he guides a product through its various stages of development.

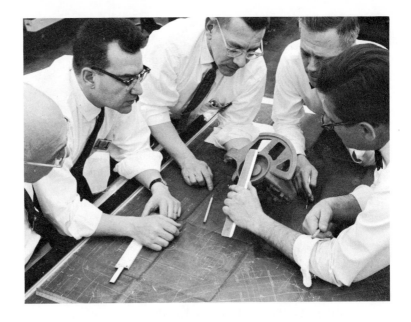

roughness has an important bearing on the fatigue life of parts which are subjected to high stress or repeated loads, much attention must be given to specifying in designs that surface finishes must meet certain requirements.

Since design work involves a production phase, the design engineer is always considering costs as a factor in our competitive economy. One of the ways in which costs can be minimized in manufacture or construction is to use standard parts, and standard sizes and dimensions for raw material. For example, if a machine were designed using nonstandard bolt threads or a bridge designed using nonstandard steel I-beams, the design probably would be more expensive than needed to fulfill its function. Thus, the design engineer must be able to coordinate the parts of his design so that it functions acceptably and is produced at minimum cost.

The design engineer soon comes to realize also that there usually is more than one acceptable way to solve a design problem. Unlike an arithmetic problem with fixed numbers which give one answer, his problem can have many answers and many ways of obtaining a solution, *and all may be acceptable.* In such a case his decision becomes a matter of experience and judgment. At other times it may become just a matter of making a decision one way or the other. Regardless of the method used, his solution to a problem should be a conscious effort to provide the *best* method considering fabrication, costs, and sales.

What are the qualifications of a design engineer? He, of course, must be creative. His every design will embody a departure from what has been done before. At the same time, he is constrained by the reality of the physical properties of materials and by economic factors. Therefore, he must be thoroughly knowledgeable in fundamental engineering in a rather wide range of subjects. In addition, he must be familiar with basic principles of economics, both from the standpoint of employing people and using machines. As he progresses upward into supervisory and management duties, the employment of principles of psychology and economics become of even more importance. For this reason design engineers usually will have more use for management courses than will research or development engineers.

Production and construction

In the fields of production and construction, the engineer is more directly associated with the technician, mechanic, and laborer. The production or construction engineer must take the design engineer's drawings and supervise the assembly of the object as it was conceived and illustrated by drawings or models.

Usually a production or construction engineer is associated closely with the process of estimating and bidding for competitive jobs. In this work he employs his knowledge of structural materials, fabricating processes, and general physical principles to estimate both time and cost to accomplish tasks. In construction work the method of competitive bidding is usually used to award contracts, and the ability to reduce an appropriate amount from an estimate by skilled engineering practices may mean the difference between a successful bid and one that is either too high or too low.

Once a bid has been awarded, it is usual practice to assign a "project engineer" as the person who assumes overall responsibility and supervision of the work from the standpoint of materials, labor, and money. He will have other production or construction engineers working under his direction who will be concerned with more specialized features of the work, such as civil, mechanical, electrical, or chemical engineering. Here the engineer must complete the details of the designers' plans. He must provide the engineering for employment of special tools needed for the work. He must also set up a schedule for production or construction, and he must be able to answer questions that technicians or workmen may raise concerning features of the design. He should be prepared to advise design engineers concerning desirable modifications that will aid in the construction or fabrication processes. In addition, he must be able to work effectively with construction or production crafts and labor unions.

Preparation of a schedule for production or construction is an important task of the engineer. In the case of an industrial plant, all planning for the procurement of raw materials and parts will be based upon this production schedule. An assembly line in a modern automobile manufacturing plant is one example which illustrates the necessity for scheduling the arrival of parts and subassemblies at predetermined time. As another example, consider the construction of a modern multistory office building. The necessity for parts and materials to arrive at the right time is very important. If they arrive too soon, they probably will be in the way, and if they arrive too late, the building is delayed, which will cause an increase in costs to the builder.

Qualifications for a production or construction engineer include a thorough knowledge of basic engineering principles. In addition, he must have the ability to visualize the parts of an operation, whether it be the fabrication of a solid-state computer circuit or the building of a concrete bridge. From his understanding of the operations involved, he must be able to arrive at a realistic schedule of time, materials, and manpower. Therefore, emphasis should be placed upon courses in engineering design, economics, business law, and psychology.

Illustration 4-4
The construction engineer is responsible for seeing that a project is carried out as designed. Usually he is working with large projects where weather and terrain are complicating factors. Construction work requires the exercise of all the capabilities of the engineer. This picture shows two engineers in consultation concerning the structural drawings of the building under construction.

Operations

In modern industrial plants, the number and complexity of machines, the equipment and buildings to be cared for, and the planning needed for expansion has brought out the need for specialized engineers to perform services in these areas. If a new manufacturing facility is to be constructed, or an addition made to an existing facility, it will be the duty of a plant engineer to perform the basic design, prepare the proposed layout of space and location of equipment, and to specify the fixed equipment such as illumination, communication, and air conditioning. In some cases, the work of construction will be contracted to outside firms, but it will be the general responsibility of the plant engineer to see that the construction is carried on as he has planned it.

After a building or facility has been built, the plant engineer and his staff are responsible for maintenance of the building, equipment, grounds, and utilities. This work varies from performing routine tasks to setting up and regulating the most complex and automated machinery in the plant.

The plant engineer must have a wide knowledge of several branches of engineering in order to perform these functions. For land acquisition and building construction, he will need courses in civil engineering; for equipment and machinery he will need mechanical training; for power he will need mechanical and electrical backgrounds, and for the specialized parts of the plant, his knowledge may need to be in such fields as chemical, metallurgical nuclear, petroleum, or textile engineering.

In many plants, particularly in utility plants, the engineer also is concerned with operation of the plant. It is his duty to see that boilers, generators, turbines, and accessory equipment are operated at their best efficiency. He should be able to

Illustration 4-5
In the operation of a plant, the engineer must make certain that all parts of the plant remain in service. In this picture, a periodic check is being made of electrical power generation equipment.

compare costs of operating under various conditions, and he attempts always to set schedules for machines so that best use will be made of them. In the case of chemical plants, he also will attempt to regulate the flows and temperatures at levels that will produce the greatest amount of desired product at the end of the line.

In his dual role as a plant and operations engineer, he will be constantly evaluating new equipment as it becomes available to see whether additional operating economies can be secured by retiring old equipment and installing new types. In this, he frequently must assume a salesman's role in order to convince management that it should discard equipment that, apparently, is operating perfectly and spend money for newer models. Here the ability to combine facts of engineering and economics is invaluable.

Plant engineering, of course, will be associated closely with production engineering processes. The production engineer will create needs for new machines, new facilities, and new locations. The plant engineer will correlate such things as the building layout, machine location, power supplies, and materials handling equipment so that they best will serve the needs of production.

The general qualifications of plant and operations engineers have already been mentioned. They must have basic knowledge of a wide variety of engineering fields such as civil, chemical, electrical, and mechanical, and also they must have specialized knowledge of areas peculiar to their plant and its operation. In addition, plant and operations engineers must be able to work with men and machines and to know what results to expect from them. In this part of their work, a knowledge of industrial engineering principles is valuable. In addition, it is desirable to have basic understanding and knowledge of economics and business law. In this work, in general, training in detailed research procedures and abstract concepts is of lesser importance.

Sales

An important and sometimes unrecognized function in engineering is the realm of applications and sales. As is well known, the best designed and fabricated product is of little use unless a demand either exists or has been created for it. Since many new processes and products have been developed within the past few years, a field of work has opened up for engineers in presenting the use of new products to prospective customers.

Discoveries and their consequent application have occurred so rapidly that a product may be available about which even a recent graduate may not know. In this case, it will fall to the engineer in sales who has intimate knowledge of the principles involved to go out and educate possible users so that a demand can be created. In this work the engineer must assume the role of a teacher. In many instances he must present his product primarily from an engineering standpoint. If his audience is composed of engineers, he can "talk their language" and answer their technical questions, but if his audience includes nonengineers, he must present the features of the product in terms that they can comprehend.

In addition to his knowledge of the engineering features of his own product, the sales and application engineer must also be familiar with the operations of his customer's plant. This is important from two standpoints. First, he should be able to show how his product will fit into the plant, and also he must show the economics involved to convince the customer that he should buy it. At the same time, the engineer must point out the limitations of his product and the possible changes necessary to incorporate it into a new situation. For example, a new bonding material may be available, but in order for a customer to use it in an assembly of parts, a special refrigerator for storage may be necessary. Also the customer would need to have emphasized the necessity for proper cleaning and surface preparation of the parts to be bonded.

A second reason that the sales and application engineer must be familiar with a customer's plant operation is that many times new requirements are generated here. By finding an application area in which no apparatus is available to do the work, the sales engineer is able to report back to his company that a need exists and that a development operation should be undertaken to produce a device or process to meet the need.

Almost all equipment of any complexity will need to be accompanied by introductory instructions when it is placed in a customer's plant. Here the application engineer can create good will by conducting an instruction program outlining the capabilities and limitations of the equipment. Also, after the equipment is in service,

Illustration 4-6
In sales, the engineer must be able to describe a technical product to customers and show how they will benefit from using the latest developments.

maintenance and repair capabilities by competent technical personnel will serve to maintain the confidence of customers.

The sales and applications engineer should have a basic knowledge of engineering principles and should, of course, have detailed knowledge in the area of his own products. Here the ability to perform detailed work on abstract principles is of less importance than the ability to present one's ideas clearly. A genuine appreciation of people and a friendly personality are desirable personal attributes. In addition to basic technical subjects, courses in psychology, sociology, and human relations will prove valuable to the sales and applications engineer.

Usually an engineer will spend several years in a plant learning the processes and the details of his plant's operation and management policies before starting out to be a member of the sales staff. Since the sales engineer represents his company in the mind of the customer, he must present a pleasing appearance and give a feeling of confidence in his engineering ability.

Management

Results of recent surveys show that the trend today is for corporate leaders in the United States to have backgrounds in engineering and science. In a survey of some 600 large industrial firms, 20 technical and engineering colleges and universities have four or more of their graduates serving as board chairmen, presidents, or senior vice presidents in these firms.

It has been predicted that within ten years, the *majority* of corporation executives will be men who are trained in engineering and science as well as in business and the humanities, and who can bridge the gap between these disciplines.

Since the trend is toward more engineering graduates moving into management positions, let us examine the functions of an engineer in management.

The basic functions of the management of a company are largely similar whether the company objective is dredging for oyster shells or building diesel locomotives or digital computers. These basic functions involve using the capabilities of the company to the best advantage to produce a desirable product in a competitive economy. The use of the capabilities, of course, will vary widely depending upon the enterprise involved.

The executive of a company, large or small, has the equipment in the plant, the labor force, and the financial assets of the organization to use in conducting the plant's operations. In management, he must make decisions involving all three of these items.

In former years it was assumed that only persons trained and educated in business administration should aspire to management positions. However, now it has been recognized that the education and other abilities which make a good engineer also provide the background to make a good management executive. The training for correlating facts and evaluating courses of action in making engineering decisions can be carried over to management decisions on machinery, men, and money. In general, the engineer is technically strong but may be quite naïve in the realm of business practicability. Therefore, it is in the business side of an operation that the engineer usually must work harder to develop his skills.

Illustration 4-7

Many engineers are selected for positions of management because of their ability to relate the technical aspects of a problem with economic and human factors to arrive at the optimum management decision.

The engineer in management is concerned more intimately with the long-range effects of policy decisions. Where the design engineer considers first the technical phases of a project, the engineer in management must consider how a particular decision will affect the men who work to produce a product and how the decision will affect the people who provide the financing of the operation. It is for this reason that the management engineer is concerned less with the technical aspects of his profession and relatively more with the financial, legal, and labor aspects.

This does not imply that engineering aspects should be minimized or deleted. Rather the growing need for engineers in management shows that the type and complexity of the machines and processes used in today's plants requires a blending of technical and business training in order to carry forward effectively. Particularly is this trend noted in certain industries such as aerospace and electronics, where the vast majority of executive managerial positions are occupied by engineers and scientists. As other industries become automated, a similar trend in those fields also will become apparent.

The education that an engineer in management receives should be identical to the basic engineering education received in other engineering functions. However, a young engineer can usually recognize early in his career whether or not he has an aptitude for working with men and directing their activities. If the young engineer has the ability to "sell his ideas" and to get others to work with him, he probably can channel his activities into managerial functions. He may start out as a research engineer, a design engineer, or a sales engineer, but the ability to influence others to his way of thinking, a genuine liking for people, and a consideration for their responses, will indicate that he probably has capabilities as a manager.

Of course, management positions are not always executive positions, but the ability to apply engineering principles in supervisory work involving large numbers of men and large amounts of money is a prerequisite in management engineering.

Other engineering functions

A number of other engineering functions can be considered that do not fall into the categories previously described. Some of these functions are testing, teaching, and consulting.

As in the other functions, there are no specific curricula leading directly toward these types of work. Rather a broad background of engineering fundamentals is the best guide to follow in preparing for work in these fields.

In testing, the work resembles design and development functions most closely. Most plants maintain a laboratory section that is responsible for conducting engineering tests of proposed products or for quality control on existing products. The test engineer must be qualified to follow the intricacies of a design and to build suitable test machinery to give an accelerated test of the product. For example, in the automotive industry, not only are the completed cars tested, but also individual components, such as engines, brakes, and tires, are tested on stands to provide data to improve their performance. The test engineer must be able also to set up quality control procedures for production lines to ensure that production meets certain standards. In this work, mathematics training in statistical theory is helpful.

A career in teaching is rewarding for many persons. A desire to help others in their learning processes, a concern for some of their personal problems, and a thorough grounding in engineering and mathematics are desirable for those considering teaching engineering subjects. In the teaching profession, the trend today is toward the more theoretical aspects of engineering, and a person will usually find that teaching is more closely allied with research and development functions than with others. Almost all colleges now require the faculty to obtain advanced degrees, and a person desiring to be an engineering teacher should consider seriously the desirability of obtaining a doctorate in his chosen field.

Illustration 4-8
Teaching is a rewarding activity of engineering. Frequently the engineering professor is the first person to introduce the student to the ethics and responsibilities of the profession.

More and more engineers are going into consulting work. Work as an engineering consultant can be either part time or full time. Usually a consulting engineer is a person who possesses specific skills in addition to several years of experience. He may offer his services to advise and work on engineering projects either part time or full time.

Frequently two or more engineers will form an engineering consulting firm that employs other engineers, technicians, and draftsmen and will contract for full engineering services on a project. The firm may restrict engineering work to rather narrow categories of work such as the design of irrigation projects, power plants, or aerospace facilities, or a staff may be available that is capable of working on a complete spectrum of engineering problems.

On the other hand, a consulting engineer can operate alone. His firm may consist of a single individual with skills such that, in a minimum time, he is able to advise and direct an operation to overcome a given problem. For instance, he may be employed by an industrial plant. In this way the plant may be able to solve a given problem more economically, particularly if the required specialization is seldom needed by the plant.

As may be inferred, a consulting engineer must have *specific* skills to offer, and he must be able to use his creative ability to apply his skills to unfamiliar situations. Usually these skills and abilities are acquired only after several years of practice and postgraduate study.

For a person who desires self-employment together with its business risks but also with the opportunity for financial reward, consulting work is an inviting part of the engineering profession.

Engineering functions in general

As described in previous paragraphs, training and skills in all functions are basically the same, that is, fundamental scientific knowledge of physical principles and mathematics. However, it can be seen that research on one hand and management on the other require different educational preparations.

For work in research, emphasis is on theoretical principles and creativity, with little emphasis on economic and personnel considerations. On the other hand, in management, primary attention is given to financial and labor problems and relatively little to abstract scientific principles. Between these two extremes, we find the other functions with varying degrees of emphasis on the research oriented or managerial oriented concepts.

Figure 4-1 shows an idealized concept of this distribution. Bear in mind that this diagram merely depicts a trend and does not necessarily apply to specific instances.

To summarize the functions of the engineer, we can say that in all cases he is a problem solver. Whether it be a mathematical abstraction that may have an application to a nuclear process or a meeting with a bargaining group at a conference table, it is a problem that must be reduced to its essentials and the alternatives explored to reach a solution. The engineer then must apply his knowledge and inventiveness to select a reasonable method to achieve a result, even in the face

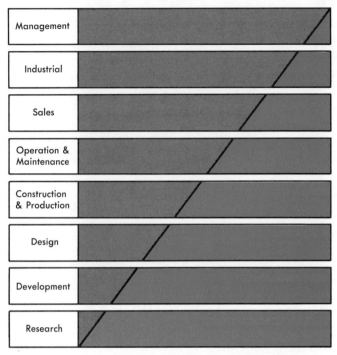

Management

Industrial

Sales

Operation & Maintenance

Construction & Production

Design

Development

Research

ABSTRACT SCIENTIFIC PRINCIPLES

Figure 4-1 Application of principles in various engineering functions.

of vague and sometimes contradictory data. That the engineer has been able, in general, to accomplish this is proven by a long record of successful industrial management and productivity.

Problems on work of the engineer

4-1. Discuss an important scientific breakthrough of the past year that was brought about by an engineering research effort.

4-2. Discuss the differences between engineering research and engineering development.

4-3. Interview an engineer and estimate the percentage of his work that is devoted to research, development, and design.

4-4. Discuss the importance of the engineer's design capability in modern industry.

4-5. Investigate the work functions of the engineer and write a brief essay describing the function that most appeals to you.

4-6. Discuss the importance of the sales engineer in the total engineering effort.

4-7. Interview an engineer in management. Discuss the reasons that many engineers rise to positions of leadership as managers.

4-8. Compare the engineering opportunities in teaching with those in industry.

4-9. Investigate the opportunities for employment in a consulting engineering firm. Discuss your findings.

4-10. Discuss the special capabilities required of the engineer in construction.

Bibliography

Bronwell, Arthur B. (ed.), *Science and Technology in the World of the Future,* Wiley-Interscience, New York (1970).

Richter, Jean, *The Notebooks of Leonardo Da Vinci,* Vol. 1 and Vol. 2, Dover, New York (1970).

Smith, R. J., *Engineering as a Career,* McGraw-Hill, New York (1969).

Williams, Clement C., and Erich A. Farber, *Building an Engineering Career,* McGraw-Hill, New York (1957).

5
Engineering careers of challenge

Much of the change in our civilization in the past 100 years has been due to the work of the engineer. We hardly appreciate the changes that have occurred in our environment unless we attempt to picture the world of a few generations ago, without automobiles, telephones, radios, electronics, transportation systems, supersonic aircraft, automatic machine tools, electric lights, television, and all the modern appliances in our homes. In the growth of all these things the role of the engineer is obvious.

Development in the field of science and engineering is progressing so rapidly at present that within the last ten years we have acquired materials and devices that are now considered commonplace but which were unknown to our parents. Through research, development, and mass production, directed by engineers, ideas are made into realities in an amazingly short time.

The engineer is concerned with more than research, development, design, construction, and the operation of technical industries, however, since many are engaged in businesses that are not concerned primarily with production. Formerly, executive positions were held almost exclusively by men whose primary training was in the field of law or business, but the tendency now is to utilize engineers more and more as administrators and executives.

No matter what kind of work the engineer may wish to do, he will find opportunities for employment not only in purely technical fields but also in other functions, such as general business, budgeting, rate analysis, purchasing, marketing, personnel, labor relations, and industrial management. Other opportunities also exist in such specialized fields of work as teaching, writing, patent practice, and work with the military establishment.

Although college engineering curricula contain many basic courses, there will be some specialized courses available that are either peculiar to a certain curriculum or are electives. These specializations permit each student to acquire a particular proficiency in certain subjects so that, for example, he can be designated as an electrical, civil, chemical, mechanical, or industrial engineer.

Education in the application of certain subject matter to solve technological problems in a certain engineering field constitutes engineering specialization. Such training is not for manual skills as in trade schools, but rather is planned to provide preparation for research, design, operation, management, testing, maintenance of projects, and other engineering functions in any given specialty.

The principal engineering fields of specialization that are listed in college curricula and that are recognized in the engineering profession are described in the following sections.

Aerospace and astronautical engineering

The powered flight of man began in 1903 at Kitty Hawk, North Carolina. Perhaps no other single technological achievement has been so significant for mankind. Through faster transportation and improved communications almost every aspect of man's daily life has been affected. However, not all challenges are associated with spaceflight. Problems associated with conventional aircraft, and the development of special vehicles such as hydrofoil ships, ground-effect machines, and deep-diving vessels for oceanographic research are all concerns of the industry.

Within the past few years many changes have taken place which have altered the work of the aeronautical engineer—not the least of which is man's successful conquest of space. Principal types of work vary from the design of guided missiles and spacecraft to analyses of aerodynamic studies dealing with the performance, stability, control, and design of various types of planes and other devices that fly. Most of such activity is concerned with the design, development, and performance testing of supersonic commercial transports and their propulsion systems.

Although aerospace engineering is one of the newer fields, it offers many possibilities for employment. Continued exploration and research in previously uncharted

Illustration 5-1
Aeronautical engineers frequently work with models of their designs to confirm the validity of their calculations.

areas is needed in the fields of propulsion, materials, thermodynamics, cryogenics, navigation, cosmic radiation, and magnetohydrodynamics.[1] It is predicted that within the near future the chemically fueled rocket engine, which has enabled man to explore lunar landscapes, will become obsolete as the need increases to cover greater and greater distances over extended periods of time.

The rapidly expanding network of airlines, both national and international, provides many openings for the engineering graduate. Since the demand for increasing numbers of aircraft of various types exists, there are opportunities for work in manufacturing plants and assembly plants and in the design, testing, and maintenance of aircraft and their component parts. The development of new types of aircraft, both civilian and military, requires the efforts of well-trained aeronautical engineers, and it is in this field that the majority of positions exist. Employment opportunities exist for specialists in the design and development of fuel systems using liquid oxygen propellants and solid propellants. Control of the newer fuels involves precision valving and flow sensing at very low and very high temperatures. Air traffic control is a problem that is becoming increasingly more complex, and trained people are needed here. The design of ground and airborne systems that will permit operation of aircraft under all kinds of weather conditions is also a part of the work of aeronautical engineers.

The aerospace engineer works on designs that are not only challenging and adventuresome but also play a major role in determining the course of present and future world events.

Agricultural engineering

Agricultural engineering is that discipline of engineering that spans the area between two fields of applied science—agriculture and engineering. It is directly concerned with supplying the means whereby food and fiber are supplied in sufficient quantity to fill the basic needs of all mankind.[2] In the next 30 years the world's population is expected to double. This factor, plus the increasing demands of people throughout the world for increased standards of living, provide unparalleled challenges to the agricultural engineer. Not only must the quantity of food and fiber be increased, but the efficiency of production also must be steadily improved in order that manpower may be released for other creative pursuits. Through applications of engineering, principles, materials, energy, and machines may be used to multiply the effectiveness of man's effort. This is the agricultural engineer's domain.

In order that the agricultural engineer may understand the problems of agriculture and the application of engineering methods and principles to their solution, instruction is given in agricultural subjects and the biological sciences as well as in basic engineering. Agricultural research laboratories are maintained at schools for research and instruction using various types of farm equipment for study and testing. The young person who has an analytical mind and a willingness to work,

[1] *Your Career As an Aerospace Engineer,* The American Institute of Aeronautics and Astronautics, New York (1970).

[2] *Agricultural Engineering and You,* American Society of Agricultural Engineers, Saint Joseph, Michigan (1967), p. 1.

Illustration 5-2
In this picture agricultural engineers at a research center test the safety features of a farm tractor. Agricultural engineers apply fundamental engineering principles of analysis and design to improve our methods of food production and land utilization.

together with an interest in the engineering aspects of agriculture, will find the course in agricultural engineering an interesting preparation for his life's work.

Many agricultural engineers are employed by companies that serve agriculture and some are employed by firms that serve other industries. Opportunities are particularly apparent in such areas as (1) research, design, development, and sale of mechanized farm equipment and machinery, (2) application of irrigation, drainage, erosion control, and land and water management practices, (3) application and use of electrical energy for agricultural production; feed and crop processing, handling and grading, (4) research, design, sale, and construction of specialized structures for farm use, and (5) the processing and handling of food products.

Architectural engineering

The architectural engineer is interested primarily in the selection, analysis, design, and assembly of modern building materials into structures that are safe, efficient, economical, and attractive. The education he receives in college is designed to teach him how best to use modern structural materials in the construction of tall buildings, manufacturing plants, and public buildings.

The architectural engineer is trained in the sound principles of engineering and at the same time is given a background which enables him to appreciate the point of view of the architect. The architect is concerned with the space arrangements, proportions, and appearance of a building, whereas the architectural engineer is more nearly a structural engineer and is concerned with safety, economy, and sound construction methods.

Opportunities for employment will be found in established architectural firms, in consulting engineering offices, in aircraft companies, and in organizations specializing in building design and construction. Excellent opportunities await the graduate who may be able to associate himself with a contracting firm or who may form a partnership with an architectural designer. In the field of sales an interesting and profitable career is open to the individual who is able to present his ideas clearly and convincingly.

Illustration 5-3
The architectural engineer may work either in an engineering firm or in an architectural firm. As part of a team of engineers, he combines fundamental principles of architecture and engineering in the design of structures to harmonize beauty and utility. The architectural engineer shown in this picture has designed a new lightweight high-strength extruded aluminum set of structural members which permit rapid construction of prefabricated housing units.

Chemical engineering

Chemical engineering is responsible for new and improved products and processes that affect every person. This includes materials that will resist extremities of heat and cold, processes for life-support systems in other environments, new fuels for reactors, rockets, and booster propulsion, medicines, vaccines, serum, and plasma for mass distribution, and plastics and textiles to serve a multiplicity of human needs.[3] Consequently, chemical engineers must be able to apply scientifically the principles of chemistry, physics, and engineering to the design and operation of plants for the production of materials that undergo chemical changes during their processing.

The courses in chemical engineering cover inorganic, analytical, physical, and organic chemistry in addition to the basic engineering subjects; and the work in the various courses is designed to be of a distinctly professional nature and to develop capacity for original thought. The industrial development of our country makes large demands on the chemical engineer. The increasing uses for plastics, synthetics, and building materials require that a chemical engineer be employed in the development

[3] *Will You Be a Chemical Engineer?,* American Institute of Chemical Engineers, New York (1970), p. 2.

and manufacture of these products. While well trained in chemistry, the chemical engineer is more than a chemist in that he applies the results of chemical research and discovery to the use of mankind by adapting laboratory processes to full scale manufacturing plants.

The chemical engineer is instrumental in the development of the newer fuels for turbine and rocket engines. Test and evaluation of such fuels and means of achieving production of suitable fuels are part of the work of a chemical engineer. This testing must be carefully controlled to evaluate the performance of engines before the fuel is considered suitable to place on the market.

Opportunities for chemical engineers exist in a wide variety of fields of manufacture. Not only are they in demand in strictly chemical fields but also in nearly all types of manufacturing. The production of synthetic rubber, the uses of petroleum products, the recovery of useful materials from what was formerly considered waste products, and the better utilization of farm products are only a few of the tasks that will provide work for the chemical engineer. Although the first professional work of a graduate chemical engineer may be in production, other opportunities exist in the fields of engineering design, research and development, patents, and sales engineering.

Illustration 5-4
Chemical engineers work with elaborate chemical apparatus to study minute details of materials in order to reveal structural secrets that cannot be uncovered by any other means. Here chemical engineers test equipment at frigid temperatures considerably below the lowest found in nature.

Illustration 5-5
An important phase of civil engineering is the planning for orderly growth and development of urban areas to include water purification and waste disposal. These civil engineers are making a site visitation to confirm the accuracy of design calculations pertaining to a city water supply.

Civil engineering

The civil engineer plans, designs, constructs, and operates physical works and facilities that are deemed essential to modern life.[4] These include the broad categories of construction, soil mechanics and foundations, transportation systems, water resources, sanitation, city planning and municipal engineering, and surveying and mapping. Construction engineering is concerned with the design and supervision of construction of buildings, bridges, tunnels, and dams. The construction industry is America's largest industry today. Soil mechanics and foundations investigations are essential not only in civilized areas but also for successful conquest of new lands such as Antarctica and the lunar surface. Transportation systems include the planning, design, and construction of necessary roads, streets, thoroughfares, and superhighways. Engineering studies in water resources are concerned with the improvement of water availability, harbor and river development, flood control, irrigation, and drainage. Pollution is an ever-increasing problem, particularly in urban areas. The sanitary engineer is concerned with the design and construction of water supply systems, sewerage systems, and systems for the reclamation and disposal of wastes. City planning and municipal engineers are concerned primarily with the planning of urban centers for the orderly, comfortable, and healthy growth and development of business and residential areas. Surveying and mapping is concerned with the

[4]Alfred R. Golzé, *Your Future in Civil Engineering,* Richards Rosen Press, New York (1965), p. 15.

measurements of distances over a surface (such as the earth or the moon) and the location of structures, rights of way, and property boundaries.

Civil engineers engage in technical, administrative, or commercial work with manufacturing companies, construction companies, transportation companies, and power companies. Other opportunities for employment exist in consulting engineering offices, in city and state engineering departments, and in the various bureaus of the federal government.

Electrical engineering

Electrical engineering is concerned, in general terms, with the utilization of electric energy, and it is perhaps more far reaching in its contacts with human endeavor than any of the other branches of engineering. Electricity used in one form or another reaches nearly all our daily lives and is truly the servant of mankind. Electrical engineering is divided into broad fields such as information systems, automatic control, and systems and devices.

A need arose after World War II for improved information systems. Electronic computers were designed to help fill this need. The increase in the complexity of computers has created a need for specialists in the field who can adapt existing knowledge of mechanical and electrical devices to extend the capabilities of computers.

Computers can provide answers to specific sets of questions. However, engineers have designed them for a variety of purposes, and computers drastically reduce the time necessary to explore a variety of concepts of a design or to control the multitude of processes within a manufacturing plant.

The electrical engineer is concerned with the application of sound engineering principles, both mechanical and electrical, in the design and construction of computers. He must be familiar with the basic requirements of a computer so that he can design to provide for the necessary capabilities. In addition he must strive to build a machine that will furnish solutions of greater and greater problem complexity and at the same time have a means of introducing the problem into the machine in as simple a manner as possible.

Although there are relatively few companies that build elaborate computing machines, employment possibilities in the design and construction part of the industry are not limited. Many industrial firms, colleges, and governmental branches have set up computers as part of their capital equipment, and opportunities exist for employment as computer applications engineers, who serve as liaison between computer programmers and engineers who wish their problems evaluated on the machines. Of course, in a field expanding as rapidly as computer design, increasing numbers of employment opportunities become available. More and more dependence will be placed on the use of computers in the future, and an engineer educated in this work will find ample opportunity for advancement.

The automatic control of machines and devices, such as autopilots for spacecraft and missiles, has become a commonplace requirement in today's technically conscious society.

Automatic controlling of machine tools is an important part of modern machine shop operation. Tape systems are used to furnish signals to serve units on automatic lathes, milling machines, boring machines, and other types of machine tools so that they can be programmed to perform repeated operations. Not only can individual machines be controlled but also entire power plants can be operated on a program system. The design of these systems is performed usually by an electrical or mechanical engineer.

Energy conversion systems, where energy is converted from one form to another, also are a necessity in almost every walk of life. Power plants are constituted to convert heat energy from fuels into electrical energy for transmission to industry and homes. In addition to power systems, communication systems are a responsibility of the electrical engineer. Particularly in communications the application of modern electronics has been most evident. The electrical engineer who specializes in electronics will find that the majority of communication devices employ electronic circuits and components.

Other branches of electrical engineering that may include power or communication activities, or both, are illumination engineering, which deals with lighting using electric power; electronics, which has applications in both power and communications; and such diverse fields as x-ray, acoustics, and seismograph work.

Employment opportunities in electrical engineering are extremely varied. Electrical manufacturing companies use large numbers of engineers for design, testing, research, and sales. Electrical power companies and public utility companies require a staff of qualified electrical engineers, as do the companies which control the networks of telegraph and telephone lines and the radio systems. Other opportunities for employment exist with oil companies, railroads, food processing plants, lumbering enterprises, biological laboratories, chemical plants, and colleges and universities. The aircraft and missile industries use engineers who are familiar with circuit design and employment of flight data computers, servomechanisms, analog computers, vacuum tubes, transistors, and other solid-state devices. There is scarcely any industry of any size that does not employ one or more electrical engineers as members of its engineering staff.

The engineering graduate must be familiar with the various sciences, but it is especially desirable that he be well versed in the fundamental principles of physics, chemistry, and mathematics. A thorough understanding of the underlying phe-

Illustration 5-6
The electrical engineer works with many types of apparatus, both electrical and mechanical. In this picture, an electrical engineer adjusts an ultrasonic device to measure composite response to resonance. The superimposed resonance curve is a test result.

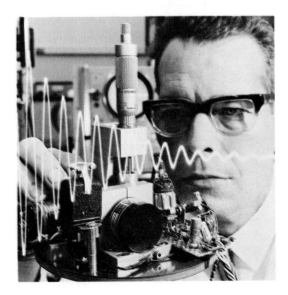

nomena is necessary if the engineer is to direct the forces of nature to the best advantage. In addition to basic science courses, the electrical engineer will take courses in machinery, electronics, communication, and wave phenomena. As in other engineering courses, the demand for breadth and culture is met by studies in history, literature, economics, English, and public speaking.

Industrial engineering

The field of industrial engineering is a wide and all-inclusive one dealing with the design and installation of manufacturing systems. Whereas other branches of engineering tend to specialize in some particular phase of science, the realm of industrial engineering may include parts of all engineering fields. The industrial engineer then will be more concerned with the larger picture of management of industries and production of goods than with the detailed development of processes.

The work of the industrial engineer is rather wide in scope, so it is difficult to designate any specializations that the industrial engineer may choose. His general work is with men and machines, and as a result he is trained in both personnel administration and in the relations of men and machines to production.

The advent of the electronic digital computer and other electronic support equipment has revolutionized the business world.[5] Many of the resultant changes have been made as a result of industrial engineering designs. Systems analysis, operations research, statistics, queuing theory, information theory, symbolic logic, and linear programming are all mathematics-based disciplines that are used in industrial engineering work.

The industrial engineer must be capable of preparing plans for the arrangement of plants for best operation and then of organizing the workers so that their efforts will be coordinated to give a smoothly functioning unit. In such things as production lines, the various processes involved must be timed perfectly to ensure smooth operation and efficient use of the worker's efforts. In addition to coordination and automating of manufacturing activities, the industrial engineer is concerned with the development of data processing procedures and the use of computers to control production, the development of improved methods of handling materials, the design of plant facilities and statistical procedures to control quality, the use of mathematical models to simulate production lines, and the measurement and improvement of work methods to reduce costs.

Opportunities for employment exist in almost every industrial plant and in many businesses not concerned directly with manufacturing or processing goods. In many cases the industrial engineer may be employed by department stores, insurance companies, consulting companies, and as engineers in cities. The industrial engineer is trained in fundamental engineering principles, and as a result may also be employed in positions which would fall in the realm of the civil, electrical, or mechanical engineer.

The courses prescribed for the student of industrial engineering follow the pattern of the other branches of engineering by starting with a thorough foundation in the

[5] Ross W. Hammond, *Your Future in Industrial Engineering,* Richards Rosen Press, New York (1965). p. 24.

Illustration 5-7
The industrial engineer is concerned with man-machine relationships. In this picture the engineers are using a treadmill experiment to find out the type of environment and the conditions under which humans can best function on the job.

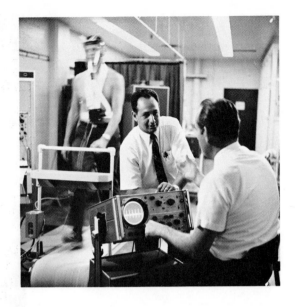

engineering sciences. The engineering courses in the later semesters will be of a more general nature, and the curriculum will include such courses as economics, psychology, business law, personnel problems, and accounting principles.

Mechanical engineering

Mechanical engineering deals with power and the design of machines and processes used to generate power and apply it to useful purposes. These designs may be simple or complex, inexpensive or expensive, luxuries or essentials. Such items as the kitchen food mixer, the automobile, air conditioning systems, nuclear power plants, and interplanetary space vehicles[6] would not be available for man's use today were it not for the mechanical engineer. In general, the mechanical engineer works with systems, subsystems, and components that have motion. The range of work that may be classed as mechanical engineering is wider than that in any of the other branches of engineering, but it may be grouped generally under two heads: work that is concerned with power-generating machines, and work that deals with machines that transform or consume this power in accomplishing their particular tasks.

Some of the general subdivisions of mechanical engineering are as follows: Power or combustion engineers deal with the production of power from fuels. Design specialists may work with parts that vary in size from the microscopic part of the most delicate instrument to the massive parts of heavy machinery. Railway engineers work with the complex railway equipment that is part of our transportation system. Automotive engineers work constantly to improve the vehicles and engines that we now have. Heating, ventilating, air conditioning, and refrigeration engineers deal with the design of suitable systems for making our buildings more comfortable and for providing proper conditions in industry for good working conditions and efficient machine operation.

[6] *Mechanical Engineering*, The American Society of Mechanical Engineers, New York (1967), p. 2.

Illustration 5-8
The mechanical engineer may be called upon to design a wide variety of complex machines. In this picture, the engineer is working with a continuous-wave argon ion laser.

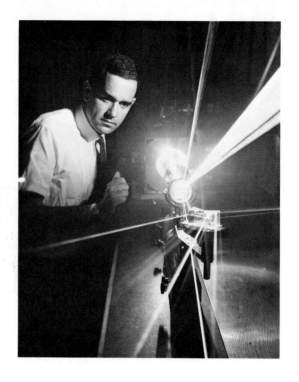

Employment may be secured by mechanical engineering graduates in almost every type of industry. Manufacturing plants, power-generating stations, public utility companies, transportation companies, airlines, and factories, to mention only a few, are examples of organizations that need mechanical engineers. Experienced engineers are needed in the missile and space industries in the design and development of such items as gas turbine compressors and power plants, air-cycle cooling turbines, electrically and hydraulically driven fans, and high-pressure refrigerants. Mechanical engineers are also needed in the testing of airborne and missile fuel systems, servo-valves, and mechanical-electrical control systems. In addition, an engineer may be employed for research endeavor as a university professor, or in the governments of cities, states, and the nation.

The courses in mechanical engineering include courses both in power and in machine principles. Courses include thermodynamics, fluid mechanics, design, energy conversion, electricity and electronics, vibrations, and heat transfer. In the senior year elective courses may enable one to specialize in any of the various fields of mechanical engineering.

Metallurgical engineering and materials science

In many respects the past 25 years may be said to be an "age of materials"—an age which has seen the maturing of space exploration, nuclear power, digital computer technology, and ocean conquest. None of these engineering triumphs could have been achieved without the contributions of the metallurgical engineer. Although his world is not confined to this planet, the unsolved problems of private industry are his menu. Metals are found in every part of the earth's crust, but rarely in immediately usable form. It is the metallurgical engineer's job to separate them from their ores and from other materials with which they exist in nature.[7]

Metallurgical engineering may be divided into two branches. One branch deals with the location and evaluation of deposits of ore, the best way of mining and concentrating the ore, and the proper method of refining the ore into the basic metals. The other branch deals with the fabrication of the refined metal or metal alloy into various machines or metal products.

The metallurgist performs pure and applied research on vacuum melting, arc melting, and zone refining to produce metallic materials having unusual properties of strength and endurance. In addition the metallurgist in the aircraft and missile industries is called upon to recommend the best materials to use for special applications and is frequently called on to give an expert opinion on the results of fatigue tests of metal parts of machines.

In addition to the two branches listed above, ceramic engineering is frequently included as a branch of this type of engineering. Requirements for the design of inorganic materials that will be flexible at $-60°$ Celsius or have strength at $2000°$ Celsius have given impetus to the study of ceramic engineering. In addition some materials may need to have properties that will not be changed by exposure to high concentrations of radioactivity. Use is made of the newer techniques of sintering in the field of high-temperature inorganic materials, some of which are unusual blends of ceramic and matallic materials. An example of one of the newer uses of ceramics in industry is in the manufacture of the parts of turbine and rocket engines that are exposed to hot gases. These frequently are protected with refractory ceramic materials developed by research teams.

The engineer who has specialized in materials science is in great demand today because of the urgent need for man-made composites—the joining of two or more

---

[7] *Careers in Metallurgy, Materials Science, and Metallurgical Engineering,* The Metallurgical Society of AIME, New York (1970).

Illustration 5-9
Materials and metallurgical engineers are specialists in their knowledge of the properties of mineral, metallic, and man-made materials. Recently their work has been extended to extraterrestial investigations. This moon fragment (photograph enlarged 990 times) was among the lunar material collected by the Apollo 11 astronauts. Research is currently underway to ascertain cosmic-ray damage in lunar materials, to "date" the ages of the materials, and to probe their structure.

different materials for the purpose of gaining advantageous characteristics or overcoming disadvantageous ones of each.

Nuclear engineering

Nuclear engineering is one of the newest and most challenging branches of engineering. Although much work in the field of nucleonics at present falls within the realm of pure research, a growing demand for people educated to utilize recent discoveries for the benefit of mankind has led several colleges and universities to offer courses in nuclear engineering. The nuclear engineer is familiar with the basic principles involved in both fission and fusion reactions; and by applying fundamental engineering concepts, he is able to direct the enormous energies involved in a proper manner. Work involved in nuclear engineering includes the design and operation of plants to concentrate nuclear reactive materials, the design and operation of plants to utilize heat energy from reactions, and the solution of problems arising in connection with safety to persons from radiation, disposal of radioactive wastes, and decontamination of radioactive areas.

The wartime uses of nuclear reactions are well known, but of even more importance are the less spectacular peacetime uses of controlled reactions. These uses include such diverse applications as electrical power generation and medical applications. Other applications are in the use of isotopes in chemical, physical, and biological research, and in the changing of the physical and chemical properties of materials in unusual ways by subjecting them to radiation.

Recent advances in our knowledge of controlled nuclear reactions have enabled engineers to build power plants that use heat from reactions to drive machines. Submarine nuclear power plants, long a dream, are now a reality, and experiments

Illustration 5-10
The nuclear engineer is a member of one of the newer branches of engineering. As part of his work, he explores all possible methods of utilizing nuclear energy for the benefit of mankind. In the above photograph, nuclear engineers and technicians supervise the removal of radioactive materials.

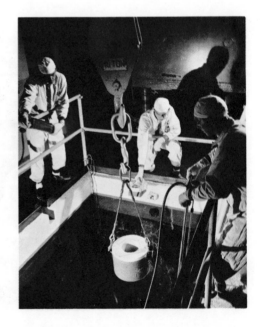

are being conducted on smaller nuclear power plants that can be used for airborne or railway applications.

At present, ample opportunities for employment of nuclear engineers exist in both privately owned and government-operated plants, where separation, concentration, or processing of nuclear materials is performed. Nuclear engineers are also needed by companies that may use radioactive materials in research or processing involving agricultural, medical, metallurgical, and petroleum products.

Petroleum engineering

Throughout history the energy available to man beyond his own musclepower has been a measure of his hope for a more secure and improved material life. In early Greek and Roman civilizations wind and water provided much of man's energy needs. In early America, wood was the primary source of energy. Today the major source of energy is petroleum.[8] It is the most widely used of all energy sources because of its mobility and flexibility in utilization. Approximately three fourths of the total energy needs of the United States are currently supplied by petroleum products, and this condition will likely continue for many years. Petroleum engineering is the practical application of the basic sciences (primarily chemistry, geology, and physics) and the engineering sciences to the development, recovery, and field processing of petroleum.

Petroleum engineering deals with all phases of the petroleum industry, from the location of petroleum in the ground to the ultimate delivery to the user. Petroleum products play an important part in many phases of our everyday life in providing our clothes, food, work, and entertainment. Because of the complex chemical structure of petroleum, we are able to make an almost endless number of different articles. Owing to the wide demand for petroleum products, the petroleum engineer strives to satisfy an ever-increasing demand for oil and gas from the ground.

The petroleum engineer is concerned first with finding deposits of oil and gas in quantities suitable for commercial use, in the extraction of these materials from the ground, and the storage and processing of the petroleum above ground. The petroleum engineer is concerned with the location of wells in accordance with the findings of geologists, the drilling of wells and the myriad problems associated with the drilling, and the installation of valves and piping when the wells are completed. In addition to the initial tapping of a field of oil, the petroleum engineer is concerned with practices that will provide the greatest recovery of the oil, considering all possible factors that may exist many thousand feet below the surface of the earth.

After the oil or gas has reached the surface, the petroleum engineer will provide the means of transporting it to suitable processing plants or to places where it will be used. Pipelines are providing an ever-increasing means of transporting both oil and gas from field to consumer.

Many challenges face the petroleum engineer. Some require pioneering efforts, such as with the rapidly developing Alaska field. Other opportunities lie closer at hand. For example, it is known that because of excessive costs in recovery less than one half of the oil already discovered in the United States *has yet to be brought*

---

[8] *Careers in Petroleum Engineering*, Society of Petroleum Engineers of AIME, New York (1968), p. 2.

Illustration 5-11
One of the tasks of the petroleum engineer is to locate oil deposits and to devise methods for oil recovery. As is the case in this photograph, design calculations frequently must be made at the drilling site.

to the surface of the earth. It is estimated that even a 10 per cent increase in oil recovery would produce 3 billion barrels of additional oil, a worth of over 10 billion dollars.

Owing to the expanding uses for petroleum and its products, the opportunities for employment of petroleum engineers are widespread. Companies concerned with the drilling, producing, and transporting of oil and gas will provide employment for the majority of engineers. Because of the widespread search for oil, employment opportunities for the petroleum engineer exist all over the world; and for the young man wishing a job in a foreign land, oil companies have crews in almost every country over the globe. Other opportunities for employment exist in the field of technical sales, research, and as civil service employees of the national government.

The curriculum in petroleum engineering includes courses in drilling methods, engines, oil and gas recovery, storage and transportation, and geology.

Problems on engineering careers of challenge

5-1. Discuss the changing requirements for aerospace and astronautical engineers.

5-2. Investigate the opportunities for employment in agricultural engineering. Discuss your findings.

5-3. Write a short essay on the differences in the utilization and capability of the architectural engineer and the civil engineer who has specialized in structural analysis.

5-4. Interview a chemical engineer. Discuss the differences in his work and that of a chemist.

5-5. Assume that you are employed as an electrical engineer. Describe your work and comment particularly concerning the things that you most like and dislike about your job.

5-6. Explain why the demand for industrial engineers has increased significantly during the past ten years.

5-7. Write a 200-word essay describing the challenging job opportunities in engineering that might be particularly attractive for young ladies.

5-8. Explain the importance of mechanical engineers in the electronics industry.

5-9. Describe the changes that might be brought about to benefit mankind by the development of new engineering materials.

5-10. Investigate the need for nuclear and petroleum engineers in your state and report on your findings.

Bibliography

Amstead, B. H., and Wilbourn McNutt, *Engineering As a Career Today*, Dodd, Mead, New York (1968).

Burstall, Aubrey, *A History of Mechanical Engineering*, M.I.T. Press, Cambridge, Mass. (1963).

Coy, Harold, *Engineers and What They Do*, Franklin Watts, New York.

Cressy, Edward, *A Hundred Years of Mechanical Engineering*, Macmillan, New York (1937).

Electric Development from 600 B.C., National Manufacturers Association, New York (1946).

Goddard, Robert H., "A Method of Reaching Extreme Altitudes," Smithsonian Institution Publication No. 2540, Washington, D.C. (1919).

Golzé, Alfred R., *Your Future in Civil Engineering*, Richards Rosen Press, New York (1965).

Hammond, Ross W., *Your Future in Industrial Engineering*, Richards Rosen Press, New York (1965).

Kelly, Mervin J., "Should You Be an Electronics Engineer?," *Career Opportunities*, New York Life Insurance Co. (September 1962).

Pollack, Philip, *Careers and Opportunities in Engineering*, Dutton, New York (1959).

Rutherford, Ernest R., The Newer Alchemy, Macmillan, New York (1951).

Steinman, David B., *The Builders of the Bridge*, Harcourt, New York (1945).

Straub, Hans, *A History of Civil Engineering*, M.I.T. Press, Cambridge, Mass. (1964).

Timoshenko, Stephen P., *History of the Strength of Materials*, McGraw-Hill, New York (1953).

Wells, Robert, *What Does a Civil Engineer Do?*, Dodd, New York (1960).

Part Two

Preparation for a career in engineering

The successful engineer of the future
will be one who prepares himself well today.
The pace of discovery is too great
to consider any other course of action
than to study and to keep abreast
of the expanding realm of science
and technology.

6

The professional role of the engineer

The word "professional" is used in many ways and has many meanings. It can be used in the sense of the skill of a professional actor who receives pay for his efforts, as distinguished from an amateur who performs more for the joy of performing. It can be used in the sense of a type of work as in describing a professional job of house painting done by an experienced painter. Also, it can be used merely to describe a degree of effort or line of conduct over a period of time as used in the expression "a professional beggar." However, in the sense that engineers would employ the word "professional," it should be restricted to a particular and specialized group of people, identified by distinguishing characteristics, that separate its members from nonprofessionals.

Within the last century, three groups have emerged with the title "learned professions." These professional groups are law, medicine, and theology. These groups came into being gradually over a long period of time and had certain characteristics in common, among which were higher levels of educational achievement and a sincere desire for performing a service for people. There is no formal naming of a person or group of persons to professional status, nor is there a schedule or procedure to follow to achieve recognition as a professional. Rather the group itself sets standards of training, skills, achievement, and service in order to call itself a professional group, and the public accepts the group's evaluation of itself.

Who is a professional? As generally used in the sense of the learned professions, a professional person is one who applies certain knowledge and skill, usually obtained by college education, for the service of people. In addition, a professional person observes an acceptable code of conduct, uses discretion and judgment in dealing with people, and respects their confidences. Also, professional persons usually have legal status, use professional titles, and associate together in groups. Although engineering has met most of these criteria for a long time, it has been only within the last few decades that legal status has been conferred upon the engineering profession.

The engineer as a professional person

Knowledge and skill above that of the average person is a characteristic of the professional man. Where a workman will have specific skills in operating a particular machine, a professional person is considered able to apply fundamental principles that are usually beyond the range of the average workman. The knowledge of these principles as well as the skills necessary to apply them distinguishes a professional man. The engineer, because of his education in the basic sciences, mathematics, and engineering sciences, is capable of applying basic principles for such diverse things as improving the construction features of buildings, developing processes that will provide new chemical compounds, or designing tunnels to bring water to arid areas.

An important concept in the minds of most persons is that a professional person will perform a service for people. This means that service must be considered ahead of any monetary reward that a professional man may receive. In this respect the professional person should, by himself, recognize a need for personal services and seek ways to provide a solution to these needs. Almost all engineering is performed to fill a need in some phase of our society. It may be to develop better appliances for the household, or to provide better transportation facilities, or to make possible a better life in regions of unfavorable climate.

Discretion and judgment also characterize a professional person. In most situations a choice of several methods to accomplish a given task will be available. The engineer must consider the facts available and the principles that apply and make decisions based upon these rather than upon expediency. Consideration must be given not only to the mechanical aspects of a solution but also to the effects that a particular decision will have upon the persons concerned.

A professional person is one in whom confidence can be placed. This confidence is not only in his skill and ability but also that his knowledge of his client's business or trade information or personal matters will not be divulged improperly. The engineer works in a relation of confidence to his client or employer not to divulge trade secrets or to take any advantage of his knowledge that may harm the client or employer. The public, in general, will have confidence that the engineer's design of buildings, bridges, or power systems will be adequate and safe to use. The engineer must not fail the public in this responsibility.

All professionals adhere to a code of ethical conduct. This code of ethics outlines the standards to which members of the group subscribe and gives an understanding of what the public can expect in its relationship with the profession. The code of ethics also serves as a guide to the members of the profession in their conduct and relations with each other. In engineering, the professional society is the National Society of Professional Engineers. A general code of ethics for professional engineers has been set up by the Society. This code is given in Appendix V.

Legal status usually is a characteristic of a professional. A medical doctor, for example, has certain rights and privileges afforded by law. Legal recognition of a professional group is afforded by a procedure of certification, licensing, or registration. In all states, a registration law is in effect which provides for legal registration of an engineer following submission of evidence of education and technical ability. Registration confers the legal title of "engineer" to the recipient, and he may use the initials "P.E." after his name to denote his registration as a "Professional Engineer."

Professionalism for the engineer[1]

Professionalism is an individual state of mind. It is a way of thinking and living rather than the development of specific skills or the acquiring of certain knowledge. While the mere acquisition of knowledge may make a person more skilled as a clerk or laborer, knowledge alone does not often promote the desire within oneself to serve or be responsive to the needs of people. It is in this realm of service that the engineer joins with members of other learned professional groups in placing honesty and integrity of action above the legal or minimum level allowable.

Although knowledge and skill often exist apart from professionalism, professionalism can mature only where such competence creates a proper atmosphere. Where competence is an impersonal quality, professionalism, in contrast, is personal. In addition to a state of mind, it is a way of working and living—a way of adding something valuable to competence. For the engineer professionalism implies that he will make *maximum* use of his skill and knowledge, and that he will use his competence to its fullest extent:

- ☐ With complete honesty and integrity.
- ☐ With his best effort in spite of the fact that frequently neither client nor employer is able to evaluate that effort.
- ☐ With avoidance of all possible conflicts of interest.
- ☐ With the consciousness that the profession of engineering is often judged by the performance of a single individual.

Professionalism for an engineer begins with good moral character, because he occupies a position of trust where he personally must set the standards. Consequently he is required to made decisions that sometimes differ from the preferences of his company or his client.

Professionalism for an engineer means:

- ☐ Striving to improve his work until it becomes a model for those in his field, as a minimum using the most up-to-date techniques and procedures.
- ☐ Proper credit for work done and ideas developed by subordinates.
- ☐ Loyalty to his employer or client, always with concern for the public safety in construction, product design, plant operation, and all other phases of engineering.
- ☐ Leadership of less experienced colleagues and subordinates toward personal development and an enthusiasm for the profession.

[1] Drawn from a statement on professionalism by Professional Engineers In Education, National Society of Professional Engineers Washington, D.C., "Engineer In Education Newsletter", Vol. 4, No. 2 (1969). Used by permission.

□ Activity in technical societies in order to keep current in his field, and encouragement of those working under him to improve their technical competence the same way.
□ Participation in professional societies, as well as technical societies, thereby demonstrating his interest in the profession and encouraging his coworkers to recognize the technical and the professional as of equal-ranking importance.
□ Registration, not simply because it may be a legal requirement, but more particularly as a demonstration to his coworkers and the public that this is one important hallmark of a professional, a willingness to go beyond the minimum to help and encourage others to realize their full potential.

For engineers in various areas of work, professionalism will include special facets that are more particularly related to a particular field. For example, engineers in industry should be especially conscious of their responsibility in protecting "company proprietary" designs or processes. It also means the establishment of performance standards and safety criteria which protect the purchaser while maintaining a satisfactory return to the manufacturer. For the engineer in government or the engineer in private practice, professionalism may mean capitalizing on a special opportunity to project the profession to the public as a constructive force in society. For the engineer in education, professionalism means practicing at the frontier of knowledge in some field and pushing against that boundary, thus impressing on his students that boundaries need not be (and are rarely) static.

Professionalism for all engineers means an active participation in community life. Engineering cannot achieve general recognition as a profession unless engineers are publicly visable. It is in the realm of public and social service that professionalism shows up strongest. For this reason service to the public and the community and to those less fortunate is particularly significant.

Professionalism can be taught since it is an acquired condition and is not inherent in one's nature. It is most effectively taught by example by individuals whose lives are themselves models of integrity. The beginnings of a professional attitude for the engineering student should be established in the formative college years since, like character, it grows stronger with reinforcement. In laboratory work, for example, an honest reporting of facts and an intelligent evaluation of results are important ingredients in the development of the student's professional training. Design experiences in general involve many compromises—time, money, materials, and so on. Ethical consideration should necessarily become a part of each compromise (decision) made by the young engineer. His professional career will, in fact, become one of compromise and he must prepare himself to face the realities of such a life.

Probably the student will not have achieved a mature professional attitude by the date of his graduation. However, responsibility of thought and decision should be firmly established by this time in order that entry into employment will be a continuation rather than the beginning of his professional advancement.

After graduation, opportunities for public service will present themselves. The engineer, as part of his professional responsibility, should seek and accept places of service in schools, community government, religious organizations, and charitable groups. Not only will he be able to contribute his talents to these causes, but also he will enhance his own outlook by contacts with both professionals and nonprofessional persons. Each individual engineer should recognize within himself the need for a professional attitude and assume the ultimate responsibility for upholding this concept.

To sum up professionalism, engineering may be considered to be a profession insofar as it meets these characteristics of a learned professional group:

Illustration 6-1
Responsibility of thought and decision are hallmarks of the professionally oriented engineer. Such characteristics are molded at an early age and matured in school.

- ☐ Knowledge and skill in specialized fields above that of the general public.
- ☐ A desire for public service and a willingness to share discoveries for the benefit of others.
- ☐ Exercise of discretion and judgment.
- ☐ Establishment of a relation of confidence between the engineer and client or the engineer and employer.
- ☐ Acceptance of overall and specific codes of conduct.

□ Formation of professional groups and participation in advancing professional ideals and knowledge.

□ Recognition by law as an identifiable body of knowledge.

With these as objectives, the student should pursue his college studies and his training in his employment so as to meet these characteristics within their full meaning and take his or her place as a professional engineer in our society.

Technical societies

As suggested above, professionals band themselves together for the mutual exchange of ideas, to improve their knowledge, and to learn new skills and techniques. Meeting and discussing problems with others in the same field of endeavor affords an opportunity for the stimulation of thought to improve learning and skills. In addition to the National Society of Professional Engineers, which is concerned primarily with the *professional* aspects of the whole field of engineering, engineers have organized a number of technical societies in their fields of specialization. Table 6-1 lists the major engineering and scientific societies in the United States.

Problems on the professional role of the engineer

6-1. Discuss the factors that are common to all professions.

6-2. Investigate the laws of the state that pertain to serving as an expert engineering witness in court. What would you need to do to qualify as such a witness?

Illustration 6-2
Engineering technical societies perform an important function in stimulating communication between individuals. Through the publication of journals and the coordination of local, regional, and national meetings the most current technical information in the discipline is made available for all to use.

*Table 6-1**

Code	Name	Address	Year organized	Total member-ship
AcSoc	Acoustical Society of America	335 East 45th St. New York, N.Y. 10017	1929	4100
APCA	Air Pollution Control Association	4400 Fifth Ave. Pittsburgh, Pa. 15213	1907	5012
AAAS	American Association for the Advancement of Science	1515 Massachusetts Ave., N.W. Washington, D.C. 20005	1848	125,000
AACE	American Association of Cost Engineers	University of Alabama P.O. Box 5199 University, Ala. 35486	1956	1880
AAPM	American Association of Physicists in Medicine	335 East 45th St. New York, N.Y. 10017	1958	500
Am. Ceram. Soc.	American Ceramic Society, Inc.	4055 North High Street Columbus, Ohio 43214	1898	7400
ACI	American Concrete Institute	22400 West 7 Mile Road Detroit, Mich. 48219	1905	14,446
ACM	Association for Computing Machinery	1133 Avenue of the Americas New York, N.Y. 10036	1947	25,747
ACSM	American Congress on Surveying and Mapping	430 Woodward Bldg 733 15th St. N.W. Washington, D.C. 20005	1941	6000
AES	Audio Engineering Society, Inc.	60 East 42nd St., Room 428 New York, N.Y. 10017	1948	4590
AGU	American Geophysical Union	2100 Pennsylvania Ave., N.W. Washington, D.C. 20037	1919	9706
AIAA	American Institute of Aeronautics and Astronautics	1290 Avenue of the Americas New York, N.Y. 10019	1932	40,614
AIA	American Institute of Architects	1735 New York Ave., N.W. Washington, D.C. 20006	1857	38,459
AIChE	American Institute of Chemical Engineers	345 East 47th St. New York, N.Y. 10017	1908	36,379
AICE	American Institute of Consulting Engineers	345 East 47th St. New York, N.Y. 10017	1910	420
AIIE	American Institute of Industrial Engineers	345 East 47th St. New York, N.Y. 10017	1948	20,000
AIME	American Institute of Mining, Metallurgical, and Petroleum Engineers, Inc.	345 East 47th St. New York, N.Y. 10017	1871	46,865
AIP	American Institute of Physics	335 East 45th St. New York, N.Y. 10017	1931	66,925
AIPE	American Institute of Plant Engineers	1056 Delta Ave. Cincinnati, Ohio 45208	1954	4026
AMS	American Mathematical Society	P.O. Box 6248 Providence, R.I. 02904	1888	13,362
ANS	American Nuclear Society	244 East Ogden Ave. Hinsdale, Ill., 60521	1954	9384
APS	American Physical Society	335 East 45th St. New York, N.Y. 10017	1899	26,000
APHA	American Public Health Association	1740 Broadway New York, N.Y. 10019	1872	21,791
ASAE	American Society of Agricultural Engineers	2950 Niles Ave. St. Joseph, Mich. 49085	1907	7200
ASCE	American Society of Civil Engineers	345 East 47th St. New York, N.Y. 10017	1852	64,695
ASEE	American Society For Engineering Education	National Center for Higher Education One Dupont Circle Washington, D.C. 20036	1893	13,615
ASM	American Society for Metals	Metals Park, Ohio 44073	1913	39,855

*The majority extracted from *Directory of Engineering Societies and Related Organizations,* Engineers Joint Council, New York (1970).

Table 6-1 (*continued*)

Code	Name	Address	Year organized	Total member-ship
ASNT	American Society for Nondestructive Testing	914 Chicago Ave. Evanston, Ill. 60202	1941	7310
ASQC	American Society for Quality Control	161 West Wisconsin Ave. Milwaukee, Wisc. 53203	1946	23,296
ASHRAE	American Society of Heating, Refrigerating and Air-Conditioning Engineers, Inc.	345 East 47th St. New York, N.Y. 10017	1894	24,250
ASLE	American Society of Lubrication Engineers	838 Busse Highway Park Ridge, Ill. 60068	1944	3470
ASME	American Society of Mechanical Engineers	345 East 47th St. New York, N.Y. 10017	1880	64,598
ASNE	American Society of Naval Engineers, Inc.	1012 14th St. N.W. Suite 507 Washington, D.C. 20005	1888	3881
ASSE	American Society of Safety Engineers	850 Busse Highway Park Ridge, Ill. 60068	1911	9100
ASSE	American Society of Sanitary Engineering	228 Standard Building Cleveland, Ohio 44113	1906	2342
ASTM	American Society for Testing and Materials	1916 Race St. Philadelphia, Pa. 19103	1898	16,500
AWRA	American Water Resources Association	905 West Fairview Urbana, Ill. 61801	1964	1622
AWWA	American Water Works Association, Inc.	2 Park Ave. New York, N.Y. 10016	1881	21,500
CEC	Consulting Engineers Council of the United States of America	1155 15th St., N.W. Washington, D.C. 20005	1959	2300
IES	Illuminating Engineering Society	345 East 47th St. New York, N.Y. 10017	1906	10,735
IEEE	Institute of Electrical & Electronics Engineers, Inc.	345 East 47th St. New York, N.Y. 10017	1884	154,734
IES	Institute of Environmental Sciences	940 East Northwest Highway Mt. Prospect, Ill. 60056	1959	2339
ITE	Institute of Traffic Engineers	2029 K Street, N.W., 6th Floor Washington, D.C. 20006	1930	3488
ISA	Instrument Society of America	520 William Penn Place Pittsburgh, Pa. 15219	1945	20,400
NACE	National Association of Corrosion Engineers	2400 West Loop South Houston, Tex. 77027	1945	7425
NAPE	National Association of Power Engineers, Inc.	174 West Adams St., Suite 1411 Chicago, Ill. 60603	1882	12,000
NICE	National Institute of Ceramic Engineers	4055 North High St. Columbus, Ohio 43214	1938	1625
NSPE	National Society of Professional Engineers	2029 K Street, N.W. Washington, D.C. 20006	1934	68,000
ORSA	Operations Research Society of America	428 East Preston St. Baltimore, Md. 21202	1952	6407
SAM	Society for Advancement of Management, Inc.	1472 Broadway New York, N.Y. 10036	1912	15,500
SESA	Society for Experimental Stress Analysis	21 Bridge Square Westport, Conn. 06880	1943	2669
SIAM	Society for Industrial and Applied Mathematics	33 South 17th St. Philadelphia, Pa. 19103	1952	4000
SAE	Society of Automotive Engineers	Two Pennsylvania Plaza New York, N.Y. 10001	1905	31,533
SME	Society of Manufacturing Engineers	20501 Ford Rd. Dearborn, Mich. 48128	1932	42,452
SNAME	Society of Naval Architects and Marine Engineers	74 Trinity Place New York, N.Y. 10006	1893	9038
SPE	Society of Plastics Engineers, Inc.	656 West Putnam Ave. Greenwich, Conn. 06830	1941	15,000
SWE	Society of Women Engineers	345 East 47th St. New York, N.Y. 10017	1952	1091

6-3. What engineering fields of specialization are recognized by the state registration board for licensing as professional engineers?

6-4. Using the Code of Ethics as a guide, discuss the procedures that professional engineers in private practice may utilize to attract clients.

6-5. Discuss the value of humanities and social studies courses in relation to the work of the professional engineer in industry.

6-6. Investigate the need for graduate engineering education for the engineer in private practice.

6-7. List the reasons why it is important for engineers in education to become registered professional engineers.

6-8. Engineer Brown, P. E., is approached by Engineer Smith (nonregistered) who offers a fee of $100.00 to Brown if he will "check over" a set of engineering plans and affix his professional P.E. seal to them. Describe Brown's responsibilities and actions.

6-9. Discuss the reasons why a professional person such as a registered engineer, an attorney, or a physician will not bid competitively on the performance of a service.

6-10. In interviewing for permanent employment, a senior student in a California engineering school agreed to visit on two successive days a company in Chicago and a company in Detroit. Upon his return home both companies sent him checks to cover his expenses, including round-trip airfare. Discuss the appropriate actions that should have been taken by the student.

6-11. The majority of all engineering designs require some extension of the engineer's repertoire of scientific knowledge and analytical skills. How can the engineer determine whether or not this extension lies beyond the "training and experience" referred to in Section 6 of the Code of Ethics?

6-12. Engineer Jones, P.E., is the only registered engineer living in Smileyville. Two individuals, Green and Black, approach him with regard to employing his services in estimating the cost of constructing a small dam that would make it possible to reclaim 500 acres of swampland that is now owned by the city but will soon be offered for sale to the highest bidder. Jones learns that both individuals will be bidding against each other to purchase the acreage. Discuss Jones' responsibilities and actions.

6-13. Engineer White is approached by several of his neighbors to urge him to announce his candidacy for city mayor. In previous months the city administration has been accused of "selling rezoning authorizations" and of "enhancing personal fortunes" through the sale of privileged information pertaining to the location of the new proposed freeway. Discuss the course of action that you would recomment for White.

6-14. Engineer Williams and Contractor Smart have been good friends for several years. In March Smart is to begin construction on a multistory building that Williams designed. On Christmas a complete set of children's play equipment (swings, slides, gymnastic bars, etc.) is delivered to Williams' house—compliments of the Smart Construction Company. What course of action do you recommend for Williams?

Bibliography

Alger, Philip, N. A. Christensen, and Sterling P. Olmsted, *Ethical Problems in Engineering*, Wiley, New York (1965).

Cross, Hardy, *Engineers and Ivory Towers*, McGraw-Hill, New York (1952).

Hoover, Theodore J, and John Charles Lounsbury Fish, *The Engineering Profession*, Stanford U.P., Stanford, Calif. (1950).

Mantell, Murray I., *Ethics and Professionalism in Engineering*, Macmillan, New York (1964).

7

Study habits of the engineer

From high school to college

Students who have enrolled in a college or university for the first time often ask, "Is there a difference between a high school course and a college course?" and "Will I need to make any adjustments in my study habits, now that I have enrolled in college?"

The answer to both of there questions is probably *yes*, but let us examine some of the reasons why this may be so.

First, in high school you were competing against the *average* of high school students. However, of the total numbers graduating from high school in the United States each year, fewer than one third go to college. Thus, you are now competing with the average of *very good* high school students.

The study habits and learning process that you used in high school may not be adequate to cope with the increased requirements of college courses because of both the limited time available and the large quantity of material to be covered. A refinement of your study habits or perhaps a complete change in study habits may be necessary to enable you to keep up with the demands of new course material.

Many students, as they enter college, do not realize what will be expected of them. In general they are expected to bring basic skills in mathematical manipulation, in reading rapidly and comprehending, and in possessing a broadbased vocabulary. Engineering educators have observed that a high school graduate who has the ability to *read* and *add* also possesses the capability to succeed in a college engineering program. In high school, much time was taken in class to outline and drill on the daily assignments. In college, relatively less time is taken in class, and much more study and preparation is expected from the student outside of class. The student is largely on his own, and his time can be used to a considerable extent as he sees fit. It can be used efficiently and profitably or it can be dissipated without plan and, in effect, be wasted.

Without parental urging or strong encouragement from teachers, the student must adopt personal methods of study that will produce desirable results. Specifically he must budget his time to permit adequate preparation for each course. There must be more than a casual desire to improve study habits. Positive steps must be taken to ensure effective study and learning conditions. It is for this reason that the following topics are included as suggestions to aid in improving the students effectiveness in study.

Preclass study

The object of study is to learn. Mere idle reading is not study. Particularly in scientific and technical courses, extreme attention to detail is necessary. With the learning process in mind, let us examine some basic principles.

1. The material must be organized into appropriate learning units. Random facts and concepts are more difficult to learn than facts which are related. For example, in learning the names of the bones of the body it is easier to remember the names if groups such as the arm or leg bones are studied as a unit.
2. Attempt to form the correct pattern of facts on the first try. This is necessary to eliminate the need for "unlearning" and relearning factual material. In the case of research or exploratory study, trial-and-error methods are necessary and frequently incorrect assumptions are made. However, by conscious effort to use reasoning and to incorporate other correct facts, false assumptions are minimized.

Illustration 7-1
The object of study is to learn. The engineering student must be able to focus his attention on specific topics for extended periods of time.

3. Correct errors immediately and reinforce correct learning responses. Experiments have shown that immediate confirmation of correct learning is more effective in remembering than when the confirmation is delayed. For example if a mathematics problem is solved and its correctness verified immediately, the principle involved in the solution is retained better than if the verification is delayed.

4. Relate realistic experiences with the facts. Experiments have demonstrated that most people learn and retain information better if it is related in some way to their experiences. For example, an abstract idea such as "democracy" is difficult to present as a realistic picture unless the student has some related background of government upon which to draw a conclusion. On the other hand a description of a new type of internal combustion engine may be simple to present to an experienced automobile mechanic because of his related experience with similar devices.

5. Give concise meanings to the facts. Particularly in scientific work the meanings of words may not always be clear. Frequently we misunderstand one another because we each may give different meanings to the same word. The use of dictionaries, encyclopedias, and reference books is therefore necessary to gain a common understanding of new words.

6. Practice, review, and provide application for facts. Education specialists believe that facts are not actually learned until at least one perfect recitation or response is completed. After this has been accomplished, review and repeated use of the facts will greatly aid retention. Research also has shown that if the review is broken into spaced periods, retention and recall are increased (sometimes as much as doubled) over the retention when the reviewing is done all at one sitting. One should be alert to applications for the ideas being learned. This will help to relate them to previous experience and to place them into a pattern where they will become bricks in a wall of knowledge upon which other ideas can be added.

7. Evaluate the adequacy of the learning: A self-evaluation of the understanding of the new ideas which have been presented is one of the most valuable learning experiences in which a student can participate. Memorizing facts does not encourage self-evaluation. However, the ability to apply principles and *to use* facts is one important way in which a person can evaluate the adequacy of learning. For example, after studying a portion of text material in a physics book, are you able at once to apply the facts and principles discussed to the solution of related problems?

The realm of factual information available is so tremendous that a student should acquire at first only the essential and basic facts in a particular field of study. From this set of basic facts, the student then enlarges or details his information into more specialized subjects. For example, the electrical engineering student should begin his study of electricity with an inspection of basic principles, such as Ohm's Law, before beginning to consider the design of amplifiers.

Setting the stage

Provide a designated study area. It is desirable to find a place where you can concentrate and where other people will not bother you. Unfortunately distractions frequently abound in large study areas and interfere with study schedules. Other people in your home or your dormitory may have conflicting schedules and may not be concerned with respecting your own study periods. Radios, televisions, and

Illustration 7-2
It is very important that the student's place for study be well arranged, adequately lighted, and free from distraction.

"bull sessions" are always inviting diversions from study. For this reason many students find that libraries afford good study areas because of the absence of distractions and the ready availability of reference materials. Although a secluded spot is not always essential for study, for most people it does require a conscious effort to reject distracting sounds and backgrounds in order to concentrate.

The best place to study is usually at a desk or table, not on a bed. The effort of sitting helps to keep most people alert and in a mood for study. Good lighting is especially helpful and it is desirable for the whole study area to be illuminated, rather than a small portion of the area. Studies have shown that it is less fatiguing on the eyes if sharply defined regions of light and dark are excluded from the immediate study area. In addition, the work area should be large enough so that reference materials can be kept close at hand.

Prepare a schedule

Time is one of the most important factors to be considered in college study. In every course there is usually more material assigned than can be studied in detail in the time available. In addition outside activities will always compete for a student's time. Athletic events, social and educational programs, recreational activities, and unscheduled meetings with other people seem to disrupt the best laid plans. The student must realize that these contradictory conditions for study will always exist. Positive steps must be taken to insure that the time for study is not taken away piecemeal by nonessentials.

In preparing a daily schedule, the question arises concerning the amount of time to allocate for study. Several rule-of-thumb principles are in common use, but the individual's capabilities in learning each specific subject will necessarily need to be the final guide. A recent survey of a cross section of students at a large university showed that the greatest number of students spent an average of 28 to 32 hours of study per week. Engineering students usually spend considerably more than this amount. Actually the number of hours of study is not always the most significant criterion to be used. Rather *how well* one studies is the factor that counts most. The results of study as shown by grades and by one's own personal satisfaction in doing a good job are usually the best indicators of the effective use of time.

A positive and direct approach to a schedule is necessary in the same way that a budget is necessary to manage the fiscal affairs of a business. No commercial enterprise can long exist that does not plan ahead for meeting expenses as they arise. In a similar way a student should prepare a budget of time for his school work and adhere to it, unless circumstances definitely indicate that it should be altered. Not only should the daily time be budgeted on a weekly basis, but also extra time must be allocated for major quizzes, term papers, and final examinations. It has been found, for instance, that the majority of the better students budget their time so that final examinations do not have to be prepared for on a frantic last minute rush. Study skills, no matter how effective, will not be of much value if a student's time is not properly scheduled so that they can be employed.

Scheduling helps to allocate more time to the more difficult courses and to assign less time to the less demanding courses. It also helps to space the available study time so that it will be distributed in a manner to aid in better retention. (Refer to the sixth principle of learning on page 120.)

Studying to learn

Studying to learn is a skill that can be developed just as other skills are developed. All good golfers do not use exactly the same stance or swing, yet they all accomplish a reasonably consistent pattern of results. In like manner, good students may employ slightly different techniques of study and still accomplish an acceptable learning pattern. However, despite individual differences, in any activity a general set of principles can be found that will produce good results, whether it be golf or studying. Some of these principles for study are discussed below.

1. Remove or minimize distractions.
2. Arrange all necessary pencils, reference books, notebooks, note paper, and other supplies before beginning.
3. Put your full attention on the work at hand, and insist that your brain work accurately and rapidly. If the brain is not employed to its full capacity, it will tend to let other thoughts enter to distract it from the task at hand. Read with a purpose—to extract details from the printed page and to comprehend important ideas.
4. Practice reading as fast as feasible. This does not mean skipping from word to word randomly, but rather training the eyes and brain to group words, phrases, and even lines of reading material and to understand the thoughts therein. Many good books are available on how to improve your reading speed for comprehension. Time spent in learning this skill will aid immensely in the faster grasping of ideas.
5. Study as though you were going to teach someone else the subject matter. This will provide motivation for learning and also will encourage self-appraisal of the adequacy of learning as discussed in the seventh principle of learning on page 120.
6. Plan for review and repetition of the assignment. Principle of learning number six on page 120 points out the desirability of spaced periods of review.

The suggested methods and practices described above have been found to aid most students in their learning and the majority of good students follow the general outline of these practices

Preparation for class recitation

A plan of study for each course is necessary to gain the greatest return in learning from your investment of study time. The plan will vary with the teacher, the textbook, the nature of the course, and the type of recitation and examination that is expected. However, before considering suggestions for specific types of courses, we should investigate study techniques that are applicable in general to all subjects.

Learning proceeds best from the general to the specific. It is therefore recommended at the beginning of a course to first skim the chapter and topic headings of the text without reading in detail any of the discussion material. This is done to get an overview of the whole organization of the book. Notice the order in which the topics appear and how the author has arranged the ideas to proceed from one to another. Next, read the lesson quickly to gain an insight into the nature of the material to be covered. Do not attempt to learn details nor to analyze any but the most emphasized points. If there is a summary, read it as part of your lesson survey to prepare you with background material that will be useful in understanding details.

Second, after a rapid survey of the material to be studied, start at the beginning of the assignment with the idea in mind that you will make notes during your study. Remember, you are going to learn as though you would have to teach the lesson content to someone else. Mere superficial reading here will not suffice. The notes can take various forms. They may include summaries of important facts, definitions of words, sample problems or examples, answers to questions, sketches, diagrams, and graphs. A better mental picture is formed and retained if the hand and eye work together on an idea and if you are forced to participate more actively and completely in the learning process.

These notes should be made in semipermanent form, not on random scraps of paper. Bound notebooks or loose-leaf notebooks can be used, but it is important that the notes be organized and retrievable. In addition to separate notes, it is helpful to underline key words and phrases in the text. Don't worry about the appearance of the book. However, do not overdo the underlining; it is better to note the crucial words and phrases so that they are more obvious for review than to underline whole sentences and paragraphs. Usually from three to eight words per paragraph will point out the central idea that has been presented.

Third, reread and review the lesson assignment and prepare your own questions and answers to the topics. At first this may seem to be an unnecessary step but it will pay dividends. Attempt, if possible, to foresee the questions the instructor may ask later concerning the material. Your notes on these predictions can be invaluable at examination time. Check to see that you have noted all of the important details and related facts that bring out the main ideas. Particularly in the technological courses, you can do this easily, since much of the material is completely factual.

Fourth, if given an opportunity, plan to participate in the classroom recitation. Force yourself, if necessary, to volunteer to recite. Recitation is a form of learning and it aids in acquiring ideas from others. If the class does not afford an opportunity for recitation, recite the lesson in your room. Review and recitation are the best methods for making a final check of your retention of information. Tests show that you begin to forget even while learning, but if you participate in some form of recitation as soon after study as possible, the retention of facts may be increased by as much as 50 per cent.

Recitation is an effective way of self-appraisal of learning. Just reading a book is not enough to convince anyone—yourself included—that you have learned what you should. When you study, break the topics into groups, and upon completion of each group of topics, as a summary close the book and see if you can recite the important facts either mentally or in writing. When you can repeat them satisfactorily then continue; if you cannot repeat them, for further study, go back and pick out the ones that you have missed. It is particularly important to recite if the subject matter consists of somewhat disconnected material such as names, dates, formulas, rules, laws, or items. If the material to be studied is more narrative in style and well organized, the recitation time can occupy a small part of the study period, but it should never be left out altogether.

The general principles above apply to all courses, but certain study plans will apply better to one course than to another. We shall examine study plans for several types of courses in more detail.

Technical courses

In this type of course your study plan should be to direct your study toward understanding the meanings of words and toward grasping the laws and principles involved. In order to understand the words, a dictionary, encyclopedia, and reference books are necessary. The first step is to write down definitions of unfamiliar terms. Remember also that a word does not always have the same meaning in different courses. For example, the word "work" as used in economics has a meaning quite different from the word "work" as used in physics.

When the definitions of words are obtained, study for complete understanding. Texts in technical courses tend to be concise and extremely factual. A technique of reading must be adopted here for reading each word and fitting it into its place in the basic idea. Except for the initial survey reading of the lesson, do not skim rapidly through the explanations, but rather read to locate the particular ideas in each paragraph. If example problems are given, try working them yourself without reference to the author's solution.

After definitions and basic ideas are studied, apply the principles to the solution of problems. It has been said by students that it is impractical to study for examinations where problems are to be solved because you are unable to predict the problem questions. This statement is not correct, for you can predict the principles which will be used in solving the problems. For example, in chemistry a vast number of compounds can be used in equation-balancing problems. However, a very few basic principles are involved. If the principle of balancing is learned, all problems, regardless of the chemical material used, are solved the same way. The objective of this part of study then is to determine the few principles involved and the few problem patterns that can be used. After this, all problems, regardless of their number arrangement and descriptive material, can be classified into one of the problem patterns for which a general method of solution is available. For instance, a problem in physics may involve an electrical circuit in which both current and voltage are known and an unknown resistance is to be determined. Another problem may suggest a circuit containing a certain resistance and with a given current in it. In this case a voltage is to be found. The problems are worded differently, but a general principle involving Ohm's Law applies to each situation. The same problem structure is used in each case. The only difference appears in where the unknown quantity lies in the problem pattern.

Illustration 7-3
The library is an excellent place to study since it is quiet and numerous reference works are readily available.

Do not become discouraged if you have difficulty in classifying problems. One of the best ways to aid in learning to classify problems is to work an abundance of problems. It is then likely that any examination problem will be similar to a problem that you have solved before.

Learn to analyze each problem in steps. Examine the problem first for any operations that may simplify it. Sometimes a change in units of measure will aid in pointing toward a solution. Try rewriting the problem in a different form. Frequently in mathematical problems, this is a useful approach. Write down each step as the solution proceeds. This approach is particularly helpful if the solution will involve a number of different principles. If a certain approach is not productive, go back and reexamine the application of the principles to the data. For problems which have definite answers, these techniques usually will provide a means for obtaining a solution.

It usually is better in studying technological courses to divide the study periods into several short sessions, rather than one continuous and long study period. For most people a period of incubation (where the idea is allowed to soak into the subconscious) is helpful in grasping the new ideas presented. After returning to do subsequent study, make a quick review of the material previously studied, and look at the notes you have prepared to provide continuity for your thinking.

Literature courses

Most writings classed as literature are written to be interesting and to entertain. For this reason, not as much attention to detail and to individual words is needed as is required in technological books. Usually the ideas are presented descriptively and are readily distinguished. However, the interpretation of the ideas may vary from person to person, and it is with this in mind that the following suggestions are given.

Examine the ideas not only from your point of view but also from the point of view of your teacher. Try to find out from his discussions and examinations the pattern of thought toward which he is directing you, and study the things *in which he is interested.*

Consciously look for these items while you read prose: the setting, central characters (note the realism or symbolism of each), the theme, the point of view of the author (first person, omniscent, etc.), the author's style of writing, the tone, and the type of the writing. For poetry, the ideas may be more obscure, but certain things may be noted. For example, the authors' style, the type of verse, the rhyme scheme, the theme, the symbols, allusions, images, similes, metaphors, personifications, apostrophes, and alliterations are all basic and important parts of the study of poetry.

Social science courses

These courses can be interesting and satisfying or dull and dry, depending upon the student's attitude and interest. Most texts use a narrative style in presenting the material and, as a consequence, the assignment should be surveyed quickly for content and then in more detail for particular ideas. Here the use of notes and underlining is invaluable, and summaries are very helpful in remembering the various facts.

If the course is history, government, sociology, psychology, or a related subject, consider that it contains information that is necessary to help you as a citizen. A knowledge of these subjects will aid you in dealing with other people and it will give you background information to aid in the evaluation of material that has been specifically designed to influence and control people's thinking. Study the course for basic ideas and information and, unless the instructor indicates otherwise, do not exaggerate the importance of detail and descriptive information.

These principles apply also to courses in economics, statistics, and related courses except that they frequently are treated on a more mathematical basis. Here a combination of techniques described above together with problem solving procedures can be helpful. Again, since the volume of words usually is quite large, it is necessary to use notes and summaries to keep the ideas in a space to be handled easily.

Language courses

Many techniques have been developed to aid in learning foreign languages. In the absence of specific study guides from your instructor, the following procedures have been found to be helpful.

Learn a vocabulary first. Study new foreign words and form a mental image of them with a conscious effort to think in the new language. As you study, practice putting words together, and, if the course includes conversation, say the words aloud. Space your vocabulary study and review constantly, always trying to picture objects and actions in the language rather than in English.

Rules of grammar are to be learned as any rule or principle: first as statements and then by application. Reading and writing seem to be the best ways of aiding retention of grammar rules. Read a passage repeatedly until it seems natural to see or hear the idea in that form. Write a summary in the language, preferably in a form that will employ the rules of grammar which you are studying. Unfortunately, there is no way to learn a new language without considerable effort on your part. Even English, our native tongue, when studied as a subject, gives some students trouble. However, many students have said that they really understand basic English much better after having taken a foreign language.

Classroom learning

The discussion so far has been concerned with learning by study. An equally effective and more widely used method of learning is by listening. From earliest childhood you have learned by listening and imitating. Do not stop now but rather use the classroom to supplement your home study. You will find that things are covered in classroom work that you do not find in your texts. The interchange of ideas with others stimulates your thinking and retention processes. The classroom can also be a place to practice and to demonstrate your learning and problem solving skills before the examination periods.

The skill of listening seldom is used to the fullest extent: If your attention is only partly on the lecture, the part missed may make a major difference in your grade. Use the time in class to evaluate your instructor, find out what he will expect of you, watch for clues for examination questions, and make notes to be used for later study. If you plan to make the classroom time profitable, you will find it also will be enjoyable.

Come to class with a knowledge of the assignment to be discussed. The instructor then can fill in your knowledge pattern rather than present entirely new material. This also saves time in taking notes because the notes will be needed only for amplification rather than as semiverbatim recording. If a point arises at variance with your knowledge from study, you have an opportunity to question it. Prior study also permits you to predict what the instructor will say next. This serves as a valuable psychological device to hold your attention throughout the class period.

Note taking during class is a skill that can be learned. The inexperienced will try to take notes verbatim and thus get so involved in writing that they cannot listen for ideas. Usually, they cannot write fast enough to copy all of the words anyway. Rather than take notes verbatim, practice your listening skills and evaluate the critical points in the lecture. A few critical points will be amplified with descriptive materials. Practice taking down these critical points in your own words. Such note taking serves to keep your attention focused and to encourage a better understanding of the principles being discussed. If you do not understand the points completely, make notes for later study or for questioning the instructor.

If the course is such that you can, recite during the class period. Push your shyness aside, and place your ideas and information before the class. It stimulates your thinking and retention, it will help to clear up obscure points, and will give you much needed practice in hearing your voice in the presence of others.

Attention and listening during a class period together with participation, either in recitation or in anticipating what the instructor will cover next, will save you hours of study time outside the classroom.

Preparation for themes, papers, and reports

The purpose of writing is to transmit information. For an engineer this is a valuable means of communicating his ideas to others and the practicing engineer takes pride in the conciseness and adequacy of his reports. No matter how good your ideas may be, if you cannot communicate them to others, they are of little value. Since part of the work of an engineer is writing reports and papers, the opportunity to learn and to practice this skill in school should be exploited. There are many good books on composition and manuals on writing that will help you. For this reason the

Illustration 7-4 (*opposite*)
Adequate study gives confidence when reciting in class.
Courtesy Brown University, Division of Engineering

suggestions given here are to be considered as supplementary helps in the preparation of written work.

In general, good writing involves good grammar, correct spelling, and an orderly organization of ideas. The basic rules of grammar should be followed and a logical system of punctuation used. If in doubt as to the application of a somewhat obscure rule in grammar, either look it up or reword your idea in a more conventional manner. Punctuation is used to separate ideas and should follow, in general, the pauses you would use if you were reading the material aloud. Usually, reports are written in an impersonal manner; seldom is the first person used in formal writing.

Little needs to be said about spelling except to say, spell correctly. There is so little room for choice in spelling that there is no excuse for a technical student to misspell words. If you don't know how to spell a word, look it up in a dictionary or reference book and remember how to spell it correctly thereafter.

The last characteristic of good writing is a clear orderly organization of ideas. They may take several forms depending upon the type of writing. For themes, usually a narrative or story form is used in which a situation is set up, possibly with characters, and a story is told or a condition is described. Engineering papers and reports generally are concerned with technical subjects. Therefore they describe the behavior of objects or processes, or they provide details of events in technical fields. Frequently, the first paragraph summarizes the thoughts in the whole report in order to give the reader a quick survey without his having to skim through the manuscript first. Following paragraphs outline the contents in more detail. They frequently end with graphs, drawings, charts, and diagrams to support the conclusions reached.

In preparation of written work, some research usually is needed. In order to aid in keeping the notes for the material in usable form, it is helpful to record abbreviated notes from research works on cards in order that the arrangement of the writing of the paper can be made in a logical order. Usually, in compiling information you do not know how much will be used so the notes on cards provide a flexibility of choice that is a great aid in the final organization of the paper. The cards can be 3″ by 5″ or 4″ by 6″, with the latter usually being the better choice because of more available space.

An outline of the material to be discussed or described is necessary, even for brief reports. An outline ensures a more logical arrangement of ideas and helps to make the writing follow from concept to concept more smoothly.

Write a draft copy first and plan on making alterations. Write first to get your ideas down on paper, and then go over the copy to improve the rough places in grammar, spelling, punctuation, and wording. If possible, wait a short time before taking these corrective steps to get a more detached and objective approach to the suggested changes. When the rework of the draft has been made, copy it over neatly, still maintaining a critical attitude on the mechanics of the writing. It is helpful if the final draft can be typed, but if not, you will find that good handwriting or lettering frequently makes a favorable impression upon the person who grades your paper.

Preparation for examinations

Have you ever felt after taking an examination (for which you studied) that everything you studied was inappropriate? Perhaps you used the wrong techniques in studying for the examination. Certain rules have been found to be very useful in preparation for tests of any kind. The type of preparation you make is often more important in the final grading than how long you spend in preparation. Let us discuss some of these rules that have been found to be effective.

Start preparing for tests the day the course starts. You know that they will be assigned, so do not close your eyes to this fact. From the very first, start studying two things: (1) the big overall ideas of the course, and (2) the instructor. Keeping these two things in mind will help you to learn while in class and while studying. This will also mean shorter reviews before tests.

Keep writing reminders of important points—as notes in the margins of your books, as flagged notes in class, or as short statements while studying. Use nontext material as it becomes available, such as outlines, old tests, and information from students who have taken the course.

It is not unethical to study the instructor. After all, he is a person qualified to present the subject matter, and, because of his training and experience, frequently you will learn much more from him than you will from any text. From a study of the instructor, you can follow his pattern of lesson organization and find out what he wants from you. In your preparation, attempt to think and study along these lines. Close attention in class frequently will give major clues pertaining to the nature of future examination questions.

Make a final review of the subject matter. This should be a planned review and not a "last ditch" cramming session. Schedule it in several short sessions and do these things: First, review the general organization of the material before the final class periods of the semester in order to take advantage of the instructor's summaries and reviews. Second, set up the major topics or ideas and associate them with specific facts or examples. In the case of problem courses, this is the time to work out and review sample problems that will illustrate laws or principles. Third, study for more detailed information and to complete the areas of uncertainty. If the first two phases of the review have been adequate, this last phase should take relatively little time.

Predict the type of test that will be given. If the test is to be an essay type, practice outlining key subject matter, summarizing important concepts, comparing or contrasting trends, and listing factual data. This may seem to be an excessive amount of work, but if you have noted the points the instructor has stressed during the course, you can narrow the field considerably. However, a word of caution here: Do not try to outguess the instructor; it usually will not pay. Study the topics you honestly feel are important, and avoid unjustified evaluation of different concepts in hope that there will not be questions on them. Remember that on this type of test not only are the ideas to be recalled but also the organization and sequence of the ideas is important.

For objective or short-answer type tests, follow the three-step program of study given above, giving more attention to relating key ideas to specific items of information. Here, short periods of highly concentrated study usually are to be preferred. Think about each idea long enough to form mental pictures and precise answers, but guard against merely memorizing words. Frequently sketches and diagrams will aid in retaining a mental picture of a concept.

If the test is to be a problem solving test, first review the principles that may be encountered in a problem. Work at least one sample problem that will illustrate the principle. Ask yourself, "If there is a change in the quantity to be solved for, can I still place this problem in the correct problem solving pattern?" This is important because, although the variation in problem statements is infinite, the applicable principles and consequently the problem patterns are relatively few.

What if you have more than one examination on the same day? Most students have found it better to do the last review on the subject that comes first. A quick check of notes then can be made before the next examination begins. An old but useful maxim states that the best preparation for taking tests is to practice the things you will need to do on the test.

Taking examinations

We shall assume that a primary objective in taking an examination is to make a high grade on it. Your grade will be based on what you put down on the test paper—not on what you know. It is crucially important then to get the correct sampling of your knowledge on record. Sometimes students fail, not because of lack of knowledge, but rather because of lack of skill in proving on the test paper that they do understand the material.

In taking any examination, be prepared. The ability to think clearly is of most importance, but the ability to recall facts is also very important. Enter the examination room with a feeling of confidence that you have mastered the subject and, while waiting for the questions to be distributed, be formulating plans for taking the test so that your mind will not be blocking itself with worry.

If the test is an objective type, turn quickly through the pages and note the kinds of questions; true-false, multiple choice, matching, completion. Make a rapid budget of time, and read the directions for answering the questions. If there is no penalty for guessing, answer every question; otherwise plan to omit answers to questions on which you are not reasonably sure. Be certain you understand the ground rules for marking and scoring so that you will not lose points on technicalities.

A basic principle of taking any examination is: *Answer the easy questions first.* If time runs out, at least you have had an opportunity to consider the questions you could answer readily; and usually an answer to an easy question counts as much as an answer to a difficult question. Do not carry over thoughts from one question to another. Concentrate on one question at a time and do not worry about a previous answer until you return to it on the next trial. It helps to relax for a moment between questions and get a fresh breath, and to help dismiss one set of thoughts before concentrating on another. Look for key words that may point to whether a statement is true or false. Usually statements are worded so that a key word or phrase tips the balance one way or the other. In case of doubt, try substituting a similar word into the statement and see whether it may aid in identification of truth or falsity. When you go back over the examination, do not change your answers unless you have obviously misread the questions or you are reasonably certain your original answer is incorrect. Tests have shown that your first response to a question on which you have some doubt is more likely to be correct than not.

If the test is an essay type, again read quickly through the questions, budget your time, and answer the easy questions first. It is helpful to plan to put an answer to each question on a separate sheet of paper unless the answer obviously will be short. The one-answer-per-page system permits easy addition of material after your initial trial. Watch your time schedule, since it is easy to write so much on one question that you are forced to slight others. A help on answering lengthy questions is to jot down a hasty outline of points to include so they will not be overlooked in the process of composition.

After the questions have been answered, take a final critical look at your paper to correct misspelling, grammatical errors, punctuation, and indistinct writing. If time permits, add sketches, examples, or diagrams that may come to mind. Sometimes a period of quiet contemplation, mentally reviewing your notes, will help recall needed additional facts.

If the test has mathematical problems to solve, again read through the questions and budget your time. Plan to answer the easy questions first. Determine the "ground rules" such as whether points will be given for correct procedure regardless of the correctness of the arithmetic. Unless the problem solution is obviously short, plan to work only one problem per page. If a mistake is detected you can more easily and more quickly line out the mistake than attempt erasure. One answer per page also permits room for computations and makes checking your work easier. Usually it is better to do all the work on that page and avoid scratch paper.

If the test is an open book test, use the reference books only for tabular or formula data that you reasonably could not remember. If you try to look up things you should already know, you will surely run out of time.

Let each problem stand by itself. First, analyze it from the standpoint of a pattern into which it can be fitted. Consider then what steps will need to be used in the solution, and finally determine how these solution steps will be presented. When the analysis is complete, solve the problem in the framework of the analysis.

Usually it is better to go ahead and work through all problems and then come back and check for arithmetic mistakes and incorrect algebraic signs. This is the place also to take an objective look at the answer and ask whether it seems reasonable. A questioning attitude here may reveal mistakes that can be corrected.

Analysis of results of tests

Finally, when the test is ended and you get an opportunity to see your graded paper, analyze it and yourself critically. Assuming that you knew the material but that your grade did not reflect your knowledge, find out why the grade was not as good as it should have been. Blame only yourself for any deficiencies. Look for clues such as the ones given below that will help you not to make the same mistake again.

If it was an essay test, was your trouble poor handwriting, incorrect grammar, incorrect spelling, or incorrect punctuation? Correction of these faults is a matter of the mechanics of learning the rules and making a conscious effort to improve on your shortcomings.

Was your trouble failure to follow instructions, lack of organization of ideas, or lack of examples? Look for clues such as marks on your paper by graders stating "not clear," "not in sequence," "why?," "explain," "?," "trace," "compare," "contrast," and so forth, which indicate a failure on your part to follow instructions. The remedies are twofold. Look for key words in instructions on tests, and practice before hand the listing, contrasting, or comparing of factual data.

When the grader's marks include words such as "incomplete," "hard to follow," "meaning not clear," or "rambling," these comments indicate that your ideas need to have better organization. A remedy is to consider carefully what is being asked for in the question. Make a brief outline before you start writing. This affords a means of placing ideas in the most effective sequence and also helps to avoid omitting good points.

The grader's marks may be "for example," "explain," "be more specific," or "illustrate." These marks usually indicate a need for illustrations and examples. Your answers may show that you know something about the subject, but they may not convey precise information. Examples will convince the grader that you know the material covered.

For objective tests, evaluate the patterns of the questions missed. Did you misread the questions? Were you tripped up by double negatives in true-false questions? Did you fail to look for key words in multiple choice questions? Did you realize immediately after the examination that you had answered incorrectly? Some aids in improving grades on objective tests follow.

For true-false questions, did you give each question undivided attention, and were you careful not to read something into the question that was not there. If you missed several questions in sequence, you probably were thinking about more than the question at hand. Try rewording questions that have double negatives next time if you show a pattern of missing them.

For multiple choice questions, determine whether you concentrated on each question alone and determined, if possible, what the answer was before looking at the set of multiple choice answers. You should have eliminated as quickly as possible answers that obviously did not fit the question and concentrated on key words that would have provided clues to select from the remainder.

If the test consisted of problems to be solved, check for mistakes in two things: analysis and arithmetic. If your paper shows false starts on a problem, if you worked part-way and could go no further, or if the solution process was incorrect from the beginning, your principal trouble probably is lack of skill in problem analysis. The remedy, of course, is to work more problems illustrating the principles so that the test situations will be more familar. If you use no scratch paper on tests, and keep all parts of your solution on the page, checking to ascertain your mistakes should be easy.

If the processes are correct but the answers are incorrect, look for careless mistakes: in arithmetic, in employing algebraic signs, in mixing systems of units such as feet and centimeters, in copying the problem or in copying from one step to the next, or in making numbers so indistinct that they are misread. The remedy for these mistakes is to go over the solution carefully checking for these things. If time permits, one independent solution will help. Finally, look at the answer—does it seem reasonable?

The employment of the techniques discussed above should help you to achieve grades based on your knowledge of a subject without a handicap in the skill of presenting the knowledge on an examination. No more should you have to say, "I knew it but I couldn't put it down on paper."

Bibliography

Crow, Lester D., *How to Study,* Collier Books, New York (1963).

Morgan, Clifford T., and James Deese, *How to Study,* McGraw-Hill, New York (1957).

Nason, Leslie J., *You Can Get Better Grades,* U. of Southern California Press, Los Angeles (1961).

Pauk, Walter, *How to Study in College,* Houghton Mifflin, Boston (1962).

Preston, Ralph C., and Morton Botel, *How to Study,* Science Research Assoc., Chicago (1956).

Wrenn, C. Gilbert, and Robert Larsen, *Study Habits Inventory,* Stanford Univ. Press, Stanford, Calif. (1955).

8

Spoken and written communication

Skills in communication are important for the engineering student and for the engineer in practice. If an engineer cannot express clearly his ideas and the results of his endeavor to others, even though he may have the intellect of a genius and the capability of performing the most creative work, the benefits of his intellect and creative abilities will be of little use to others.

What are the skills that are needed in communications? For the engineer they generally are classed as verbal, graphical, and mathematical. In this respect we shall consider that *verbal* means language communication, either oral or written; that *graphical* constitutes all pictorial language such as engineering drawings, charts, diagrams, graphs, and pictures; and that *mathematical* includes all symbolic language in which concepts and logic processes are presented by use of a system of prearranged symbols.

A question may arise as to whether models and demonstrations constitute communication. In the truest sense, they do but usually they are inadequate within themselves to convey all concepts. Since usually words, pictures, or symbols are used as a supplement to explain such devices, these methods should not be considered to be a separate means of communication.

Verbal communication

We begin practicing our oral communication at an early age. As we progress through school, we add to our vocabulary and pick up experience in presenting ideas in writing. By the time a student is a freshman in college, he is expected to have a working vocabulary of several thousand words, to be able to organize ideas into a coherent pattern, and to present these ideas either orally or in writing. How does the objective of verbal communication for an engineer differ from this objective of other people?

136

Illustration 8-1

The engineer must be able to explain his ideas to his fellow engineers, and also to technicians and craftsmen who will fabricate his designs.

Primarily, the engineer communicates to present ideas and to gain ideas. For some people, talking or writing is purely an entertainment, or an outlet for creative feelings. On the other hand, for the engineer, verbal communication is a part of his professional life. He communicates on a technological level with other engineers and with scientists and technicians and on a layman's level with nontechnically trained people.

For example, suppose you have been working on a device for inclusion in the design of an autopilot control for an airplane. This device includes a potentiometer and a gyroscope. Consider how different your description of the device would be to an engineer and to an accountant. The ability to "speak their language" is an important skill which the engineer should possess in dealing with diverse people.

Not only should the engineer's verbal skill be descriptive, but also it should be persuasive. Frequently, good ideas are considered by the uninformed to be too impractical or too revolutionary. The engineer should have not only an adequate vocabulary, but also skills in presenting his ideas in a way that others will be led to accept them. In situations like this, practice in idea organization, a knowledge of psychology, and training in debate are all helpful.

In college, many opportunities are available for participation in group discussions, for the presentation of concepts both written and oral, and for gaining vocabulary skills. This is the time for the engineering student to learn by trial and error his best ways to communicate. After graduation, trial-and-error methods may be economically impractical. A conscious effort while in college to improve one's ability to communicate verbally will make the transition to work as a practicing engineer after graduation much easier.

Graphical communication

How often have you heard someone exclaim, after a futile attempt to describe an object to another person, "Here, let me draw you a picture of it!" The old adage of a picture being worth a thousand words is still true. The ability to present ideas by such means as pictures, diagrams, and charts is a valuable asset. In general, the engineer is expected by nontechnical people to be able to sketch and draw better than the average person. Today, most engineering curricula include some work in engineering graphics, and although the engineer may not be a professional draftsman, he should be able to attain and maintain an acceptable level of performance in engineering drawing and lettering.

Since ideas in research and development are frequently somewhat abstract, diagrams and graphs not only help to present ideas to others but also help the engineer to crystalize his own thought processes.

For the design engineer, the ability to present ideas graphically is a necessity. In almost every case, instructions prepared by a design engineer for use by technicians or workmen in building or fabricating articles are transmitted in the form of drawings. In the case of machined parts, for example, usually the workman has only the vaguest idea of the application of the part, so the drawing prepared by the design engineer must tell the complete story to the machinist.

The engineer engaged in sales will need to make frequent use of graphic aids. It usually is easier and faster to project ideas and application by graphic means than by verbal communication alone. Pictures fill the gap between verbal description and actual observance of an operating device. So effective are these techniques that considerable experimentation is now being done in teaching by means of television.

Mathematical communication

Mathematics involves the use of symbols to represent concepts and their manipulation in logic processes. It has been stated humorously, but nevertheless somewhat truthfully, that mathematics is a form of shorthand used to describe science and that higher mathematics is shorter shorthand. In his study of mathematics, the engineer learns the meaning of symbols such as π, $+$, and $\int$, the rules for manipulating mathematical quantities, and the logic processes involved.

The question sometimes arises as to why an engineer needs so much mathematical training. The answer in simple terms is that it is such a valuable and powerful tool that the engineer cannot afford to ignore its use. By using mathematics, not only is space conserved in the presentation of ideas but also the task of carrying the ideas through logic processes is simplified. Since many engineering science operations follow elementary mathematical laws, it is much easier to transform ideas into symbols, and manipulate the symbols according to prearranged mathematical procedures, and finally to come up with a set of symbols which can be reconverted into ideas.

The engineer's way of thinking is so consistently geared to mathematical processes that it becomes almost impossible for him to think otherwise. For example, if you are asked to find the area of a circle whose radius is known, you may immediately visualize $A = \pi r^2$. Now try to think of finding the area of a circle without using such a mathematical formula—you will probably find such thought to be difficult and unnatural.

Since your mathematical training has given you a skill in communication, as an engineer you should make full use of it. As has been pointed out, the logic processes enable one to predict mathematically the behavior of many engineering science operations. In addition, the mathematical presentation of the ideas enables others familiar with mathematical rules to envision the practical application of the concepts.

For example, if the effects of gravitational forces, air loads, centrifugal forces, temperatures, and humidity are expressed properly in a mathematical formulation, the path of a missile over the earth's surface can be predicted with surprising accuracy. It is not actually necessary to perform the flight and to measure the trajectory if the parameters involved are accurately known.

Of course, mathematics is not restricted to an application of the known behavior of objects. By mathematical extrapolation, fundamentals of natural laws have been determined even before it has become known that such behavior is possible. For example, the principles of atomic fission were predicted mathematically many years before it was possible to verify them experimentally.

The use of mathematics by engineers permits more time to be given to creative thought, since ideas can be explored symbolically without having to make physical determinations. Of course, the advent of high-speed automatic computing machines also has aided both in accelerating exploratory research and in executing routine mathematical operations.

Technical reporting

Much of the engineer's communication is executed by reports. These reports may be oral presentations in the form of technical talks or they may be written presentations as technical reports. In either case, information must be presented in a form so that the desired meaning can be understood.

Since the objective of a report is to present information, it must be prepared with the reader in mind. Clarity is therefore a prerequisite for a good report. A report that uses rare words or uncommon foreign phrases may serve to point up the brilliance of the author, but it may also discourage readers from attempting to unravel the meaning. A report should be prepared using words and phrases with which the reader will be familiar.

In addition to clarity, a report should state clearly and honestly the results obtained. In the case of reporting on tests, frequently data are taken and the test assembly is dismantled before the test results are available. Therefore, the tests cannot always be rerun, and the data are usually used as recorded. If the results should turn out to be less than desirable, as an engineer you are obligated to report the facts completely and honestly. Even though reporting the true facts may be distressing to the writer, an honest statement will instill a feeling of confidence in the reader that the results are trustworthy.

In preparing reports, in general, only factual material should be covered. There is often a temptation to include irrelevant subjects, or personal opinions as a part of the factual material. In some cases, it may be desirable to give a personal opinion, but such opinion should be identified clearly as a matter of judgment and not as factual data.

The technical report

Much of the formal communication between engineers is in the form of written technical reports. There are a number of excellent references that describe in detail the preparation of technical reports, and the student is encouraged to use them when preparing his reports. The following paragraphs outline some of the mechanics of report preparation and are given as a supplement to more complete references in report preparation.

There are a number of ways in which a report can be organized. One sequence which is used by many engineers follows the general procedure of an engineering test. This sequence is

1. Introduction   **4.** Results
2. Equipment   **5.** Discussion
3. Tests   **6.** Conclusions

Material that is included in each of these sections will be reviewed briefly.

1. *Introduction:* In this section, the background of the problem should be described in sufficient detail to show why the investigation or test was undertaken. After this, outline the general nature of the work that was done, previous investigations of others if applicable, and the extent of the testing proposed. This section is included basically to inform the reader about the test program and to detail reasons for its execution. It is designed to lead the reader into the more detailed parts of the report.

2. *Equipment:* This section describes the apparatus used, how the parts of the test apparatus were employed, and techniques that were used in manipulating the apparatus.

3. *Tests:* This section should outline the test procedure step by step. Such an

outline is desirable to help the reader to understand the test apparatus arrangement and its employment to acquire data. In some cases where the apparatus is simple, the sections on Equipment and Tests may be combined into a single section.

4. *Results:* In most test work it is desirable to present the results as tabular data or as graphs. In cases where data presentation in this form is not feasible, a brief description of results should be given.

5. *Discussion:* In this section, describe the ways in which the data have served to provide answers to the problems. Essentially, this section should answer questions and describe problem areas that were discussed in the introduction part of the report.

6. *Conclusions:* In this section, it is customary to gather together the main parts of the problem and its answers and to state them in a concise summary. In general, this section should answer the question, "What was the test and what were the results of the test?" If the results were inconclusive or if further testing seems desirable, a brief description of the remaining problem areas should be included with a discussion of the situation and recommendations for future research.

Another sequence frequently employed in industry is as follows:

1. Summary
2. Introduction
3. Apparatus and Tests
4. Discussion
5. Results and Conclusions
6. Tables, Charts, and Figures

In this sequence, the first part of the report gives a short outline of the problem and a summary of the results. For a person who is evaluating a number of reports, the summary will make it possible for him to decide quickly whether a more detailed reading of the report is desirable. The content of each section is substantially the same as for corresponding sections given in the first example. However, in the second example, the first part of the report is brief and general while the remainder is more detailed.

Writing the report

In writing a report, let us consider a few of the major principles of the mechanics of report preparation. One of the first considerations should be the choice of words. As pointed out previously, consider the educational level of the reader. Use words that the reader reasonably could be expected to understand without having to refer to a dictionary.

The next consideration should be the sentence structure of the report. Sentences should not be too long; in general, a sentence should not exceed about 35 words. Simple sentences, although they can convey meanings readily, frequently cause abrupt discontinuities in the flow of words. Complex sentences with introductory clauses and phrases usually provide the smoothest reading. A useful device is to tie a sentence or thought into a previous sentence by an opening phrase such as "This conclusion indicates," or "For example," or "Another way in which." This phraseology in effect leads the reader from thought to thought and helps to provide a coherent flow of ideas as the topics develop.

As a final consideration, sentences should be organized into paragraphs. In general, a paragraph should tell a fairly complete story within itself. The opening sentence should give the reader an idea of what is in the body of the paragraph, just as the title of a technical book should give the reader an idea of the nature of its contents. After the opening sentence, the ideas are developed within the paragraph. Here again, the use of opening and transitional words and phrases aids in providing continuity. The last sentence of a paragraph should indicate a relationship to the next paragraph. Like sentences, paragraphs should not be too long. Usually a paragraph should not exceed one fourth to one third of a page. If a single idea appears to require a long paragraph, it is better to break it into subideas for better paragraphing.

Technical talks

The technical talk, like the written report, should convey information. However, the methods of presenting information differ for these two types of reports. Because of this difference, it is desirable to examine some of the recognized principles of preparing and presenting technical talks.

A primary requirement of a technical talk should be simplicity. In preparing a talk an engineer should remember that his listeners have an opportunity to receive an item of information only once. Someone seeking information can reread parts of a written report, but in listening to a talk he must understand the crucial ideas when they are first expressed. In order to insure that the listener does grasp the ideas, they must be simple and must be expressed in understandable language.

There are many faults possible in technical talks, but two of the most common are compressing the subject matter unnecessarily and using unfamiliar words. If a talk is scheduled to last 20 minutes and the subject matter is general, a common tendency will be to compress the subject matter into the time allotted by talking rapidly and rushing through each topic. In a few minutes, the listeners are so

Illustration 8-2
The engineer must be able to convey his ideas to others by means of spoken and written communication. Conciseness without loss of clarity is most desirable.

confused that they will not attempt to follow the thread of the discussion further. At the end of the time, you can say that the subject was presented to the listeners; but probably they would have gained more information had fewer ideas been presented.

The same problem exists if unfamiliar words are used. Although the audience may be amazed at your command of language, they will be using even less of their perceptive powers to follow your thoughts, since the words do not convey ideas to them. In most cases, it is impossible to make the wording of a talk too simple. Inherently, in a technical talk, technical words will be used. However, the meanings of unfamiliar words should be explained, or the ideas should be expressed in two or more different ways so that the real meanings will be evident.

Organizing a talk

The organization of a technical talk should follow generally the organization used for a written report. Usually, the introduction outlines the problem, gives reasons for attempting solutions to the problem, and summarizes the work that has been done. A description of the equipment and its use should follow. The presentation of results and a discussion of the significance of the results will usually conclude the talk.

The question of preparing a talk in written form so that it can be read arises frequently. In presentations to technical groups, there is often a requirement that written copies of talks be submitted in advance. With a carefully phrased copy available, the temptation is always present to *read* the material to the audience. It is advisable to resist this temptation! Except in the case of short sections of especially complex subject matter, the material should not be read. You should familiarize yourself enough with the subject so that you can at least give a major portion of the material without reading it. There are few things less appealing in technical education than looking at the top of the head of a person who is droning over his paper in a rapid monotone.

In gathering material for a talk, screen the subject matter carefully. There is always a tendency to present more concepts than can be grasped. A few ideas that have been successfully related in the period allocated for the talk are superior to many ideas that are presented without being very well understood or remembered.

Since the attention span of most people is about 25 minutes, it is advisable to arrange talks so they will not exceed this limit. If a talk will be longer than 25 minutes, a useful method to maintain attention is to divide the talk essentially into two or more units using such devices as telling a humorous anecdote, providing a demonstration, or changing the style of delivery.

After the talk has been prepared, it is often helpful to rehearse it with a friend who can offer suggestions regarding such things as (1) revisions of subject matter to improve clarity, (2) changing posture or mannerisms to reduce distractions, and (3) improving diction to aid in understanding the subject matter. There is no rigid pattern which all speakers must follow. However, a sympathetic critic can help make your presentation more effective, regardless of the style you use. It is helpful to realize that the audience will listen to your talk because of the worth of its technical content. You need not be a polished speaker, but you should be a clear and understandable

Illustration 8-3
*Technical talks should be supplemented with appropriate charts, slides, graphs,
models, and so on, to add clarity and interest.*

one. Remember that your listeners are not interested in judging you but in learning
what you have to say.

A question may arise concerning the desirability of using visual aids. In almost
all cases, the use of visual aids is recommended. First, they help to illustrate your
points because the audience has an opportunity to see as well as hear information
relating to the subject. Second, they will assist you in your speaking role by affording
you an opportunity for movement to help you relax and speak more naturally. Also
they serve as a supplement to notes to help keep the organization of the talk in
the proper sequence.

Visual aids that are most useful to supplement a talk are charts, diagrams, graphs,
models, slides, and movies. However, in preparing the talk, prepare the visual aids
in such a manner that they supplement the talk, rather than dominate the presentation. If it becomes necessary to make lengthy explanations of a visual aid, the
aid should be simplified or subdivided into simpler parts.

Of course, practice helps in presenting talks, but if you have mastered a definite group of ideas that you have organized properly, lack of experience in making talks is not a great handicap. Actually, your mission in presenting a talk usually will be accomplished successfully if you leave each individual in the audience with a fairly clear impression of your work and its most significant results or contributions.

Problems on spoken and written communication

8-1. Write a 250-word paper concerning your career objectives.

8-2. Assume that at the end of the semester you are scheduled to graduate from college with a bachelor's degree in engineering. Compose a letter to the Quality Electronics Company, Inc., concerning your desire to secure employment.

8-3. Visit a company that manufactures a product. Write a 200-word report concerning improvements that you believe could be made in the manufacturing process.

8-4. Prepare a five-minute talk on the topic, "Man's Desire vs. Man's Need for Energy."

8-5. Prepare a brief talk concerning the importance of electronic digital computers to our way of life.

Bibliography

Estrin, Herman A., *Technical and Professional Writing*, Harcourt, Brace & World (1963).

Glidden, H. K., *Reports, Technical Writing, and Specifications*, McGraw-Hill, New York (1964).

Graves, Harold F., and Lyne S. Hoffman, *Report Writing*, Prentice-Hall, Englewood Cliffs, N.J. (1965).

Hays, Robert, *Principles of Technical Writing*, Addison-Wesley, Reading, Mass. (1965).

Hicks, Tyler G., *Successful Technical Writing*, McGraw-Hill (1959).

Katzoff, S., *Clarity in Technical Reporting*, NASA, Washington, D.C. (1964).

Marder, Daniel, *The Craft of Technical Writing*, Macmillan, New York (1960).

Miller, W. J., and L. E. A. Saidla, *Engineers As Writers*, Van Nostrand Reinhold, New York (1953).

Rathbone, Robert R., and James B. Stone, *A Writer's Guide for Engineers and Scientists*, Prentice-Hall, Englewood Cliffs, N.J. (1961).

Rosenstein, Allen B., Robert R. Rathbone, and William F. Schneerer, *Engineering Communications*, Prentice-Hall, Englewood Cliffs, N.J. (1964).

Van Hagan, Charles E., *Report Writers' Handbook*, Prentice-Hall (1961).

Weisman, Herman M., *Technical Report Writing*, Merrill (1966).

Wilcox, Sidney W., *Technical Communication*, International, Scranton, Pa. (1962).

Part Three

Preparation for problem solving

The engineer's work is distinguished by clarity of thinking, systematic analysis, and conciseness of presentation. These are trademarks of his profession.

9

Presentation of engineering calculations

Format

In problem solving, both in school and in industry, considerable importance is attached to a proper analysis of the problem, to a logical recording of the problem solution, and to the overall professional appearance of the finished calculations. Neatness and clarity of presentation are distinguishing marks of the engineer's work. Students should strive always to practice professional habits of problem analysis and to make a conscious effort to improve the appearance of each paper, whether it is submitted for grading or is included in a notebook.

The computation paper used for most calculations is $8\frac{1}{2}$ by 11 inches in size, with lines ruled both vertically and horizontally on the sheet. Usually these lines divide the paper into five squares per inch, and the paper is commonly known as cross-section paper or engineering calculation paper. Many schools use paper that has the lines ruled on the reverse side of the paper so that erasures will not remove them. A fundamental principle to be followed is that the problem work shown on the paper should not be crowded and that all steps of the solution should be included.

Engineers use slant or vertical lettering (see Figure 9-1); either is acceptable as long as there is no mixing of the two forms. The student should not be discouraged if he finds that he cannot letter with great speed and dexterity at first. Skills in making good letters improve with hours of patient practice. Use a well-sharpened H or 2H pencil and follow the sequence of strokes recommended in Figure 9-1.

Several styles of model problem sheets are shown in Figures 9-2 to 9-5. Notice in each sample that an orderly sequence is followed in which the known data are given first. The data are followed by a brief statement of the requirements, and then the engineer's solution.

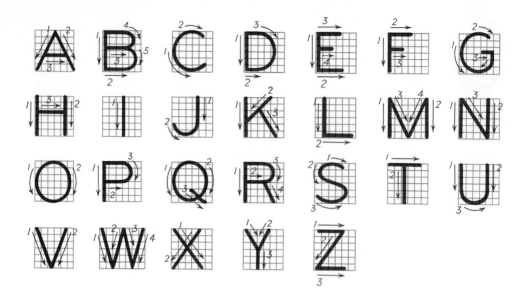

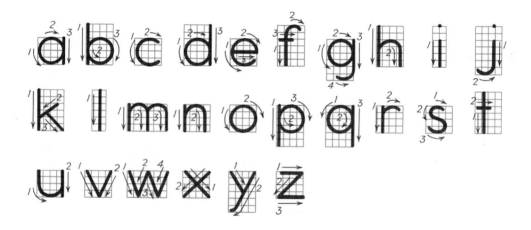

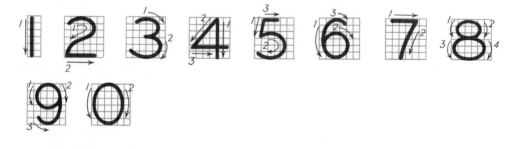

Figure 9-1 Vertical lettering.

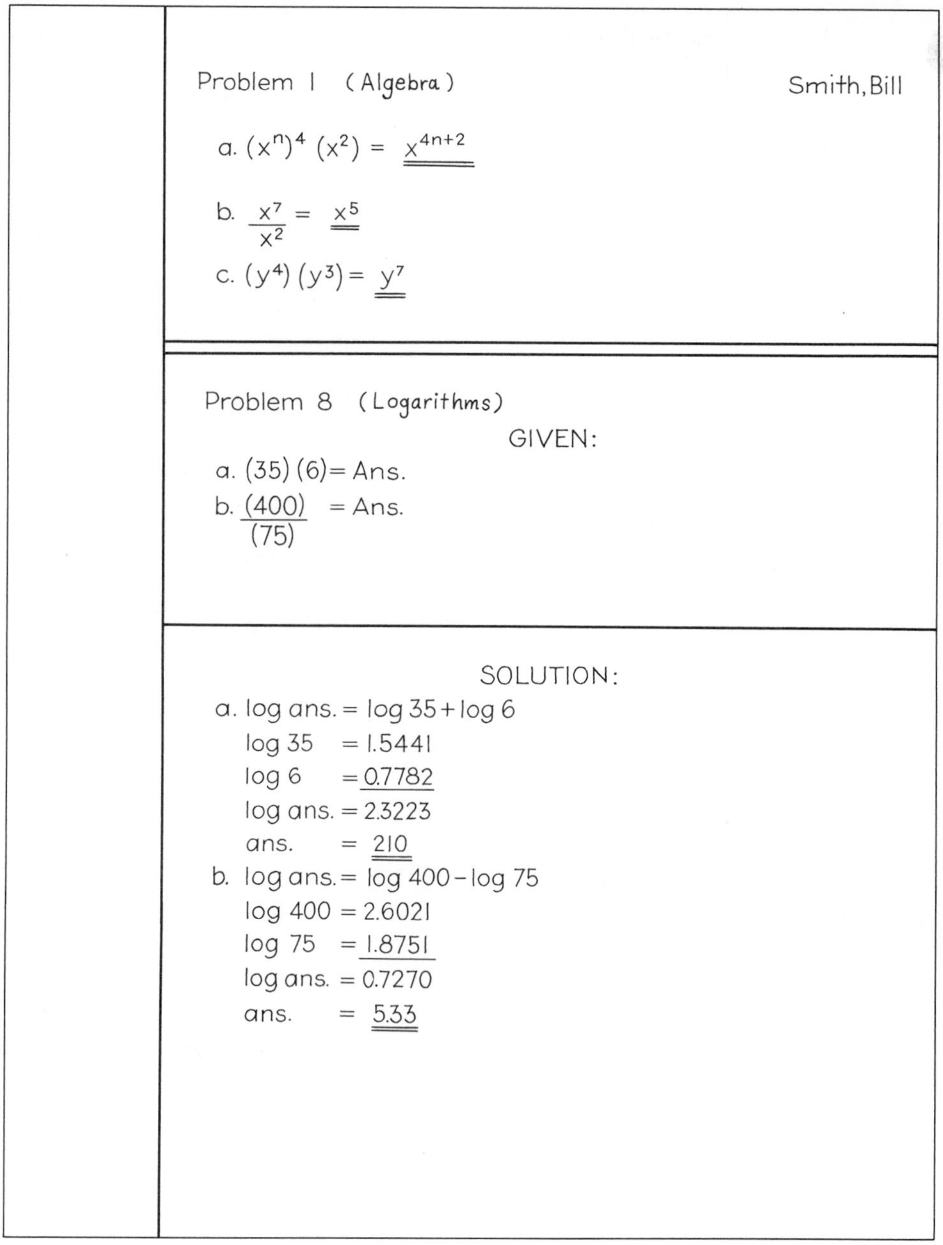

Problem 1 (Algebra)   Smith, Bill

a. $(x^n)^4 (x^2) = \underline{\underline{x^{4n+2}}}$

b. $\dfrac{x^7}{x^2} = \underline{\underline{x^5}}$

c. $(y^4)(y^3) = \underline{\underline{y^7}}$

Problem 8 (Logarithms)

GIVEN:

a. $(35)(6) = $ Ans.
b. $\dfrac{(400)}{(75)} = $ Ans.

SOLUTION:

a. log ans. = log 35 + log 6
   log 35   = 1.5441
   log 6   = $\underline{0.7782}$
   log ans. = 2.3223
   ans.   = $\underline{\underline{210}}$
b. log ans. = log 400 − log 75
   log 400 = 2.6021
   log 75   = $\underline{1.8751}$
   log ans. = 0.7270
   ans.   = $\underline{\underline{5.33}}$

Figure 9-2 Model problem sheet, style A. This style shows a method of presenting short, simple exercises.

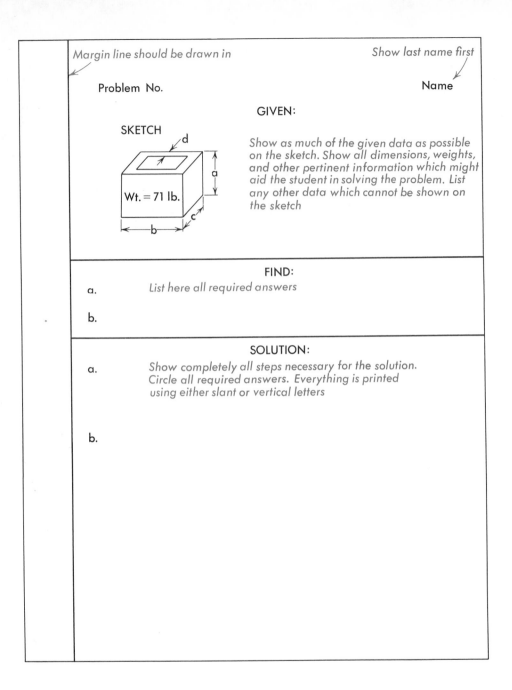

Margin line should be drawn in

Show last name first

Problem No.

Name

GIVEN:

SKETCH

Wt. = 71 lb.

Show as much of the given data as possible on the sketch. Show all dimensions, weights, and other pertinent information which might aid the student in solving the problem. List any other data which cannot be shown on the sketch

FIND:

a.

List here all required answers

b.

SOLUTION:

a.

Show completely all steps necessary for the solution. Circle all required answers. Everything is printed using either slant or vertical letters

b.

Figure 9-3 Model problem sheet, style B. This style shows a general form which is useful in presenting the solution of mensuration problems.

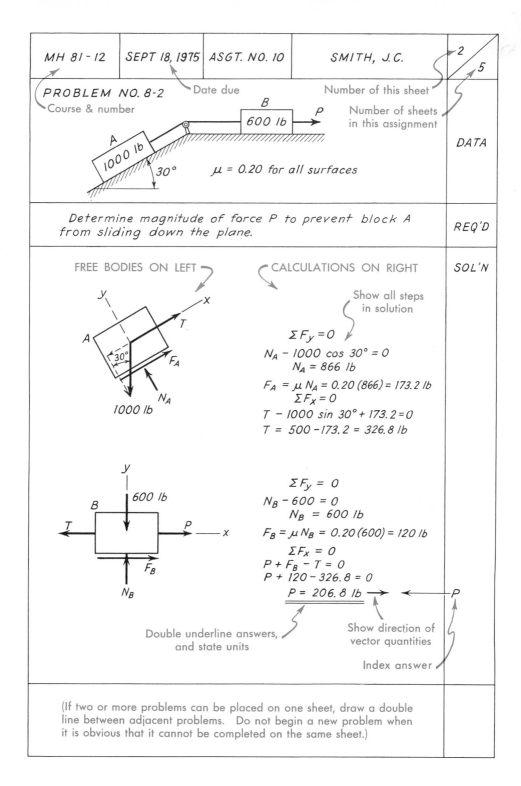

| MH 81-12 | SEPT 18, 1975 | ASGT. NO. 10 | SMITH, J.C. | 2 / 5 |

MH 81-12 (Course & number)
SEPT 18, 1975 — Date due
ASGT. NO. 10
SMITH, J.C. — Number of this sheet

PROBLEM NO. 8-2

Course & number

Number of sheets in this assignment

DATA

B
600 lb P

A
1000 lb
30° $\mu = 0.20$ for all surfaces

REQ'D

Determine magnitude of force P to prevent block A from sliding down the plane.

SOL'N

FREE BODIES ON LEFT

CALCULATIONS ON RIGHT

Show all steps in solution

$\Sigma F_y = 0$

$N_A - 1000 \cos 30° = 0$
$N_A = 866$ lb

$F_A = \mu N_A = 0.20 (866) = 173.2$ lb
$\Sigma F_x = 0$
$T - 1000 \sin 30° + 173.2 = 0$
$T = 500 - 173.2 = 326.8$ lb

A $30°$ T F_A N_A 1000 lb

$\Sigma F_y = 0$
$N_B - 600 = 0$
$N_B = 600$ lb
$F_B = \mu N_B = 0.20 (600) = 120$ lb
$\Sigma F_x = 0$
$P + F_B - T = 0$
$P + 120 - 326.8 = 0$
$\underline{\underline{P = 206.8 \text{ lb}}}$ →   ← P

B 600 lb T P F_B N_B

Double underline answers, and state units

Show direction of vector quantities

Index answer

(If two or more problems can be placed on one sheet, draw a double line between adjacent problems. Do not begin a new problem when it is obvious that it cannot be completed on the same sheet.)

Figure 9-4 Model problem sheet, style C. This style shows a method of presenting stated problems. Notice that all calculations are shown on the sheet and that no scratch calculations on other sheets are used.

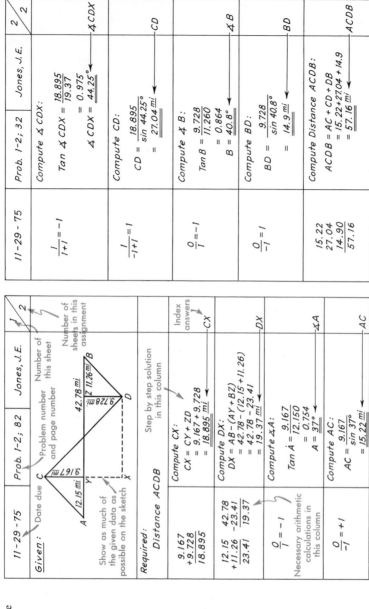

Figure 9-5 Model problem sheet, style D. This style employs a sheet with heading and margin lines preprinted. Notice that all calculations are shown on the solution sheet.

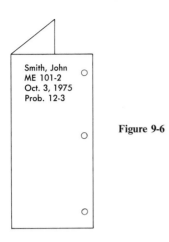

Figure 9-6

When the problem solution is finished, the paper may be folded and endorsed on the outside or may be submitted flat in a folder. Items that appear on the endorsement should include the student's name, and the course, section, date, problem numbers, and any other prescribed information. An example of a paper that has been folded and endorsed is shown in Figure 9-6.

Measurements and the scientific presentation of measured data

The purpose of measurement

Measurements are made by the engineer in order to gain quantitative information about processes within the vast complex of physical systems. Not only do measurements enable the engineer to understand more about objects and their behavior but measurements also help him to communicate ideas about his physical surroundings to others.

The ability to make measurements and to employ measurements is a basic requirement of engineering design. Both in science and engineering the ability to organize and evaluate measurements is an essential part of any interpretation of the behavior of physical bodies. In addition, measurements are necessary in order that scientific discoveries can be employed in the design of new devices. For example, every new type of aircraft is tested rigorously, and measurements are made on it to see whether its performance agrees with earlier design predictions. Since some of the original design concepts may have been hypothetical, measured results of tests serve to verify the hypothesis and to provide a sound basis for any extensions of the design to other situations.

Engineering is essentially a science of measurements. The engineer finds that the quantities which he can measure most easily and accurately are the quantities that he employs most confidently in the design, operation, and use of devices. Actually, much of the significant progress in science and engineering is made when effective measuring techniques are devised to support a new discovery. From the time of the Babylonians, when measurements of length were first used in earth work, to modern times, when man has desired to measure interatomic distances and intergalactic space, the limits of his knowledge have been generally the limits of his ability to make accurate measurements.

In the words of the famous scientist Lord Kelvin, ". . . . when you cannot express it in numbers, your knowledge is of a meager and unsatisfactory kind." When measurements are made and data are being secured, it is necessary to understand how accuracy is affected when various measuring devices are used and to know how measured quantities can be used in computations. It is also necessary to understand that every measurement will disturb to some degree the state or process on which the measurement is being made.

Measured quantities

"Measured quantities" are not the same as "counted quantities." We can get an exact count of the number of pennies in a sack, and this always should be the same number each time the pennies are counted, regardless of who counts them. This is an example of a counted quantity. However, if the sack of pennies is weighed several times by different persons, using different scales, it is unlikely that each of the measured weights would be exactly the same. This is an example of a measured quantity. The true value of any measured quantity is seldom known.

Measurements generally imply that a quantity is compared with a standard value of some sort. Most countries maintain standards of length, mass or weight, and time to which secondary standards periodically are compared. In addition, legal definitions of such quantities as temperature, electrical current, and land area are made for use in industry and trade.

For measurements of length or weight (mass), direct comparison with a standard is a common method of determination. Frequently, however, other measurements are made through indirect comparison with a standard. A thermometer, for example, permits a measurement of temperature by converting a volumetric thermal expansion of a fluid into a lineal dimension change. In a similar manner, a spring balance, a pressure gage, or a voltmeter give indications that indirectly are measurements of basic quantities. In many cases complex but much faster indirect methods have supplanted cumbersome direct methods of measurement.

Measuring devices

Instruments of various types are employed to enable an engineer or technician to make measurements of physical quantities. Regardless of the type of device used, consideration must be given to the limitations of the instruments and to the factors that enter into the precision of measurements.

Some of the factors in instrument use that affect the accuracy of measurement are (a) readability, (b) sensitivity, (c) lag and hysteresis, (d) environmental effects, (e) calibration errors, and (f) effect of the measurement on the quantity being measured.

Readability Since many instruments are analog devices, a pointer or cursor serves to indicate the location on a scale at which a reading is to be made. Readability is affected by such things as scale size, shape or length, color and contrast, parallax or position errors, and spacing of graduations. For instance, the physical arrangement of the scale has a considerable effect on the ability of an observer to make accurate

Illustration 9-1
The ability of the engineer to make and employ measurements is essential to achieving good engineering design. Consideration must be given to the limitations of the measuring instruments and to the factors that enter into the precision of measurements.

readings. Tests have shown that a digital readout can be read without mistakes about 99 per cent of the time but that a vertical scale and pointer arrangement may be read without mistakes only about 70 per cent of the time.

Sensitivity The sensitivity of an instrument is determined principally by its physical configuration. For instance, an electrical voltmeter may have a sensitivity of 0.5 volt, which means that the smallest change in applied voltage that can be detected is 0.5 volt. Usually it is desirable to have the size of the smallest subdivision, or least count, about the same as the change in the input that will give a readable movement.

Lag and hysteresis There are inherent errors in readout devices due to mechanical, electrical, magnetic, elastic, or thermal effects. The inability of a readout device to return to the same place when approached from two different directions is called hysteresis. It is caused many times by friction, but it can be caused by any delaying action. Closely allied with hysteresis is lag, which is a slowing of the indicator as it nears its rest position. The effects of lag and hysteresis in general are to produce a zone of uncertainty of reading around, for example, the rest position of a pointer on a scale. When hysteresis and lag effects are noticeable, it frequently is desirable to take the average of several readings to obtain an idea of the deviation and to use the mean value of the readings rather than a single reading value.

Environmental effects Many types of measuring devices are affected by changes in the environment in which the instrumentation is located. The principal effects are produced by changes in temperature, pressure, humidity, vibration, and position.

For example, in using electrical measuring devices, temperature effects must be taken into account, since temperature usually strongly affects circuit resistance and the behavior of electronic devices. In other cases, vibration may distort the reading pattern of pointer-type instruments. Usually ambient environmental effects can be evaluated by varying the conditions surrounding an instrument while maintaining constant input signals.

Calibration errors An instrument, such as a pointer type of meter, frequently will need corrections applied to the readings at various scale locations. These corrections may be necessary because of nonlinearity of the movement or nonlinearity of the scale divisions, because of environmental conditions changing the instrument response, or because of aging effects changing the basic response of the device. A calibration of an instrument may show the correction to be applied to any given reading to give a value in accord with an accepted standard, or it may show that the difference between the instrument readings and standard values falls within specified limits.

Standards are maintained, usually in laboratories, to be used in the calibrations of instruments. These standards ordinarily have their calibrations traceable to National Bureau of Standards measuring devices. Usually periodic recalibration of standards is scheduled in a manner similar to scheduling periodic recalibration of working instruments.

Loading errors Measurement is the transfer of information about a state or process, with accompanying energy transfer. If energy is drawn from the process being observed, the process has been altered. The measurement will have influenced the process and this influence may be more or less severe depending on the selection of the instrument.

Measurement of length

The process of measuring lengths, areas, volumes, and angles is called *mensuration*. A number of devices are available for making these measurements, ranging in accuracy from conventional wooden scales to light interference devices that have accuracies of a few wavelengths of light.

Some of the frequently used devices to measure length or "changes in length" (listed in order of increasing precision) are graduated scales, vernier calipers, dial indicators, measuring microscopes, strain gages, gage blocks, and interferometers.

The usual standard of length found in laboratories and gage rooms is the gage block. These steel blocks have two very smooth parallel surfaces whose dimensions are known accurately. A reasonable value of the precision for gage blocks is that the error or uncertainty in length is in the order of five millionths of an inch. The surfaces are so smooth and flat that when two blocks are placed together by a process called "wringing," they stick together by molecular attraction.

Measurement of mass or weight

Standards of weight have been used for thousands of years and usually have consisted of a standard size object to which the weight of other objects is compared. The difference between mass and weight is discussed on page 238 in Chapter 11.

Two common methods are employed to determine weight. As mentioned above, comparison with a standard, using a beam balance for the measurement, permits the measurement of mass, and indirectly, weight. Another frequently employed method involves the elastic deformation of a body due to a weight. A spring scale is an example of this type of system in which a pointer moves over a graduated scale. The pointer position indicates the force of attraction between an object being weighed and the earth. This force of attraction is called the weight of the object.

In laboratories standard masses are maintained with which other masses are compared in conducting calibration tests.

Measurement of time

Since the time of the Babylonians, from whom we have inherited our "units of 60" system of time measurement, time has been reckoned principally from movements of heavenly bodies. The length of the day, the phases of the moon, and the occurrence of solstices have provided our basic time units for centuries. It is only within comparatively recent times that the engineer has recognized a need for more precise time standards.

Our basic time unit in most laboratory work is the second. It is usually reckoned from the apparent movements of stars or of the sun. Since these apparent movements have some irregularity, several proposals for other time standards have been made based on the frequency of vibration of molecules under standard pressure and temperature conditions.

Since most direct measurements of time are somewhat cumbersome, many indirect methods have been developed. Some of the more common methods involve using escapement drives powered by torsion springs, weights, or electrical solenoids.

Measurement of electrical quantities

Two general methods of measuring quantities in electrical circuits are in use. One method involves direct measurement by deflection of an indicating instrument's pointer. The ordinary voltmeter or ammeter is an example of this sort of device. The other method is a "null" method and involves balancing electrical parameters, one against another, until an indicating device shows no deflection. The first method might be compared to mechanically weighing an object on a spring scale, and the second method to balancing one mass against another in a beam balance.

Portable indicating meters used to measure current or voltage usually have errors of 5 per cent or less. Laboratory meters having mirrors behind the pointers to reduce parallax errors usually have errors of 1 per cent or less. In fact, in making many mechanical measurements, an electrical analog device is employed because the basic error of the system can be made smaller.

Null balance methods of measurements usually involve comparisons with standard values. A Wheatstone bridge network is an example of an unknown resistance being compared in its electrical behavior with a known resistance. Impedance bridges permit the measurements of inductances and capacitances by comparison with standard values.

Measurements of mechanical quantities

Measurements of mechanical quantities such as power, pressure, speed, flow, acceleration, or angle, in general, use the basic concepts of measurements of mass, length, and time. Although the discussion of measurements of each of these parameters is beyond the scope of this book, it may be pointed out that in many cases analog methods of measurement of these quantities is a much faster process than the direct measurement of the quantity.

As an example, in measuring the flow of fuel to a rocket engine, a direct measurement of flow would involve a scale to measure mass, a timing device to measure time, and perhaps a force sensing transducer to measure pressure. In practice, a common flow measuring system employing analog methods uses a windmill type of vane, which rotates in the fuel-carrying pipe, at a rate proportional to the volume of flow. A magnetic sensing element detects the passage of each vane as the windmill-like assembly rotates and converts this signal to a pulsating electrical voltage. At the same time, a thermocouple senses the fuel temperature. The voltage pulses and the thermocouple signals are transmitted to a computer circuit that converts the input information into a readout in terms of pounds per second of fuel flow.

Use of measurements

A large part of engineering work involves measurements. They may be used in planning, in designing, in testing, or in certifying engineering work. Although the actual measurements may be made by technicians or subprofessionals, their planning and direction is the responsibility of the professional engineer whose understanding of the basic principles involved is a guide for the work.

Scientific presentation of measured data

Since measured data inherently are not exact, it is necessary that methods of manipulating data be examined so that information derived therefrom can be evaluated properly. It should be obvious that the diameter of a saucepan and the diameter of a diesel engine piston, although each may measure about 6 in., usually will be measured with different accuracies. Also a measurement of the area of a large ranch which is valued at $50 per acre would not be made as accurately as a measurement of a piece of commercial property that is valued at $1000 per square foot. In order to describe the accuracy of a single measurement, it can be given in terms of a set of significant figures.

Significant figures

A significant figure in a number can be defined as a figure that may be considered reliable as a result of measurements or of mathematical computations. In making measurements, it is customary to read and record all figures from the graduations on the measuring device and to include one estimated figure which is a fractional part of the smallest graduation. Any instrument can be assumed to be accurate *only* to one half of the smallest scale division that has been marked by the manufacturer. All figures read are considered to be significant figures. For example, if we examine the sketch of the thermometer in Figure 9-7, we see that the mercury column, represented in the sketch by a vertical line, lies between 71° and 72°. Since the smallest graduation is 1°, we should record 71° and include an estimated 0.5°. The reading would then be recorded as 71.5° and would contain three significant figures.

As another example, suppose that it is necessary to record the voltmeter reading shown in Figure 9-8. The needle obviously rests between the graduations of 20 and 30 volts. A closer inspection shows that its location can be more closely determined

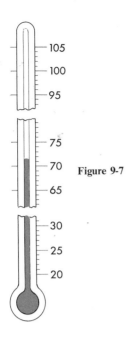

Figure 9-7

as being between 25 and 26 volts. However, this is the extent of the aid which we can get from the individual graduations. Any further refinement must be accomplished by eye.[1] Since the scale of the voltmeter is calibrated to the nearest volt, we can estimate the reading to the nearest half volt—in this case 25.5 volts. An attempt to obtain a more precise reading (such as 25.6 or 25.7) would result only in false accuracy, as discussed below.

The designated digits, together with one doubtful digit, are said to be "significant figures." In reading values previously recorded, assume that only one doubtful digit has been recorded. This usually will be the last digit retained in any recorded measurement.

False accuracy

In analysis of engineering problems one must prevent false accuracy from appearing in the calculations. False accuracy occurs when data are manipulated without regard to their degree of precision. For example, it may be desirable to find the sum of

[1]In most cases, estimation by eye (beyond the precision obtainable from the graduations) is acceptable. It should be recognized that this final subdivision (by eye) will give doubtful results.

Figure 9-8

three lengths, each having been measured with a different type of instrument. These lengths might have been recorded in tabular form (rows and columns) as:

Columns

		a b c d e f g	
First Measurement:	Row A	1 5 7 . 3 9	±0.02 ft
Second Measurement:	Row B	1 8 . 0 2 5	±0.001 ft
Third Measurement:	Row C	8 5 3 .	±2 ft
		1 0 2 8 . 4 1 5	(By regular addition)

Although the sum of the columns would be 1028.415, it would not be proper to use this value in other calculations. Since the last measurement (Row C) could vary from 851 to 855 (maximum variation in Column d), it would be trivial to include the decimal numbers in Rows A and B in the sum. The final answer should be expressed as 1028 ± 2, or merely 1028. In this case the last digit (8) is of doubtful accuracy.

In the tabulation of data (readings from meters, dials, gages, verniers, scales, etc.), only one doubtful digit may be retained for any measurement. In the preceding example, the doubtful digits are 9 (Row A), 5 (Row B), and 3 (Row C). The example also shows that when numbers are added, the sum should not be written to more digits than the digit under the first column which has a doubtful number.

Scientific notation

The decimal point has nothing to do with how many significant figures there are in a number, and therefore it is impossible to tell the number of significant figures if written as 176,000., 96000., or 1000. This doubt can be removed by the following procedure:

1. Move the decimal point to the left or right until a number between 1 and 10 remains. The number resulting from this process should contain *only* significant figures.

2. This remaining number must now be multiplied by a power of ten, $(10)^{\text{number of decimal moves}}$. If the decimal is moved to the left, the power of 10 is positive.

Example   Express the number 1756000 to five significant figures:

$1_x 7\ 5\ 6\ 0\ 0\ 0$.   (Move the decimal point to the left
to get a number between 1 and 10.)

Answer   **(1.7560) (10)^6**   (The power of 10 is the number of decimal moves.)

Note   Only the five significant figures remain to be multiplied by the power of 10.

Example   Express the number 0.016900 to three significant figures:

$0\ .\ 0\ 1_x\ 6\ 9$ (Move the decimal point to the right
to get a number between 1 and 10.)

Answer   **(1.69) (10)$^{-2}$**   (The power of 10 is the number of decimal moves and is negative in sign.)

Note The three significant figures remain to be multiplied by the power of 10.

Examples of significant figures:

385.1	four significant figures
38.51	four significant figures
0.03851	four significant figures
3.851×10^7	four significant figures
7.04×10^{-4}	three significant figures
25.5	three significant figures
0.051	two significant figures
0.00005	one significant figure
27,855	five significant figures
8.91×10^4	three significant figures
2200	May have two, three, or four significant figures depending on the accuracy of the measurement that obtained the number. Where such doubt may exist, it is better to write the number as 2.2×10^3 to show two significant figures; or as 2.20×10^3 to show three significant figures.
55	two significant figures
55.0	three significant figures. The zero is significant in this case, since it is not otherwise needed to show proper location of the decimal point.

In engineering computations it is necessary to use standard computed constants, such as π (3.14159265 . . .) and ϵ (2.71828 . . .). It is feasible to simplify these values to fewer significant figures, since most calculations will be done on the slide rule where five, six, and seven significant figures are impossible to read. Usually three or four significant figures are sufficient, but this may vary somewhat with the nature of the problem. Since we do not need a large number of significant figures, let us examine some rules concerning "rounding off" the excess figures which need not be used in a given calculation.

Retention of significant figures

1. In recording measured data, only one doubtful digit is retained, and it is considered to be a significant figure.

2. In dropping figures which are not significant, the last figure retained should be increased by 1 if the first figure dropped is 5 or greater.

3. In addition and subtraction, do not carry the result beyond the first column which contains a doubtful figure.

4. In multiplication and division, carry the result to the same number of significant figures that there are in the quantity entering into the calculation which has the least number of significant figures.

9-1. Determine the proper value of X for each problem.

a. $0.785 = 7.85(10^x)$

b. $0.005066 = 5.066(10^x)$

c. $6.45 = 64.5(10^x)$

d. $10.764 = 10764(10^x)$

e. $1973. = 0.01973(10^x)$

f. $0.3937 = 3937000(10^x)$

g. $30.48 = 0.03048(10^x)$

h. $2.54 = 254(10^x)$

i. $1000 = 10(10^x)$

j. $0.001 = 1(10^x)$

k. $44.2 = 0.442(10^x)$

l. $0.737 = 73.7(10^x)$

m. $1.093 = 10930(10^x)$

n. $4961. = 0.4961(10^x)$

o. $1.02 = 0.000102(10^x)$

p. $0.0914(10^{-3}) = 9.14(10^x)$

q. $745.6(10^4) = 7,456,000(10^x)$

r. $7.78(10^0) = 778(10^x)$

s. $14,800,000(10^{-2}) = 14.8(10^x)$

t. $23,700,000(10^6) = 23.7(10^x)$

Addition of laboratory data

9-2. Add and then express the answer to the proper number of significant figures.

a.	11.565	d.	757.1	g.	6282.6	j.	17.306
	4.900		54.540		545.81		1.6535
	226.55		11.5		122.55		0.0762
	82.824		1.0375		334.75		653.22
	17.668		378.64		98.88		29.969
	108.77		4372.1		28.77		0.02202
					1.059		

b.	858.7	e.	16.59	h.	38.808	k.	61.309
	404.3		0.0531		11.955		1.9792
	54.42		11.72		35.306		0.005531
	19.8		285.5		67.332		122.88
	8.775		4.41		105.65		52.8
	12.04		0.0748		575.75		37.075

c.	1.39395	f.	0.32	i.	0.005754	l.	1.0585
	8.7755		6171.0		0.006434		18.08
	10.6050		255.5		0.018466		675.5
	49.201		80.60		0.085405		70.08
	88.870		715.55		0.131876		111.0
	108.887		3707.		0.97574		828.

Subtraction of laboratory data

9-3. Subtract and then express the answer to the proper number of significant figures.

a.	6508.	f.	10276.	k.	−933.0
	3379.		61581.		77.12

b.	8.104	g.	118.72	l.	−156.2
	7.891		366.		0.0663

c.	0.04642	h.	0.016	m.	−610.01
	0.0199		0.1513		−355.66

d.	731.16	i.	766.	n.	−1.9767
	189.28		−516.16		−113.54

e.	7.114	j.	0.8280		
	16.075		−0.023		

Multiplication of laboratory data

9-4. Multiply and then express the answer to the proper number of significant figures.

a.	5167.	b.	32105.	c.	535.58	d.	84.636
	238.		5.28		0.2759		30869.

e. 1.03975	*h.* 47.738	*k.* 7.5427	*n.* 558.0
54682.	0.065	−542.16	80.08
f. 0.0548	*i.* 15903.	*l.* −0.0989	*o.* 141.8
0.00376	0.00469	−11.6507	0.37
g. 14.7410	*j.* −9757	*m.* 17.66	*p.* 0.0051
0.7868	0.05478	0.0307	1.06

Division of laboratory data

9-5. Divide and then express the answer to the proper number of significant figures:

a. $\dfrac{3928.}{5636.}$ *g.* $\dfrac{73.65}{127.1}$ *m.* $\dfrac{3.58}{100}$

b. $\dfrac{216.75}{53.83}$ *h.* $\dfrac{4.91}{1598.}$ *n.* $\dfrac{13.550}{120}$

c. $\dfrac{7.549}{3.069}$ *i.* $\dfrac{0.2816}{5383.}$ *o.* $\dfrac{4.001}{2.5}$

d. $\dfrac{539.77}{1.6303}$ *j.* $\dfrac{-0.005295}{1728.}$ *p.* $\dfrac{0.0507}{350.1}$

e. $\dfrac{0.5322}{0.343}$ *k.* $\dfrac{0.07737}{-0.1293}$ *q.* $\dfrac{1.8}{0.006075}$

f. $\dfrac{8831.}{128.75}$ *l.* $\dfrac{-0.3343}{-52.1}$

Calculation of error

The word "error" is used in engineering work to express the *uncertainty* in a measured quantity. When used with a measurement, it shows the probable reliability of the quantity involved. *Error,* as used here, does not mean the same as the word "mistake," and care should be exercised to call operations or results which are mathematically incorrect "mistakes" and not "errors."

Errors are inherent in making any measurement and as such cannot be eradicated by any practical means. Errors can be made smaller by care in making measurements, by employing more precise measuring instruments, and by performing repeated measurements to afford statistical accuracy. Statistical accuracy defines a region in which the true value probably will fall.

Since the reliability of engineering data is of extreme importance, familiarity with methods of computing probable error is essential. As the student has more opportunity to collect his own data, the need for means of expressing the reliability or uncertainty involved in measured quantities will become even more apparent. Although a detailed study of theory of errors is beyond the scope of this book, a general discussion of some of the basic computations of errors is desirable.

Measurement and error

Experimentation in the laboratory is necessary to verify the engineer's design analysis and to predict results in processes of manufacture. For certain tests the laboratory technician will attempt to secure data to prove the analytical results as predicted by the engineer. At other times, emphasis will be directed to routine testing of items for acceptance. In any case, the results obtained in the laboratory will only approximate the true values, and the data tabulated will not be exact. Rather, every measurement taken and every gage reading or scale deflection noted will reflect the accuracy with which the individual measuring instruments were designed and manufactured—as well as the human errors that may have appeared in the readings.

For example, it is convenient and many times expedient to estimate distances by eye when under other circumstances an unknown distance could be more accurately measured by using a surveyor's tape or perhaps a graduated scale. In a similar manner we may lift a given object and, from experience, estimate its weight. A more accurate procedure would be to weigh it on some type of balance. In general, the more precise the measuring device, the more accurate the measurement obtained.

As we know from practical experience, length, weight, or time can be measured to various degrees of precision, depending upon the accuracy that has been designed into the measuring instrument being used. The engineer must therefore have some method whereby he can evaluate the degree of accuracy obtained in any given measurement. Where a numerical error of plus or minus ($\pm$) 1 in. would not ordinarily make too much difference in a measured distance of 100 mi., the same numerical error (of 1 in.) would cause considerable concern if it occurred in a measured distance of 2 in. For this reason the engineer will frequently express the maximum error present in a measurement as "per cent error" instead of "numerical error."

By "per cent error" is meant how may parts out of each 100 parts that a number is in error. For example, if a yardstick is too long by 0.02 yd, the numerical error is 0.02 yd, the relative error is 0.02 yd in 1.00 yd, and the "per cent error" is therefore 2 per cent. In other words:

$$\text{per cent error} = \frac{(\text{numerical error})(100 \text{ per cent})}{(\text{measured value})}$$

$$= \frac{(1.02 - 1.00)(100 \text{ per cent})}{(1.00)} = \textbf{2 per cent}$$

In any measured quantity, the true value is never known. The measured value is usually expressed to the number of digits corresponding to the precision of measurement followed by a number showing the maximum probable error of the measurement. For example, if we measure the length of a desk to be 5.712 ft and we have estimated the last digit, 2, because of our inability to read our measuring device closely, we would need to know what the probable variation in this last digit could be. Assuming that we can estimate to the nearest 0.001 ft, we could show this measurement with its error as

$$5.712 \pm 0.001 \text{ ft}$$

In order to compute the per cent error of our measurement, we proceed as follows:

$$\text{per cent error} = \frac{\text{numerical error} \times 100 \text{ per cent}}{\text{measured value}}$$

$$= \frac{0.001 \times 100 \text{ per cent}}{5.712}$$

$$= \textbf{0.02 per cent}$$

The error in measurement could be less than 0.02 per cent, but this shows the maximum probable error in the measurement.

As another example, a measurement can be shown as a number, and a per cent error as

$$7.64 \text{ lb} \pm 0.2 \text{ per cent}$$

To express this measurement as a number and a numerical error, the procedure is as follows:

$$\text{numerical error} = (\text{measured value})\frac{(\text{per cent error})}{100 \text{ per cent}}$$

$$= (7.64)\frac{(0.2 \text{ per cent})}{100 \text{ per cent}}$$

$$= 0.02 \text{ lb}$$

Expressing the measurement as a number,

7.64 ± 0.02 lb

Problems

(Note that the proper number of significant figures may not be given in the reading.)

9-6. Compute the per cent error:
- a. Reading of 9.306 ± 0.003
- b. Reading of 19165 ± 2.
- c. Reading of 756.3 ± 0.7
- d. Reading of 2.596 ± 0.006
- e. Reading of 13.750 ± 0.009
- f. Reading of 0.0036 ± 0.0006
- g. Reading of 0.7515 ± 0.02
- h. Reading of 12,835 ± 20
- i. Reading of 382.5 ± 5
- j. Reading of 0.03 ± 0.03

9-7. Compute the numerical error:
- a. Reading of 35.219 ± 0.03 per cent
- b. Reading of 651.79 ± 0.01 per cent
- c. Reading of 11.391 ± 0.05 per cent
- d. Reading of 0.00365 ± 2 per cent
- e. Reading of 0.03917 ± 0.6 per cent
- f. Reading of 152 ± 4.0 per cent
- g. Reading of 0.0575 ± 10 per cent
- h. Reading of 7.65(10^7) ± 7 per cent
- i. Reading of 3.080(10^{-4}) ± 2.5 per cent
- j. Reading of 32.5(10^{-2}) ± 30 per cent

9-8. A surveyor measures a property line and records it as being 3207.7 ft long. The distance is probably correct to the nearest 0.3 ft. What is the per cent error in the distance?

9-9. The thickness of a spur gear is specified as 0.875 in., with an allowable variation of 0.3 per cent. Several gears that have been received in an inspection room are gaged, and the thickness measurements are as follows: 0.877, 0.881, 0.874, 0.871, 0.880. Which ones should be rejected as not meeting dimensional specifications?

9-10. A rectangular aluminum pattern is laid out using a steel scale which is thought to be exactly 3 ft long. The pattern was laid out to be 7.42 ft by 1.88 ft, but it was subsequently found that the scale was incorrect and was actually 3.02 ft long. What were the actual pattern dimensions and by what per cent were they in error?

9-11. A resident of a city feels that his bill for water is considerably too high, probably because of a defective water meter. He proposes to check the meter on a do-it-yourself basis by using a gallon milk bottle to measure a volume of water. He believes that the volume of the bottle is substantially correct and that the error of filling should not exceed plus or minus 2 tablespoons.

a. What would be the probable maximum error in gallons per 1000 gallons of water using this measurement?

b. Using the milk bottle, he draws ten full bottles of water and observes that the meter indicates a usage of 1.345 ft^3 of water. If the average rate for water is $1.05 per 1000 ft^3, by how much could his water bill be too high?

Part Four

Engineering tools of analysis

The slide rule is a useful instrument
at all levels of engineering.

10

The slide rule

The slide rule is not a modern invention although its extensive use in business and industry has been common only in recent years. Since the slide rule is a mechanical device whereby the logarithms of numbers may be manipulated, the slide rule of today was made possible over three and a half centuries ago with the invention of logarithms by John Napier, Baron of Merchiston in Scotland. Although Napier did not publicly announce his system of logarithms until 1614, he had privately communicated a summary of his results to Tycho Brahe, a Danish astronomer in 1594. Napier set forth his purpose with these words:

> Seeing there is nothing (right well beloved Students of Mathematics) that is so troublesome to mathematical practice, nor doth more molest and hinder calculators, than the multiplications, divisions, square and cubical extractions of great numbers, which besides the tedious expense of time are for the most part subject to many slippery errors, I began therefore to consider in my mind by what certain and ready art I might remove those hindrances.

In 1620 Edmund Gunter, Professor of Astronomy at Gresham College, in London, conceived the idea of using logarithm scales that were constructed with antilogarithm markings for use in simple mathematical operations. William Oughtred, who lived near London, first used "Gunter's logarithm scales" in 1630 in sliding combination, thereby creating the first slide rule. Later he also placed the logarithm scales in circular form for use as a "circular slide rule."

Sir Isaac Newton, John Warner, John Robertson, Peter Roget, and Lieutenant Amédée Mannheim further developed these logarithmic scales until there exist today many types and shapes of rules. Basically all rules of modern manufacture are variations of a general type of construction that utilizes sliding scales and a movable indicator. The principles of operation are the same and they are not difficult to master.

Description of the slide rule

The slide rule consists of three main parts, the "body," the "slide," and the "indicator" (see Figure 10-1). The "body" of the rule is fixed; the "slide" is the middle sliding portion; and the "indicator," which may slide right or left on the body of the rule, is the transparent runner. A finely etched line on each side of the indicator is used to improve the accuracy in making settings and for locating the answer. This line is referred to as the "hairline."

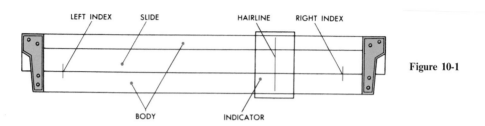

Figure 10-1

The mark opposite the primary number 1 on the C and D scale is referred to as the "index" of the scale. An examination of the C and D scales indicates that each scale has two indexes: one at the left end (called the "left index") and one at the right end (called the "right index").

Regardless of the manufacturer or the specific model of slide rule that may be used, the principles of operation are the same. The nomenclature used here is general although some specific references are made to the Deci-Lon (Keuffel & Esser Co.), the Model 10,000 KOH-I-NOOR, Inc., the Versalog (Frederick Post Co.), the Maniphase Multiplex (Eugene Dietzgen Co.), and the Model N4 (Pickett, Inc.) rules. These models are those most frequently used by engineers, scientists, and technicians.

Care of the slide rule

The slide rule is a precision instrument and should be afforded reasonable care in order to preserve its accuracy. Modern rules stand up well under normal usage, but dropping the rule or striking objects with it will probably impair its accuracy.

In use, the rule may collect dirt under the glass of the indicator. Inserting a piece of paper under the glass and sliding the indicator across it will frequently dislodge the dirt without necessitating the removal of the indicator glass from the frame. If the glass has to be removed for cleaning, it should be realigned when replaced, using the techniques described below.

The rule should never be washed with abrasive materials, alcohol, or other solvents, since these may remove markings. If the rule needs to be cleaned, it may be wiped carefully with a damp cloth, but the excessive use of water should be avoided because it will cause wooden rules to warp.

The metal-frame rules are not subject to warping due to moisture changes, but they must be protected against blows which would bend them or otherwise throw them out of alignment. A light layer of lubricant of the type specified by the manufacturer of the metal rule will increase the ease with which the working parts move. This is particularly important during the "breaking in" period of the new rule.

Manipulation of the rule

Some techniques in manipulation of the rule have been found to speed up the setting of the slide and indicator. Two of these suggested procedures are described in the following paragraphs.

1. Settings usually can be made more rapidly by using two hands and holding the rule to that the thumbs are on the bottom with the backs of the hands toward the operator.

2. In moving either the indicator or the slide, the settings are easier to make if the index fingers and thumbs of both hands are used to apply forces toward each

Illustration 10-1
In setting the indicator, a rolling motion with the forefingers will permit rapid and precise locations to be made. Keeping the fingers of both hands in contact with the indicator, exert slight forces toward each other with both hands.

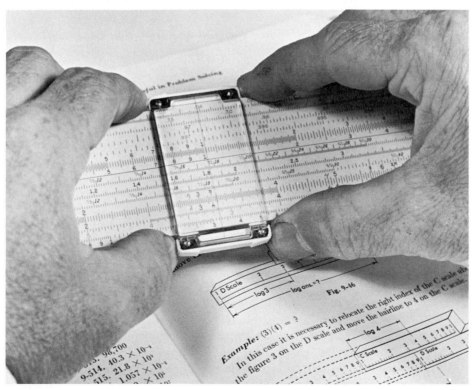

Illustration 10-2
In moving the slide, use fingers to exert forces toward each other. A rolling motion with the forefinger aids in setting the indexes. Avoid pinching the frame because this will make the slide bind.

other than if only one hand is used to apply force. For example, in setting the indicator, put the forefinger of each hand against the respective edges of the indicator and move it by a combined squeezing and rolling motion of the forefingers. The same general procedure is used in setting the slide, where both hands exert forces toward each other. The student is cautioned in setting the slide not to squeeze the frame of the rule, since this will cause the slide to bind.

Adjusting the rule

Regardless of the make, most rules have the same general form of adjustment. The method of adjustment is simple but should not be applied in a hurry. It is desirable to use a magnifying glass, if one is available, to aid in lining up the scales and hairline.

To determine whether or not a rule needs adjustment, line up the indexes of the C and D scales. The indexes of the scales above and below the C and D scales should also be aligned. If they do not coincide, slightly loosen the screws that clamp the top bar of the frame and carefully move the frame to the right or left until the indexes are aligned. Tighten the screws slightly and move the slide to check for proper friction. If the alignment and friction are satisfactory, tighten the frame screws to complete that part of the adjustment.

Next, test the hairline for proper alignment by setting the hairline over the indexes of the C and D scales and checking to see that the hairline also coincides with the other indexes on this side of the rule. If it does not coincide with all the scale indexes, slightly loosen the screws which hold the glass frame to the indicator. Rotate the frame slowly until the hairline coincides with the indexes on this side of the rule. Tighten the screws holding this frame; then, while the hairline is aligned on the indexes of the C and D scales, turn the rule over and check for the alignment of the hairline with the indexes of the scales on the other side of the rule. If the hairline does not coincide with the indexes on this side of the rule, loosen the screws on the indicator and make the necessary adjustment as before.

Check the tightness of all screws when the adjustment is completed. The student is cautioned not to use excessive force in tightening any screws, as the threads may become stripped. With reasonable care, a slide rule will usually require very little adjustment over a considerable period of time.

Accuracy of the rule

Most measurements made in scientific work contain from two to four significant figures; that is, digits which are considered to be reliable. Since the mathematical operations of multiplication, division, and processes involving roots and powers will not increase the number of significant figures when the answer is obtained, the slide rule maintains an accuracy of three or four significant figures. The reliability of the digits obtained from the rule depends upon the precision with which the operator makes his settings. It is generally assumed that with a 25-cm. slide rule, the error of the answer will not exceed about a tenth of 1 per cent. This is one part in a thousand.

A common tendency is to use more than three or four significant digits in such numbers as π (3.14159265 . . .) and ϵ (2.71828 . . .). The slide rule automatically "rounds off" such numbers to three or four significant figures, thus preventing false accuracy (such as can occur in longhand operations) from occurring in the answer.

In slide rule calculations the answer should be read to four significant figures if the first digit in the answer is 1 (10.62, 1.009, 1195., 1,833,000., etc.). In other cases the answer is usually read to three significant figures (2.95, 872., 54,600., etc.). The chance for error is increased as the number of operations in a problem increases. However, for average length operations, such as those required to solve the problems in this text, the fourth significant digit in the slide rule answer should not vary more than ± 2 from the correct answer. Where only three significant digits are read from the rule, the third digit should be within ± 2 of the correct answer.

Example

$$+ \left. \begin{array}{l} 16.27 \\ 16.26 \end{array} \right\} \text{within slide rule accuracy} \left\{ \begin{array}{l} 0.0859 \\ 0.0858 \end{array} \right. +$$

| Correct Answer   16.25 |

| 0.0857   Correct Answer |

$$- \left. \begin{array}{l} 16.24 \\ 16.23 \end{array} \right\} \text{within slide rule accuracy} \left\{ \begin{array}{l} 0.0856 \\ 0.0855 \end{array} \right. -$$

Rules of modern manufacture are designed so that results read from the graduations are as reliable as the naked eye can distinguish. The use of magnifying devices may make the settings easier to locate but usually do not have an appreciable effect on the accuracy of the result.

Instructions for reading scale graduations

Before studying the scales of the slide rule, let us review the reading of scale graduations in general. First let us examine a common 12-in. ruler (Figure 10-2).

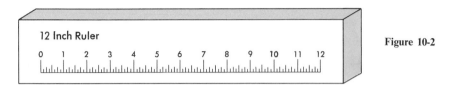

Figure 10-2

Example We see that the total length of 1 ft has been divided into 12 equal parts and that each part is further divided into quarters, eighths, and sixteenths. This subdivision is necessary so that the workman need not estimate fractional parts of an inch.

Example Measure the unknown lengths L_1 and L_2 as shown in Figure 10-3.

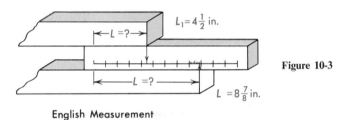

Figure 10-3

English Measurement

The English system of measurement as shown in Figure 10-3 is probably familiar to all students. The unit of length in the metric system which corresponds to the yard in the English system is called the *meter*. The meter is 39.37 in. in length. For convenience, the meter is divided into 100 equal parts called *centimeters,* and each centimeter is divided into ten equal parts called *millimeters.* Since we can express units and fractional parts of units as tenths or hundredths of the length of a unit, this system of measurement is preferred many times for engineering work.

Example Measure the unknown lengths L_1 and L_2 as shown in Figure 10-4.

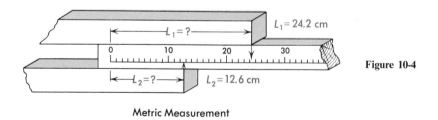

Figure 10-4

Metric Measurement

The scales of the slide rule are basically divided as in the metric system in that between each division there are ten subdivisions. However, the student will find that the main divisions are not equal distances apart. Sometimes the divisions will be subdivided by graduations, and at other times the student will need to estimate the subdivisions by eye. Let us examine the D scale of a slide rule (Figure 10-5).

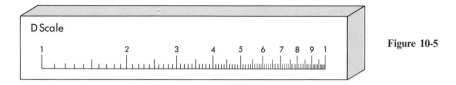

Figure 10-5

Since the graduations are so close together, let us examine the rule in three portions: from left index to 2, from 2 to 4, and from 4 to the right index.

Example Left index to 2 as shown in Figure 10-6.

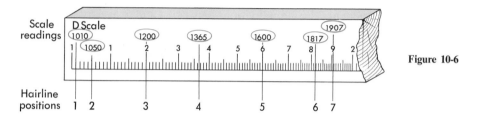

Figure 10-6

The student should refer to his own rule for comparisons as he studies the diagrams in this chapter. In the example using Figure 10-6, we note that from the left index (read as one-zero-zero) to the digit 1 (read as one-one-zero), there are ten graduations. The first is read as *one-zero-one* (101), the second as *one-zero-two* (102), and so on. Digit 2 is read as *one-two-zero* (120), digit 3 as *one-three-zero* (130), and so on. If need be, the student can subdivide by eye the distance between each of the small, unnumbered graduations. Thus, if the hairline is moved to position 4 (see example above), the reading would be *one-three-six-five* or 1365. Position 6 might be read as 1817 and position 7 as 1907. The student is reminded that each small graduation on this portion of the rule has a value of 1.

Example 2 to 4 as shown in Figure 10-7.

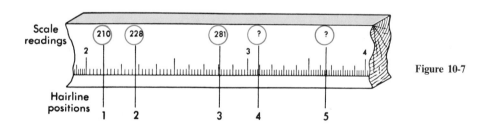

Figure 10-7

Since the distance between 2 and 3 is not as long as the distance from the left index to 2, no numbers are placed over the graduations. However, we can use the same reasoning and subdivide as in the previous examples. Set the hairline in position 1 (see example) and read *two-one-zero,* or 210. We note that the distance between 200 and 210 has been divided into five divisions. Each subdivision would thus have a value of 2. Consequently, if the hairline is in position 2, a reading of

228 would be obtained. Remember that each of the smallest graduations is valued at 2 and not 1. What are the readings at 3, 4, and 5?[1]

Example: 4 to the right index as shown in Figure 10-8.

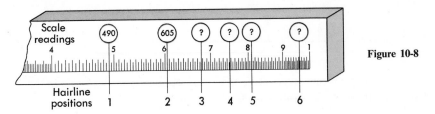

Figure 10-8

The distance between 4 and 5 is still shorter than the distance between 3 and 4, and it becomes increasingly more difficult to print such small subdivisions. For this reason there are ten main divisions between 4 and 5, each of which is subdivided into two parts. With this type of marking it is possible to read two figures and

[1] Readings at 3, 4, and 5 are, respectively, 281, 309, and 365.

Problems on scale readings

Set hairline to	Read answer on								
	ST scale	T scale	LL_3 scale	CI scale	K scale	DF scale	LL_{01} scale	LL_2 scale	L scale
1. 210 on D									
2. 398 on D									
3. 1056 on D									
4. 1004 on D									
5. 866 on D									
6. 222 on D									
7. 1196 on D									
8. 439 on D									
9. 1705 on D									
10. 2325 on D									
11. 917 on D									
12. 323 on D									
13. 1077 on D									
14. 1854 on D									
15. 268 on D									
16. 833 on D									
17. 551 on D									
18. 667 on D									
19. 8125 on D									
20. 406 on D									
21. 918 on D									
22. 5775 on D									
23. 1466 on D									
24. 288 on D									
25. 466 on D									
26. 798 on D									
27. 1107 on D									
28. 396 on D									
29. 1999 on D									
30. 998 on D									

estimate the third, or to get three significant figures on all readings. If the hairline is set as indicated in position 1, the reading would be *four-nine-zero* (490), and position 2 would give *six-zero-five* (605). What are the readings at hairline positions 3, 4, 5, and 6?[2]

If the student has followed the reasoning thus far, he should have little trouble in determining how to read an indicated value on any scale of the slide rule. Several of the problems on page 178 should be worked, and the student should thoroughly understand the principle of graduation subdivision before he attempts to delve further into the uses of the slide rule.

It is suggested that one have a good understanding of logarithms before proceeding to learn the operational aspects of the slide rule. Those who may desire to review these principles should refer to Appendix I.

Construction of the scales

Let us examine how the main scales (C and D) of the rule are constructed. As a basis for this examination, let us set up a scale of some length with a beginning graduation called a *left index* and an end graduation called a *right index* as in Figure 10-9.

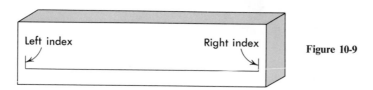

Figure 10-9

Next let us subdivide this scale into ten equal divisions and then further subdivide each large division into ten smaller divisions as shown in Figure 10-10. We call this the *L scale.*

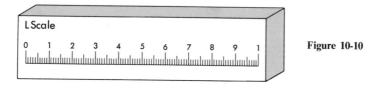

Figure 10-10

Let us place a blank scale beneath this L scale so that the left index of the L scale will coincide with the left index of the blank scale as shown in Figure 10-11. We shall call the blank scale the *D scale.*

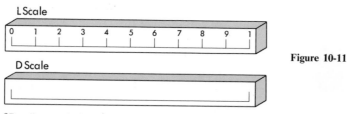

Figure 10-11

[2] Readings at 3, 4, 5, and 6 are, respectively, 678, 746, 810, and 963.

Now let us graduate the D scale in such a way that each division mark is directly beneath the mark on the L scale that represents the mantissa of the logarithm of the number. Before examining the scales closer, we should note that the mantissa of 2 is 0.3010, the mantissa of 3 is 0.4771, the mantissa of 4 is 0.6021, and the mantissa of 5 is 0.6990 as shown in Figure 10-12.

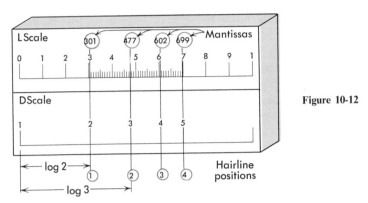

Figure 10-12

If the student will examine his rule, he will find a C or D scale and an L scale. The C and D scales are identical, so use the D scale since it is printed on the body of the rule. Several problems should be worked, determining the logarithms of numbers by using the slide rule.

Remember to:

1. Set the number on the D scale.
2. Read the mantissa of the number on the L scale.
3. Supply the characteristic, using the *characteristic rules* given in the discussion on logarithms in Appendix I.

Example   What is the logarithm of 55.8? Use Figure 10-13.

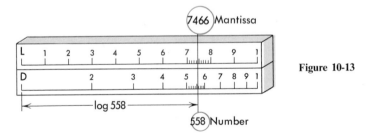

Figure 10-13

From slide rule: Mantissa of 55.8 = 0.7466
From characteristic rules: Characteristic of 55.8 = 1.0000
Therefore   log of 55.8 = **1.7466**

From the preceding example, we can see that the D scale is so constructed that each number lies below the mantissa of its logarithm. Also we note that the distance from the left index of the D scale to any number on the D scale represents (in length) the mantissa of the number as shown in Figure 10-14. Since the characteristic of a logarithm is governed merely by the location of the decimal point, we can delay its determination for the time being.

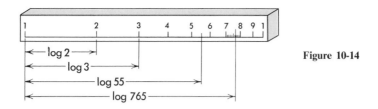

Figure 10-14

Problems

10-1. Use the slide rule and find the logarithms.

a. 894.	j. 5.91×10^7	s. 33.67×10^{-9}
b. 1.845	k. 9.06×10^{-4}	t. 4.40×10^3
c. 0.438	l. 66.9×10^8	u. 98,700
d. 81.5	m. 155.8×10^2	v. 40.3×10^{-9}
e. 604.	n. 23.66×10^{-4}	w. 21.8×10^9
f. 7.41	o. 0.06641×10^8	x. 1.057×10^{-3}
g. 11.91	p. 9.33×10^{-2}	y. $719. \times 10^5$
h. 215.	q. 29.88×10^{-1}	z. 49.2×10^7
i. 993,000.	r. 0.552×10^6	

Multiplication

As shown in Figure 10-15, the C and D scales are divided logarithmically with all graduations being marked with their corresponding antilogarithms. These scales can be used for multiplication by adding a given logarithmic length on one of the scales to another logarithmic length which may be found on the other scale.

Example   (2)(3) = 6, as shown in Figure 10-15.

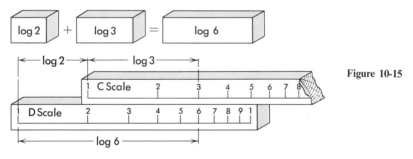

Figure 10-15

Procedure
1. Set the left index of the C scale above the digit 2 on the D scale.
2. Move the hairline to the right until it is directly over 3 on the C scale.
3. Read the answer (6) directly under the hairline on the D scale.

The A and B scales are also divided logarithmically, but their overall lengths are only one half the lengths of the C and D scales. Therefore, although the A and B scales can also be used for multiplication and division, their shortened lengths will diminish the accuracy of the readings.

Similarly other pairs of scales of the slide rule may be used to perform multiplication if they are graduated logarithmically. A majority of slide rules have at least one set of folded scales that can be used for this purpose. Most frequently they are folded at π (3.14159 . . .). Special use of these scales will be explained later in this chapter.

In some cases, when the logarithm of one number is added to the logarithm of another number, the multiplier extends out into space, and it is impossible to move the indicator to the product (Figure 10-16).

Example $(3)(4) = ?$, as shown in Figure 10-16.

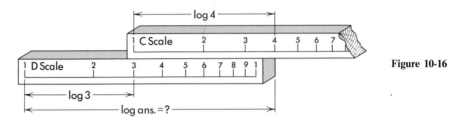

Figure 10-16

In this case it is necessary to relocate the right index of the C scale above the figure 3 on the D scale and move the hairline to 4 on the C scale as shown in Figure 10-17.

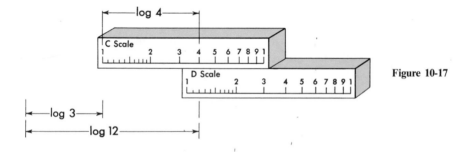

Figure 10-17

Procedure
1. Set the right index of the C scale above the digit 3 on the D scale.
2. Move the hairline to the left until it is directly over 4 on the C scale.
3. Read answer (12) directly under the hairline on the D scale.

The location of the decimal point in multiplication problems is ascertained either by inspection or by applying one of the several methods explained in the following paragraphs.

Methods of determining decimal point location

Several methods which may be used are given below. Although these methods by no means include all ways to determine the decimal point location, they will be suitable for instruction of students, particularly those having an elementary mathematical background.

Inspection method

This is the simplest method and consists of determining the decimal point location by observing the location of the decimal point in the numbers involved in a slide rule operation and locating the decimal point in the answer by a quick estimation.

Example $$\frac{(28.1)}{(7.20)} = \textbf{390} \text{ (decimal point to be determined)}$$

A quick examination of the numbers involved shows that the answer will be somewhere near the number "4," so the answer evidently will be 3.90. This method will have its widest application where only one or two operations are involved and where the numbers lie between 1 and 100.

Example $$(1.22)(58.2) = \textbf{71.0}$$

In the example above, it is seen that the number 58.2 is multiplied by a number which is a little more than 1. Therefore, the answer will be slightly greater than 58.2.

Approximate number method

This method is an extension of the inspection method. It involves the same general procedures except that the numbers used in a problem are "rounded off" and written down and an approximate answer is obtained that will show the decimal point location.

Example $(37.6)(0.188)(5.71)(11.92) = \textbf{482}$ (decimal point to located)

Rewrite, using simple numbers that are near in value to the problem numbers.
$$[(40)(0.2)][(6)(10)] = (8)(60) = \textbf{480}$$

This shows that the answer in the example problem should be expressed as 482.
A problem that is more involved can be solved by this method, as shown by the following example.

Example $$\frac{(12,560)(0.0387)}{(594,000)} = \textbf{819} \text{ (decimal point to be determined)}$$

Using simple numbers near in value to the problem numbers, write the same problem:

$$\frac{(12,000)(0.04)}{(600,000)} = \textbf{0.0008}$$

By cancellation the numbers can be simplified still further to obtain an approximate answer of 0.0008. One way of doing this would be to divide 12,000 into 600,000, obtaining a value of 50 in the denominator. This value of 50 divided into 0.04 gives 0.0008. Referring to the original problem, the decimal point must be located to give an answer of 0.000819.

Scientific notation or power-of-ten method

The power-of-ten or scientific notation method is a variation of the characteristic method discussed on page 185. In this method the numbers in the problem are expressed as a single digit, a decimal point, the remaining digits, and followed by the number "10" raised to the appropriate power. This process simplifies the numbers, and the decimal point in the answer can be determined by inspection or by the approximation method. For a review of scientific notation refer to page 162.

Example

$$(15.9)(0.0077)(30500)(4660) = \mathbf{1741} \text{ (decimal point to be located)}$$

Write the same problem with each number expressed as a digit, decimal point, and the remaining digits followed by the appropriate power of 10.

$$(1.59 \times 10^1)(7.7 \times 10^{-3})(3.05 \times 10^4)(4.66 \times 10^3) \times \mathbf{174.1 \times 10^5}$$

Since all the numbers are now expressed as numbers between 1 and 10, followed by 10 to a power, the approximate value of the multiplication can be determined rapidly, by inspection, to be about 170. The power of 10 is obtained by adding algebraically the powers of 10 of each of the rewritten numbers. The answer to the original problem is therefore 174.1×10^5, or 17,410,000, or 1.741×10^7.

Example
$$\frac{(28,500)(307)}{(0.552)} = \mathbf{1585} \text{ (decimal point to be located)}$$

Rewrite the problem using powers of 10:

$$\frac{(2.85 \times 10^4)(3.07 \times 10^2)}{(5.52 \times 10^{-1})} = \mathbf{1.585 \times 10^7}$$

By inspection and approximation the product of the numerator will be found to be near 9, and dividing 5.52 into it will give about 1.6. This procedure determines the decimal point location for the digits of the answer. The powers of 10 are added algebraically to give 10^7, which completes the decimal point location in the answer. The answer may be rewritten as 15,850,000 if desired.

Digit method

In this method the numbers of digits in each number are counted and the following rules apply.

Multiplication   Add the number of digits to the left of the decimal of each number to be multiplied. This will give the number of digits to the left of the decimal in the answer. If the slide projects to the right, subtract 1 from the number of digits to be pointed off.

Example
$$(27,300)(15.1) = \mathbf{412,000}$$

There are five digits to be counted in the first number and only two digits in the second number. Since the slide projects to the right, subtract 1. There will be six digits to the left of the decimal point in the answer.

Division Subtract the number of digits to the left of the decimal in the denominator from the number of digits to the left of the decimal in the numerator to obtain the number of digits to the left of the decimal in the answer. If the slide projects to the right in division, add one digit more to be pointed off.

Example
$$\frac{(12.88)}{(466)} = 0.0276$$

Subtracting three digits in the denominator from two digits in the numerator gives (-1) digit to be located in the answer. Inspection shows that the answer will be a decimal quantity. In any case where decimal numbers are encountered, the method of counting the digits is to begin at the decimal point and count the number of zeroes between the decimal point and the first digit that is not zero to the right of the decimal. Since the digit difference shown above is (-1), there must be one zero between the decimal point and the first significant figure, which gives an answer of 0.0276. The student will observe that the digit count of decimal numbers is considered as a minus quantity and that the addition and subtraction of the digit count must take into account any minus signs.

Variations and extensions of these methods may readily be set up to solve problems involving roots and powers. Many schools prefer the "characteristic" or "projections method" to determine decimal point location, and this method is given in detail in the discussions which follow.

Characteristic method

Projection rule for multiplication   This method of decimal point location is recommended for students who are inexperienced in slide rule computations:

1. Before attempting to solve the problem, place the characteristic of each quantity above or below it.
2. Solve for the sum of the characteristics by simple addition, and place this number above the space for the answer.
3. Begin the multiplication with the slide rule, and each time the left index of the C scale extends past the left index of the D scale, add a $(+1)$ to the sum of the characteristics previously determined.
4. Add the original sum to the $+1$'s obtained from left extensions. The total number is the characteristic of the answer.

Example

one left extension
↓
Characteristics   (0) + (0) → (0) + 1 = +1 ← characteristic of answer
(5)   (3) =   **15**   Answer

ESTIMATION OF ANSWER BY SCIENTIFIC NOTATION:
$(5)(3) = \mathbf{1.5(10)^1}$ ← ESTIMATED ANSWER

Example

one left extension
↓

Characteristics $(+2) + (-3) \rightarrow (-1) + 1 = 0$
$(390) \quad (0.0030) = \quad \textbf{1.17} \quad \text{Answer}$

ESTIMATION OF ANSWER BY SCIENTIFIC NOTATION:

$(4)(10)^2(3)(10)^{-3} = \textbf{1.2(10)}^0 \leftarrow$ ESTIMATED ANSWER

Example

two left
↓ extensions

Characteristics $(-3) \quad + (+1) + (+2) + \quad (+4) \quad \rightarrow (+4) + 2 = +6$
$(0.001633) \quad (79.1) \quad (144) \quad (96,500) = \textbf{1,800,000} \quad \text{Answer}$

ESTIMATION OF ANSWER BY SCIENTIFIC NOTATION:

$(2)(10)^{-3}(8)(10)^1(1)(10)^2(10)^5 = \textbf{1.6(10)}^6 \leftarrow$ ESTIMATED ANSWER

Example

three left
↓ extensions

Characteristics $(+1) + (+3) + \quad (-3) \quad + \quad (-4) \quad \rightarrow (-3) + 3 = 0$
$(73.7) \quad (4460) \quad (0.00704) \quad (0.000853) = \quad \textbf{1.975} \quad \text{Answer}$

ESTIMATION OF ANSWER BY SCIENTIFIC NOTATION:

$(7)(10)^1(4)(10)^3_7(7)(10)^{-3}(9)(10)^{-4} = 1.8(10)^0 \leftarrow$ ESTIMATED ANSWER

Example

two left extensions
↓

Characteristics $(+2) + (+2) + (0) \rightarrow \quad (+4) \quad + \quad \overbrace{1+1} \quad = +6$
$(861) \quad (204) \quad (9.0) = 1,580,000 \text{ or } (1.58)(10)^6 \quad \text{Answer}$

ESTIMATION OF ANSWER BY SCIENTIFIC NOTATION:

$(9)(10)^2(2)(10)^2(9) = \textbf{1.6(10)}^6 \leftarrow$ ESTIMATED ANSWER

Multiplication practice problems

10-2. $(23.8)(31.6) = \textbf{(7.52)(10)}^2$

10-3. $(105.6)(4.09) = \textbf{(4.32)(10)}^2$

10-4. $(286,000)(0.311) = \textbf{(8.89)(10)}^4$

10-5. $(0.0886)(196.2) = \textbf{(1.738)(10)}^1$

10-6. $(0.769)(47.2) = \textbf{(3.63)(10)}^1$

10-7. $(60.7)(17.44) = \textbf{(1.059)(10)}^3$

10-8. $(9.16)(115.7) = \textbf{(1.060)(10)}^3$

10-9. $(592.)(80.1) = \textbf{(4.74)(10)}^4$

10-10. $(7.69 \times 10^3)(0.722 \times 10^{-6}) = \textbf{(5.55)(10)}^{-3}$

10-11. $(37.5 \times 10^{-1})(0.0974 \times 10^{-3}) = \textbf{(3.65)(10)}^{-4}$

10-12. $(23.9)(0.715)(106.2) = \textbf{(1.815)(10)}^3$

10-13. $(60.7)(1059)(237,000) = \textbf{(1.523)(10)}^{10}$

10-14. $(988)(8180)(0.206) = \mathbf{(1.665)(10)^6}$

10-15. $(11.14)(0.0556)(76.3 \times 10^{-6}) = \mathbf{(4.73)(10)^{-5}}$

10-16. $(72.1)(\pi)(66.1) = \mathbf{(1.497)(10)^4}$

10-17. $(0.0519)(16.21)(1.085) = \mathbf{(9.13)(10)^{-1}}$

10-18. $(0.001093)(27.6)(56{,}700) = \mathbf{(1.710)(10)^3}$

10-19. $(0.379)(0.00507)(0.414) = \mathbf{(7.96)(10)^{-4}}$

10-20. $(16.05)(23.9)(0.821) = \mathbf{(3.15)(10)^2}$

10-21. $(1009)(0.226)(774) = \mathbf{(1.765)(10)^5}$

10-22. $(316)(825)(67{,}600) = \mathbf{(1.762)(10)^{10}}$

10-23. $(21{,}000)(0.822)(16.92) = \mathbf{(2.92)(10)^5}$

10-24. $(0.707)(80.6)(0.451) = \mathbf{(2.57)(10)^1}$

10-25. $(1.555 \times 10^3)(27.9 \times 10^5)(0.902 \times 10^{-7}) = \mathbf{(3.91)(10)^2}$

10-26. $(0.729)(10)^3(22{,}500)(33.2) = \mathbf{(5.45)(10)^8}$

10-27. $(18.97)(0.216)(899)(\pi)(91.2) = \mathbf{(1.055)(10)^6}$

10-28. $(7160)(0.000333)(26)(19.6)(5.01) = \mathbf{(6.09)(10)^3}$

10-29. $(1.712)(89{,}400)(19.5)(10^{-5})(82.1) = \mathbf{(2.45)(10)^3}$

10-30. $(62.7)(0.537)(0.1137)(0.806)(15.09) = \mathbf{(4.66)(10)^1}$

10-31. $(10)^6(159.2)(144)(7{,}920{,}000)(\pi) = \mathbf{(5.70)(10)^{17}}$

10-32. $(0.0771)(19.66)(219)(0.993)(7.05) = \mathbf{(2.32)(10)^3}$

10-33. $(15.06)(\pi)(625)(0.0963)(43.4) = \mathbf{(1.236)(10)^5}$

10-34. $(2160)(1802)(\pi)(292)(0.0443) = \mathbf{(1.582)(10)^8}$

10-35. $(437)(1.075)(0.881)(43{,}300)(17.22) = \mathbf{(3.09)(10)^8}$

10-36. $(\pi)(91.6)(555)(0.673)(0.00315)(27.7) = \mathbf{(9.38)(10)^3}$

10-37. $(18.01)(22.3)(1.066)(19.36)(10)^{-5} = \mathbf{(8.29)(10)^{-2}}$

10-38. $(84.2)(15.62)(921)(0.662)(0.1509) = \mathbf{(1.210)(10)^5}$

10-39. $(66{,}000)(25.9)(10.62)(28.4)(77.6) = \mathbf{(4.00)(10)^{10}}$

10-40. $(55.1)(7.33 \times 10^{-8})(76.3)(10)^5(0.00905) = \mathbf{(2.79)(10)^{-1}}$

10-41. $(18.91)(0.257)(0.0811)(92{,}500)(\pi) = \mathbf{(1.145)(10)^5}$

Multiplication problems

10-42. $(46.8)(11.97)$

10-43. $(479.)(11.07)$

10-44. $(9.35)(77.8)$

10-45. $(10.09)(843{,}000.)$

10-46. $(77{,}900)(0.467)$

10-47. $(123.9)(0.00556)$

10-48. $(214.9)(66.06)$

10-49. $(112.2)(0.953)$

10-50. $(87.0)(1.006)$

10-51. $(1{,}097{,}000)(1.984)$

10-52. $(43.8)(0.000779)$

10-53. $(31.05)(134.9)$

10-54. $(117.9)(98.9)$

10-55. $(55.6)(68.1)$

10-56. $(1.055)(85.3)$

10-57. $(33{,}050.)(16{,}900.)$

10-58. $(6.089)(44.87)$

10-59. $(34.8)(89.7)$

10-60. $(43{,}900.)(19.07)$

10-61. $(41.3)(87.9)$

10-62. $(99.7)(434{,}000.)$

10-63. $(0.0969)(0.1034)(0.1111)(0.1066)$

10-64. $(1.084 \times 10^{-5})(0.1758 \times 10^{13})(66.4)(0.901)$

10-65. $(234.5)(10)^4(21.21)(0.874)(0.0100)$

10-66. $(\pi)(26.88)(0.1682)(0.1463)(45.2)(1.007)$

10-67. $(75.8)(0.1044 \times 10^8)(10)^{-2}(54{,}000)(0.769)$

10-68. $(34.5)(31.09)(10)^{-6}(54.7)(0.677)(0.1003)$

10-69. $(6.08)(5.77)(46.8)(89.9)(3.02)(0.443)(\pi)$

10-70. $(1.055)(6.91)(31.9)(11.21)(\pi)(35.9)(4.09)$

10-71. $(10.68)(21.87)$

10-72. $(88{,}900.)(54.7)$

10-73. $(113{,}900.)(48.1)$

10-74. $(95{,}500.)(0.000479)$

10-75. $(0.0956)(147.2)(0.0778)$

10-76. $(15.47)(82.5)(975{,}000.)$

10-77. $(37.8)(22{,}490{,}000.)(0.15)$

10-78. $(1.048)(0.753)(0.933)$

10-79. $(1.856)(10)^3(21.98)$

10-80. $(57.7)(46.8)(3.08)$

10-81. $(0.045)(0.512)(115.4)$

10-82. $(0.307)(46.3)(7.94)$

10-83. $(2.229)(86.05)(16,090.)(\pi)$

10-84. $(44,090.)(38.9)(667.)(55.9)$

10-85. $(568.)(46.07)(3.41)(67.9)$

10-86. $(75.88)(0.0743)(0.1185)(0.429)$

10-87. $(10)^{-7}(69.8)(11.03)(0.901)$

10-88. $(46.3)(0.865)(10)^{-9}(0.953)(\pi)$

10-89. $(665.)(35,090)(0.1196)(0.469)$

10-90. $(888.)(35.9)(77.9)(0.652)$

10-91. $(43.4)(0.898)(70.09)(0.113)(\pi)$

Division

Multiplication is merely the process of mechanically adding the logarithms of the quantities involved. From a review of the principles of logarithms, it follows that division is merely the process of mechanically subtracting the logarithm of the divisor from the logarithm of the dividend.

Example $\qquad \dfrac{(8)}{(2)} = 4$, as shown in Figure 10-18.

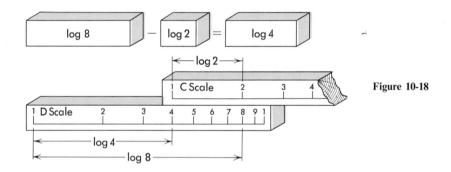

Figure 10-18

Procedure

1. Set the divisor (2) on the C scale directly above the dividend (8), which is located on the D scale.

2. Read the answer (4) on the D scale directly under the left index of the C scale.

For location of the decimal point in division problems the following *Projection Rule* should be observed.

Projection rule for division

1. Locate the characteristic of the dividend above it and the characteristic of the divisor below it.
2. Subtract the characteristic of the divisor from the characteristic of the dividend.
3. For every left extension of the C scale's left index, add a (-1) to the total characteristic already obtained.
4. The sum is the characteristic of the answer.

Example

left extension ↓
characteristic of answer ↓

$(+2)$ $(+2) - (0) \rightarrow +2 - 1 = +1$

$$\frac{(575)}{(6.05)} = (9.50)(10)^1$$

(0)

ESTIMATION OF ANSWER BY SCIENTIFIC NOTATION:

$$\frac{6(10)^2}{6} = 1(10)^2 \leftarrow \text{ESTIMATED ANSWER}$$

Example

left extension ↓
characteristic of answer ↓

(-1) $(-1) - (+1) \rightarrow -2 - 1 = -3$

$$\frac{(0.465)}{(54)} = (8.61)(10)^{-3}$$

$(+1)$

ESTIMATION OF ANSWER BY SCIENTIFIC NOTATION:

$$\frac{5(10)^{-1}}{5(10)^1} = 1(10)^{-2} \leftarrow \text{ESTIMATED ANSWER}$$

Division practice problems

10-92. $(29.6) \div (18.02) = \mathbf{1.641}$
10-93. $(1.532) \div (72.6) = \mathbf{(2.11)(10)^{-2}}$
10-94. $(0.1153) \div (70.3) = \mathbf{(1.64)(10)^{-3}}$
10-95. $(89.3) \div (115.6) = \mathbf{(7.72)(10)^{-1}}$
10-96. $(0.1052) \div (33.6) = \mathbf{(3.13)(10)^{-3}}$
10-97. $(40.2) \div (50.8) = \mathbf{(7.91)(10)^{-1}}$
10-98. $(0.661) \div (70,500) = \mathbf{(9.38)(10)^{-6}}$
10-99. $(182.9) \div (0.00552) = \mathbf{(3.31)(10)^4}$
10-100. $(0.714) \div (98,200) = \mathbf{(7.27)(10)^{-6}}$
10-101. $(4.36) \div (80,300) = \mathbf{(5.43)(10)^{-5}}$
10-102. $(1.339) \div (22.6 \times 10^4) = \mathbf{(5.92)(10)^{-6}}$
10-103. $(17.03) \div (76.3) = \mathbf{(2.23)(10)^{-1}}$
10-104. $(0.511) \div (0.281) = \mathbf{1.819}$
10-105. $(67.7) \div (91,300) = \mathbf{(7.42)(10)^{-4}}$
10-106. $(5.04) \div (29,800) = \mathbf{(1.691)(10)^{-4}}$
10-107. $(18.35) \div (0.921) = \mathbf{(1.992)(10)^1}$
10-108. $(29.6 \times 10^5) \div (0.905) = \mathbf{(3.27)(10)^6}$
10-109. $(0.1037) \div (92.5 \times 10^5) = \mathbf{(1.121)(10)^{-8}}$
10-110. $(537) \div (15.63 \times 10^{-7}) = \mathbf{(3.44)(10)^8}$
10-111. $(26,300) \div (84.3 \times 10^5) = \mathbf{(3.12)(10)^{-3}}$
10-112. $(6.370) \div (0.733) = \mathbf{(8.69)(10)^3}$
10-113. $(1.066) \div (7.51 \times 10^3) = \mathbf{(1.419)(10)^{-4}}$
10-114. $(29.6 \times 10^4) \div (0.973) = \mathbf{(3.04)(10)^5}$
10-115. $(0.912) \div (10.31 \times 10^{5}) = \mathbf{(8.85)(10)^3}$

10-116. $(17.37 \times 10^{-4}) \div (0.662) = $ **(2.62)(10)$^{-3}$**
10-117. $(0.693 \times 10^5) \div (1.008 \times 10^{-6}) = $ **(6.88)(10)^{10}**
10-118. $(89.1 \times 10^3) \div (189.3 \times 10^4) = $ **(4.71)(10)$^{-2}$**
10-119. $(0.617) \div (29,600) = $ **(2.08)(10)$^{-5}$**
10-120. $(18.06 \times 10^7) \div (15.29) = $ **(1.181)(10)^7**
10-121. $(56.8)(10)^4 \div (29.6)(10)^{-3} = $ **(1.919)(10)^7**
10-122. $(183,600) \div (76.3 \times 10^{-3}) = $ **(2.41)(10)^6**
10-123. $(75.9 \div (0.000813) = $ **(9.34)(10)^4**
10-124. $(43.6) \div (0.0837) = $ **(5.21)(10)^2**
10-125. $(156.8 \times 10^3) \div (0.715) = $ **(2.19)(10)^5**
10-126. $(216 \times 10^{-3}) \div (1557) = $ **(1.387)(10)$^{-4}$**
10-127. $(88.3 \times 10^{-1}) \div (29.1 \times 10^{-4}) = $ **(3.03)(10)^3**
10-128. $(1.034 \times 10^3) \div (0.706 \times 10^{-8}) = $ **(1.465)(10)^{11}**
10-129. $(55.2)(10)^3 \div (0.1556 \times 10^3) = $ **(3.55)(10)^2**
10-130. $(0.01339) \div (1896 \times 10^5) = $ **(7.06)(10)$^{-11}$**
10-131. $(4,030 \times 10^{-7}) \div (75.3 \times 10^{-9}) = $ **(5.35)(10)^3**

Problems in division

10-132. $\dfrac{89.9}{45.}$

10-133. $\dfrac{147.}{22.}$

10-134. $\dfrac{9.06}{7.1}$

10-135. $\dfrac{1,985.}{78.55}$

10-136. $\dfrac{19,230.}{64.88}$

10-137. $\dfrac{87,600.}{43.8}$

10-138. $\dfrac{54.8}{9.10}$

10-139. $\dfrac{0.877}{33.07}$

10-140. $\dfrac{11.44}{24.9}$

10-141. $\dfrac{187,900.}{71.45}$

10-142. $\dfrac{0.00882}{87.04}$

10-143. $\dfrac{0.675}{54.8}$

10-144. $\dfrac{87.9}{45.7}$

10-145. $\dfrac{164,800.}{3.88}$

10-146. $\dfrac{7.09 \times 10^3}{18.45}$

10-147. $\dfrac{(0.001755)}{(6.175)}$

10-148. $\dfrac{(0.0000559)}{(0.00659)}$

10-149. $\dfrac{(5.065)}{(0.0003375)}$

10-150. $\dfrac{(469,000)}{(793)}$

10-151. $\dfrac{(5,100,000)}{(933 \times 10^5)}$

10-152. $\dfrac{(3765 \times 10^3)}{(760.3)}$

10-153. $\dfrac{(4917)}{(0.391)}$

10-154. $\dfrac{(5516)}{(1.65)}$

10-155. $\dfrac{(0.0916)}{(0.331)}$

10-156. $\dfrac{(193.7)}{5.06}$

10-157. $\dfrac{(113.05)}{(72.35)}$

10-158. $\dfrac{(32.33)}{(46.77)}$

10-159. $\dfrac{(3.17)}{(3.1416)}$

10-160. $\dfrac{(0.221)}{(56.91)}$

10-161. $\dfrac{(233.17)}{(5506)}$

10-162. $\dfrac{(72.13)}{(52.03)}$

10-163. $\dfrac{(6607)}{(1.91 \times 10^5)}$

10-164. $\dfrac{(1.993 \times 10^{-8})}{(72.31 \times 10^{-6})}$

10-165. $\dfrac{(461 \times 10^3)}{(0.003617)}$

10-166. $\dfrac{(9903 \times 10^{-5})}{(47.31 \times 10^3)}$

10-167. $\dfrac{0.711}{11,980.}$

10-168. $\dfrac{0.01253}{66.8}$

10-169. $\dfrac{0.974}{1.058}$

10-170. $\dfrac{0.000497}{38.9 \times 10^{-5}}$

10-171. $\dfrac{48.6 \times 10^{-9}}{1.977 \times 10^5}$

10-172. $\dfrac{69,990. \times 10^{18}}{43.9 \times 10^{-2}}$

10-173. $\dfrac{5.06 \times 10^{-7}}{0.001853 \times 10^9}$

10-174. $\dfrac{1.097 \times 10^{-6}}{458. \times 10^{-1}}$

10-175. $\dfrac{89.99 \times 10^{-3}}{40.7 \times 10^{-6}}$

10-176. $\dfrac{659{,}000}{0.1148 \times 10^{-3}}$ 10-178. $\dfrac{15.06 \times 10^{-7}}{33.8 \times 10^{-1}}$ 10-180. $\dfrac{33.97 \times 10^{7}}{56.98 \times 10^{3}}$

10-177. $\dfrac{883.8}{3.89 \times 10^{-11}}$ 10-179. $\dfrac{1.095}{24.66}$ 10-181. $\dfrac{22{,}900. \times 10^{-6}}{76.4 \times 10^{4}}$

Combined multiplication and division

Since most scientific calculations involve both multiplication and division, the student should master the technique of combined multiplication and division. The projection rules for both multiplication and division also apply in a combination problem.

Example

$$\frac{(+2)\quad(+4)}{(513)\quad(15{,}300)} \quad (+6)\ -\ (+2) \to +4$$
$$\frac{}{\underset{+2}{(238)}} = 32{,}900,\ \text{or}\ \mathbf{3.29 \times 10^{4}}$$

ESTIMATION OF ANSWER BY SCIENTIFIC NOTATION:

$$\frac{5(10)^{2}(1.5)(10)^{4}}{(2.5)(10)^{2}} = \mathbf{3(10)^{4}} \leftarrow \text{ESTIMATED ANSWER}$$

In order to work the problem above, first set 513 divided by 238 on the C and D scales. Now, instead of reading this answer, move the hairline to 15,300 on the C scale (thus multiplying this latter quantity by the quotient of the first setting).

The student should always alternate the division and multiplication settings and should not try to take readings as he progresses with the steps. Only the final result is desired and since each reading of the rule further magnifies any error, the fewest readings possible should be allowed.

Example

(left extension
from the division)
↓

$$\frac{(+1)\quad(-4)\quad(+2)}{(47.30)(0.000391)(693.5)} \quad (-1)-(+2) \to -3-1 = -4$$
$$\frac{}{\underset{(-1)\ (+1)\ (+2)}{(0.312)(55.1)(773.1)}} = \mathbf{9.66 \times 10^{-4}}$$

ESTIMATION OF ANSWER BY SCIENTIFIC NOTATION:

$$\frac{5(10)^{1}\ 4(10)^{-4}\ 7(10)^{2}}{3(10)^{-1}\ 6(10)^{1}\ 8(10)^{2}} = \mathbf{1(10)^{-3}} \leftarrow \text{ESTIMATED ANSWER}$$

Remember that when you want to divide, you move the slide, and when you want to multiply, you move the hairline.

A common mistake made by many students is to multiply all the quantities in the dividend and all the quantities in the divisor and then divide these two results.

This is a bad habit and such practice should not be followed. There are too many chances for mistakes, in addition to the method's being slower.

Combined multiplication and division practice problems

10-182. $\dfrac{(29.6)(18.01)}{(937)} = (5.69)(10)^{-1}$

10-183. $\dfrac{(625,000)(0.0337)}{(48.2)} = (4.37)(10)^2$

10-184. $\dfrac{(0.887)(1,109)}{(5.22)} = (1.884)(10)^2$

10-185. $\dfrac{(0.1058)(937,000)}{(0.218)} = (4.55)(10)^5$

10-186. $\dfrac{(43,800)(0.0661)}{(87.2 \times 10^5)} = (3.32)(10)^{-4}$

$\dfrac{43.8 \cdot 10^3 \times 6.61 \cdot 10^{-2}}{87.2}$

10-187. $\dfrac{(114.3)(0.567)}{(66,400)} = (9.76)(10)^{-4}$

10-188. $\dfrac{(76.5 \times 10^4)}{(0.733)(49.7 \times 10^{-6})} = (2.10)(10)^{10}$

10-189. $\dfrac{(11.03)}{(20,100)(8.72 \times 10^3)} = (6.29)(10)^{-8}$

10-190. $\dfrac{(0.226)}{(87.3 \times 10^4)(0.717)} = (3.61)(10)^{-7}$

10-191. $\dfrac{(43.2)}{(9.09)(0.000652)} = (7.29)(10)^3$

10-192. $\dfrac{(94.9 \times 10^{-9})}{(33,800)(0.609)} = (4.61)(10)^{-12}$

10-193. $\dfrac{(737,000)}{(0.1556)(61.9 \times 10^3)} = (7.65)(10)^1$

10-194. $\dfrac{(17.01)(0.0336)}{(52,600)(0.01061)} = (1.024)(10)^{-3}$

10-195. $\dfrac{(66.6)(0.937)}{(7.05 \times 10^2)(184,300)} = (4.80)(10)^{-7}$

10-196. $\dfrac{(2.96)(1000)(62.1)}{(0.911)(432,000)} = (4.67)(10)^{-1}$

10-197. $\dfrac{(45.8)(10.33)}{(29,200)(0.702)} = (2.31)(10)^{-2}$

10-198. $\dfrac{(0.604)(9,270)}{(0.817 \times 10^4)(1.372)} = (4.99)(10)^{-1}$

10-199. $\dfrac{(176,300)(42.8 \times 10^3)}{(68.3)(15.01)} = (7.36)(10)^6$

10-200. $\dfrac{(39,200)(89.3 \times 10^{-7})}{(20.4 \times 10^{-6})(155.5)} = (1.104)(10)^2$

10-201. $\dfrac{(0.763 \times 10^{-4})(0.01004)}{(44.3)(7,150,000)} = (2.42)(10)^{-15}$

10-202. $\dfrac{(152,300)(88,100)}{(0.00339)(60.4)} = (6.55)(10)^{10}$

10-203. $\dfrac{(90,400)(2.05 \times 10^6)}{(24.3 \times 10^{-2})(0.0227)} = (3.36)(10)^{13}$

10-204. $\dfrac{(14.36 \times 10^2)(0.907)}{(51.6 \times 10^2)(0.00001118)} = (2.26)(10)^4$

10-205. $\dfrac{(991,000)(60.3 \times 10^4)}{(23.3 \times 10^{-1})(0.1996)} = (1.285)(10)^{12}$

10-206. $\dfrac{(8.40)(10)^3(29.6 \times 10^{-5})}{(0.369)(10.02 \times 10^9)} = (6.72)(10)^{-10}$

10-207. $\dfrac{(54.9)(26.8)(0.331)}{(21.6)(11.03)(54.6)} = (3.74)(10)^{-2}$

10-208. $\dfrac{(17,630)(0.1775)(92.3)}{(0.433)(0.0061)(57.3)} = (1.908)(10)^6$

10-209. $\dfrac{(0.821)(0.221)(0.811)}{(0.0907)(10.72)(66,300)} = (2.28)(10)^{-6}$

10-210. $\dfrac{(0.00552)(89.6)(0.705)}{(19.52 \times 10^3)(18.03)(22.4)} = (4.42)(10)^{-8}$

10-211. $\dfrac{(30,600)(29.9)(0.00777)}{(485)(19.32)(62.6)} = (1.212)(10)^{-2}$

10-212. $\dfrac{(54.1)(0.393)(16,070)}{(49.3 \times 10^3)(11.21)(61.6)} = (1.00)(10)^{-2}$

10-213. $\dfrac{(44.2)(100.7)(62,400)}{(90.3)(75,100)(0.01066)} = (3.84)(10)^3$

10-214. $\dfrac{(78.4)(15.59)(0.01669)}{(33.6)(88,100)(0.432)} = (1.594)(10)^{-5}$

10-215. $\dfrac{(994,000)(21,300)(0.1761)}{(44.4)(71.2)(32.1 \times 10^4)} = 3.67$

10-216. $\dfrac{(16.21)(678,000)(56.6)}{(0.01073)(4,980)(30.3)} = (3.84)(10)^5$

10-217. $\dfrac{(61.3 \times 10^3)(0.1718)(0.893)}{(21.6)(0.902)(0.01155)} = (4.18)(10)^4$

10-218. $\dfrac{(20,900)(16.22 \times 10^4)(0.1061)}{(877)(20.1 \times 10^{-4})(5.03)} = (4.06)(10)^7$

10-219. $\dfrac{(999,000)(17.33)(0.1562)}{(0.802)(0.0443)(29.3 \times 10^{-1})} = (2.60)(10)^7$

10-220. $\dfrac{(16.21)(0.0339)(151.6)(0.211)}{(0.00361)(0.785)(93.2)(406)} = (1.640)(10)^{-1}$

10-221. $\dfrac{(84.3)(0.916)(0.1133)(21.3)}{(66.2)(0.407)(55.3)(462)} = (2.72)(10)^{-4}$

Problems

Solve by combined multiplication and division method:

10-222. $\dfrac{(0.916)}{(90.5)(13.06)}$

10-223. $\dfrac{(0.00908)}{(22.3)(33.2)}$

10-224. $\dfrac{(24.5)(43)}{(36)}$

10-225. $\dfrac{(82)(9.3)}{(56.5)}$

10-226. $\dfrac{(167)(842)}{(0.976)}$

10-227. $\dfrac{(5.72)(3690)}{(95.7)}$

10-228. $\dfrac{(925)(76.9)}{(37.6)}$

10-229. $\dfrac{(9.87)}{(1.76)(89)}$

10-230. $\dfrac{(85.4)}{(26.3)(213)}$

10-231. $\dfrac{(1525)}{(73.6)(0.007)}$

10-232. $\dfrac{(84,500)}{(126)(37.3)}$

10-233. $\dfrac{(76)(23.7)}{(13.5)(373)}$

10-234. $\dfrac{(6.23)(2.14)}{(0.00531)}$

10-235. $\dfrac{(21.3)(370)}{(10.9)(758)}$

10-236. $\dfrac{(0.00215)(2520)}{(7.57)(118)}$

10-237. $\dfrac{(755)(1.15)}{(51.4)(0.093)}$

10-238. $\dfrac{(916)(0.752)}{(5.16)}$

10-239. $\dfrac{(23.1)(1.506)}{(6.27)}$

10-240. $\dfrac{(42.6)(1.935)}{(750.3)}$

10-241. $\dfrac{(77.1)(10.53)}{(331.0)(73)}$

10-242. $\dfrac{(56.7)(0.00336)}{(15.06)(8.23)}$

10-243. $\dfrac{(14.5)(10)^3(6.22)}{(53.3)(0.00103)}$

10-244. $\dfrac{(42)(1000)}{(5.23)(0.00771)}$

10-245. $\dfrac{(1.331)}{(916)(506)}$

10-246. $\dfrac{(4320)(0.7854)}{(134)(0.9)}$

10-247. $\dfrac{(0.00713)(329)}{(0.0105)(1000)}$

10-248. $\dfrac{(103.4)(0.028)}{(0.0798)}$

10-249. $\dfrac{(1573)(4618)}{(3935)(97)}$

10-250. $\dfrac{(47.2)(0.0973)}{(85)(37.6)}$

10-251. $\dfrac{(0.0445)(0.0972)}{(0.218)(0.318)}$

10-252. $\dfrac{(39.1)(680,000)(3.52)(1.1 \times 10^6)}{(0.0316)(9.6 \times 10^6)(26.3)}$

10-253. $\dfrac{(7.69)(76,000)(5.63)(0.00314)}{(0.00365)(10 \times 10^6)}$

10-254. $\dfrac{(3.97)(6.71 \times 10^{-3})(0.067)}{(63.1)(3 \times 10^7)(7.61)(80,175)}$

10-255. $\dfrac{(697)(0.000713)(68.1)}{(234)(9.68)(5.1 \times 10^4)}$

10-256. $\dfrac{(43,400)(9.16)(8.1 \times 10^{-6})}{(0.00613)(67,000)(0.416)}$

10-257. $\dfrac{(691.6)(7.191)(3 \times 10^7)}{(410,000)(6.39)(0.0876)}$

10-258. $\dfrac{(37.615)(81.4)(9.687)(0.0017)}{(13.13)(0.076)(43)}$

10-259. $\dfrac{(51.2 \times 10^{-6})(3.41 \times 10^5)(36.1)}{(96.69)(7 \times 10^{-2})(0.134)}$

10-260. $\dfrac{(6.716)(3.2 \times 10^3)(0.0173)(413)}{(0.0000787)(6.6 \times 10^4)}$

10-261. $\dfrac{(1.061) \times 10^{-1})(96,000)(3.717)}{(7.34 \times 10^{-6})(3.9 \times 10^4)(13.5)}$

10-262. $\dfrac{(361)(482)(5.816)(38.91)(0.00616)}{(0.07181)(3 \times 10^3)(39.36)}$

10-263. $\dfrac{(0.019) \times 10^8)(111.15)(0.0168)}{(7.96)(58.6)(0.0987)(3,000)}$

10-264. $\dfrac{(21.4)(0.82)(39.6 \times 10^{-1})}{(10.86)(6.7 \times 10^{-2})(37,613)}$

10-265. $\dfrac{(63,761)(43,890)(0.00761)}{(8 \times 10^6)(0.0781)(67.17)}$

10-266. $\dfrac{(516.7)(212 \times 10^3)(0.967)(34)}{(76,516)(2 \times 10^{-6})(618)}$

10-267. $\dfrac{(5.1 \times 10^8)(370)(8.71)(3,698)}{(0.00176)(36,170)}$

10-268. $\dfrac{(59.71 \times 10^{-6})(0.00916)(0.1695)(55.61)}{(17.33 \times 10^5)(0.3165)(10.56)(1.105)}$

10-269. $\dfrac{(773.6)(57.17)(0.316)(912.3)}{(56,000)(715,000)(471.3)}$

10-270. $\dfrac{(51.33)(461.3)(919)(5.03)}{(66,000)(71.52)(0.3316)(12.39)}$

10-271. $\dfrac{(0.6617)(75.391)(0.6577)(91.33)}{(0.3305)(5.69 \times 10)(0.00317 \times 10^{-5})}$

Proportions and ratios

A "ratio of one number to another is the quotient of the first with respect to the second. For example, the ratio of a to b may be written as $a:b$ or $\dfrac{a}{b}$. A "proportion" is a statement that two ratios are equal. Thus, $2:3 = 6:B$ means that $\dfrac{2}{3} = \dfrac{6}{B}$.

The slide rule is quite useful in solving problems involving ratio or proportion because these fractions may be handled on any pair of matching identical scales of the rule. The C and D scales are most commonly used for this purpose.

In the example, $\dfrac{2}{3} = \dfrac{6}{B}$, 2, 3, and 6 are known values and B is unknown. The procedure to solve for B would be as follows:

1. Divide 2 by 3 (using the C and D scales). In this position the value 2 on the D scale would be located immediately beneath 3 on the C scale.

2. The equal ratio of $\dfrac{6}{B}$ would also be found on the C and D scales. The unknown value B may be read on the C scale immediately above the known value 6 on the D scale; $B = 9$.

With this particular location of the slide, every value read on the C scale bears the identical ratio of $2:3$ to the number directly below it on the D scale. It is also important to remember that the cross products of a proportion are equal. In the above example, $3 \times 6 = 2 \times B$.

Examples

$\qquad$ a. $\dfrac{47}{21} = \dfrac{18}{A}$ $\qquad\qquad$ *Answer,* $A = $ **8.04**

$$b. \quad \frac{0.721}{1.336} = \frac{B}{89.3} \qquad \textit{Answer, } B = \mathbf{48.2}$$

$$c. \quad \frac{15.9}{C} = \frac{72.1}{166.7} \qquad \textit{Answer, } C = \mathbf{36.7}$$

$$d. \quad \frac{D}{0.1156} = \frac{0.921}{0.473} \qquad \textit{Answer, } D = \mathbf{0.225}$$

$$e. \quad \frac{42,100}{7,060} = \frac{E}{0.0321} \qquad \textit{Answer, } E = \mathbf{0.1912}$$

Folded scales

The CF and DF scales are called *folded scales.* They are identical with the C and D scales except that their indexes are in a different position. On the majority of slide rules, the CF and DF scales begin at the left end with the value π, which means that their indexes will be located near the center of the rule. On some rules the CF and DF scales may be folded at ϵ (2.718) or at some other number.

Since the CF and DF scales are identical in graduations with the C and D scales, they can be used in multiplication and division just as the C and D scales are. Another important fact may be noticed when the scales are examined; that is, if a number such as 2 on the C scale is set over a number such as 3 on the D scale, then 2 on the CF scale coincides with 3 on the DF scale. This means that operations may be begun or answers obtained on either the C and D scales or on the CF and DF scales.

For example, if we wish to multiply 2 by 6, and we set the left index of the C scale over 2 on the D scale, we observe that the product cannot be read on the D scale because 6 on the C scale projects past the right end of the rule. Ordinarily this would mean that the slide would need to be run to the left so that the right index of the C scale could be used. However, by using the folded scales, we notice that the 6 on the CF scale coincides with 12 on the DF scale, thereby eliminating an extra movement of the slide (See Figure 10-19). In many cases the use of the folded scales will reduce the number of times the slide must be shifted to the left because an answer would fall beyond the right end of the D scale.

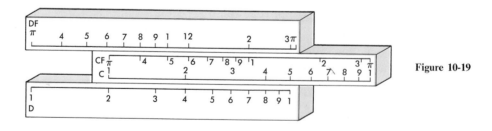

Figure 10-19

There are several methods by which the location of the decimal point in the answer can be determined. The decimal point location can best be found by using the method of scientific notation.

The projection rule can be used if it is always remembered that an answer read on the DF scale to the right of the index (near the center of the rule) corresponds to a left projection. Since in many operations the decimal point location in the answer can be determined by inspection, the decimal point can often be placed without reference to projection rules.

A convenient method of multiplying or dividing by π is afforded by the use of the folded scales. For example, to find the product 2π, set the hairline over 2 on the D scale. The product 6.28 is read on the DF scale under the hairline. Of course this same operation may be performed by using either index of the slide.

Reciprocal scales

The CI, DI, and CIF scales are known as *reciprocal scales* or *inverted scales*. They are identical with the C, D, and CF scales, respectively, except that they are inverted; that is, the numbers represented by the graduations on these scales increase from right to left. On some slide rules, the inverted scale graduations are printed in red to help distinguish them from the other scale markings.

An important principle to remember when using these scales is that a number on the C scale will have its reciprocal in the same position on the CI scale. Conversely, when the hairline is set to a number on the CI scale, its reciprocal is under the hairline on the C scale.

The inverted scales are useful in problems involving repeated multiplication or division because some movements of the slide may be eliminated.

Example Find the product:

$$(1.71)(8.30)(0.252)(4910)(53.8)$$

In order to perform this operation, using the inverted scales, the following steps are used:

1. Set the hairline to 1.71 on the D scale.
2. Move the slide until 83 on the CI scale is under the hairline.
3. Move the hairline until it is set on 252 on the C scale.
4. Move the slide until 491 on the CI scale is under the hairline.
5. Move the hairline until it is set on 538 on the C scale.
6. Read the product 94600 under the hairline on the D scale.

The actual process has involved the use of reciprocal quantities in division in Steps 2 and 4 of the sequence above. Rewritten as the operation is actually performed, the problem appears as follows:

$$\frac{(1.71)(0.252)(53.8)}{(1/8.30)(1/4910)}$$

ESTIMATION OF ANSWER BY SCIENTIFIC NOTATION:
$$(2)(8)(2)(10)^{-1}(5)(10)^{3}(5)(10)^{1} = (8)(10)^{5} \leftarrow \text{ESTIMATED ANSWER}$$

Since the digits read on the slide rule were 946, the actual product would be $9.46(10)^5$. The projection rule should not be used with inverted scales, since the number of left projections are sometimes difficult to determine.

Proper use of the folded and inverted scales will enable one to work each practice problem below with only one setting of the slide.

Use of folded and reciprocal scales practice problems

10-272. $(264)(564)(522) = (7.77)(10)^7$
10-273. $(387)(7.32)(176) = (4.99)(10)^5$
10-274. $(0.461)(4.79)(1140) = (2.52)(10)^3$
10-275. $(6.69)(1548)(92,000) = (9.53)(10)^8$
10-276. $(561)(3.30)(1.94) = (3.59)(10)^3$
10-277. $(1456)(0.351)(0.835) = (4.27)(10)^2$
10-278. $(1262)(0.405)(65,100) = (3.33)(10)^7$
10-279. $(0.1871)(5.04)(53,000) = (5.00)(10)^4$
10-280. $(7.28 \times 10^{-5})(4.16)(14.10) = (4.27)(10)^{-3}$
10-281. $(10.70)(19,400)(0.0914) = (1.897)(10)^4$
10-282. $(4.56)(47.4)(87.1) = (1.883)(10)^4$
10-283. $(0.510)(68.9)(3.370) = (1.184)(10)^5$
10-284. $(2,030)(14.72)(129.7) = (3.88)(10)^6$
10-285. $(1824)(29.1)(21,800) = (1.157)(10)^9$
10-286. $(0.0255)(0.0932)(0.867) = (2.06)(10)^{-3}$
10-287. $(93.6)(3.99)(5,680) = (2.12)(10)^6$
10-288. $(4.48)(103.5)(0.198) = (9.18)(10)^1$
10-289. $(0.580)(43,700)(40.3) = (1.021)(10)^6$
10-290. $(7.05)(62.0)(34.9) = (1.525)(10)^4$
10-291. $(74.8)(8.)(483,000) = (2.89)(10)^8$

10-292. $\dfrac{(208)(90.2)}{(30,600)} = (6.13)(10)^{-1}$

10-293. $\dfrac{(0.387)(25,200)}{(0.118)} = (8.26)(10)^4$

10-294. $\dfrac{(0.458)(14.05 \times 10^{-15})}{(75.5 \times 10^8)} = (8.52)(10)^{-25}$

10-295. $\dfrac{(18,100)(84.4)}{(10.92)} = (1.40)(10)^5$

10-296. $\dfrac{(477)(9,720)}{(19,150)} = (2.42)(10)^2$

10-297. $\dfrac{(25,600)}{(68,500)(12,080)} = (3.09)(10)^{-5}$

10-298. $\dfrac{(3050)(1.00 \times 10^{-20})}{(71.4)(0.946)} = (4.52)(10)^{-19}$

10-299. $\dfrac{(1,670)}{(0.000570)(24,700)} = (1.186)(10)^2$

10-300. $\dfrac{(51.5)}{(15.14)(0.00194)} = (1.753)(10)^3$

10-301. $\dfrac{(917,000)}{(54.3)(119.8 \times 10^{-4})} = (1.41)(10)^6$

Squares and square roots

The A and B scales have been constructed so that their lengths are one half those of the C and D scales (see Figure 10-20). Similarly some slide rules are so constructed that they have a scale (Sq 1 and Sq 2, or R_1 and R_2) which is twice as long as the D scale. This means that the logarithm of 3 as represented on the D scale would be equivalent in length to the logarithm of 9 on the A scale. Where the Sq 1 and

Sq 2 or the R_1 and R_2 scales are used in conjunction with the D scale, the logarithm of 3 on the Sq 2 (R_2) scale would be equivalent in length to the logarithm of 9 on the D scale.

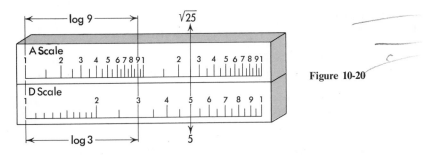

Figure 10-20

To find the square root of a number using the A and D scales

1. Get an estimate of the intended answer by placing a bar over every two digits, starting at the decimal point and working outward. There will be a digit in the answer for each bar marked.
2. Set the number on the A scale and read the square root on the D scale under the hairline. Note that the estimated answer will always indicate which A scale to use, since only one of the scales will give a square root near the estimated value.

Greater accuracy can be obtained by using the D scale in conjunction with the Sq 1 and Sq 2 scales (R_1 and R_2).

Examples for finding the location of decimal points:

a. $\sqrt{\overset{9}{97} \ \overset{x}{65}}$ The estimated answer is somewhere between 90 and 100.

b. $\sqrt{\overset{.\,0}{.00} \ \overset{5}{30}}$ The estimated answer is approximately 0.05.

Note In the last example, since the given value was 0.003, an extra zero would have to be added after the 3 to complete the digits beneath the bar.

Examples for finding the square root of a number:

a. $\sqrt{\overset{1}{1} \ \overset{x}{03} \ \overset{x}{57}}$ The estimated answer is somewhere between 100 and 200.

$$\sqrt{1 \ 03 \ 57} = 101.8 = \mathbf{1.018 \times 10^2}$$

b. $\sqrt{\overset{0.\,0}{0.00} \ \overset{2}{05} \ \overset{x}{20}}$ The estimated answer is approximately 0.02.

$$\sqrt{0.00 \ 05 \ 20} = 0.02280 = \mathbf{2.280 \times 10^{-2}}$$

Examples for finding squares:

1. Express the number in scientific notation.

a. $(0.0000956)^2 = (9.56 \times 10^{-5})^2$

2. Square each part of the converted term by setting the number to be squared on the D scale and reading its square on the A scale under the hairline.

a. $(9.56)^2 \times (10^{-5})^2 = 91.4 \times 10^{-10} = \mathbf{9.14 \times 10^{-9}}$

b. $(90100)^2 = (9.01 \times 10^4)^2$
   $(9.01)^2 \times (10^4)^2 = 81 \times 10^8 = \mathbf{8.1 \times 10^9}$

c. $(357000000)^2 = (3.57 \times 10^8)^2$
   $(3.57)^2 \times (10^8)^2 = 12.7 \times 10^{16} = \mathbf{1.27 \times 10^{17}}$

d. $(0.00000001050)^2 = (1.05 \times 10^{-8})^2$
   $(1.05)^2 \times (10^{-8})^2 = \mathbf{1.10 \times 10^{-16}}$

Squares and square roots practice problems

10-302. $(408)^2 = \mathbf{(1,665)(10)^5}$

10-303. $(8.35)^2 = \mathbf{(6.97)(10)^1}$

10-304. $(3,980)^2 = \mathbf{(1.584)(10)^7}$

10-305. $(0.941)^2 = \mathbf{(8.85)(10)^{-1}}$

10-306. $(57.4)^2 = \mathbf{(3.29)(10)^3}$

10-307. $(0.207)^2 = \mathbf{(4.28)(10)^{-2}}$

10-308. $(784)^2 = \mathbf{(6.15)(10)^5}$

10-309. $(296,000)^2 = \mathbf{(8.76)(10)^{10}}$

10-310. $(1037)^2 = \mathbf{(1.075)(10)^6}$

10-311. $(8.93)^2 = \mathbf{(7.97)(10)^1}$

10-312. $(30.9)^2 = \mathbf{(9.55)(10)^2}$

10-313. $(43,300)^2 = \mathbf{(1.875)(10)^9}$

10-314. $(0.00609)^2 = \mathbf{(3.71)(10)^{-5}}$

10-315. $(0.846)^2 = \mathbf{(7.16)(10)^{-1}}$

10-316. $(55.2 \times 10^3)^2 = \mathbf{(3.05)(10)^9}$

10-317. $(0.0707)^2 = \mathbf{(5.00)(10)^{-3}}$

10-318. $(11.92 \times 10^{-4})^2 = \mathbf{(1.421)(10)^{-6}}$

10-319. $(0.291 \times 10^{-5})^2 = \mathbf{(8.47)(10)^{-12}}$

10-320. $(449,000)^2 = \mathbf{(2.02)(10)^{11}}$

10-321. $(0.000977)^2 = \mathbf{(9.55)(10)^{-7}}$

10-322. $(33.5 \times 10^{-6})^2 = \mathbf{(1.122)(10)^{-9}}$

10-323. $(8,810)^2 = \mathbf{(7.76)(10)^7}$

10-324. $(50.9 \times 10^6)^2 = \mathbf{(2.59)(10)^{15}}$

10-325. $(99,300)^2 = \mathbf{(9.86)(10)^9}$

10-326. $(0.0714 \times 10^{-6})^2 = \mathbf{(5.10)(10)^{-15}}$

10-327. $\sqrt{96,100} = \mathbf{(3.10)(10)^2}$

10-328. $\sqrt{0.912} = \mathbf{(9.55)(10)^{-1}}$

10-329. $\sqrt{24.9} = \mathbf{4.99}$

10-330. $\sqrt{0.01124} = \mathbf{(1.06)(10)^{-1}}$

10-331. $\sqrt{5,256} = \mathbf{(7.25)(10)^1}$

10-332. $\sqrt{0.3764} = \mathbf{(6.14)(10)^{-1}}$

10-333. $\sqrt{43,800,000} = \mathbf{(6.62)(10)^3}$

10-334. $\sqrt{0.01369} = \mathbf{(1.17)(10)^{-1}}$

10-335. $\sqrt{73.6} = \mathbf{8.58}$

10-336. $\sqrt{1.1025} = \mathbf{1.05}$

10-337. $\sqrt{487,000} = \mathbf{(6.98)(10)^2}$

10-338. $\sqrt{580.8} = \mathbf{(2.41)(10)^1}$

10-339. $\sqrt{0.00002767} = \mathbf{(5.26)(10)^{-3}}$

10-340. $\sqrt{0.1399} = \mathbf{(3.74)(10)^{-1}}$

10-341. $\sqrt{6,368} = \mathbf{(7.98)(10)^1}$

10-342. $\sqrt{1.142 \times 10^{-3}} = \mathbf{(3.38)(10)^{-2}}$

10-343. $\sqrt{6.496 \times 10^1} = \mathbf{8.06}$

10-344. $\sqrt{190,970} = \mathbf{(4.37)(10)^2}$

10-345. $\sqrt{3,204,000} = \mathbf{(1.79)(10)^3}$

10-346. $\sqrt{0.003807} = \mathbf{(6.17)(10)^{-2}}$

10-347. $\sqrt{0.08352} = \mathbf{(2.89)(10)^{-1}}$

10-348. $\sqrt{3069} = \mathbf{(5.54)(10)^1}$

10-349. $\sqrt{61.78 \times 10^{-4}} = \mathbf{(7.86)(10)^{-2}}$

10-350. $\sqrt{3.648 \times 10^{-8}} = \mathbf{(1.91)(10)^{-4}}$

10-351. $\sqrt{9.92 \times 10^5} = \mathbf{(9.96)(10)^2}$

Problems

Solve by method of squares and square roots.

10-352. $(1468.)^2$

10-353. $(0.886)^2$

10-354. $(67.4)^2$

10-355. $(11.96)^2$

10-356. $(0.00448)^2$

10-357. $(0.000551)^2$

10-358. $(9.22)^2$

10-359. $(64,800.)^2$

10-360. $(0.0668)^2$

10-361. $(16.85)^2$

10-362. $(1.802 \times 10^9)^2$

10-363. $(0.00358)^2$

10-364. $(5089)^2$

10-365. $(44,900.)^2$

10-366. $(64.88)^2$

10-367. $\sqrt{11.81}$

10-368. $\sqrt{4567.}$

10-369. $\sqrt{0.01844}$

10-370. $\sqrt{0.9953}$

10-371. $\sqrt{1395.}$

10-372. $\sqrt{0.0001288}$

10-373. $\sqrt{1.082 \times 10^2}$

10-374. $\sqrt{75.9}$

10-375. $\sqrt{\pi}$

10-376. $\sqrt{73,800.}$

10-377. $\sqrt{13.38}$

10-378. $\sqrt{93.07}$

10-379. $\sqrt{0.1148}$

10-380. $\sqrt{0.2776}$

10-381. $\sqrt{9.31}$

10-382. $(0.774)^2(11.47)^{1/2}$

10-383. $(0.1442)^{1/2}(33.89)^{1/2}$

10-384. $(54.23)^2(88,900)^{1/2}$

10-385. $\sqrt{234.5} \sqrt{55,900.}$

10-386. $\sqrt{16.38} \sqrt{45.6} \sqrt{0.9}$

10-387. $\sqrt{415.} \sqrt{\pi} \sqrt{86.4}$

10-388. $\sqrt{15.66} \sqrt{0.1904} \sqrt{\pi}$

10-389. $(34.77)^2(54.8)^2(0.772)^{1/2}$

10-390. $\sqrt{7.90} \sqrt{7.02} \sqrt{11.54}$

10-391. $\sqrt{31.19} \sqrt{56.7} \sqrt{54.8}$

$3620,5$

$\sqrt{31.19} \times \sqrt{415} = 113,77$

Cubes and cube roots

The D and K scales are used to find the cube or cube root of a number as shown in Figure 10-21. The same general procedure is used as that followed for squaring numbers and taking the square root of a number. The K scale is divided into scales K_1, K_2, and K_3, which are each one third the length of the D scale. Thus, if a number is located on the D scale, the cube of the number will be indicated on the K scale. It follows that if a number is located on one of the K scales, the root of the number would appear on the D scale.

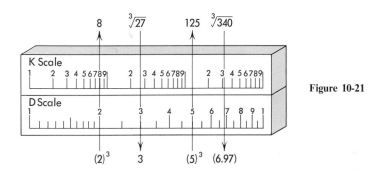

Figure 10-21

To find the cube root of a number

1. Get an estimate of the intended answer by placing a bar over every three digits, starting at the decimal point and working outward. There will be a digit in the answer for each bar marked.

2. Set the number on the K scale and read the cube root on the D scale under the hairline. (Some slide rules, such as those made by Pickett, have three cube root scales instead of the conventional K scale. These cube root scales are used with the D scale to determine cubes and cube roots of numbers. When they are used, however, the number should be set on the D scale and the cube root read on the appropriate cube root scale.)

Examples for finding the location of decimal points:

a. $\sqrt[3]{\overline{44,}\ \overline{800.}}$ The estimated answer is somewhere between 30 and 40.

b. $\sqrt[3]{\overline{0.}\ \overline{000}\ \overline{011}}$ The estimated answer is approximately 0.02.

Note In estimating the answer by marking bars over the digit groupings, be sure that the bars cover three digits instead of two, as was the case in square roots.

Since an estimated answer [see Example *a* above] has been obtained, it is easy to pick the proper K scale (K_1, K_2, or K_3) to use. Remember that only one of these will give an answer between 30 and 40 [see Example *a*].

Examples for finding the cube roots of a number:

$$\overset{\displaystyle 1 \quad x \quad x}{a. \ \sqrt[3]{1 \ \overline{490} \ \overline{000}}.}$$ The estimated answer is somewhere between 100 and 200.

$$\sqrt[3]{1 \ \overline{490} \ \overline{000}}. = 114.1 = \mathbf{(1.141)(10)^2}.$$

$$\overset{\displaystyle 0. \quad 0 \quad 6}{b. \ \sqrt[3]{0. \ \overline{000} \ \overline{156} \ \overline{9}}}$$ The estimated answer is approximately 0.06.

$$\sqrt[3]{0. \ \overline{000} \ \overline{156} \ \overline{9}} = 0.0537 = \mathbf{(5.37)(10)^{-2}}.$$

Examples for finding cubes:

1. Convert the number to a number between 1 and 10 (scientific notation) that must be multiplied by 10 raised to some power.

    a. $(0.00641)^3 = (6.41 \times 10^{-3})^3$

2. Cube each part of the converted term by setting the number to be cubed on the D scale and reading its cube on the K scale under the hairline.

  a. $(6.41 \times 10^{-3})^3 = (264)(10)^{-9} = \mathbf{2.63 \times 10^{-7}}$

  b. $(93.88)^3 = (9.388 \times 10^1)^3$
       $(9.388)^3(10^1)^3 = 830 \times 10^3 = \mathbf{8.27 \times 10^5}$

  c. $(2{,}618{,}000.)^3 = (2.618 \times 10^6)^3$
       $(2.618)^3(10^6)^3 = (17.95 \times 10)^{18} = \mathbf{1.794 \times 10^{19}}$

  d. $(0.000001194)^3 = (1.194 \times 10^{-6})^3$
       $(1.194)^3(10^{-6})^3 = \mathbf{1.701 \times 10^{-18}}$

Cubes and cube roots practice problems

10-392. $(206)^3 = \mathbf{(8.74)(10)^6}$
10-393. $(7.68)^3 = \mathbf{(4.53)(10)^2}$
10-394. $(0.00519)^3 = \mathbf{(1.398)(10)^{-7}}$
10-395. $(33.5)^3 = \mathbf{(3.76)(10)^4}$
10-396. $(0.229)^3 = \mathbf{(1.201)(10)^{-2}}$
10-397. $(1090)^3 = \mathbf{(1.295)(10)^9}$
10-398. $(0.0579)^3 = \mathbf{(1.94)(10)^{-4}}$
10-399. $(9.89)^3 = \mathbf{(9.67)(10)^2}$
10-400. $(419)^3 = \mathbf{(7.36)(10)^7}$
10-401. $(52.4)^3 = \mathbf{(1.439)(10)^5}$
10-402. $(0.0249)^3 = \mathbf{(1.544)(10)^{-5}}$
10-403. $(14.9)^3 = \mathbf{(3.31)(10)^3}$

10-404. $(2.96)^3 = \mathbf{(2.59)(10)^1}$
10-405. $(397)^3 = \mathbf{(6.26)(10)^7}$
10-406. $(63.4)^3 = \mathbf{(2.55)(10)^5}$
10-407. $(9040)^3 = \mathbf{(7.39)(10)^{11}}$
10-408. $(0.0783)^3 = \mathbf{(4.80)(10)^{-4}}$
10-409. $(0.844)^3 = \mathbf{(6.01)(10)^{-1}}$
10-410. $(5.41)^3 = \mathbf{(1.583)(10)^2}$
10-411. $(35.5)^3 = \mathbf{(4.47)(10)^4}$
10-412. $(0.1270)^3 = \mathbf{(2.05)(10)^{-3}}$
10-413. $(20.7)^3 = \mathbf{(8.87)(10)^3}$
10-414. $(691)^3 = \mathbf{(3.30)(10)^8}$
10-415. $(0.719)^3 = \mathbf{(3.72)(10)^{-1}}$

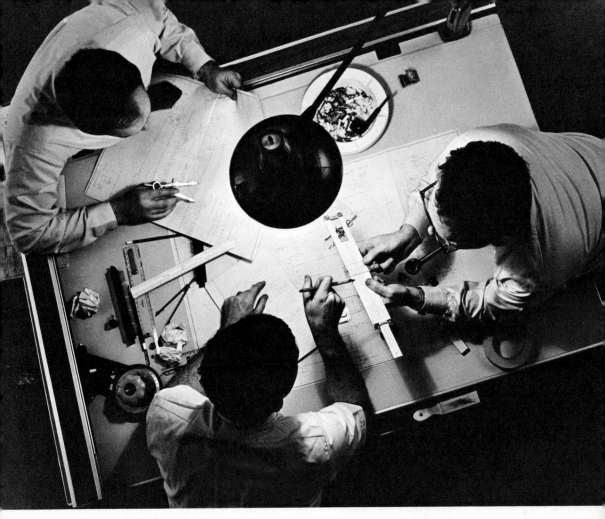

Illustration 10-3

Electronic computers of all types are very important to the engineer. However for many years to come the slide rule will continue to be the "workhorse" tool of analysis.

$$20.96 \times 10^{3\overset{6}{|}}$$
$$3.14 \times 10^{2}$$

10-416. $(4.34)^3 = (8.17)(10)^1$

10-417. $\sqrt[3]{30,960,000} = (3.14)(10)^2$

10-418. $\sqrt[3]{0.001728} = (1.20)(10)^{-1}$

10-419. $\sqrt[3]{491} = 7.89$

10-420. $\sqrt[3]{9.91 \times 10^{11}} = (9.97)(10)^3$

10-421. $\sqrt[3]{0.272} = (6.48)(10)^{-1}$

10-422. $\sqrt[3]{118,400} = (4.91)(10)^1$

10-423. $\sqrt[3]{22.91} = 2.84$

10-424. $\sqrt[3]{527,500} = (8.08)(10)^1$

10-425. $\sqrt[3]{1.295} = 1.09$

10-426. $\sqrt[3]{0.0001804} = (5.65)(10)^{-2}$

10-427. $\sqrt[3]{460,100,000} = (7.72)(10)^2$

10-428. $\sqrt[3]{261,000} = (6.39)(10)^1$

10-429. $\sqrt[3]{0.11620} = (4.88)(10)^{-1}$

10-430. $\sqrt[3]{0.0030486} = (1.45)(10)^{-1}$

10-431. $\sqrt[3]{0.03096} = (3.14)(10)^{-1}$

10-432. $\sqrt[3]{504.4} = 7.96$

10-433. $\sqrt[3]{8,869,000} = (2.07)(10)^2$

10-434. $\sqrt[3]{174,700,000} = (5.59)(10)^2$

10-435. $\sqrt[3]{5.886 \times 10^{10}} = (3.89)(10)^3$

10-436. $\sqrt[3]{5.885 \times 10^{-1}} = (8.38)(10)^{-1}$

10-437. $\sqrt[3]{76.105 \times 10^{-5}} = (9.13)(10)^{-2}$

10-438. $\sqrt[3]{327.1} = 6.89$

10-439. $\sqrt[3]{0.02567} = (2.95)(10)^{-1}$

10-440. $\sqrt[3]{0.0004118} = (7.44)(10)^{-2}$

10-441. $\sqrt[3]{68,420} = (4.09)(10)^1$

Problems

Solve by method of cubes and cube roots.

10-442. $(86)^3$

10-443. $(148)^3$

10-444. $(395,000)^3$

10-445. $(47.6)^3$

10-446. $(1.074)^3$

10-447. $(76.9)^3$

10-448. $(220.8)^3$

10-449. $(9.72)^3$

10-450. $(110.7)^3$

10-451. $(91.3)^3$

10-452. $(1.757 \times 10^4)^3$

10-453. $(3.06 \times 10^{-7})^3$

10-454. $(44.8 \times 10^{-1})^3$

10-455. $(0.933 \times 10^{-2})^3$

10-456. $(0.1184 \times 10^8)^3$

10-457. $(51.5 \times 10^2)^3$

10-458. $\sqrt[3]{118}$

10-459. $\sqrt[3]{2,197}$

10-460. $\sqrt[3]{9}$

10-461. $\sqrt[3]{0.0689}$

10-462. $\sqrt[3]{0.001338}$

10-463. $\sqrt[3]{0.1794}$

10-464. $\sqrt[3]{0.0891}$

10-465. $\sqrt[3]{34,690}$.

10-466. $\sqrt[3]{0.3329}$

10-467. $\sqrt[3]{1,258,000}$

10-468. $\sqrt[3]{0.1853}$

10-469. $\sqrt[3]{12.88}$

10-470. $\sqrt[3]{4.98 \times 10^7}$

10-471. $\sqrt[3]{1.844 \times 10^{-5}}$

10-472. $\sqrt[3]{3.86 \times 10^{-1}}$

10-473. $(9.94)(0.886)^{1/3}$

10-474. $(284.)(11.98)^{1/3}$

10-475. $(0.117)(0.0964)^{1/3}$

10-476. $(\pi)^3(44.89)^3$

10-477. $(6.88)^3(0.00799)^3$

10-478. $(0.915)^{1/3}(0.366)^{1/3}\sqrt[3]{11,250}(36.12)^{1/3}$

10-479. $(2.34)^3(3.34)^3(4.56)^3(5.67)^3$

10-480. $(8.26)^{1/3}(8.26)^3(1000)^{1/3}(10)^3$

10-481. $\sqrt[3]{2670}\ \sqrt[3]{3165}\ \sqrt[3]{1065}\ \sqrt[3]{7776}$

10-482. $\sqrt[3]{206}\ \sqrt[3]{0.791}\ (12.35)^3(26.3)^3$

Trigonometric functions

Finding trigonometric functions on a log-log rule is a rather simple process. The angle may be read on the S (sine), ST (sine and tangent of small angles), or T (tangent) scales. The functions may be read under the hairline on the C, D, or DI scales without any movement of the slide.

Sine 0° to 0.574° It is not often that the student needs to know the function of extremely small angles, but if he does need them, it is possible to get approximate values for these functions without consulting tables.

Method 1 (Based upon the relation that the sine of small angles is approximately equal to the size of the angle expressed in radians)

1. This method is more accurate than the following Method 2, and is preferable.
2. Express the angle in question in degrees.
3. Change the degrees to radians by dividing by 57.3.

Note $57.3° = 1$ radian (approximately)

4. The value obtained is the approximate answer.

Example

$$\sin 6' = ?$$
$$6' = \tfrac{6}{60} = 0.10°$$
$$\sin 6' = \frac{0.10}{57.3}$$
$$\sin 6' = \mathbf{0.00174} \text{ approximately}$$

Method 2

1. Keep in mind the following values:

sin 1″ = **0.000005** (five zeros-five) approximately
sin 1′ = **0.0003** (three zeros-three) approximately

2. For small angles, multiply the value of 1′ or 1″, as the case may be, by the number of minutes or seconds in question.

Example

sin 6′ = ?
sin 6′ = (6)(sin 1′)
sin 6′ = (6)(0.0003)
sin 6′ = **0.0018** approximately

Sine 0.574° to 5.74° To find the sine of an angle between 0.574° and 5.74°, the ST and D scales are used as shown in Figure 10-22.

Example   sin 1.5° = ?   .04 94

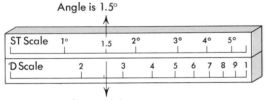

Figure 10-22

Sine of the angle is 0.0262

Instructions

1. Be certain that the left index of the D scale is directly under the left index of the ST scale.
2. Set the hairline to the angle on the ST scale.
3. Read the answer on the D scale. The answer will be a decimal number and will have one zero preceding the digits read from the rule.

Sine 5.74° to 90° To find the sine of an angle between 5.74° and 90°, the S and D scales are used as shown in Figure 10-23.

Example   sin 45° = ?

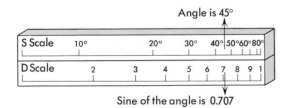

Figure 10-23

Sine of the angle is 0.707

Instructions

1. Be certain that the left index of the D scale is directly under the left index of the S scale.
2. Set the hairline to the angle on the S scale. If the rule has more than one set of figures on the S scale, the angles for sine functions are usually shown to the right of the longer graduations.

3. Read the answer on the D scale. Place the decimal preceding the first digit read from the rule.

10.1
10.17
10.2

Sines practice problems

all odd ans

10-483. sin 26° = **0.438**
10-484. sin 81° = **0.988**
10-485. sin 16° = **0.276**
10-486. sin 15.5° = **0.267**
10-487. sin 42.6° = **0.677**
10-488. sin 3.33° = **0.0581**
10-489. sin 10.17° = **0.1765**
10-490. sin 63.2° = **0.893**
10-491. sin 70.83° = **0.945**
10-492. sin 26.67° = **0.449**
10-493. sin 7.33° = **0.1276**
10-494. sin 2.83 = **0.0494**
10-495. sin 51.5° = **0.783**

10-496. sin 5.17° = **0.0901**
10-497. sin 33.8° = **0.556**
10-498. sin 20.3° = **0.348**
10-499. sin 68.2° = **0.928**
10-500. arc sin 0.557 = **33.8°**
10-501. sin⁻¹ 0.032 = **1.83°**
10-502. sin⁻¹ 0.242 = **14.0°**
10-503. arc sin 0.709 = **45.15°**
10-504. sin⁻¹ 0.581 = **35.5°**
10-505. arc sin 0.999 = **87.5°**
10-506. sin⁻¹ 0.569 = **34.68°**
10-507. sin⁻¹ 0.401 = **23.6°**

10.7

Cosine 0° to 84.26° To find the cosine of an angle between 0° and 84.26°, the markings to the left of the long graduations on the S scale are used in conjunction with the D scale. Note that the markings begin with 0° at the right end of the scale and progress to 84.26° at the left end of the scale as shown in Figure 10-24.

Example   cos 74.1° = ?

.06 9

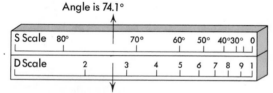

Figure 10-24

Cosine of the angle is 0.274

Cosine 84.26° to 89.4° To find the cosine of an angle between 84.26° and 89.4°, the complement of the angle on the ST scale is used in conjunction with the D scale.

Example

$$\cos 88.5° = ?$$
$$\text{complement of } 88.5° = 1.5°$$
$$\sin 1.5° = 0.0262$$
$$\cos 88.5° = \mathbf{0.0262}$$

Cosine 89.4° to 90° To find the cosine of an angle between 89.4° and 90°, determine the complement of the angle and find the value of the sine of this angle as previously discussed.

Example

$$\cos 89.94° = ?$$
$$\text{complement of } 89.94° = 0.06°$$

$$\sin 0.06° = \frac{0.06}{57.3} = 0.001048$$

$$\cos 89.94° = \mathbf{0.001048}$$

Note In finding the cosine of any angle, it is sometimes more convenient to look up the sine of the complement of the angle.

Example

$$\cos 60° = ?$$
$$\text{complement of } 60° = 30°$$
$$\sin 30° = 0.500$$

Therefore,

$$\cos 60° = \mathbf{0.500}$$

207
old

Cosines practice problems

10-508. $\cos 18.8° = \mathbf{0.947}$
10-509. $\cos 33.17° = \mathbf{0.837}$
10-510. $\cos 71.5° = \mathbf{0.317}$
10-511. $\cos 45° = \mathbf{0.707}$
10-512. $\cos 68.3° = \mathbf{0.370}$
10-513. $\cos 26.9° = \mathbf{0.892}$
10-514. $\cos 55.7° = \mathbf{0.564}$
10-515. $\cos 5.5° = \mathbf{0.995}$
10-516. $\cos 81.3° = \mathbf{0.151}$
10-517. $\cos 8.9° = \mathbf{0.988}$
10-518. $\cos 77.6° = \mathbf{0.215}$
10-519. $\cos 39.1° = \mathbf{0.776}$
10-520. $\cos 50.7° = \mathbf{0.633}$

10-521. $\cos 11.5° = \mathbf{0.980}$
10-522. $\cos 49.2° = \mathbf{0.653}$
10-523. arc cos $0.901 = \mathbf{25.7°}$
10-524. $\cos^{-1} 0.727 = \mathbf{43.4°}$
10-525. $\cos^{-1} 0.0814 = \mathbf{85.3°}$
10-526. arc cos $0.284 = \mathbf{73.5°}$
10-527. $\cos^{-1} 0.585 = \mathbf{54.2°}$
10-528. $\cos^{-1} 0.658 = \mathbf{48.8°}$
10-529. $\cos^{-1} 0.1190 = \mathbf{83.2°}$
10-530. arc cos $0.303 = \mathbf{72.4°}$
10-531. $\cos^{-1} 0.505 = \mathbf{59.7°}$
10-532. $\cos^{-1} 0.693 = \mathbf{46.1°}$

Tangent 0° to 5.74° For small angles (0° to 5.74°) the tangent of the angle may be considered to be the same value as the sine of that angle.

Tangent 5.74° to 45° To find the tangent of an angle between 5.74° and 45°, the T scale is used in conjunction with the D scale, as shown in Figure 10-25.

Example   Find tan 30°.

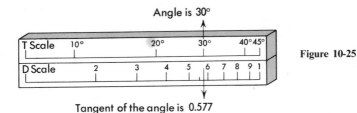

Figure 10-25

Tangent of the angle is 0.577

Instructions
1. Be certain that the left index of the D scale is directly under the left index of the T scale.
2. Set the hairline to the angle on the T scale. If the T scale has more than one set of markings, be certain that the correct markings are used.
3. Read the answer on the D scale. Place the decimal preceding the first digit read from the rule.

Tangent 45° to 84.26° To find the tangent of an angle between 45° and 84.26°, the markings to the left of the longer graduations on the T scale are used in conjunction with the CI or DI scales, as shown in Figure 10-26.

Example   tan 70° = ?

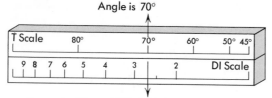

Angle is 70°

T Scale 80° 70° 60° 50° 45°

9 8 7 6 5 4 3 2 DI Scale

Tangent of the angle is 2.74

Figure 10-26

Instructions

1. be certain that the left index of the DI or CI scale is aligned with the left index of the T scale.

2. Set the hairline to the angle on the T scale.

3. Read the answer on the CI or DI scale. Note that these scales read from right to left. Place the decimal after the first digit read from the rule.

Tangent 84.26° to 89.426° To find the tangent of an angle between 84.26° and 89.426°, the complement of the angle on the ST scale is used in conjunction with the CI or DI scales, as shown in Figure 10-27.

Example tan 88° = ?

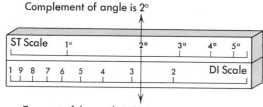

Complement of angle is 2°

ST Scale 1° 2° 3° 4° 5°

1 9 8 7 6 5 4 3 2 DI Scale

Tangent of the angle is 28.6

Figure 10-27

Instructions

1. Be certain that the left index of the DI or CI scale is aligned with the left index of the ST scale.

2. Complement of 88° = 2°.

3. Read the answer on the DI or CI scale. Note that these scales read from right to left.

4. Place the decimal point after the first two digits read from the rule.

Frequently the value of the function of an angle is known and it is desired to find the value of the angle.

Example

$$\sin \theta = 0.53;$$
$$\theta = ?$$

This may be written in the inverse form in either of two ways:

$$\text{arc} \sin 0.53 = \theta$$
or
$$\sin^{-1} 0.53 = \theta$$
then
$$\theta = 32°$$

The forms arc sin, arc cos, and arc tan are usually preferred in modern practice.

Tangents practice problems

10-533. tan 29.6° = **0.568**
10-534. tan 48.2° = **1.118**
10-535. tan 11.5° = **0.203**
10-536. tan 71.9° = **3.06**
10-537. tan 5.7° = **0.0993**
10-538. tan 61.4° = **1.834**
10-539. tan 33.3° = **0.657**
10-540. tan 69.2° = **2.63**
10-541. tan 40.6° = **0.857**
10-542. tan 8.7° = **0.1530**
10-543. tan 17.5° = **0.315**
10-544. tan 85.1° = **11.66**
10-545. tan 58.6° = **1.638**

10-546. tan 39.3° = **0.818**
10-547. tan 20.9° = **0.382**
10-548. tan 42.1° = **0.904**
10-549. arc tan 0.362 = **19.9°**
10-550. arc tan 0.841 = **40.1°**
10-551. $\tan^{-1}$ 0.119 = **6.78°**
10-552. $\tan^{-1}$ 0.0721 = **4.13°**
10-553. $\tan^{-1}$ 1.732 = **60°**
10-554. arc tan 21.6 = **87.3°**
10-555. $\tan^{-1}$ 0.776 = **37.8°**
10-556. arc tan 89.3 = **89.36°**
10-557. $\tan^{-1}$ 0.661 = **33.5°**

The following tables have been prepared for reference purposes. The student should check all the examples with his rule as he proceeds.

Function	Angle	Read angle on	Read function on	Decimal	Examples
sine or tangent	0°–0.574° Convert the angle to radians (1 radian = 57.3°), and this value is assumed to be equal to the sine or tangent of the angle.				
sine or tangent	0.574°–5.74°	ST	D	0.0xxx	tan 2° = 0.0349 sin 3° = 0.0523
sine	5.74°–90°	S (right markings)	D	0.xxxx	sin 29° = 0.485
cosine	0°–84.26°	S (left markings)	D	0.xxxx	cos 43° = 0.7314
tangent	5.74°–45°	T (right markings)	D	0.xxxx	tan 13° = 0.231
tangent	45°–84.26°	T (left markings)	DI	x.xxx	tan 78° = 4.70
tangent	84.26°–89.426	Set complement on ST	DI	xx.xxx	tan 89° = 57.3
cosecant	5.74°–90°	S (right markings)	DI	x.xxx	csc 63° = 1.122
secant	0°–84.26°	S (left markings)	DI	x.xxx	sec 48° = 1.494
cotangent	0.574°–5.74°	ST	DI	xx.xx	cot 3.5° = 16.35
cotangent	5.74°–45°	T (right markings)	DI	x.xxx	cot 23° = 2.36
cotangent	45°–84.26°	T (left markings)	D	0.xxxx	cot 68° = 0.404

Trigonometric functions: problems

Solve, using the slide rule.

10-558. sin 35°	10-587. cot 3.77°	10-616. cos 36.6°
10-559. sin 14°	10-588. cot 66.4°	10-617. tan 32.6°
10-560. sin 78°	10-589. csc 38.1°	10-618. tan 16.34°
10-561. sin 3.7°	10-590. csc 75.2°	10-619. tan 88°30′
10-562. sin 88.3° .999	10-591. csc 88.3°	10-620. arc tan 0.62
10-563. sin 55.3°	10-592. csc 12.8°	10-621. tan⁻¹ 0.75
10-564. cos 35°	10-593. csc 46.4°	10-622. arc tan 0.392
10-565. cos 66°	10-594. csc 81.1°	10-623. tan⁻¹ 1.53
10-566. cos 21.3° .9316	10-595. csc 32.6°	10-624. tan 37°24′
10-567. cos 11.1°	10-596. csc 9.03°	10-625. arc tan 0.567
10-568. cos 7.9°	10-597. sec 6.14°	10-626. tan⁻¹ 0.0321
10-569. cos 43.8°	10-598. sec 59.2°	10-627. cot 19°33′
10-570. tan 33.8°	10-599. sec 79.4°	10-628. sec 46°46′
10-571. tan 9.4°	10-600. sec 19.5°	10-629. csc 32°12′
10-572. tan 37.7° .773	10-601. sec 2.77°	10-630. sin 37°
10-573. tan 22.5° .414	10-602. sec 45.9°	10-631. sin 51°50′
10-574. tan 86.1°	10-603. arc sin 0.771	10-632. sin 68°37′
10-575. tan 54.4° 1.39	10-604. arc cos 0.119	10-633. sin 75°10′
10-576. tan 70.3°	10-605. arc tan 34.8	10-634. arc sin 0.622
10-577. tan 29.7°	10-606. arc sec 7.18	10-635. sin 13.6°
10-578. tan 36.5°	10-607. arc csc 1.05	10-636. sin⁻¹ 0.068
10-579. tan 13.3°	10-608. cos 33.4°	10-637. sin 14.6°
10-580. tan 45.8°	10-609. cos 3.6°	10-638. arc sin 0.169
10-581. cot 14.7°	10-610. arc cos 0.992	10-639. sin 34.67°
10-582. cot 81.8°	10-611. cos 24.67°	10-640. cos 26.26°
10-583. cot 36.9°	10-612. cos⁻¹ 0.496	10-641. csc 20°20′
10-584. cot 61.2°	10-613. cos 36°6′	10-642. (csc 20°)(sin 46°)
10-585. cot 54.3°	10-614. arc cos 0.238	10-643. (cos 32°)(tan 43°)
10-586. cot 18.7° 2.954	10-615. cos 0.75°	

Handwritten margin notes: 1.29, 2.41, .715

$$10\text{-}644. \quad \frac{(\sin 13.9°)}{(\cot 13.9°)}$$

$$10\text{-}651. \quad \frac{(\sin 1.36°)(\cot 26°)}{(\sqrt[3]{0.00916})}$$

$$10\text{-}645. \quad \frac{\cot 33°22′}{\sec 4°53′}$$

$$10\text{-}652. \quad \frac{\cot \sin^{-1} 0.916}{(1.32)(5.061)}$$

$$10\text{-}646. \quad \frac{(\cos 33°15′)}{(\cot 46°19′)}$$

$$10\text{-}653. \quad \frac{(77.19)(\sec 46°)}{(\tan 3.91°)}$$

$$10\text{-}647. \quad \frac{(\sec 10°)(\cot 10°)}{(\sin 10°)(\csc 10°)}$$

$$10\text{-}654. \quad \frac{(\sqrt[3]{\tan 25.9°})(\sin \cos^{-1} 0.5)}{(\sin 5.16°)(\tan 22°)}$$

$$10\text{-}648. \quad \frac{(\sin 35°)(\tan 22°)}{(\sqrt[3]{\sin 5.96°})}$$

$$10\text{-}655. \quad \frac{(0.0311)(\sec 69°)\sqrt[3]{9.0}}{(\sin 9°)(\cos 9°)}$$

$$10\text{-}649. \quad \frac{(\sec 11°)(\tan 4°)}{(\cot 49°)}$$

$$10\text{-}656. \quad \frac{(1.916)(\sqrt[3]{1.916})(\sqrt[3]{\sin 20°})}{(\sqrt[3]{\sec 40°})(\tan 10°22′)}$$

$$10\text{-}650. \quad \frac{(\sin 8°)(\tan 9°)}{(\cot 82°)}$$

$$10\text{-}657. \quad \frac{(6.17)(\tan 6.17°)(\sqrt[3]{6.17})}{(6.17)^2(\sin 61.7°)(\cos 6.17°)}$$

Right triangle solution (log-log rule)

In the study of truss design, moments, and free body diagrams, the right triangle plays an important role. Since the Pythagorean theorem is sometimes awkward to use, and mistakes in arithmetic are likely to occur, it is suggested that the following method be used to solve right triangles.

Given: Right triangle with sides *a, b,* and *c* and angles *A, B,* and *C* (90°), as shown in Figure 10-28.

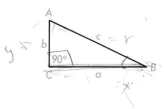

Figure 10-28

$$\sin B = \frac{b}{c}$$

$$\cos B = \frac{a}{c}$$

If the smaller side (*b*) is divided by the longer side (*a*) and the quotient is greater than 0.100, use *Solution 1*. If the quotient is between 0.100 and 0.0100, use *Solution 2*. If the quotient is less than 0.0100, assume that the hypotenuse (*c*) is equal in length to the longest side (*a*) and that $B \cong 0°$.

Solution 1

1. Set the index of the T scale above the larger side (*a*) on the D scale.
2. Move the hairline to the smaller side (*b*) on the D scale.
3. Read the two angles of the right triangle on the T scale. The larger angle is always opposite the larger side.
4. Move the slide until the smaller of the two angles just read is under the hairline on the sine scale.
5. Read the hypotenuse (*c*) on the D scale as indicated by the index of the sine scale.

Example $a = 4$ $A = ?$ $33\frac{1}{3} = \frac{24'}{60}$
                     $b = 3$ $B = ?$
                     $c = ?$

a. Set right index of T to 4 on the D scale.
b. Move the hairline to 3 on the D scale.
c. Read $B = 36.9°, A = 53.1°$ on the T scale. (Note that the smaller angle is opposite the smaller side.)
d. Move the slide so that 36.9° on the S scale is under the hairline.
e. Read side $c = 5$ at the right index of the S scale on the D scale.

Solution 2

1. Set the index of the T scale above the largest side (*a*) on the D scale.
2. Move the hairline to the smaller side (*b*) on the D scale.
3. Read the smaller angle (*B*) on the ST scale. The other angle (*A*) is the complement of *B*.
4. The hypotenuse is assumed to be equal in length to the largest side.

Solution 3   This solution is used where the hypotenuse and one side are given.

Example $a = 5.26$ $A = ?$
                               $b = ?$ $B = ?$
                               $c = 8.75$

a. Set index over 8.75 on D scale.
b. Move hairline to 5.6 on D scale.
c. Read $A = 37.0°$; $B = 53.0°$ on the S scale. (Note that the angle read on the sine scale is opposite the given side.)
d. Set hairline to 37° on the cosine scale.
e. Read $b = 7.0$ on the D scale.

Problems

Solve by right triangle method.

10-658.	$a = 53$ $b = 4$	$B = ?$ $c = ?$		10-668.	$a = 11.33$ $B = 26.1°$	$b = ?$ $c = ?$
10-659.	$a = 69.3$ $c = 95$	$b = ?$ $A = ?$		10-669.	$a = 0.00197$ $A = 11.36°$	$b = ?$ $c = ?$
10-660.	$a = 37$ $c = 40.3$	$b = ?$ $B = ?$		10-670.	$c = 1904$ $A = 18.33°$	$a = ?$ $b = ?$
10-661.	$a = 1.97$ $c = 2.33$	$B = ?$ $b = ?$		10-671.	$c = 4.0059$ $B = 86.3°$	$a = ?$ $b = ?$
10-662.	$a = 29.3$ $c = 55.3$	$b = ?$ $A = ?$		10-672.	$c = 4.266$ $B = 31.06°$	$a = ?$ $b = ?$
10-663.	$a = 49.3$ $b = 29.6$	$c = ?$ $A = ?$		10-673.	$a = 0.00397$ $c = 0.00512$	$b = ?$ $A = ?$
10-664.	$a = 57.3$ $b = 42.1$	$c = ?$ $A = ?$		10-674.	$a = 1069$ $A = 85.3°$	$b = ?$ $c = ?$
10-665.	$a = 3.95$ $b = 1.06$	$c = ?$ $B = ?$		10-675.	$b = 42.1$ $B = 3.56°$	$a = ?$ $c = ?$
10-666.	$a = 333$ $b = 20$	$A = ?$ $c = ?$		10-676.	$a = 0.0317$ $c = 0.0444$	$b = ?$ $B = ?$
10-667.	$a = 591$ $b = 25$	$c = ?$ $B = ?$		10-677.	$a = 21.67$ $b = 20.06$	$c = ?$ $B = ?$

The log-log (Lon) scales

There are two groups of log-log scales (also called "Lon" scales) on the slide rule. Scales within the two groups are arranged in matched sets. Some slide rules have four matched sets, whereas others have three. These scales are used to obtain the roots, powers, and logarithms of numbers. The matched sets are arranged as follows:

Matched sets of log-log scales

Four sets		Three sets	
For numbers larger than one (called "Lon" scales)	For numbers smaller than one (called "Lon-minus" scales)	(called LL scales)	(called LL_0 scales)
Ln0 . . . . .Ln–0			
Ln1 . . . . .Ln–1		LL_1 . . . . .LL_{01}	
Ln2 . . . . .Ln–2		LL_2 . . . . .LL_{02}	
Ln3 . . . . .Ln–3		LL_3 . . . . .LL_{03}	

The C and D scales are used in conjunction with these matched sets of log-log scales. In former years other rules were manufactured with only two LL_0 scales, and these are marked LL_0 and LL_{00}. The A and B scales were used with LL_0 and LL_{00} scales on this type of rule. The general principles discussed below apply to all of the various types of log-log scales.

Scale construction

If the Lon scales Ln0, Ln1, Ln2, and Ln3 were placed end to end, they would form a continuous scale, as shown in Figure 10-29. Similarly, if the Lon-minus scales Ln-0, Ln-1, Ln-2, Ln-3 were placed end to end, they would form a continuous scale. The Lon-minus scales are graduated from approximately 0.999 to 0.00003 (representing the values of $\epsilon^{-0.001}$ to ϵ^{-10}). The Lon scales are graduated from approximately 1.001 to 22,026 (representing the values of $\epsilon^{0.001}$ to ϵ^{10}). Since $\epsilon^0 = 1$, values on both the Lon and Lon-minus scales approach the value 1.0000.

Figure 10-29

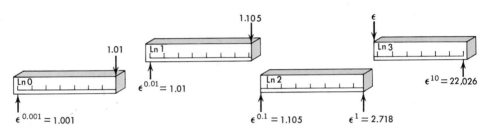

Each division on the Lon and Lon-minus scales represents a single unique number. Thus the decimal point is already marked on these scales for all of the numbers located on the scales. For example, there is only one place on the Lon scales that the number 125.0 may be found. The number 125.0 is found on the Ln3 (LL_3) scale, whereas the number 1.25 is found on the Ln2 (LL_2) scale. Since the manner in which settings are read on the log-log scales is distinctly different from the method of reading the scales previously studied, the student should be very careful in making his slide rule settings.

Reciprocal values

The only case where the Lon and Lon-minus (LL and LL_0) scales may be used together is in the finding of reciprocals of numbers. The reciprocal of any number on the Lon (LL) scales can be read on the corresponding Lon-minus (LL_0) scale.

Examples
 1. Find 1.25 on Ln2 (LL_2) scale. On the Ln-2 (LL_{02}) scale its reciprocal can be read as 0.80.
 2. Find 236 on the Ln3 (LL_3) scale. On the Ln-3 (LL_{03}) scale its reciprocal can be read as 0.00424.

Raising a number to a power

If such problems as $(5.3)^3 = ?$ were worked entirely by logarithms, the following procedure would be required:

1. $(5.3)^3 = ?$
2. log ans. $= 3(\log 5.3)$
3. log [log ans.] $= \log 3 + \log (\log 5.3)$
4. Answer $= \mathbf{(1.488)(10)^2}$

Step 3 is rather involved in many instances. It is for this reason that the log-log scales have been added to the slide rule. Since log-log values of numbers are recorded on the Lon (LL) scales and the log values of numbers have been recorded on the C and D scales, it is quite convenient to perform Step 3 in the preceding example.

The Lon (LL) and Lon-minus (LL$_0$) scales are also used in conjunction with the C and D scales to find powers, roots, and logarithms to the base ϵ of numbers.

In order to raise any number greater than 1.01 to any power:

$$(X)^n = A$$

1. Set the index of the C scale over the value X found on the appropriate Lon (LL) scale (Ln0, Ln1, Ln2, or Ln3).
2. Move the hairline to the value n on the C scale.
3. Read the answer A on the appropriate Lon (LL) scale.

Example   As shown in Figure 10-30,

$$(1.02)^{2.5} = ?$$
$$\log [\log \text{ans.}] = \log 2.5 + \log (\log 1.02)$$
$$\text{Answer} = \mathbf{1.0507}$$

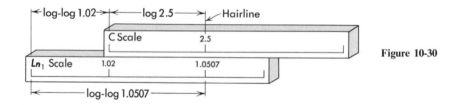

Figure 10-30

Solution
1. Set the index of the C scale over the value 1.02 on the Ln1 (LL$_1$) scale.
2. Move the hairline to the value 2.5 on the C scale.
3. Read the answer 1.0507 on the Ln1 (LL$_1$) scale.

These scales are arranged so that a number on the Ln3 (LL$_3$) scale is the tenth power of the number directly below it on the Ln2 (LL$_2$) scale, and the Ln2 (LL$_2$) scale gives the tenth power of a number in the corresponding position on the Ln1 (LL$_1$) scale. Therefore the Ln3 (LL$_3$) scale would give the one-hundredth power of a number in the corresponding position on the Ln1 (LL$_1$) scale.

Example $(1.034)^{0.23} = \mathbf{1.00773}$ ans. on the Ln0
$(1.034)^{2.3} = \mathbf{1.0799}$ ans. on the Ln1 (LL$_1$)
$(1.034)^{23.} = \mathbf{2.156}$ ans. on the Ln2 (LL$_2$)
$(1.034)^{230.} = \mathbf{2160}$ ans. on the Ln3 (LL$_3$)

In order to raise any number less than 0.99 to any power:

$$(X)^n = A$$

1. Set the index of the C scale over the value X found on the appropriate Lon-minus (LL_0) scale Ln-0, Ln-1, Ln-2, or Ln-3 (LL_{01}, LL_{02}, or LL_{03}).
2. Move the hairline to the value n on the C scale.
3. Read the answer A on the appropriate Ln-0 (LL_0) scale.

Example $\qquad$ $(0.855)^{4.8} = A$, as shown in Figure 10-31.

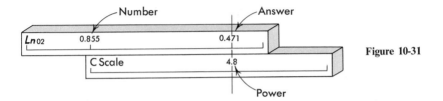

Figure 10-31

Method of scale selection—powers of numbers

To use this method, we must consider three factors: (1) the particular log-log scale upon which the *number* is located, (2) the power of ten of the exponent when it is expressed in scientific notation, and (3) the particular index of the C scale that is used in the calculation.

1. Each log-log scale is given a positive value as follows:

Ln0 = 0	Ln-0 = 0
Ln1 = +1 (Also LL_1)	Ln-1 = +1 (Also LL_{01})
Ln2 = +2 (Also LL_2)	Ln-2 = +2 (Also LL_{02})
Ln3 = +3 (Also LL_3)	Ln-3 = +3 (Also LL_{03})

2. The exponent should be expressed in scientific notation and the power of ten indicated.
3. Assume that the *left* index of the C scale has a value of zero (0) and that the *right* index has a value of plus one (+1).

Rule for scale selection of powers of numbers

The number of the scale upon which the answer will be read is the algebraic sum of (1) the value of the scale on which the number to be raised is found plus (2) the C scale index value plus (3) the power of ten of the exponent.

Example $\qquad$ $(1.015)^{56} = ?$
Rewrite as $\qquad$ $(1.015)^{5.6(10)^1} = ?$

Factor	Description of factor	Value
1.015	1.015 is found on LL_1 scale	+1
Left Index	Use left index of C scale	0
56	Power of ten of exponent = 1	+1
?	Sum = Scale location of answer	+2 ← Answer on Ln2 (LL_2)

Therefore, the answer will be read under the hairline on the Ln2 (LL_2) scale.

$$(1.015)^{56} = \mathbf{2.30} \qquad \text{Answer, as shown in Figure 10-32.}$$

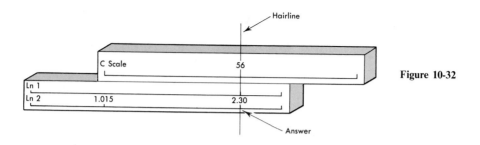

Figure 10-32

Negative exponents

In solving problems which involve raising numbers to a negative power, either of two methods may be employed.

Method 1 Set the number and its exponent on the proper scales in the usual manner. Instead of reading the answer on the usual log-log scale, read it on the corresponding scale of the other group.

Example $$(9.2)^{-3.5} = ?$$

Instead of reading the answer as 2355 on the Ln3 (LL_3) scale, read its reciprocal value on the Ln-3 (LL_{03}) as 0.000425; therefore

$$(9.2)^{-3.5} = \mathbf{4.25 \times 10^{-4}} \text{ (Answer)}$$

Method 2 Set the numbers on the rule in the usual manner, ignoring the negative exponent. When the answer by this operation has been obtained, determine its reciprocal, using the CI scale.

On the slide rules that have only the LL_0 and LL_{00} scales, Method 2 is the only method that can be used.

Powers of numbers: practice problems

10-678. $(53.2)^{0.84} = \mathbf{28.2}$

10-679. $(4.65)^{3.68} = \mathbf{285.}$

10-680. $(0.836)^{0.47} = \mathbf{0.919}$

10-681. $(1.0042)^{217} = \mathbf{2.48}$

10-682. $(0.427)^4 = \mathbf{0.0332}$

10-683. $(0.3156)^4 = \mathbf{0.00988}$

10-684. $(0.159)^{0.67} = \mathbf{0.292}$

10-685. $(1.0565)^{49.5} = \mathbf{15.2}$

10-686. $(32.5)^{0.065} = \mathbf{1.254}$

10-687. $(3.45)^{4.65} = \mathbf{318.}$

10-688. $(0.759)^5 = \mathbf{0.252}$

10-689. $(2.127)^4 = \mathbf{20.5}$

10-690. $(2.03)^{-5} = \mathbf{0.0290}$

10-691. $(4.00)^{0.0157} = \mathbf{1.022}$

10-692. $(0.0818)^{-0.777} = \mathbf{7.00}$

10-693. $(1.382)^{21.3} = \mathbf{980.}$

10-694. $(0.071)^{-0.46} = \mathbf{3.38}$

10-695. $(0.232)^{0.0904} = \mathbf{0.876}$

10-696. $(2.718)^{0.405} = \mathbf{1.50}$

10-697. $(0.916)^{0.724} = \mathbf{0.9384}$

10-698. $(1.1106)^{1.72} = \mathbf{1.197}$

10-699. $(59.2)^{-0.43} = \mathbf{0.1727}$

10-700. $(883)^{0.964} = \mathbf{688.}$

10-701. $(7676)^{0.001102} = \mathbf{1.0099}$

10-702. $(4.30)^{0.521} = \mathbf{2.14}$

Finding roots of numbers

The process of finding roots of numbers is easier to understand if it is remembered that

$$\sqrt[2.1]{576} = X$$

may be written as $(X)^{2.1} = 576$

Therefore we can "work backward" and apply the principles learned in raising a number to a power. Proceed as follows:

Example $\qquad\qquad\qquad\qquad \sqrt[n]{A} = X$

1. Locate the root n on the C scale to coincide with the value A found on the appropriate log-log scale.
2. Move the hairline to the particular index of the C scale which is located within the body of the rule.
3. Read the answer on the appropriate log-log scale.

Example $\quad \sqrt[3.2]{120} = 4.46$ ans. on Ln3 (LL_3), as shown in Figure 10-33.

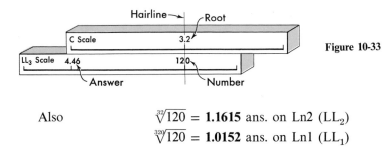

Figure 10-33

Also $\qquad\qquad\qquad \sqrt[32]{120} = \mathbf{1.1615}$ ans. on Ln2 (LL_2)

$\qquad\qquad\qquad\qquad \sqrt[320]{120} = \mathbf{1.0152}$ ans. on Ln1 (LL_1)

In taking the root of a number, students usually are less certain of the appropriate scale upon which the answer is found. Therefore, a method of scale selection similar to that employed for powers of numbers should be used.

Method of scale selection for roots of numbers

As before there are three factors which must be considered: (1) the particular log-log scale upon which the *number* is located; (2) the power of ten of the exponent when it is expressed in scientific notation, and (3) the particular index of the C scale which is used in the calculation.

1. Each log-log scale is given a negative value as follows:

$$\text{Ln0} = 0 \qquad\qquad\qquad \text{Ln-0} = 0$$
$$\text{Ln1} = -1 \text{ (Also } LL_1) \qquad \text{Ln-1} = -1 \text{ (Also } LL_{01})$$
$$\text{Ln2} = -2 \text{ (Also } LL_2) \qquad \text{Ln-2} = -2 \text{ (Also } LL_{02})$$
$$\text{Ln3} = -3 \text{ (Also } LL_3) \qquad \text{Ln-3} = -3 \text{ (Also } LL_{03})$$

2. The root should be expressed in scientific notation and the power of ten indicated.
3. Assume that the *left* index of the C scale has a value of zero (0) and that the *right* index has a value of plus one ($+1$).

Rule for scale selection for roots of numbers

The number of the scale upon which the answer will be read is the algebraic sum of (1) the value of the scale on which the *number whose root is to be determined* is located, plus (2) the C scale index value, plus (3) the power of ten of the root.

Example $\qquad \sqrt[4.37]{0.0092}$ = Answer, as shown in Figure 10-34.

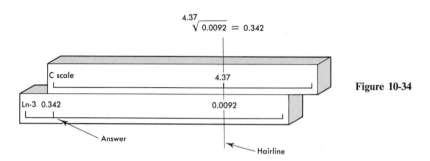

Figure 10-34

Factor	Description of factor	Value
0.0092	0.0092 is found on Ln-3 (LL$_{03}$) Scale	-3
Left Index	Use left index of C scale	0
4.37	Power of ten of root = 0	0
?	Sum = Scale location of Answer	-3 ← Answer on Ln-3 (LL$_{03}$)

Therefore, the answer will be read on the Ln-3 (LL$_{03}$) scale as **0.342.**

Roots of numbers practice problems

10-703. $\sqrt[7.81]{5.85} = $ **1.254**

10-704. $\sqrt[6]{0.0835} = $ **0.661**

10-705. $\sqrt[5]{0.0763} = $ **0.598**

10-706. $\sqrt[194]{460.} = $ **1.0321**

10-707. $\sqrt[6]{0.0001} = $ **0.215**

10-708. $\sqrt[1.65]{8.26} = $ **3.60**

10-709. $\sqrt[0.34]{0.862} = $ **0.646**

10-710. $\sqrt[2.3]{85.9} = $ **6.92**

10-711. $\sqrt[60]{45.} = $ **1.0655**

10-712. $\sqrt[21.5]{1.606} = $ **1.0223**

10-713. $\sqrt[1.91]{92.5} = $ **10.7**

10-714. $\sqrt[50]{0.05} = $ **0.9418**

10-715. $\sqrt[7]{0.0108} = $ **0.524**

10-716. $\sqrt[0.006]{0.9762} = $ **0.018**

10-717. $\sqrt[5.21]{2000} = $ **4.30**

10-718. $\sqrt[0.04]{0.9792} = $ **0.592**

10-719. $\sqrt[2.7]{81} = $ **5.09**

10-720. $\sqrt[2.81]{1.218} = $ **1.0726**

10-721. $\sqrt[2.15]{52.5} = $ **6.31**

10-722. $\sqrt[400]{100} = $ **1.0116**

10-723. $\sqrt[0.75]{2.37} = $ **3.16**

10-724. $\sqrt[0.073]{1.060} = $ **2.22**

10-725. $\sqrt[1.51]{6.50} = $ **3.45**

10-726. $\sqrt[5.6]{0.0018} = $ **0.323**

10-727. $\sqrt[0.67]{0.954} = $ **0.932**

General guides for decimal location

The student should be able to estimate the approximate answer and thereby know on which scale the answer will be found.

The following suggestions are presented so that the student can more easily decide whether the answer is to be larger or smaller than the original quantity.

$$(\text{Number})^{\text{Exponent}} = \text{Answer}$$

1. If the number is larger than 1.00 and the exponent is larger than 1.00, the answer will be greater than the number.
2. If the number is less than 1.00 and the exponent is less than 1.00, the answer will be greater than the number.
3. If the number is less than 1.00 and the exponent is greater than 1.00, the answer will be less than the number.
4. If the number is greater than 1.00 and the exponent is less than 1.00, the answer will be less than the number.

Results that do not fall within the limits of the scales

In many computations the final answer may be larger than 22,026 and hence cannot be read within the limits of the scales. In such cases the original expression must be factored before attempting to use the log-log scales. Several such methods of factoring are explained below.

These methods are for use in finding the powers of numbers. For problems involving roots of numbers convert the problem to one involving the power of a number and then apply the appropriate method.

Example
$$\sqrt{5} = (5)^{1/2} = (5)^{0.5}$$
$$\sqrt[4]{5} = (5)^{1/4} = (5)^{0.25}$$
$$\sqrt[0.5]{5} = (5)^{1/0.5} = (5)^{2}$$

Method 1 Express the number in scientific notation and raise each part to the given power.

Example
$$(35.3)^4 = ?$$
$$(35.3)^4 = (3.53 \times 10)^4$$
$$= (3.53)^4 \times (10)^4$$

Now, using the Lon (LL) scales, and since $(3.53)^4 = 155$, we obtain

$$(35.3)^4 = 155. \times 10^4$$
$$= \mathbf{1.55 \times 10^6} \text{ (Answer)}$$

Method 2 Factor the number which is to be raised to a power and then treat each part separately, as in Method 1.

Example
$$(15)^5 = ?$$
$$(15)^5 = (3 \times 5)^5$$
$$= (3)^5 \times (5)^5$$
$$= (243)(3125)$$
$$= \mathbf{7.59 \times 10^5} \text{ (Answer)}$$

Method 3 Divide the exponent into two or more smaller parts and, using the log-log scales, compute each part separately. A final computation is made using the C and D scales as in Method 1 and Method 2.

Example

$$(2.36)^{15} = ?$$
$$(2.36)^{15} = (2.36)^5 \times (2.36)^5 \times (2.36)^5$$
$$= (73.2)(73.2)(73.2)$$
$$= \mathbf{3.93 \times 10^5} \text{ (Answer)}$$

or

$$(2.36)^{15} = (2.36)^8 \times (2.36)^7$$
$$= (960)(410)$$
$$= \mathbf{3.93 \times 10^5} \text{ (Answer)}$$

$$(2.36)^{15} = (2.36)^{7.5} \times (2.36)^{7.5}$$
$$= (620)^2$$
$$= \mathbf{3.93 \times 10^5} \text{ (Answer)}$$

Example

$$(0.000025)^{1.3} = ?$$
$$(0.000025)^{1.3} = (2.5 \times 10^{-5})^{1.3}$$
$$= (2.5)^{1.3} \times (10^{-5})^{1.3}$$
$$= 3.29 \times (10)^{-6.5}$$
$$= (3.29)(10)^{-6}(10)^{-0.5}$$
$$= (3.29)(10)^{-6}\left(\frac{1}{3.16}\right)$$
$$= (3.29)(10)^{-6}(0.316)$$
$$= \mathbf{1.041 \times 10^{-6}} \text{ (Answer)}$$

Method 4 Express the number in scientific notation and then express the power of 10 in logarithmic form.

Example

$$(250)^{3.2} = ?$$
$$(250)^{3.2} = (2.50 \times 10^2)^{3.2} = (2.50)^{3.2}(10)^{6.4}$$

where $(10)^{6.4} = x$ may be expressed as $\log_{10} x = 6.4$ or $x = (2.51)(10)^6$.

Then

$$(2.50)^{3.2}(10)^{6.4} = (1.87 \times 10^1)(2.51 \times 10^6)$$
and
$$(1.87 \times 10^1)(2.51 \times 10^6) = \mathbf{4.71 \times 10^7}$$

Method 5 This method is more suitable for those numbers which have 5, 6, 7, 8, or 9 as the first digit.

Example

$$(645)^{13} = ?$$
$$(645)^{13} = (0.645)^{13}(10^3)^{13}$$
$$= (0.00335)(10)^{39}$$
$$= \mathbf{3.35(10)^{36}} \text{ (Answer)}$$

Method 6 Factor the exponent such that one part is equivalent to an exact power of ten.

Example
$$(2)^{52} = ?$$

First raise the base (2) to a power such that the answer is an exact power of ten.

$$(2)^k = 10,000 = (10)^4$$
$$k = 13.29$$

Also
$$(2)^{52} = (2)^{13.29+13.29+13.29+12.13}$$
$$= (10^4)(10)^4(10)^4(2)^{12.13}$$
$$= (10^4)^3(2)^{12.13}$$
$$= (10)^{12}(4500)$$
$$= (4.5)(10)^{15} \text{ (Answer)}$$

Example
$$(1.324)(10)^{-9} = (0.815)^m$$

First choose a factor such that anexact power of ten is obtained.
$$(0.815)^{45} = 0.0001 = (10)^{-4}$$

Then
$$(1.324)(10)^{-9} = (0.815)^{45+45+t}$$
$$= (0.815)^{45}(0.815)^{45}(0.815)^t$$
$$= (10)^{-4}(10)^{-4}(0.815)^t$$

$$\frac{(1.324)(10)^{-9}}{(10)^{-8}} = (0.815)^t$$

$$1.324(10)^{-1} = (0.815)^t$$
$$t = 9.87$$

Therefore
$$(1.324)(10)^{-9} = (0.815)^{45+45+9.87}$$
$$(1.324)(10)^{-9} = (0.815)^{99.87}$$
and
$$m = 99.9 \text{ (Answer)}$$

Methods 1 and 6 are generally preferred over the other methods because they usually make greater accuracy possible in the final answer.

Finding the natural logarithm of a number

The natural base for logarithms is $\epsilon(2.71828—)$. The logarithm of any number (to the base ϵ) may be found as follows:

For numbers greater than 1.00
$$\log_\epsilon X = A$$

1. Locate the number X on the Ln0, Ln1 (LL$_1$), Ln2 (LL$_2$), or Ln3 (LL$_3$) scale.
2. Read the logarithm of the number under the hairline on the D scale.

Location of Decimal Point

If the number X is on	Decimal point in the answer is
Ln3 or LL$_3$	x.xxx
Ln2 or LL$_2$	0.xxx
Ln1 or LL$_1$	0.0xxx
Ln0	0.00xx

Examples
$$\log_\epsilon 62 \ = 4.13$$
$$\log_\epsilon 1.271 = 0.240$$
$$\log_\epsilon 1.026 = 0.0257$$

For numbers less than 1.00
$$\log_\epsilon X = A$$

1. Locate the number X on the Ln-0, Ln-1 (LL_{01}), Ln-2 (LL_{02}), or Ln-3 (LL_{03}) scales.

2. Read the logarithm (to the base ϵ) of the number A directly above X on the D scale.

Location of Decimal Point

If the number X is on	Decimal point in the answer is
Ln-3 or LL_{03}	$-$x.xxx
Ln-2 or LL_{02}	$-$0.xxx
Ln-1 or LL_{01}	$-$0.0xxx
Ln-0	$-$0.00xx

3. The logarithm (to the base ϵ) of all numbers less than 1.000 is a negative number.

Examples

$$\log_\epsilon 0.0045 = -5.40$$
$$\log_\epsilon 0.745 = -0.294$$
$$\log_\epsilon 0.954 = -0.0471$$

Problems

Solve, using the log-log scales.

10-728. $(2.89)^6$
10-729. $(4.11)^{5.2}$
10-730. $(19.01)^{1.6}$
10-731. $(1.185)^{2.7}$
10-732. $(1.033)^{5.8}$
10-733. $(1.0134)^{25}$
10-734. $(3.95)^{0.65}$
10-735. $(8.46)^{0.134}$
10-736. $(81.2)^{0.118}$
10-737. $(7850.)^{0.0775}$
10-738. $(1.399)^{0.883}$
10-739. $(10.06)^{0.0621}$
10-740. $(0.569)^4$
10-741. $(0.157)^8$
10-742. $(0.985)^{1.568}$
10-743. $(0.318)^{4.65}$
10-744. $(0.078)^{0.458}$
10-745. $(17.91)^{0.012}$

10-746. $(4780.)^{0.913}$
10-747. $(253.)^{0.269}$
10-748. $(0.428)^{0.559}$
10-749. $(4.08)^{24}$
10-750. $(3.91)^{20}$
10-751. $(8.45)^{16}$
10-752. $(7.77)^{42}$
10-753. $(16.89)^{1.402}$
10-754. $(87.8)^8$
10-755. $(0.1164)^{0.33}$
10-756. $(0.779)^{0.43}$
10-757. $(867.)^6$
10-758. $(91.05)^{14}$
10-759. $(0.775)^{0.0259}$
10-760. $\sqrt[6]{8.69}$
10-761. $\sqrt[7]{1.094}$
10-762. $\sqrt[1.3]{8.74}$

10-763. $\sqrt[0.6]{19.77}$
10-764. $\sqrt[18]{54.8}$
10-765. $\sqrt{1.004}$
10-766. $\sqrt[1.95]{0.642}$
10-767. $\sqrt[14]{0.1438}$
10-768. $\sqrt[3.6]{0.952}$
10-769. $\sqrt[2.4]{0.469}$
10-770. $\sqrt[1.7]{0.1975}$
10-771. $\sqrt[0.55]{0.2218}$
10-772. $\sqrt[0.46]{16,430}$
10-773. $\sqrt[0.133]{507.}$
10-774. $\sqrt[0.57]{0.964}$
10-775. $\sqrt[5.09]{6.49}$
10-776. $\sqrt[13.6]{0.1574}$
10-777. $\sqrt[2.09]{0.1268}$

Solve for X.

10-778. $X = (43.8)^{6.4}$
10-779. $X = (1.853)^{0.447}$
10-780. $(31.77)^x = 1.164$
10-781. $(2.388)^{3x} = 3.066$
10-782. $(1.064)^{0.2x} = 4.99$
10-783. $(X)^{5.8} = 8.57$
10-784. $(4.92)^{0.66x} = 24.1$
10-785. $(0.899)^{4.7x} = (1.552)(10)^{-8}$

10-786. $(0.1135)^{0.77x} = 0.775$
10-787. $(11.774)^{8.31x} = 12.88$
10-788. $(18.73)^{6.4x} = 8688.$
10-789. $(34.86)^{1.117x} = 9.44$
10-790. $(0.631)^{0.64x} = 0.318$
10-791. $(0.1299)^{0.68x} = 0.443$
10-792. $(15.84)^x = 4.87$
10-793. $(0.679)^x = 0.337$

10-794. $(1.461)^{19.66x} = 9.07$

10-795. $(0.766)^{5.8x} = 0.239$

10-796. $(X)^{7.99} = 0.775$

10-797. $(X)^{0.175} = 8.53$

10-798. $(X)^{3.33} = 1.055$

10-799. $(X)^{0.871} = 0.1557$

10-800. $(X)^{4.77} = 1.088$

10-801. $(X)^{0.771} = 0.0521$

10-802. $(4.51)^{0.199} = \dfrac{X}{3}$

Solve for the natural logarithms of the following numbers.

10-803. 15.77

10-804. 19,850

10-805. 0.7789

10-806. 0.1845

10-807. 1.896

10-808. 56.87

10-809. 13.09

10-810. 33.4

10-811. 8.09

10-812. 1.571

10-813. 0.1345

10-814. 0.915

10-815. 0.001233

10-816. 13,890.

10-817. 2.066

10-818. 1.3157

10-819. 1.0047

10-820. 89.78

10-821. 0.664

10-822. 0.459

10-823. 0.1175

10-824. 1.9974

10-825. 0.9974

10-826. 0.2378

10-827. 0.01663

Review problems

Solve by general slide rule methods.

10-828. $(51)(9)$

10-829. $(426)(51)$

10-830. $(6.03)(5.16)$

10-831. $(561)(4956)$

10-832. $(43.2)(0.617)$

10-833. $(6617)(0.00155)$

10-834. $(99.043)(3.091)$

10-835. $(0.0617)(0.4417)$

10-836. $(1.035)(2.31 \times 10^5)$

10-837. $(79.81 \times 10^{-4})(0.617)$

10-838. $(516 \times 10^{-8})(0.391 \times 10^{-2})$

10-839. $(51)(97)(32)$

10-840. $(52.3)(759.3)$

10-841. $(716.5)(0.03166)$

10-842. $(11.65)(-0.9213)$

10-843. $(76.2)(-31.45)$

10-844. $(-0.6175)(-12,391)$

10-845. $\dfrac{(-759.6)}{(0.6175)}$

10-846. $\dfrac{(-19.96)}{(3346)}$

10-847. $\dfrac{(-1.0366)}{(29.31)}$

10-848. $\dfrac{(7575)}{(695.2)}$

10-849. $\dfrac{(-516.6)}{(0.06052)}$

10-850. $(116.5)(4619)(0.317)$

10-851. $(210.9)(151.3)(7716)$

10-852. $(706.5)(1.695 \times 10^{-6})(0.006695)$

10-853. $(1033)(7.339 \times 10^{-6})(0.0317 \times 10^{-3})$

10-854. $(4.017 \times 10^{-8})(0.0991)(0.1756)$

10-855. $(5.576)(0.0917)(1.669 \times 10^4)$

10-856. $(6.991)(0.75)(0.993)(4.217)$

10-857. $(56.88)(0.971 \times 10^{-5})$

10-858. $(59.17)(0.3617)(0.5916)(0.00552)$

10-859. $(5.691)(0.3316)(0.991)(0.00554)(0.1712)$

10-860. $(6.523)(71.22)(4.091)(591)(600)(0.1332)$

10-861. $(43.06)(0.2361)(0.905 \times 10^{-4})(3.617 \times 10^{-3})$

10-862. $(1917)^{2.16}$

10-863. $(4.216)^{1.517}$

10-864. $(2.571)^{2.91}$

10-865. $(0.3177)^{2.06}$

10-866. $\sqrt[5]{26.31}$

10-867. $\sqrt[3]{0.03175}$

10-868. $\sqrt{116.75}$

10-869. $\sqrt[3]{0.6177}$

10-870. $\sqrt{3167}$

10-871. $(179 \times 10^3)(0.3165)$

10-872. $(5033 \times 10^{-4})(0.9116)$

10-873. $(0.06105)(77.165)$

10-874. $(\sqrt{216})(34)(\pi)^2$

10-875. $(\sqrt{819})(107)(\sqrt{\pi})$

10-876. $\dfrac{(\sqrt{616})(6.767)}{(\sqrt{39.6})}$

10-877. $\dfrac{(1045)}{(X)} = \dfrac{(0.0278)}{(0.0798)}$

10-878. $\dfrac{(1.486)}{(33)} = \dfrac{(0.37)(X)}{467}$

10-879. $(816) = \dfrac{(244)(2\pi)}{(0.049)(X)}$

10-880. $(0.0036)(\sin 49.8°)$

10-881. $\dfrac{(20.5)^2(7.49)(\sin 49°)}{(30.5)(0.0987)}$

10-882. $\sqrt{\dfrac{(38)^2(6.71)^2}{\pi}}$

10-883. $(7.61)(\sqrt[3]{7.61})(\pi)$

10-884. $\dfrac{(13.1)(\sin 3.12°)}{(\tan 41.9°)}$

10-885. $\dfrac{2}{3} = \dfrac{(X)(\pi)}{8.37}$

10-886. $\dfrac{(9616)}{X} = \dfrac{(3.1416)}{(0.0142)}$

10-887. $(\sqrt[3]{64.9})(2.1 \times 10^3)$

10-888. $(4 \times 10^6)(0.007) = (X)(10,980)$

10-889. $Y = \left(\dfrac{1}{4}\right)\left(\dfrac{16}{6}\right)\left(\dfrac{1}{17}\right)$

10-890. $\dfrac{X}{\pi} = \dfrac{(\sqrt{46.2})(3.14)^2}{(\sin 3.7°)}$

10-891. $\dfrac{(3.98)(X)}{(1.07)(38)} = \dfrac{(3 \times 10^6)}{(17,680)}$

10-892. $\dfrac{(\sqrt[3]{986})}{X} = \dfrac{(14)}{(1/116)}$

10-893. $\dfrac{(X)^2}{(9.2)} = \dfrac{(18.17)(3.4)}{(166)}$

10-894. $\dfrac{(3.6)}{(X)^2} = \dfrac{(9.6 \times 10^2)}{(67.4)} = \dfrac{(Y)^{1/2}}{(64)}$

10-895. $\dfrac{(X)^{1/2}}{(31.1)} = \dfrac{(\sqrt{196})(189.1)}{4/76}$

10-896. $\dfrac{(96.5)}{(3.9)} = \dfrac{X}{(\sin 46.6°)} = \dfrac{(Y)^2}{(3.14 \times 10^{-2})}$

10-897. $\dfrac{(X)^2}{Y} = \dfrac{(67.3)^2(Y)}{(96.61)} = \dfrac{(497.1)}{\tan 75°}$

10-898. $\dfrac{(3.7)(4.9)}{X} = \dfrac{(46.7)}{564}$

Solve by general slide rule methods.

10-899. $\dfrac{Y}{(28)} = \dfrac{(3.2)}{(4/118)}$

10-900. $\dfrac{Y}{42} = \dfrac{39.1}{(1/45)}$

10-901. $(37.3)(X)(46.6) = (175)(\pi)$

10-902. $(\sqrt{256})(3) = (X)(197.6)$

10-903. $\dfrac{(54.6)(\tan 10.6°)}{(\sqrt{0.0967})(8.1 \times 10^3)}$

10-904. $\dfrac{\sqrt[3]{(15.1)^2}(31.4)^2}{(\sin \text{arc} \cos 0.617)}$

10-905. $\dfrac{(0.954)(0.06 \times 10^3)}{(\tan 59°)^{1/2}(6.5)^2}$

10-906. $\dfrac{\sqrt[3]{(15.6)^2}(0.9618)}{(0.08173)(61,508)(2\pi)}$

10-907. $\dfrac{(68)(765)(391)(0.0093 \times 10^3)}{(571)^2(\sqrt[3]{64})}$

10-908. $\dfrac{(\cos 11.5°)(\sqrt{6.87})}{(0.00081)(7.7 \times 10^4)}$

10-909. $\dfrac{\sqrt[4]{(1.71)^5}(6.87)}{(\tan 53°)(5.1)^2}$

10-910. $\dfrac{(0.000817)(\tan 81°)}{(0.00763)(\tan 81°)}$

10-911. $(273)^{1/2}(46.9)(\cos 61°)(\pi^3)$

10-912. $\dfrac{(\sin \text{arc} \tan 3.17)(71.7)}{(\sqrt{89.6})(\sqrt[4]{76.5^2})}$

10-913. $\dfrac{(\sqrt{(16)^3})(\log_{10} 100)}{(6.71 \times 10^{-1})(3.71)^3}$

10-914. $\dfrac{(6.93)(\sin \cos^{-1} 0.98)}{(0.937)^2(39.6)}$

10-915. $\dfrac{(\sqrt{91.68})(\sqrt[3]{65.9})}{(\tan 68.7°)(0.671)^2}$

10-916. $\dfrac{(4.5)^4(\sqrt{98.71})(\sin 56.4°)}{(0.09 \times 10)(38.6)^{3/2}}$

10-917. $\dfrac{(\sqrt{285})(\cos 36.6°)(1.64)^2}{(67.1 \times 10^{-1})(5780)}$

10-918. $\dfrac{(\tan \sin^{-1} 0.87)(61.7)}{(5.64)^{0.98}(3.65)^2}$

10-919. $\dfrac{(3174)(\tan 64°)}{(81.6)^2(\sqrt[3]{18})}$

10-920. $\dfrac{(44.6)(0.09 \times 10^3)(\sin 80.9°)}{(\sqrt[3]{96.7})(51.6)^2}$

10-921. $\dfrac{(\tan 50.6°)(3.4)^2}{(\sqrt{9681})(171)}$

10-922. $\dfrac{(296)(0.197 \times 10^5)}{\sqrt[4]{(76.1)}(\sin 49.6°)}$

10-923. $\dfrac{(\sin 22.6°)(9.918)}{(\tan 31.6°)(98.71)}$

10-924. $\dfrac{(68.7 \times 10^2)(\tan 56.1°)}{(96.7)^{0.86}(18,614)}$

10-925. $\dfrac{(0.0098)(\sin 17.6°)\sqrt{(0.186)}}{(41.6)^2(689.0)}$

10-926. $\dfrac{(\tan 19.8°)^2(6.71 \times 10^3)}{(1,876)(\sqrt[4]{59})}$

10-927. $\dfrac{(\sqrt{\sin 40°})(17)^2(4\pi^2)}{(0.643)(\tan 60°)}$

Hyperbolic functions on the slide rule

Hyperbolic functions are useful in several mathematical applications such as the variation of electrical current and voltage with distance in the calculation of transmission of electrical power. Several manufacturers of slide rules make special scales from which hyperbolic functions can be read directly. However, it is possible to obtain numerical values for hyperbolic functions using conventional scales by making use of the relations:

$$\frac{\epsilon^x - \epsilon^{-x}}{2} = \text{hyperbolic sine } x \ (\sinh x)$$

$$\frac{\epsilon^x + \epsilon^{-x}}{2} = \text{hyperbolic cosine } x(\cosh x)$$

$$\frac{\epsilon^{2x} - 1}{\epsilon^{2x} + 1} = \text{hyperbolic tangent } x \ (\tanh x)$$

Reading hyperbolic scales

Most slide rules that have hyperbolic scales have the scales marked as Sh and Th. Slide rules manufactured by Pickett identify the hyperbolic sine scales as *upper* and *lower* and the values of sinh x are read on the C scale. Keuffel & Esser identify the hyperbolic sine scales as Sh 1 and Sh 2 and values of sinh x are read on the D scale. Except for these minor differences, reading hyperbolic functions on slide rules made by either company is essentially the same.

Hyperbolic sines In order to read hyperbolic sine functions on the slide rule, set the value sinh x on one of the Sh scales and read the value of the function on either the C scale or the D scale under the hairline.

Example Find sinh 0.38.

Solution Locate 0.38 on the upper Sh scale or on the Sh 1 scale and read 0.389 on the C or D scale.

Example Find sinh 1.88.

Solution Using the method above read sinh 1.88 = 3.20. Note that the value 1.88 is located on the lower Sh scale (Sh 2 scale) and 3.20 is read on the C scale (D scale).

The decimal point can be determined readily by noting that numbers corresponding to function values on the upper Sh (Sh 1) scale lie between 0.1 and 1.0, and numbers corresponding to function values on the lower Sh (Sh 2) scale lie between 1.0 and 10.0.

Hyperbolic tangents Hyperbolic tangents can be read by locating the value of the tangent function on the Th scale and reading the number on the C or D scale under the hairline.

Example tanh 0.206 = **0.1990**

Example tanh 1.33 = **0.870**

Hyperbolic Cosines Most slide rules do not have a hyperbolic cosine scale. Values for the hyperbolic cosine can be determined by use of the relation:

$$\cosh x = \frac{\sinh x}{\tanh x}$$

In finding values for cosh x using the Pickett rule, first set the slide so the indexes coincide. Locate the hairline over the value of x on the appropriate Sh scale. Move the slide until the value of x on the Th scale is under the hairline and cosh x can be read on the D scale at the C index.

Example cosh 0.482 = **1.118**

Example cosh 1.08 = **1.642**

For the Keuffel & Esser Vector slide rule, this procedure can be followed. Set an index of the slide on the value of x on the Th scale. Set the hairline on the value of x on either Sh 1 or Sh 2, depending on its amount. Read the value of cosh x on the C scale.

Example cosh 0.305 = **1.046**

Example cosh 1.181 = **2.31**

When the value of cosh x is given and it is desired to find x, use can be made of the relation

$$\cosh^2 x - \sinh^2 x = 1$$

Example Find the value of x when cosh x = 2.1

Solution $\qquad\qquad \sinh x = \sqrt{\cosh^2 x - 1}$

Substituting:

$$\sinh x = \sqrt{(2.1)^2 - 1}$$
$$\sinh x = \sqrt{3.41}$$

and

$$\sinh x = 1.85$$

Set 1.85 on the C (D) scale and read the value of x on the lower Sh (Sh 2) scale. The lower scale is used because sinh x is greater than 1.

Then

$$x = \mathbf{1.372}$$

Approximations for large and small values of x   When the value of x is more than 3, it can be shown that the value of sinh x and cosh x is approximately the same as $\dfrac{\epsilon^x}{2}$.

Example

$$\sinh 4.2 = ?$$

$$\frac{\epsilon^{4.2}}{2} = 33.5$$

$$\sinh 4.2 \cong \mathbf{33.5}$$

Also for large values of x, tanh x is approximately 1.0.

Example

$$\tanh 3.7 = ?$$

Solution

$$\tanh 3.7 = \frac{\epsilon^{(2)(3.7)} - 1}{\epsilon^{(2)(3.7)} + 1}$$

$$= \frac{1650 - 1}{1650 + 1}$$

$$\tanh 3.7 \cong \mathbf{1.0}$$

When x has values below 0.1, it can be shown that sinh x and tanh x are approximately the same as x, and cosh x is approximately 1.0.

Example

$$\sinh 0.052 \cong \mathbf{0.052}$$
$$\tanh 0.037 \cong \mathbf{0.037}$$
$$\cosh 0.028 \cong \mathbf{1.00}$$

Other hyperbolic functions   While not often needed, other hyperbolic functions can be obtained by using the following defining expressions:

$$\coth x = \frac{1}{\tanh x}$$

$$\operatorname{sech} x = \frac{1}{\cosh x}$$

$$\operatorname{csch} x = \frac{1}{\sinh x}$$

Problems on hyperbolic functions

10-928. Find the values of sinh x for the following values of x: (*a*) 0.12, (*b*) 1.07, (*c*) 1.91, (*d*) 2.30, (*e*) 3.11, (*f*) 4.26, (*g*) 5.00

10-929. Find the values of x for the following values of sinh x: (*a*) 0.1304, (*b*) 0.956, (*c*) 1.62, (*d*) 4.10, (*e*) 8.70, (*f*) 19.42, (*g*) 41.96

10-930. Find the values of cosh x for the following values of x: (*a*) 0.28, (*b*) 1.03, (*c*) 1.98, (*d*) 2.37, (*e*) 3.56, (*f*) 4.04, (*g*) 5.00

10-931. Find the values of x for the following values of cosh x: (*a*) 1.204, (*b*) 1.374, (*c*) 2.31, (*d*) 5.29, (*e*) 8.50, (*f*) 21.7, (*g*) 52.3

10-932. Find the values of tanh x for the following values of x: (*a*) 0.16, (*b*) 0.55, (*c*) 1.14, (*d*) 1.94, (*e*) 2.34, (*f*) 2.74, (*g*) 5.00

10-933. Find the values of x corresponding to the following values of tanh x: (*a*) 0.1781, (*b*) 0.354, (*c*) 0.585, (*d*) 0.811, (*e*) 0.881, (*f*) 0.980, (*g*) 0.990

Slide rule solution of complex numbers

A complex number, which consists of a real part and an imaginary part, is often used to describe a vector quantity. By definition, a vector quantity, frequently referred to as a *phasor* in electrical engineering, has both magnitude and direction. For example, the expression $3 + j4$ will describe a vector which is $\sqrt{3^2 + 4^2}$ units long and makes an angle arc tan $\frac{4}{3}$ with an x axis. For a more complete discussion on complex number theory, refer to a text on basic algebra.

The symbol i or the symbol j is customarily used to represent the quantity $\sqrt{-1}$. In the discussion in this section the symbol $j = \sqrt{-1}$ will be used.

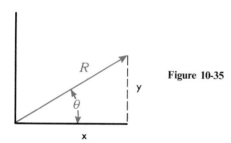

Figure 10-35

If we let the scalar length of a vector be designated as R, as shown in Figure 10-35, then we can write $R\epsilon^{j\theta} = x + jy$ in polar form as $R\underline{/\theta}$. This expression $R\underline{/\theta}$ is a shortened form of $R\epsilon^{j\theta}$ which is obtained from the identity

$$R\epsilon^{j\theta} = R\cos\theta + jR\sin\theta.$$

Complex numbers on the slide rule From trigonometric relations for a right triangle, we can show that $\tan\theta = \dfrac{y}{x}$, $R = \dfrac{y}{\sin\theta}$, and $R = \dfrac{x}{\cos\theta}$. We can use these relations to solve complex number problems on the slide rule. Take, for example, the complex number $3 + j4$ and let it be required to find $R\underline{/\theta}$.

The following method will give the solution to this problem on most types of slide rules:

1. Locate the larger of the two numbers on the D scale and set an index of the C scale at this number. Locate the smaller of the two numbers on the D scale using the hairline, and read the angle θ on the T scale under the hairline. If y is smaller than x, θ is less than 45°, and if y is larger than x, θ is larger than 45°.
2. Next move the slide until the angle θ on the S scale is in line with the smaller of the two numbers. Read R on the D scale at the index of the C scale.

Example Express $3 + j4$ in polar form.

Solution Set the right index of the C scale at 4 on the D scale.
Move the hairline to 3 on the D scale and read $\theta = 53.1°$ on the T scale. Note that the y value is larger than the x value; thus the angle is larger than 45°.
Without moving the hairline, move the slide until 53.1° on the S scale (reading angles to the left) is under the hairline.
Read 5 at the right index of the C scale.
The solution is $3 + j4 = \mathbf{5/\underline{53.1°}}$

This method can be performed on most types of rules, requiring the minimum number of manipulations of the rule. It also can be applied readily to the solution of most problems involving right triangles.
When any of the complex numbers have a minus sign, the slide rule operation to solve the problem is the same as though the sign of the numbers were positive. The angles usually are determined by inspection using trigonometric relations. The following general rules apply:
If the expression has the form $+x + jy$, θ is in the first quadrant.

For $-x + jy$, θ is in the second quadrant
For $-x - jy$, θ is in the third quadrant
For $+x - jy$, θ is in the fourth quadrant

Example Express $-7.1 + j3.8$ in polar form.

Solution Set the right index of the C scale at 7.1 on the D scale, and read on the T scale $\theta = 28.3°$ at 3.8 on the D scale.
Move the slide so that 28.3° on the S scale is over 3.8 and read $R = 8.03$ at the C index.
By inspection, the angle is in the second quadrant and the total angle is $180° - 28.3° = 151.7°$.
Therefore, the polar form is $\mathbf{8.03/\underline{151.7°}.}$

Example Express $4 - j3$ in polar form.

Solution The angle is read as 36.9° and is in the fourth quadrant. The total angle is $360° - 36.9° = 323.1°$.
The polar form is $\mathbf{5/\underline{323.1°}.}$

If the polar form is given, the rectangular form can be obtained by multiplying the value of R by the appropriate sine and cosine value. A rapid method of finding the quantities is to use the previously described slide rule manipulation in reverse.

Example Express $3.3\underline{/28°}$ in rectangular form.

Solution Set the right index of the C scale at 3.3 on the D scale and read 1.55 on D under 28° on the sine scale.

Move the slide until 28° on the T scale is over 1.55 on the D scale.

Read 2.915 on the D scale at the right index. Since the angle is less than 45°, the imaginary part of the complex number is the smaller of the two. Therefore,

$$3.3\underline{/28°} = \textbf{2.915} + \textbf{\textit{j}1.55}$$

If the polar angle is larger than 45°, angles on the T scale and S scale are read to the left, and the real part of the complex number is read first. The real part of the number will be the smaller of the two parts.

Example $\qquad\qquad\qquad 179\underline{/66°} = \textbf{72.9} + \textbf{\textit{j}163.5}$

For angles not in the first quadrant, obtain the angle of the vector with respect to the *x* axis and treat the solution as outlined above. By inspection, affix the proper signs to the real and imaginary parts after obtaining their values. A sketch will help greatly in this process.

Conversion for small angles If the ratio of the *x* value and *y* value in the complex number is greater than 10, the angle can be found on the ST scale. The real value is approximately equal to the value of *R*.

Example $\qquad\qquad\qquad 35 + j1.5 = R\underline{/\theta}$

Solution Set the C index at 35 on the D scale and read $\theta = 2.45°$ on the ST scale.

Then $R\underline{/\theta} \cong \textbf{35}\underline{\textbf{/2.45°.}}$

Example $\qquad\qquad\qquad 0.0075\underline{/4.1°} = x + jy$

Solution Set the C index at 0.075 on the D scale. Read 0.00536 on D under 4.1° on ST.

Then $x + jy \cong \textbf{0.075} + \textbf{\textit{j}0.00536.}$

Conversion for angles near 90° For angles between 84.27° and 90°, the ratio of *x* to *y* will be 10 or greater and the imaginary part of the complex number is approximately equal to the value of *R*. The angle can be read on the ST scale after subtracting it from 90°.

Example $\qquad\qquad\qquad 18\underline{/88°} = x + jy$

Solution Set the left index of C at 18 on the D scale. Read 0.6 on D under 2° on the ST scale.

Then $x + jy \cong \textbf{0.6} + \textbf{\textit{j}18.}$

Remember that for very large and very small angles, the ratio of *x* and *y* will be 10 or greater, and either the real part or the imaginary part of the complex number will be approximately equal to the value of R.

Applications of complex numbers   In solving problems involving complex numbers, addition and subtraction of complex numbers are more easily performed if the numbers are expressed in rectangular form. In this form, the respective real parts and imaginary parts can be added or subtracted directly. However, to multiply or divide complex numbers, it is more convenient to express them in polar form and solve by multiplying or dividing the vector magnitude, and adding or subtracting the angular magnitude.

Examples

$$(a + jb) + (c + jd) = (a + c) + j(b + d) \quad \text{(Addition)}$$
$$(a + jb) - (c + jd) = (a - c) + j(b - d) \quad \text{(Subtraction)}$$
$$(a/\theta_1)(b/\theta_2) = (a)(b)/\underline{\theta_1 + \theta_2} \quad \text{(Multiplication)}$$
$$\frac{a/\theta_1}{b/\theta_2} = \frac{a}{b}/\underline{\theta_1 - \theta_2} \quad \text{(Division)}$$

From the examples above, we can see that the ability to perform rapid conversions from polar form to rectangular form or vice versa will be helpful in solving problems involving complex numbers.

Problems on complex numbers

10-934. Express in polar form: (a) $8 + j3$, (b) $2 + j6$, (c) $1 + j4$, (d) $5 + j5$

10-935. Express in rectangular form: (a) $6.2/39°$, (b) $3.6/48°$, (c) $9.2/21.4°$, (d) $2.7/71°$

10-936. Express in polar form: (a) $-8.9 + j4.2$, (b) $-16.8 + j9.3$, (c) $-5.3 + j2.1$, (d) $-18.4 + j3.3$

10-937. Express in rectangular form: (a) $9.7/118°$, (b) $115/137°$, (c) $2.09/160°$, (d) $5.72/110°$

10-938. Express in polar form: (a) $-7.3 - j6.1$, (b) $-4.4 - j8.2$, (c) $-8.8 - j2.5$, (d) $-1.053 - j5.13$

10-939. Express in rectangular form: (a) $81.3/200°$, (b) $62.1/253°$, (c) $1059/197°$, (d) $0.912/231°$

10-940. Express in polar form: (a) $160.5 - j147$, (b) $89.3 - j46.2$, (c) $0.0062 - j0.0051$, (d) $3.07 - j1.954$

10-941. Express in rectangular form: (a) $557/297°$, (b) $6.03/327°$, (c) $0.9772/344°$, (d) $19,750/300°$

10-942. Express in polar form: (a) $15.61 + j7.09$, (b) $-14.9 - j61.7$, (c) $0.617 - j0.992$, (d) $-41.2 + j75.3$

10-943. Express in rectangular form: (a) $1.075/29.1°$, (b) $10.75/136°$, (c) $107.5/253°$, (d) $1075/322°$

11

Unit systems and dimensional analysis

Man interprets the universe in which he lives by evaluating those things that he perceives. Through experience he has learned that there are certain physical quantities that are unique and *fundamental* and that can be used to describe all other physical relationships. Among the fundamental dimensions most commonly recognized are *length, force,* and *time,* which are used extensively by peoples of all cultures, economic classes, and educational levels. Engineering and scientific calculations make use of measurements of all types and, therefore, use not only these, but other fundamental dimensions as well. Fundamental dimensions may be combined in numerous ways to form *derived dimensions;* it is by this means that man is able to portray accurately the physical laws of nature that he observes.

Some measurements are made with precise instruments, while others are the result of crude approximations. Regardless of the accuracy of the measurements or of the particular type of measuring instrument used, the measurements are themselves merely representative of certain comparisons previously agreed upon.

The length of a metal cylinder, for example, can be determined by laying it alongside a calibrated scale or ruler. The 12-in. ruler is known to represent one third of a yard, and a yard is recognized as being equivalent to 36.00/39.37 meter—which used to be the distance between two marks on a platinum-iridium bar kept in a vault in Sèvres, France, but is now defined in terms of the wavelength of a particularly uniform monochromatic light. All these methods of measurements are comparisons. Other similar standards exist for the measurement of temperature, time, and force.

Physical quantities to be measured may be of two types: those concerned with *fundamental dimensions* of length (L), time (T), force (F), mass (M), electrical charge (Q), luminous intensity (I), and temperature (θ); and those concerned with *derived dimensions,* such as area, volume, pressure, or density. *Fundamental dimensions* may be subdivided into various sized parts, called *units*. The dimension *time* (*T*), for example, can be expressed in the units of seconds, hours, days, and so forth, depending upon the application to be made or the magnitude of the measurement. *Derived dimensions* are categorical descriptions of some specific physical characteristic or quality of an entity, and they are brought into being by combining *fundamental dimensions*. Area, therefore, is expressed dimensionally as length times length, or length squared (L^2), pressure as force per unit area (F/L^2, or FL^{-2}), and acceleration as length per time squared (L/T^2, or LT^{-2}).

Most measured quantities must be expressed in both magnitude and units. To state that an area was 146 would have no meaning. For example, an area could be tabulated as 146 mi^2 or 146 cm^2; a pressure could be recorded as 0.0015 dyne/cm^2 or 0.0015 lb$_f$/in.^{2}; an acceleration could be indicated as 159 in./sec^2 or 159 ft/sec^2, and so forth. However, some values used in engineering computations are dimensionless (without dimensions). These should be ignored in the unit balancing of an equation. *Radians, π, coefficient of friction, ratios,* and *per cent error* are examples of dimensionless quantities.

Equations involving measured quantities must be balanced dimensionally as well as numerically. Both dimensions and units can be multiplied and divided or raised to powers just like ordinary algebraic quantities. When all of the dimensions (or units) in an equation balance, the equation is said to be *dimensionally homogeneous*.

Example An alloy has a specific weight of 400 lb$_f$/ft^3. What is the weight of 2 ft^3 of the alloy? Show the numerical and dimensional solutions to the problem.

$$W = Vp \qquad \text{[Algebraic equation]}$$

or

(Weight[1] of metal) = (volume of metal)(specific weight of metal)

Fundamental Dimensions: $F = (L^3)\left(\dfrac{F}{L^3}\right)$ [Dimensional equation]

Units: $F = (2 \text{ ft}^3)\left(400\dfrac{\text{lb}_f}{\text{ft}^3}\right) = \textbf{800 lb}_f$ [Unit equation]

Check: $\text{lb}_f = \text{lb}_f$

Frequently it will be necessary to change unit systems, that is, feet to inches, hours to seconds, pounds to grams, and so on. This process can be accomplished by the use of unity conversion factors that are multiplied by the expression to be changed. Refer to Appendix IV for a listing of commonly used conversion factors.

Example Change a speed of 3000 miles per hour (miles/hr) to feet per second (ft/sec).

Fundamental dimensions: $\dfrac{L}{T} = \dfrac{L}{T}$

Units: $V = \left(3000\,\dfrac{\text{mi}}{\text{hr}}\right)\left(\dfrac{5280 \text{ ft}}{1 \text{ mi}}\right)\left(\dfrac{1 \text{ hr}}{3600 \text{ sec}}\right) = \textbf{4400}\,\dfrac{\text{ft}}{\text{sec}}$

The two conversion factors, (5280 ft/1 mi) and (1 hr/3600 sec), are each equivalent to unity, since the numerator of each fraction is equal to its denominator (5280 ft = 1 mi, and 1 hr = 3600 sec).

[1] Weight is expressed in the dimensions of force.

Note that the word *per* means *divided by*. To avoid misunderstandings in computations, the units should be expressed in fractional form.

Example

a. $(X \text{ per } Y) \text{ per } Z = (X \div Y) \div Z = [(X/Y)/Z] = \dfrac{(X/Y)}{Z} = \dfrac{X}{YZ}$

b. Acceleration $= 156$ ft per sec per min $= 156$ ft/sec/min

$$= 156 \dfrac{\text{ft}}{(\text{sec})(\text{min})}$$

c. Pressure $= 14.7 \text{ lb}_f$ per square inch $= 14.7 \dfrac{\text{lb}_f}{\text{in.}^2}$

Example Solve for the fundamental dimensions of Q and P in the following dimensionally homogeneous equation if C is a velocity and B is an area.

$$Q = C(B - P)$$

Fundamental Dimensions: $\quad Q = \dfrac{L}{T}(L^2 - P)$

Since the equation is dimensionally homogeneous, P must also be length squared (L^2) in order that the subtraction can be carried out. If this is true, the units of Q are [2]

$$Q = \dfrac{L}{T}(L^2 - L^2) = \dfrac{L}{T}(L^2) = \dfrac{L^3}{T}$$

Example Solve for the conversion factor k:

a. $\dfrac{L^2 T^3 \theta}{F^4} = (k)\left(\dfrac{L^5 T F^2}{Q^2}\right)$

Solving for k: $\qquad\qquad\qquad\qquad k = \dfrac{T^2 \theta Q^2}{F^6 L^3}$

and $\qquad\qquad \left(\dfrac{L^2 T^3 \theta}{F^4}\right) = \left(\dfrac{T^2 \theta Q^2}{F^6 L^3}\right)\left(\dfrac{L^5 T F^2}{Q^2}\right)$

Check: $\qquad\qquad \dfrac{L^2 T^3 \theta}{F^4} = \dfrac{L^2 T^3 \theta}{F^4} = L^2 T^3 \theta F^{-4}$

b. $\left(\dfrac{F^3 T^2 \theta}{L^2 Q}\right)k = \left(\dfrac{M F^2 Q^3}{T^2 L^3}\right)$

$$k = \dfrac{M Q^4}{F T^4 L \theta}$$

Check: $\quad \left[\dfrac{F^3 T^2 \theta}{L^2 Q}\right]\left[\dfrac{M Q^4}{F T^4 L \theta}\right] = \dfrac{M F^2 Q^3}{T^2 L^3} \qquad \text{or} \qquad M F^2 Q^3 T^{-2} L^{-3}$

---

[2] Remember that the terms L^2 represent a particular length squared in each instance. Thus the remainder (depending on the numerical magnitude of each term) will also be length squared or will be zero for the special case of the original lengths being equal.

Problems

Solve for the conversion factor k.

11-1. $k = \left(\dfrac{L^{3}\theta T Q^{5}}{FM}\right) = \dfrac{M^{3}\theta Q}{L^{2}}$

11-2. $\dfrac{FTL^{2}}{\theta M^{3}} = k\dfrac{\theta^{5}M}{T^{2}}$

11-3. $k\left(\dfrac{QM}{TF^{2}}\right) = \sqrt{L^{4}I\theta Q^{8}}$

11-4. $\theta^{2}\sqrt{LM^{5}} = k\left(\dfrac{FT^{2}}{M^{3}}\right)$

11-5. $k(F\theta^{2}TL^{-2}M^{-3}) = M^{5}L\theta F^{-3}$

11-6. $M^{2}FT^{-5}L^{-2} = k\sqrt{MT\theta}$

11-7. $\sqrt{LT^{3}F^{-2}M} = k\sqrt{TF^{3}M^{6}}$

11-8. $k\dfrac{\sqrt{T^{3}Q}}{L^{2}F^{-2}} = MTLF$

11-9. $k(F^{2}T\sqrt{L\theta^{-2}}) = \theta^{-3}T^{-2}$

11-10. $FL^{3}Q^{-1}M^{-3} = k\sqrt{L^{2}Q^{-1}}$

11-11. Convert 76 newtons to dynes and lb_f.

11-12. Convert 2.67 in. to angstroms and miles.

11-13. Convert 26 knots to feet per second and meters per hour.

11-14. Convert $8.07(10)^{3}$ tons to grams and ounces.

11-15. Convert 1.075 atmospheres to dynes per cm² and inches of mercury.

11-16. Convert 596 Btu to foot-pounds and Joules.

11-17. Convert 26,059 watts to horsepower and ergs per second.

11-18. Convert 92.7 coulombs to faradays.

11-19. Convert 75 angstroms to feet.

11-20. Convert 0.344 henries to abhenries.

11-21. Express 2903 ft³ of sulphuric acid in gallons.

11-22. Change a Btu to horsepower-seconds.

11-23. A car is traveling 49 mi/hr. What is the speed in feet per second?

11-24. A river has a flow of $3(10)^{6}$ gallons per 24-hour day. Compute the flow in cubic feet per minute.

11-25. Convert 579 qt/sec to cubic feet per hour.

11-26. A copper wire is 0.0809 in. in diameter. What is the weight of 1000 ft of the wire?

11-27. A cylindrical tank 2.96 ft high has a volume of 136 gallons. What is its diameter?

11-28. A round iron rod is 0.125 in. in diameter. How long will a piece have to be to weigh 1 lb?

11-29. Find the weight of a common brick that is 2.6 in. by 4 in. by 8.75 in.

11-30. Convert 1 yd² to acres.

11-31. A white pine board is 14 ft long and 2 in. by 8 in. in cross section. How much will the board weigh? At $200.00 per 1000 f.b.m., what is its value?

11-32. A container is 12 in. high, 10 in. in diameter at the top, and 6 in. in diameter at the bottom. What is the volume of this container in cubic inches? What is the weight of mercury that would fill this container?

11-33. How many gallons of water will be contained in a horizontal pipe 10 in. in internal diameter and 15 ft long, if the water is 6 in. deep in the pipe?

11-34. A hemispherical container 3 ft in diameter has half of its volume filled with lubricating oil. Neglecting the weight of the container, how much would the contents weigh if kerosene were added to fill the container to the brim?

11-35. What is the cross-sectional area of a railroad rail 33 ft long that weighs 94 lb/yd?

11-36. A piece of cast iron has a very irregular shape and its volume is to be determined. It is submerged in water in a cylindrical tank having a diameter of 16 in. The water level is raised 3.4 in. above its original level. How many cubic feet are in the piece of cast iron? How much does it weigh?

11-37. A cylindrical tank is 22 ft in diameter and 8 ft high. How long will it take to fill the tank with water from a pipe which is flowing at 33.3 gallons/min?

11-38. Two objects are made of the same material and have the same weights and diameters. One of the objects is a sphere 16 in. in diameter. If the other object is a right cylinder, what is its length?

11-39. A hemisphere and cone are carved out of the same material and their weights are equal. The height of the cone is 3 ft, $10\frac{1}{2}$ inches while the radius of the hemisphere is 13 in. If a flat circular cover were to be made for the cone base, what would be its area in square inches?

11-40. An eight-sided wrought iron bar weighs 3.83 lb per linear foot. What will be its dimension across diagonally opposite corners?

11-41. Is the equation $a = (2S/t^2) - (2V_1/t)$ dimensionally homogeneous if a is an acceleration, V_1 is a velocity, t is a time, and S is a distance? Prove your answer by writing the equation with fundamental dimensions.

11-42. Is the equation $V_2^2 = V_1^2 + 2as$ dimensionally correct if V_1 and V_2 are velocities, a is an acceleration, and s is a distance? Prove your answer by rewriting the equation in fundamental dimensions.

11-43. In the homogeneous equation $R = B + \frac{1}{2}CX$, what are the fundamental dimensions of R and B if C is an acceleration and X is a time?

11-44. Determine the fundamental dimensions of the expression $B/g \sqrt{D - m^2}$, where B is a force, m is a length, D is an area, and g is the acceleration of gravity at a particular location.

11-45. The relationship $M = \sigma I/c$ pertains to the bending moment for a beam under compressive stress. σ is a stress in F/L^2, C is a length L, and I is a moment of inertia L^4. What are the fundamental dimensions of M?

11-46. The expression $V/K = (B - \frac{1}{3}A)A^{5/3}$ is dimensionally homogeneous. A is a length and V is a volume of flow per unit of time. Solve for the fundamental dimensions of K and B.

11-47. Is the expression $S = 0.031V^2/fB$ dimensionally homogeneous if S is a distance, V is a velocity, f is the coefficient of friction, and B is a ratio of two weights? Is it possible that the numerical value 0.031 has fundamental dimensions? Prove your solution.

11-48. If the following heat transfer equation is dimensionally homogeneous, what are the units of k?

$$Q = \frac{-kA(T_1 - T_2)}{L}$$

A is a cross-sectional area in square feet, L is a length in feet, T_1 and T_2 are temperatures (°F), and Q is the amount of heat (energy) conducted in Btu per unit of time.

11-49. In the dimensionally homogeneous equation

$$F = \frac{4Ey}{(1 - \mu^2)(Md^2)}\left[(h - y)\left(h - \frac{y}{2}\right)t - t^3\right]$$

F is a force, E is a force per (length)^2, y, d, and h are lengths, μ is Poisson's ratio, and M is a ratio of diameters. What are the fundamental dimensions of t?

11-50. In the equation

$$F = \frac{12WV^2}{gr}\left(\cos \alpha + \frac{r}{l} \cos 2\alpha\right)$$

F represents a force, *W* is a weight, *V* is a crank velocity, *g* is the acceleration of gravity at the place of experimentation, α is an angle, and *l* is a connecting rod length. What must be the fundamental dimensions of *r* if the equation is to be dimensionally homogeneous?

The most commonly used fundamental and derived units in engineering calculations are the following:

Units of length The concept of *length* as a measure of space in one direction is easily understood. People in every country use this concept because the position of any point in our universe may be described in relation to any other point by specifying three lengths. The world standard of length is the meter (m), defined now in terms of the wavelength of a particularly uniform monochromatic light. It is quite close to being equal to the distance from the earth's equator to the North Pole divided by ten million, which was its original definition. This unit of length is commonly used by engineers and scientists in most countries for the usual engineering problems as well as in the field of space mechanics.

In the United States, the most common units of length that are used in engineering calculations are the inch (in.), the foot (ft), and the mile (mi). Less common are the yard and the nautical mile. They are defined as

$$1 \text{ in.} = 2.54 \ (10)^{-2} \text{ m (exactly by definition)}$$
$$1 \text{ ft} = 12 \text{ in.}$$
$$1 \text{ yard} = 3 \text{ ft}$$
$$1 \text{ mile} = 5280 \text{ ft}$$
$$1 \text{ nautical mile} = 6080.27 \text{ ft approximately}$$

Often feet and inches or feet and miles are used in the same problem. The foot is sometimes decimalized and sometimes the last fractional foot is given in inches and fractions of an inch. Sometimes the inch is decimalized and sometimes it is fractionalized; sometimes it is both decimalized and fractionalized in the same problem. One of the disadvantages of the English system of measurement is the tendency to use a mixture of methods of showing a measured quantity.

Units of force Force is most commonly thought of as a "push" or a "pull" and represents the action of one body on another. The action may be exerted by direct contact between the bodies or at a distance, as in the case of magnetic and gravitational forces.

The most common unit of force used by American engineers is the pound (lb_f). This is the force that is required to accelerate a pound mass with the mean acceleration of gravity, or $g = 32.174 \text{ ft/sec}^2$. Its value is

$$1 \ lb_f = 4.48 \text{ newton}$$

The newton (N) is derived from the kilogram by means of Newton's law, $F = Ma$. Thus,

$$1 \text{ N} = 1 \text{ kg}_m \times 1 \text{ m/sec}^2$$

and it is the force required to accelerate a 1-kg mass 1 m/sec². This unit of force is most frequently used by the American electrical engineers and by other engineers who are engaged in space exploration activities.

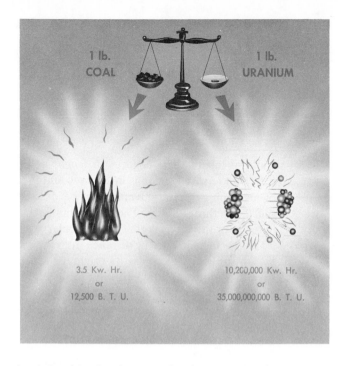

The contrast of energy sources is depicted in this picture, which shows the relative energy conversion from coal and nuclear fuels. In working with such energy sources, the engineer must be able to convert from one unit system to another.

1 lb.
COAL

1 lb.
URANIUM

3.5 Kw. Hr.
or
12,500 B. T. U.

10,200,000 Kw. Hr.
or
35,000,000,000 B. T. U.

Units of time Time cannot be defined in simple terms, but in general it is a measure of the interval separating the occurrence of two events. The mean solar day is the standard unit of time in all systems of units used at present. The hour (hr), the minute (min), and the second (sec) are all derived from the mean solar day, but not decimally. Since all four of these units are used, sometimes even in the same problem, it is easy to see how mistakes can be made and considerable extra work required. This is also the case with the International System of Units (SI), since the unit of time is the same in all systems of units. The most common unit used in engineering calculations is the second, defined as

$$1 \text{ sec} = \frac{1 \text{ mean solar day}}{86{,}400}$$

Then, 1 min = 60 sec and 1 hr = 3600 sec.

Units of mass While length, force, and time are readily understood concepts, *mass* is somewhat more difficult to perceive. The universe is filled with matter—the accumulation of electrons, protons, and neutrons. *Mass* is a measure of the quantity of these subatomic particles that a particular object possesses. Although a quantity of matter can change form—for example, as when a block of ice is melted to water and then vaporized to steam—its "quantity" does not change.

In contrast to length, force, and time, there is no direct measure for mass. Its quantity may be measured only through an examination of its properties, such as the amount of force that must be provided to give it a certain acceleration. The world standard of mass is the kilogram (kg), defined originally as being one thousandth of 1 m³ of water at a temperature of 4° Celsius and standard atmospheric pressure, but now defined as the mass of a block of platinum kept at the French Bureau of Standards. This unit is used by American electrical and space engineers.

The pound mass (lb_m) is the unit that the average American engineer thinks he is using most of the time. In most instances this is incorrect. Generally the pound that he uses is the pound force (lb_f), from which he derives units of mass by means of Newton's law, $F = Ma$. Thus,

$$1 \; lb_m = 0.4535924277 \; \text{kg (by definition)}$$

$$1 \frac{lb_f \; \sec^2}{\text{ft}} \text{(also called a slug)} = 32.174 \; lb_m$$

$$1 \frac{lb_f \; \sec^2}{\text{in.}} = 386.088 \; lb_m$$

Units of temperature   Temperature is an arbitrary measure which is proportional to the average kinetic energy of the molecules of an ideal gas. Four temperature scales are used by American engineers. The degree Celsius (°C), formerly called centigrade, reads zero at the freezing point of water and 100°C at the boiling point of water under standard conditions of pressure. It is the world standard of temperature. The temperature in degrees Kelvin (°K) is derived from the Celsius scale by the following equation:

$$\text{Temperature in } °K = \text{Temperature in } °C + 273.16$$

The degree Fahrenheit (°F) reads 32°F at the freezing point of water and 212°F at the boiling point of water under standard conditions of pressure.[3] The degree Rankine (°R) is derived from the Fahrenheit scale by the equation

$$\text{Temperature in } °R = \text{Temperature in } °F + 459.69$$

When a temperature is measured in either °K or in °R, it is said to be the *absolute* temperature, because these scales read zero for the condition where the kinetic energy of the molecules of an ideal gas is presumed to be zero.

Units of area and volume   Units of area and volume are derived from the units of length for the most part. However, the gallon is a commonly used measure of volume that is in no way related to units of length.

Units of velocity and acceleration   These units are all derived from the fundamental units of length and time.

Units of work and energy   Work is the product of a force and a distance through which that force acts. Energy is the ability or capacity for doing work. Although the two quantities are conceptually different, they are measured by the same units. Several different units are used. For example, foot-pounds, inch-pounds, and horse-power-hours are all used for work and mechanical energy; both the joule and the kilowatt-hour are used for electrical energy; and both the calorie (two types) and the British thermal unit (Btu) are used for heat energy. In some problems all of these units occur, which frequently makes the task of unit conversion the most formidable part of the solution.

Units of power   Power is the time rate of accomplishing work. The average power is the work performed divided by the time required for the performance. Since power

[3]G. D. Fahrenheit thought that 0°F was the lowest possible temperature that could be obtained and that 100°F was the uniformly standard temperature of human blood.

units are derived units, they also involve the various work and energy units described above. In addition, the ton of refrigeration (3517 watts) is sometimes used in air conditioning design calculations.

Units of pressure   Pressure is the result of a force distributed over an area. In general, the units of pressure have been derived from conventional units of force and area. However, other measures are also used. For example, the standard atmospheric pressure is commonly used as a unit, and for fractional atmospheres the millimeter of mercury, the inch of mercury, and the inch of water are used.

Units of density   Density is a measure of the mass that a body of uniform substance possesses per unit volume. The units of density are derived units that are made up by dividing the chosen unit of *mass* by the unit of volume, for example, grams per cubic centimeter.

Units of specific weight   Specific weight is a measure of the *weight* of a substance per unit volume. Many people confuse density with specific weight. Remember that they are not the same, but rather that they are related to each other by the relationship

$$(Specific\ Weight) = (Density)(Acceleration\ of\ Gravity)$$

The units most commonly used for specific weight are lb/ft^3 and $lb/in.^3$, where the lb is a unit of force, lb_f. They represent the attraction, in lb_f, of the earth on either $1\ ft^3$ or $1\ in.^3$ of the material. To convert specific weights to density for use in a gravitational system, one must divide these quantities by the acceleration of gravity, g. If one divides the first unit by $g = 32.174\ ft/sec^2$, one obtains the unit of density $lb_f\ sec^2/ft^4$, or $slugs/ft^3$; and, if one divides the second unit by $g = 386.088$ $in./sec^2$, one obtains the unity of density $lb_f\ sec^2/in^4$.

Unit systems

One serious barrier between scientists and engineers is the fact that the two groups use entirely different systems of units to describe the same things. In addition, the electrical engineers use different units than the other engineers. This situation still exists in all countries except those that have adopted the MKS system of units.

Additional handicaps to the engineers are that they use different units for thermal energy, mechanical energy (work), and electrical energy; they use both absolute and gravitational units for mass, and forces are based on the pull of gravity. These handicaps are shared by all engineers outside of the countries that have adopted the MKS system. However, even in these countries a serious burden is imposed on both engineers and scientists by the fact that their units for time and angular measure are unbelievably cumbersome, and they must use both absolute and ordinary temperature scales. These handicaps are shared by all engineers and scientists in the world today.

In the English-speaking countries an additional staggering burden is placed on the engineers by the fact that a multitude of units are used for each of the quantities length, mass, and force, and none of the units used for the same quantity is derivable from another by a simple shifting of the decimal point. These countries, therefore, have the most to gain by a change in units. In addition, the adoption of the MKS system on a worldwide basis will greatly facilitate the exchange of scientific and technical information.

There are a number of systems of units that have been used in scientific and engineering calculations. Variations in the preference of unit systems may depend not only upon the language spoken by a particular researcher but also upon whether or not he has been educated as an engineer or as a scientist.

Table 11-1   Unit systems

	Absolute			Gravitational		
	(1) MKS	**(2) CGS**	**(3) FPS**	**(4) FPS**	**(5) MKS**	**(6) American engineering**
Fundamental dimensions						
Force (F)	—	—	—	lb_f	kg_f	lb_f
Length (L)	m	cm	ft	ft	m	ft or in.
Time (T)	sec	sec	sec	sec	sec	sec
Mass (M)	kg_m	g	lb_m	—	—	lb_m
Derived dimensions						
Force (F)	$\dfrac{kg_m\text{-m}}{sec^2}$ (called a newton*)	$\dfrac{g\text{-cm}}{sec^2}$ (called a dyne)	$\dfrac{lb_m\text{-ft}}{sec^2}$ (called a poundal)	—	—	—
Mass (M)	—	—	—	$\dfrac{lb_f\text{-sec}^2}{ft}$ (called a slug)	$\dfrac{kg_f\text{-sec}^2}{m}$	—
Energy (LF)	N-m	cm-dyne (called an erg)	ft-poundal	$ft\text{-}lb_f$	$m\text{-}kg_f$	$ft\text{-}lb_f$
Power $\left(\dfrac{LF}{T}\right)$	$\dfrac{\text{N-m}}{sec}$	$\dfrac{erg}{sec}$	$\dfrac{\text{ft-poundal}}{sec}$	$\dfrac{ft\text{-}lb_f}{sec}$	$\dfrac{m\text{-}kg_f}{sec}$	$\dfrac{ft\text{-}lb_f}{sec}$
Velocity $\left(\dfrac{L}{T}\right)$	$\dfrac{m}{sec}$	$\dfrac{cm}{sec}$	$\dfrac{ft}{sec}$	$\dfrac{ft}{sec}$	$\dfrac{m}{sec}$	$\dfrac{ft}{sec}$
Acceleration $\left(\dfrac{L}{T^2}\right)$	$\dfrac{m}{sec^2}$	$\dfrac{cm}{sec^2}$	$\dfrac{ft}{sec^2}$	$\dfrac{ft}{sec^2}$	$\dfrac{m}{sec^2}$	$\dfrac{ft}{sec^2}$
Area (L²)	m^2	cm^2	ft^2	ft^2	m^2	ft^2
Volume (L³)	m^3	cm^3	ft^3	ft^3	m^3	ft^3
Density $\left(\dfrac{M}{L^3}\right)$	$\dfrac{kg_m}{m^3}$	$\dfrac{g}{cm^3}$	$\dfrac{lb_m}{ft^3}$	$\dfrac{lb_f\,sec^2}{ft^4}$	$\dfrac{kg_f\text{-}sec^2}{m^4}$	$\dfrac{lb_m}{ft^3}$
Pressure $\left(\dfrac{F}{L^2}\right)$	$\dfrac{N}{m^2}$	$\dfrac{dyne}{cm^2}$	$\dfrac{poundal}{cm^2}$	$\dfrac{lb_f}{ft^2}$	$\dfrac{kg_f}{m^2}$	$\dfrac{lb_f}{ft^2}$

*A newton (N) is the force required to accelerate a 1-kg mass at 1 m/sec². The acceleration of gravity at sea level and 45° latitude has the measured value of 9.807 m/sec². A force of 1 kg equals 9.807 N of force.

The need for unit systems was first evident when it became necessary to explain the fundamental relationships between force, mass, and acceleration. Sir Isaac Newton (1642–1727) expressed several basic laws that he believed to govern the motion of particles. Only recently has it become evident that in studying the motion of atoms and certain planets, Einstein's theory of relativity must supplant Newton's concepts. However, Newton's "second law" still serves as a basis for much of today's engineering mechanics. Briefly this law may be stated as follows:

When an external unbalanced force F acts on a rigid particle of mass, the motion of the particle will be changed. The particle will be accelerated. Its rate of change in motion will be in the direction of the unbalanced force and will be proportional to it.

Stated mathematically, $F_1/a_1 = F_2/a_2 = F_3/a_3 = F_n/a_n = $ a constant, where F_1, F_2, F_3, and so forth are external unbalanced forces acting on a particle, and a_1, a_2, a_3, and so forth, are consequential accelerations of the particle.

The quotient of (F/a) is a quantity which is invariant. The units of this term depend upon the units arbitrarily chosen to define F and a. This constant has been called the *mass* of the particle under consideration. It is properly designated by the symbol M, or in some cases by the product of the two symbols, km. In this latter case, k could be a value of 1, or it could be some other dimensional expression whose resultant value is unity. The mass M of a particular body is independent of the location of the body in the universe.

Thus
$$F = Ma$$
or
$$= kma$$

Absolute unit systems

Scientists the world over have chosen to use dimensional or unit systems that are *absolute*. That is, the fundamental units chosen do not depend upon gravitational effects on the earth or other planets. In absolute systems the dimensions of force are derived in terms of the fundamental units of time, length, and mass. There are three absolute systems.[4] Two of these are used extensively in scientific work today. These are the MKS (meter, kilogram, second) absolute system, and the CGS (centimeter, gram, second) absolute system. The other absolute system, the FPS absolute system, is used primarily in engineering computations.

The first one of these, which is also called the International System of Units, or SI units, from the French "Systéme International d'Unites", is now rapidly replacing both the CGS system and the old engineering systems in all parts of the world. The reason for this is that SI units are equally convenient for both engineers and scientists, which is a great advantage now that the two groups must cooperate closely for the purpose of making rapid technological progress. It is particularly convenient in calculations involving energy, since only one unit is used for all types of energy, whether atomic, electric, chemical, heat, or mechanical. This unit of energy is the joule, which previously was used only by electrical engineers, and the corresponding unit of power is the watt, which is 1 joule/sec.

The following is a complete list of SI units and their dimensions:

[4] See page 241.

Fundamental units

Length: 1 m

Mass: 1 kg_m

Time: 1 sec

Current = 1 ampere (amp) = 1 coulomb/sec

Temperature: $1°K$ or $1°C$

Light Source: 1 candela (International candle)

Derived units

area = 1 m^2

volume = 1 m^3

velocity = 1 m/sec

acceleration = 1 m/sec^2

force = 1 newton (N) = 1 kg_m-m/sec^2

work and energy: 1 joule (j) = 1 kg_m-m^2/sec^2

moment and torque = 1 N-m

power, 1 watt (w) = 1 kg_m-m^2/sec^3

pressure, 1 N/m^2 = 1 kg_m/sec^2-m (1 bar = 10^5N/m)

thermal conductivity = 1 w/m-$°C$ = 1 kg_m-m/sec^3-$°C$

heat transfer coefficient = 1 w/m^2-$°C$ = 1 kg_m/sec^3-$°C$

dynamic viscosity = 1 N-sec/m^2 = 1 kg_m/m-sec = 1 decapoise

kinematic viscosity = 1 m^2/sec = 1 myriastoke

density = 1 kg_m/m^3

heat coefficient = 1 j/kg_m-$°C$ = 1 m^2/sec^2-$°C$

enthalpy, heat content, and internal energy = 1 j/kg_m = 1 m^2/sec^2

electrical charge; 1 coulomb = 1 amp-sec

potential = 1 volt (v) = 1 w/amp = 1 kg_m-m^2/sec^3-amp

resistance = 1 ohm (Ω) = 1 w/amp^2 = 1 kg_m-m^2/sec^3-amp^2

capacitance = 1 farad (f) = 1 coulomb/v = 1 amp^2-sec/w =
    1 amp^2-sec^4/kg_m m^2

inductance = 1 henry (h) = 1 v-sec/amp = 1 j/amp^2 = 1 kg_m-m^2/sec^2-amp^2

capacity or permittivity $\epsilon_0 = \dfrac{10^7}{4\pi c^2} = 8.854 \times 10^{-12}$ f/m

magnetic permeability $\mu_0 = 4\pi(10)^{-7} = 1.2566(10)^{-6}$ h/m

The American engineering system of units

Early in the development of engineering analysis a system of units was developed that defined both the units of mass and the units of force. It is perhaps unfortunate that the same word, pounds, was chosen to represent both quantities, since they are physically different. In order to help differentiate the quantities, the pound-mass may be designated as lb_{mass} (or lb_m) and the pound-force as lb_{force} (or lb_f).

For many engineering applications the numerical values of lb_m and lb_f are very nearly the same. However, in expressions such as $F = Ma$, it is necessary that the difference between lb_m and lb_f be maintained. By definition, a mass of 1 lb_m will be attracted to the earth by a force of 1 lb_f at a place where the acceleration of gravity is 32.2 ft/sec^2. If the acceleration of gravity changes to some other value, the force must change in proportion, since mass is invariant.

Although the pound subscripts, *force* and *mass,* are frequently omitted in engineering and scientific literature, it is nevertheless true that lb_f is not the same as lb_m. Their numerical values are equal, however, in the case of sea level, 45°-latitude calculations. However, their values may be widely different, as would be the case in an analysis involving satellite design and space travel.

In Newton's equation, $F = Ma$, dimensional homogeneity must be maintained. If length, force, and time are taken as fundamental dimensions, the dimensions of mass must be derived. This can be accomplished as follows:

$$F = Ma$$

Then
$$M = \frac{F}{a}$$

$$= \frac{(F)}{(L/T^2)} = \frac{FT^2}{L} = FL^{-1}T^2$$

and
$$= \textbf{lb}_f\textbf{-ft}^{-1}\textbf{-sec}^2$$

For convenience, this derived unit of mass (1 lb-sec²)/ft is called a *slug*. Thus, a force of 1 lb_f will cause a mass of 1 slug to have an acceleration of 1 ft/sec².

The relationship between 1 lb_m and 1 slug is given by considering that whereas 1 lb_f will accelerate 1 lb_m with an acceleration of $g = 32.2$ ft/sec², it will accelerate 1 slug with an acceleration of only 1 ft/sec². Thus:

$$1 \ lf_f = (1 \ lb_m)(32.2 \ \text{ft/sec}^2) = (1 \ \text{slug})(1 \ \text{ft/sec}^2)$$

or
$$1 \ \text{slug} = 32.2 \ lb_m$$

It should be noted that with the FPS system a unity conversion factor must be used if a mass unit other than the slug is used. Since the acceleration of gravity varies with both latitude and altitude, the use of a gravitational system is sometimes inconvenient. A 100,000-lb rocket on the earth, for example, would not weigh 100,000 lb_f on the moon, where gravitational forces are smaller. The mass of the rocket, on the other hand, is a fixed quantity and will be a constant amount, regardless of its location in space.

For a freely falling body at sea level and 45° latitude, the acceleration[5] g of the body is 32.174 (approximately 32.2) ft/sec². As the mass is attracted to the earth, the only force than acting on it is its own weight.

then
$$F = Ma$$
If
$$W = Mg$$
and
$$M = \frac{W}{g}$$
where
$$a = g \quad \text{and} \quad F = W$$

In this particular system of units, then, the mass of a body in slugs may be calculated by dividing the weight of the body in pounds by the local acceleration of gravity in feet per second squared.

The engineer frequently works in several systems of units in the same calculation. In this case it is only necessary that the force, mass, and acceleration dimensions all be expressed in any valid set of units from any unit system. Numerical equality

---

[5] The value of the acceleration of gravity, g, at any latitude θ on the earth may be approximated from the following relationship: $g = 32.09(1 + 0.0053 \sin^2 \theta)$ ft/sec².

and unit homogeneity may be determined in any case by applying unity conversion factors to the individual terms of the expression.

Example Solve for the lb_m which is being accelerated at 3.07 ft/sec² by a force of 392 lb_f.

Solution
$$F = Ma \quad \text{or} \quad M = \frac{F}{a}$$

$$M = \frac{392 \text{ lb}_f}{3.07 \text{ ft/sec}^2} = 127.8 \frac{\text{lb}_f\text{-sec}^2}{\text{ft}}$$

The direct substitution has given mass in the units of slugs instead of lb_m units. This is a perfectly proper set of units for mass, although not in lb_m units as desired. Consequently the final equation must be altered by applying the unity conversion factor $\left(\dfrac{32.2 \text{ lb}_m}{1 \text{ lb}_f\text{-sec}^2\text{-ft}^{-1}}\right)$. The object, of course, is to cancel units until the desired units appear in the answer. Thus

$$M = \left(\frac{127.8 \text{ lb}_f\text{-sec}^2}{\text{ft}}\right)\left(\frac{32.2 \text{ lb}_m\text{-ft}}{1 \text{ lb}_f\text{-sec}^2}\right) = (4.11)(10)^3 \text{ lb}_m$$

Example Solve for the mass in slugs being accelerated at 13.6 m/sec by a force of 1782 lb_f.

Solution $\quad F = Ma$

$$M = \frac{F}{a} = \frac{(1782 \text{ lb}_f)}{(13.6 \text{ m/sec}^2)} = \left(\frac{1782 \text{ lb}_f\text{-sec}^2}{13.6 \text{ m}}\right)\left(\frac{1}{3.28}\frac{\text{m}}{\text{ft}}\right)$$

$$= 40 \frac{\text{lb}_f\text{-sec}^2}{\text{ft}} = 40 \text{ slugs}$$

It is recommended that in writing a mathematical expression to represent some physical phenomena, the engineer should avoid using stereotyped conversion symbols such as g, g_c, k, or J in the equation. If one of these, or any other conversion factor, is needed in an equation to achieve unit balance, it can *then* be added. Since many different unit systems may be used from time to time, it is best to add unity conversion factors *only* as they are needed. Unfortunately, in much engineering literature, the equations used in a particular instance have been written to include one or more unity conversion factors. Considerable care must be exercised, therefore, in using these expressions since they represent a "special case" rather than a "general condition." The engineer should form a habit of always checking the unit balance of all equations.

Remember that

$$1 \text{ slug} = 1 \frac{\text{lb}_f\text{-sec}^2}{\text{ft}} = 32.2 \text{ lb}_m$$

The foregoing discussion has shown that

1. If mass units in slugs are used in the expression $F = Ma$, the force units will come out in the usual units of pounds (lb_f).

2. If mass units in pounds (lb$_m$) are used in the expression $F = Ma$, force units will come out in an absolute unit called the *poundal* (see Table 11-1).

In engineering calculations the inch is used just as often as the foot to represent the unit of length, and this necessitates the introduction of an additional unit of mass. Consider Newton's law, $F = Ma$, where $F = 1$ lb$_f$ and $a = 1$ in./sec^2. Then

$$M = 1 \ lb_f\text{-sec}^2/\text{in.}$$

where lb$_f$ now is lb$_{force}$.

Example A body weighs W lb$_f$ at a place where $g = 386$ in./sec^2. Find the mass of the body in units of lb$_f$-sec^2/in.

Solution The relationship between weight and mass is given by

$$W = Mg$$

and if W is given in lb$_f$ and g in in./sec^2, this gives

$$M = \frac{W}{g} = \frac{W}{386} \ \text{lb}_f\text{-sec}^2/\text{in.}$$

Problems on unit systems

11-51. The kinetic energy of a moving body in space can be expressed as follows:

$$KE = \frac{MV^2}{2}$$

where KE = kinetic energy of the moving body
  M = mass of the moving body
  V = velocity of the moving body

a. Given: $M = 539 \dfrac{\text{lb}_f\text{-sec}^2}{\text{ft}}$; $V = 2900 \dfrac{\text{ft}}{\text{sec}}$

  Find: KE in ft-lb$_f$

b. Given: $M = 42.6 \dfrac{\text{lb}_f\text{-sec}^2}{\text{ft}}$; $KE = 1.20(10)^{11}$ ft-lb$_f$

  Find: V in $\dfrac{\text{ft}}{\text{sec}}$

c. Given: $KE = 16,900$ in.-lb$_f$; $V = 3960 \dfrac{\text{in.}}{\text{min}}$

  Find: M in slugs

d. Given: $M = 143$ g; $KE = 2690$ in.-lb$_f$

  Find: V in $\dfrac{\text{mi}}{\text{hr}}$

11-52. The inertia force due to the acceleration of a rocket can be expressed as follows:

$$F = Ma$$

where F = unbalanced force
  a = acceleration of the body
  M = mass of the body

a. Given: $a = 439 \dfrac{\text{ft}}{\text{sec}^2}$; $M = 89.6 \dfrac{\text{lb}_f\text{-sec}^2}{\text{ft}}$

Find: F in lb_f

b. Given: $F = 1500 \text{ lb}_f$; $M = 26.4 \dfrac{\text{lb}_f\text{-sec}^2}{\text{ft}}$

Find: a in $\dfrac{\text{ft}}{\text{sec}^2}$

c. Given: $F = (49.3)(10)^5 \text{ lb}_f$; $a = 32.2 \dfrac{\text{ft}}{\text{sec}^2}$

Find: M in $\dfrac{\text{lb}_f\text{-sec}^2}{\text{ft}}$

d. Given: $M = 9650 \dfrac{\text{lb}_f\text{-sec}^2}{\text{ft}}$; $a = 980 \dfrac{\text{cm}}{\text{sec}^2}$

Find: F in lb_f

11-53. The force required to assemble a force-fit joint on a particular piece of machinery may be expressed by the following equation:

$$F = \frac{\pi d l f P}{2000}$$

where d = shaft diameter, in.
$\quad l$ = hub length, in.
$\quad f$ = coefficient of friction
$\quad P$ = radial pressure, psi
$\quad F$ = force of press required, tons

a. Given: $d = 9.05$ in.; $l = 15.1$ in.; $f = 0.10$; $P = 10{,}250$ psi
Find: F in lb_f
b. Given: $F = 4.21 \times 10^5 \text{ lb}_f$; $f = 0.162$; $P = 8.32(10^8)$ psf; $l = 1.62$ ft
Find: d in ft
c. Given: $d = 25$ cm; $l = 30.2$ cm; $f = 0.08$; $P = 9260$ psi
Find: F in tons
d. Given: $F = 206$ tons; $d = 6.23$ in.; $l = 20.4$ in.; $f = 0.153$
Find: P in lb_f/ft^2

11-54. The dynamic stress in the rim of a certain flywheel has been expressed by the following equation:

$$\sigma = 0.0000284 \rho r^2 n^2$$

where σ = tensile stress, $\dfrac{\text{lb}_f}{\text{in.}^2}$

ρ = specific weight of material, $\dfrac{\text{lb}_f}{\text{in.}^3}$

r = radius of curvature, in.
n = number of rpm

a. Given: $\sigma = 200$ psi; $\rho = 0.282 \dfrac{\text{lb}_f}{\text{in.}^3}$; $r = 9$ in.

Find: n in rpm

b. Given: $\rho = 0.332 \dfrac{\text{lb}_f}{\text{in.}^3}$; $r = 23.1$ cm; $m = 200$ rpm

Find: σ in psi

c. Given: $\rho = 540 \dfrac{\text{lb}_f}{\text{ft}^3}$; $n = 186$ rpm; $\sigma = (31.2)(10)^3$ psf

Find: r in ft

d. Given: $\rho = 326 \dfrac{\text{lb}_f}{\text{ft}^3}$; $n = 250$ rpm; $r = 0.632$ ft

Find: σ in psf

Solve the following:

11-55. The stress in a certain column may be calculated by the following relationship:

$$\sigma = \frac{F}{A}\left[1 + \left(\frac{l}{k}\right)^2 \frac{R}{\pi^2 n E} \right]$$

where σ = induced stress, psi
F = applied force, lb_f
A = cross-sectional area of member, in.^{2}
l = length of bar, in.
k = radius of gyration, in.
R = elastic limit, $\text{lb}_f/\text{in.}^2$
E = modulus of elasticity, $\text{lb}_f/\text{in.}^2$
n = coefficient for different end conditions

a. Given: $n = 1$; $E = (3)(10)^7$ psi; $R = (4.2)(10)^4$ psi; $k = 0.29$ in; $l = 20.3$ in.; $A = 17.5$ in.^{2}; $F = 12,000$ lb_f.
Find: σ in psi

b. Given: $\sigma = 11,500$ psi; $F = 6.3$ tons; $l = 2.11$ ft; $k = 0.41$ in.; $R = 40,000$ psi; $E = (3.16)(10)^7$ psi; $n = 2$
Find: A in ft^2

c. Given: $n = \frac{1}{4}$; $E = (2.65)(10)^7$ psi; $R = (3.21)(10)^4$ psi; $k = 0.026$ ft; $A = 102$ cm^2; $F = 5.9$ tons; $\sigma = 10,000$ psi
Find: l in ft

d. Given: $\sigma = (1.72)(10)^6$ psf; $F = (1.33)(10)^4$ lb_f; $l = 1.67$ ft; $k = 0.331$ in.; $E = (7.87)(10)^7$ psi; $n = 4$; $A = 14.2$ in.^{2}
Find: R in psi

11-56. In the FPS gravitational system, what mass in slugs is necessary to produce 15.6 lb_f at standard conditions?

11-57. In the engineering gravitational system, what mass in lb_m is necessary to produce a 195.3 lb_f at standard conditions?

11-58. Using the FPS gravitational system, calculate the fundamental dimensions of E in Einstein's equation,

$$E = mc^2\left[\frac{1}{\sqrt{1 - (V^2/c^2)}} - 1 \right]$$

if m is a mass, V is a velocity, and c is the speed of light. What would be the fundamental dimensions of E in the CGS absolute system of units?

11-59. Using the relationship for g on page 244 and the FPS gravitational system of units, determine the weight, at the latitude 0°, of a stainless steel sphere whose mass is defined as 150 $\text{lb}_f\text{-sec}^2/\text{ft}$.

11-60. The mass of solid propellant in a certain container is 5 kg. What is the weight of this material in newtons at a location in Greenland, where the acceleration of gravity is 9.83 m/sec^2? What is the weight in kilograms?

11-61. Change 100 N of force to lb_f.

11-62. If a gold sphere has a mass of 89.3 lb_m on earth, what would be its weight in lb_f on the moon, where the acceleration of gravity is 5.31 fps^2?

11-63. Assuming that the acceleration due to gravitation is 5.31 fps^2 on the moon, what is the mass in slugs of 100 lb$_m$ located on the moon?

11-64. A silver bar weighs 382 lb$_f$ at a point on the earth where the acceleration of gravity is measured to be 32.1 fps^2. Calculate the mass of the bar in lb$_m$ and slug units.

11-65. The acceleration of gravity can be approximated by the following relationship:

$$g = 980.6 - (3.086)(10)^{-6}A$$

where g is expressed in cm/sec^2, and A is an altitude in cm. If a rocket weighs 10,370 lb$_f$ at sea level and standard conditions, what will be its weight in dynes at 50,000-ft elevation?

11-66. At a certain point on the moon the acceleration due to gravitation is 5.35 fps^2. A rocket resting on the moon's surface at this point weighs 23,500 lb$_f$. What is its mass in slugs? In lb$_m$?

11-67. If a 10-lb weight on the moon (where $g = 5.33$ fps^2) is returned to the earth and deposited at a latitude of 90° (see page 244), how much would it weigh in the new location?

11-68. A 4.37-slug mass is taken from the earth to the moon and located at a point where $g = 5.33$ fps^2. What is the magnitude of its mass in the new location?

11-69. Is the equation $F = WV^2/2g$ a homogenous expression if W is a weight, V is a velocity, F is a force, and g is the linear acceleration of gravity? Prove your answer, using the FPS absolute system of units.

11-70. Sir Isaac Newton expressed the belief that all particles in space, regardless of their mass, are each attracted to every other particle in space by a specific force of attraction. For spherical bodies, whose separation is very large compared with the physical dimensions of either particle, the force of attraction may be calculated from the relationship $F = Gm_1m_2/d^2$, where F is the existing gravitational force, d is the distance separating the two masses m_1 and m_2, and G is a gravitational constant, whose magnitude depends upon the unit system being used. Using the CGS absolute system of units [$G = 6.67 \times 10^{-8}$ (cm^3/gm-sec^2)], calculate the mass of the earth if it attracts a mass of 1 g with a force of 980 dynes. Assume that the distance from the center of the earth to the gram mass is 6370 km.

11-71. Referring to Problem 11-70, calculate the mass of the sun if the earth (6 $\times$ 10^{24} kg mass) has an orbital diameter of 1.49 $\times$ 10^7 km and the force of attraction between the two celestial bodies is $(1.44)(10)^{25}$ N.

11-72. From Problem 11-70, calculate the acceleration of gravity on the earth in CGS absolute units.

11-73. An interstellar explorer is accelerating uniformly at 58.6 fps^2 in a spherical space ship which has a total mass of 100,000 slugs. What is the force acting on the ship?

11-74. At a certain instant in time a space vehicle is being acted on by a vertically upward thrust of 497,000 lb$_f$. The mass of the space vehicle is 400,000 lb$_m$, and the acceleration of gravity is 32.1 fps^2. Is the vehicle rising or descending? What is its acceleration? (Assume "up" means radially outward from the center of the earth.)

11-75. Some interstellar adventurers land their spacecraft on a certain celestial body. Explain how they could calculate the acceleration of gravity at the point where they landed.

11-76. In a swimming pool manufacturer's design handbook, for a pool whose surface area is triangular, you find the following formula: $V = 3.74Rt\theta$, where $V =$ volume of pool in gallons, $R =$ length of base of triangular shaped pool in feet, $t =$ altitude of triangular shaped pool in feet if t is measured perpendicular to R, and $\theta =$ average depth of pool in feet. Prove that the equation is valid or invalid.

11-77. You are asked to check the engineering design calculations for a sphere-shaped satellite. At one place in the engineer's calculations you find the expression $A = 0.0872\Delta^2$, where A is the surface area of the satellite measured in square feet, and Δ is the diameter of the satellite measured in inches. Prove that the equation is valid or invalid.

11-78. The U.S. Navy is interested in your torus-shaped lifebelt design and you have been asked to supply some additional calculations. Among these is the request to supply the formula for the volume of the belt in cubic feet if the average diameter of the belt is measured in feet and the diameter of a typical cross-sectional area of the belt is measured in inches. Develop the formula.

11-79. From the window of their spacecraft two astronauts see a satellite with foreign insignia markings. They maneuver for a closer examination. Apparently the satellite has been designed in the shape of an ellipsoid. One of the astronauts quickly estimates its volume in gallons from the relationship $V = 33.8ACE$, where the major radius (A) is measured in meters, the minor radius (E) is measured in feet, and the endview depth to the center of the ellipsoid (C) is measured in centimeters. Verify the correctness of the mathematical relationship used for the calculations.

11-80. An engineer and his family are visiting in Egypt. The tour guide describes in great detail the preciseness of the mathematical relationships used by the early Egyptians in their construction projects. As an example he points out some peculiar indentations in a large stone block. He explains that these particular markings are the resultant calculations of "early day" Egyptians pertaining to the volume of the pyramids. He says that the mathematical relationship used by these engineers was $\odot = \square \uparrow$, where $\odot$ was the volume of pyramid in cubic furlongs, $\square$ was the area of the pyramid base in square leagues, and $\uparrow$ was the height of the pyramid in hectometers. The product of the area and the height equals the volume. The engineer argued that the guide was incorrect in his interpretation. Prove which was correct.

11-81. Develop the mathematical relationship for finding the weight in drams of a truncated cylinder of gold if the diameter of the circular base is measured in centimeters and the height of the piece of precious metal is measured in decimeters.

11-82. If a silver communications satellite has a mass of 126.3 lb_m at Houston, Texas, what would be its weight in newtons on the moon, where the acceleration of gravity is measured to be 162 cm/sec^2?

11-83. A volt is defined as the electric potential existing between two points when 1 joule of work is required to carry 1 coulomb of charge from one point to the other. An ampere is defined as a flow of 1 coulomb of charge per second in a conducting medium. From these definitions, derive an expression for power in watts in an electrical circuit.

11-84. An electric light bulb requires 100 w of power while burning. At what rate is heat being produced? What will be the horsepower corresponding to 100 w?

11-85. A 440-v electric motor which is 83 per cent efficient is delivering 4.20 hp to a hoist which is 76 per cent efficient. At what rate can a mass of 1155 kg be lifted?

11-86. How many kilograms of silver will be transferred in an electroplating tank by a passage of 560 amp for 1 hr? (Hint: 96,500 coulombs will deposit a gram-equivalent of an element in a plating solution.)

11-87. A window-mount type of air conditioning unit is rated at $\frac{3}{4}$ ton capacity for cooling. If the overall efficiency of the motor and compressor unit is 26 per cent, what electric current will be necessary to operate the unit continuously when connected to a 120-v alternating current power line?

11-88. A large capacitor is rated at 10,000 microfarads. If it is connected to a 6.3-v battery, how many coulombs will be required to charge it?

11-89. A capacitor used in transistor circuits is rated at 5 picofarads. How many coulombs will be required to charge it if it is connected to a 9-v battery?

11-90. The reactance in ohms of a coil of wire is given as $X_L = 2fL$, where f is the frequency of an electric current in cycles per second and L is the coil inductance in henries. Compute the reactance of a small solenoid coil whose inductance is 2.75 millihenries if the coil is connected to a 109-v line whose frequency is 412 hertz.

11-91. A galvanometer has a resistance of 612 ohms and gives a deflection of 18.0 cm for a current of 28 ma. What will be its current sensitivity (amperes per meter), and its voltage sensitivity (volts per meter)?

11-92. A current of 0.63 amp will produce 15.0 cal of heat in a small light bulb in 10.0 sec. What power is expended in the bulb and what is the lamp resistance?

11-93. A coil of resistance wire having a resistance of 3.11 ohms is immersed in a beaker containing 1.150 kg of water. At what rate is heat being produced when a current of 47.5 amp is flowing?

Bibliography

Ipsen, D. C., *Units, Dimensions, and Dimensionless Numbers,* McGraw-Hill, New York (1960).

Walshaw, A. C., *Engineering Units and Worked Examples,* Blackie and Son, London (1964).

12

Statistics and graphical analysis

Statistics

Certain statistical operations are commonly encountered in engineering work, particularly when data are acquired and evaluated. We might even say that science is based on statistics and that the scientific "laws" that we use relate not to how nature will certainly behave, but rather to how nature has behaved within limits and to how nature is likely to continue to behave under similar conditions. It is within the realm of statistics to determine what these limits are and to attempt to determine the probability of recurrence of any given set of events based on the frequency and regularity of their occurrence in the past.

If we consider some natural phenomena, such as the sun's rising in the east rather than in the west, we cannot say with certainty that the same thing will happen tomorrow. We can say, however, that as far as any records show, the sun has always risen in the east, and so far as we know, no changes in conditions have occurred to alter the probability of its rising in the east, so we conclude that it is highly probable that tomorrow's sunrise will be in the east.

In a like manner, we can make a general statement that at some given city in the United States, it will be colder on New Year's Day than it will be on the first day of July. Statistically, we can show that for many years it has always been colder on New Year's Day than on the first of July, but it is within the realm of possibility, knowing how local weather conditions can vary, that a set of weather circumstances can occur that could make, for a certain year, a colder July 1st than New Year's Day.

The probability of such an occurrence is slight but it definitely is greater than that of the sun's sudden appearance in the morning on the western horizon. Thus, we see that there not only is an uncertainty even in well-ordered natural phenomena, but also there is a degree of uncertainty of future happenings which is based on the variability in the past of certain occurrences.

Statistics then is the science of making decisions based on observation, collection, analysis, and interpretation of data that are affected by chance causes.[1] The importance of the use of statistics has been emphasized in recent years by the national effort to place a man on the moon and effect his safe return to earth.

The best statistical methods are useless unless the data obtained have been collected so that the methods are applicable. Accuracy in tabulation, in calculation, and in thought are essential ingredients to all statistical work, since the data used are themselves subject to chance errors. Care and neatness in preparing all calculations are important aids to accuracy. However, it is no less important that the engineer develop a natural skepticism and inquisitive attitude toward all data collected and toward their methods of collection, their analyses, and their interpretation.

Variables

From a statistical point of view, the chance variations which occur in measured data are a major problem in any evaluation. Fortunately, in the physical sciences and in engineering work the variables usually are easier to control and are better known than they are in some other fields, such as psychology, where animal and human behavior is being studied. For example, if we should desire to determine the relation between current and voltage in an electrical circuit, we can establish a test setup of a power source, a set of conductors, and a power receiver together with appropriate meters to measure the electrical quantities. However, we recognize that variables inherent in the test setup must be controlled, held constant, or evaluated for effects on the meter readings. Of all the possible variables, temperature is most likely to change the circuit resistance and consequently alter the data secured. Fortunately, it usually is fairly easy to maintain constant temperature conditions and then to obtain a relation between a voltage change and the corresponding current change in order to establish a relationship describing their behavior within the limits of error of the experiment. Again, if we should try other circuit conditions of power and resistance, we probably would arrive at substantially the same results; therefore, we can reasonably conclude that the ratio between the voltage change and the corresponding current change in a circuit is a constant.

On the other hand, if a psychological test were to be made to determine the effect of loss of sleep on ability to perform simple arithmetical operations, we would find quite a wide variance between subjects and even between the ability of the same subject at various times. We conclude then that the relationship of loss of sleep to arithmetical accomplishments involves variables of many sorts, most of which are hard to control or evaluate.

Normal probability law

If a large glass jar were filled to the top with marbles and placed in view of a large class of students and each student was asked to write down his estimate of the number

[1] Irving W. Burr, *Engineering Statistics and Quality Control*, McGraw-Hill, New York (1953), p. 3.

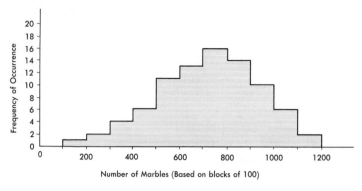

Figure 12-1   A histogram of estimates of marbles in a jar.

of marbles in the jar, it is extremely unlikely that every student would estimate the same number and that this number would be the exact number of marbles in the jar. Rather it is likely that if the answers were compiled, a pattern of distribution of estimates would focus upon a certain extimated number of marbles.

If, for simplicity in plotting, the estimates are grouped into blocks to the nearest 100 marbles, a graph of this distribution might look like Figure 12-1. This figure is plotted so that the width of a column is equal to the interval, in this case 100 marbles, and the height is equal to the frequency, which is the number of persons making any given block of estimates.

If the number of persons making estimates of the marbles were doubled and the blocks within which the estimates fall were made smaller, the histogram probably would take on an appearance similar to Figure 12-2.

If this process were to be continued, we would see that the appearance of the graph would begin to assume the shape of a smooth curve. Although the proof of this statement is beyond the scope of this book, we can show that for a large number of types of observations, the pattern becomes similar to the graph in Figure 12-3.

This graph shows the usual frequency distributions of a large number of observations and is typical of the distribution of any set of chance events. In practice, it can be taller or shorter, fatter or thinner, but it is usually symmetrical and bell shaped.

If a person should take ten coins and toss them on a table many times and keep a tally of the number of heads that show up each time, he would find that the

Figure 12-2   A histogram of a large number of estimates.

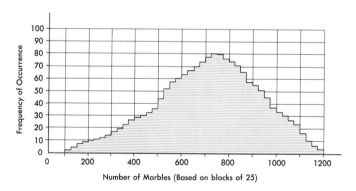

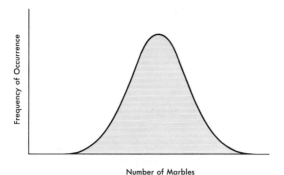

Figure 12-3 Normal probability curve.

occurrence of ten heads is extremely rare, that the occurrences of zero heads is extremely rare, and that the greatest number of occurrences is for five heads to show up. If the frequencies of occurrences is plotted against the number of heads, we would find that the bell shaped curve described above will result.

This graph, which pictures the distribution of frequencies of certain chance events, is called the *normal probability curve*. It is of great use in many forms of testing in engineering and science.

The horizontal axis (abscissa) of the graph represents the values of the measurements made (X_1, X_2, X_3, etc.) and the vertical axis (ordinate) represents the fraction of the total number of observations made corresponding to each value of X.

The general mathematical expression for the probability curve is a log function of the form $y = Ce^{Kx^2}$. From an inspection of the probability curve determined either by trial or by derivation, several principles can be observed:

1. Small errors occur more frequently than large ones.
2. Errors of any given size are as likely to be positive as they are to be negative.
3. Very large random errors seldom occur.

Some fundamental statistical measures

The terms "arithmetic mean," "median," and "mode" are used extensively in statistical work. These terms will be defined here in order that the student can gain a better appreciation of their use.

Arithmetic mean This term is used to denote the point about which the data tend to cluster. It is often referred to as the *average* or *central tendency*. It is calculated by obtaining the sum of the individual measurements and dividing this quantity by the number of measurements made. This process may be represented mathematically by:

$$\overline{X} = \sum_{i=1}^{i=n} \frac{X_i}{n} = \frac{X_1 + X_2 + X_3 \cdots X_n}{n}$$

where $\overline{X}$ = arithmetic mean
$\quad\quad X_i$ = individual measurements
$\quad\quad\ n$ = total number of measurements

Example Find the arithmetic mean of the following data:

$$7, 4, 9, 5, 6, 8, 3$$

$$\bar{X} = \frac{7 + 4 + 9 + 5 + 6 + 8 + 3}{7} = \frac{42}{7} = 6$$

Median This term is similar to the mean in that it is also a measure of the tendency of the data to collect about a central point. The median is the midpoint (not average) of a group of data. When the total number of data is odd, the median is the middle number of the set of numbers. If the total number of data is even, the median is the arithmetic mean of the two middlemost numbers in the set.

Examples

a. 4, 6, 9, 10, 11, 12, 15   Median = 10
b. 5, 7, 7, 8, 10, 11, 15, 19   Median = 9
c. 2, 5, 7, 9, 9, 11, 15, 16   Median = 9

Mode As in the other cases, the mode is also a measure of the "central tendency" of the data. The mode is that value which occurs with the greatest frequency in the set of data. It is the most common value, and for this reason it may exist in some sets of data. In other cases there may be more than one mode.

Examples

a. 2, 4, 5, 5, 5, 3, 2, 6   Mode = 5
b. 2, 3, 4, 6, 7, 8   There is no mode
c. 2, 3, 4, 4, 5, 5, 6, 7   There are two modes—4 and 5
                                (This is called bimodal)

Deviations from the normal curve

The most common deviation from the normal probability curve is a condition known as "skewness." In this condition the curve is distorted, and the high part of the curve corresponding to the greatest frequency is nearer to one end, rather than being in the middle. One of the most common causes of this nonnormality is that the distribution may be restricted from going beyond a certain point. This situation would exist, for example, if the measurement has a physical limit of zero. Such a graph could also be formed if the scores on an examination given to students were plotted, and the test had been much too easy or much too difficult. In another case, if the length of a group of parts made by an improperly adjusted machine are measured with a steel scale, the plot of the measurements could be distorted or skewed.

Another abnormal condition is produced when the group being sampled is not homogeneous. The curve produced could have two peaks and would be known as a "bimodal" distribution. Such a plot could be obtained if an examination were given to a group of students some of whom were rather dull and the remainder of whom were very apt and intelligent. As another example, if a box of similar type of resistors is measured to determine the distribution of resistance values, and the box contains resistors from two different machines set to produce slightly different values of resistance, it is likely that a "two-humped" graph would result, showing that two somewhat independent groups are present in the test sequence.

If deviations from the normal curve are excessive, accurate results cannot be obtained from the statistical tools described in the following topics. Usually it is necessary to examine the method of measurement to see whether systematic errors are present or to examine the group being measured to determine whether a proper sample is taken, so that results can be made to approximate the normal curve.

Theory of errors

As suggested above, the normal curve may be considered to be the frequency distribution of the infinite number of possible measurements of the quantity being observed. When practical, *all possible* measurements in a given situation should be tabulated. When this can be accomplished it is said to be a study of the *total population* or *universe*. In many situations such measurement is not possible. For example, if someone wanted to obtain the heights of all the men in the world, he could not do so. In such cases, it is necessary to examine a small part of the total population, called a *sample*. If the *sample* is representative of the *total population*, certain important conclusions can be drawn about the nature of the *total population*. The size of the *sample* chosen will depend upon how close it is desired to approximate the *total population*.

Standard deviation   Since, in any group of measured quantities the true value is never known, it is desirable to have a means of estimating the uncertainty, and consequently the accuracy, of a measurement. In order to do this, we must make use of several statistical tools, one of which is known as the "Standard Deviation." The standard deviation may be calculated for a *total population* (usually designated as σ)[2] and for the *sample*. For the sample, the standard deviation is given by the equation

$$s = \sqrt{\frac{\Sigma(X_i - \bar{X})^2}{n - 1}}$$

Where σ and s represent the standard deviations for the respective situations, Σ is the Greek capital letter *sigma*, which represents the sum, $(X_i - \bar{X})$ represents the deviation of a single observation from the mean, and n is the number of observations. For example, if we weigh a block of wood on ten different scales and record the weight from each weighting in a tabular form, the deviations from the mean can be obtained readily by subtracting any single reading from the mean of the values. The standard deviation for the *sample* can then be calculated as shown in Table 12-1.

From this table the value of $\Sigma(X_i - \bar{X})^2 = 274$, which, if substituted in the expression for standard deviation, gives

$$s = \sqrt{\frac{274}{10 - 1}} = \sqrt{\frac{274}{9}} = \sqrt{30.44} = 5.52 \text{ g}$$

The use of the standard deviation will be discussed in more detail later in this chapter.

[2]Greek letters are usually used to represent descriptive quantities about the population whereas Arabic letters are used to represent descriptive quantities about a sample.

Table 12-1

Trial	Weight in grams	$X_i - \bar{X}$	$(X_i - \bar{X})^2$
1	522	+10	100
2	506	− 6	36
3	513	+ 1	1
4	510	− 2	4
5	519	+ 7	49
6	508	− 4	16
7	512	0	0
8	504	− 8	64
9	512	0	0
10	514	+ 2	4
	$\Sigma = 5120$	$\Sigma = 0$	$\Sigma = 274$

$\bar{X} = \text{Mean} = {}^{5120}\!/_{10} = 512$

Population dispersion

If the plot of a series of measurements is made to produce a histogram and the tops of the rectangles are connected by a smooth curve, the bell-shaped curve is a typical probability curve.

After a normal probability curve is obtained from a histogram, if the values of σ (assuming a *total* population study) are plotted on the abscissa, it will be found that about 68.27 per cent of the measurements will fall within the $\pm 1\sigma$ range of the mean (that is, one standard deviation on either side of the mean). This means that there is a 68.27 per cent chance that the value of any single observation will fall between $+\sigma$ and $-\sigma$ of the mean, $\bar{X}$.

Referring to Figure 12-4, we can show experimentally that 68.27 per cent of the values will be plotted between $-\sigma$ and $+\sigma$. However, this percentage can be shown best where a large number of observations, 100 or more for example, are made.

If an abscissa value of $\pm 2\sigma$ is plotted on a probability curve, it can be shown that about 95.45 per cent of the observations will fall between -2σ and $+2\sigma$ of $\bar{X}$, Figure 12-5.

Figure 12-4 Normal probability curve.

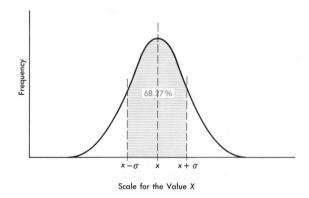

Scale for the Value X

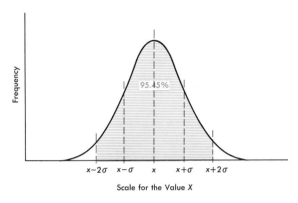

Figure 12-5 Sigma error on a normal probability curve.

Use of probability curve

A probability curve does not give the true value of a quantity being measured. If we assume that the mean, or arithmetical average, of a number of observations is acceptable as a value to use to present a measured quantity, than the standard deviation gives an indication of the reliability of any single observation.

Standard error

It usually is desirable to evaluate the uncertainty of the arithmetic mean. We know that the uncertainty of the mean, $\bar{X}$, is considerably less than the uncertainty of any single observation, (X_i). The uncertainty of the mean can be expressed in the following form:

$$\sigma_m = \frac{\sigma}{\sqrt{n}} \text{ and this is usually approximated by } s_m = \frac{s}{\sqrt{n}}$$

where σ_m is the standard error of the mean, S_m is the standard deviation of the mean, s is the standard deviation of a sample, and n is the number of observations in the sample.

Example   The mean of 25 measurements of an angle gives a value of $32°17.1'$, s is $1.2'$. What is the probable range of the true value?

Solution
   1. The mean of $32° 17.1'$ is the most likely true value.

   2. $s_m = \dfrac{1.2'}{5} = 0.24' \cong \pm 0.2'$

There is a 68.27 per cent certainty that the true value lies between $32° 16.9'$ and $32° 17.3' (\pm s_m)$.
   3. There is a 95.45 per cent certainty that the true value lies between $32° 16.7'$ and $32° 17.5' (\pm 2 s_m)$.

Since the true value is never known, an estimate based on mathematical processes can be made as to the confidence that can be placed in the mean as an assumed true value.

Problems

12-1. A series of weighings of a sample of metal powder are made with the following results:

Weight in grams of a sample

2.020	2.021	2.021	2.019	2.019
2.018	2.021	2.018	2.021	2.017
2.017	2.020	2.016	2.019	2.020

Compute the mean, s, and s_m values for the weighings. What is the probable weight of the sample?

12-2. A series of measurements of the length of a concrete runway is made using a steel tape. The results (in meters) are tabulated below:

1363.7	1364.5	1364.0	1363.8	1364.0
1364.1	1363.9	1364.1	1363.9	

Compute the mean and give the s_m limits for the measurements.

12-3. A series of readings was taken, using an electronic interval timer, for one complete swing of a pendulum to occur. The data are tabulated as follows:

Time in seconds	Number of occurrences	Time in seconds	Number of occurrences
1.851	1	1.859	18
1.852	3	1.860	15
1.853	6	1.861	12
1.854	9	1.862	10
1.855	12	1.863	5
1.856	14	1.864	4
1.857	18	1.865	2
1.858	19	1.866	1

What is the mean time of a swing, and what would be the standard error of the mean?

12-4. The test scores on an intelligence test given to a class of elementary students are tabulated as follows:

35	58	46	67	47	53
55	38	50	47	50	53
46	54	45	52	62	48
45	51	48	42	48	65
51	55	60	53	55	
56	43	47	58	34	
42	55	46	59	68	
60	52	61	39	31	
52	44	42	39	70	

Plot a histogram of the scores and sketch in a probability curve. Compute the mean, median, and mode. Is there any tendency to skewness or bimodality? Does the mean value of the scores have a significance comparable to the mean of, for example, a series of measurements of the length of a steel block?

12-5. Take ten coins and toss them at least 25 times, keeping count of the number of heads and tails for each toss. Plot a probability curve and determine whether s does represent 68.27 per cent of the total observations.

12-6. The distribution of ages of a group of recruits at an Army camp is given on page 261. Plot a histogram and sketch a probability curve for the ages. Show the s and $2s$ locations. Does this graph show any unusual departures from a standard probability curve? Compute the mean, median and mode.

Age in years and months	Number of persons	Age in years and months	Number of persons
18–1	1	19–7	9
18–2	0	19–8	5
18–3	1	19–9	3
18–4	3	19–10	3
18–5	8	19–11	0
18–6	5	19–12	2
18–7	8	20–1	5
18–8	10	20–2	1
18–9	14	20–3	0
18–10	7	20–4	2
18–11	12	20–5	6
18–12	11	20–6	0
19–1	11	20–7	1
19–2	6	20–8	0
19–3	10	20–9	2
19–4	8	20–10	0
19–5	7	20–11	0
19–6	6	20–12	0

12-7. Measurements were made of the lengths of a number of steel rods which were supposed to be cut to a length of 6.80 in. The measurements are as follows:

6.81	6.80	6.79	6.80
6.82	6.80	6.78	6.80
6.81	6.83	6.79	6.77
6.82	6.80	6.78	6.80
6.81	6.81	6.79	6.87

What is the average length of the rods, and what maximum tolerance can be set up if 95.45 per cent of the rods are to be acceptable?

Graphical analysis

Graphs are a valuable aid in presenting many types of information where facts must be readily grasped. They aid in the analysis of engineering data and facilitate the presentation of statistical information. Graphs generally can be classified as those used for technical purposes and those used for general presentation of information. To be of greatest value, graphs should be prepared in accord with the best current practice.

A graphical display of information may take any of several forms, depending upon the type of information to be presented and the use to be made of the information. For rapid dissemination of information, pictographs are convenient. Where more exact representation is desired, bar graphs or circle graphs may be employed. Most engineering data are displayed in the line graphs. Such information usually is more exact and offers opportunity to interpolate values, to extrapolate values, and to draw conclusions as to the behavior of the variable quantities involved. Examples of several types of graphs are shown in Figures 12-6 to 12-10.

Illustration 12-1

Graphs are an important method of displaying data for rapid visualization of the variations of one quantity with respect to another. In this picture engineers are discussing a curve of measured valve positions in an automobile engine as compared with theoretical curves of cam contours to determine appropriate changes that may be necessary in the manufacture of the cams.

Since line graphs offer the best opportunity to present engineering data, the discussion here will be concerned chiefly with the preparation and use of line graphs. The general form of the graph sheet illustrated by Figure 12-11 is the form used by the majority of engineering schools and is the style widely used in industry.

Notes on the preparation of graphs

1. Graphs usually are prepared in pencil on printed coordinate graph paper. Carbon paper backing should be used where sharpness of reproduction is a factor. For more permanent work or for display purposes, India ink should be used.

2. Arrange the data in tabular form for convenience in plotting, and determine the type of scales that most logically portay the functional relationship between the variables (see Figure 12-11.)

3. Graphs usually are designated by naming ordinate values first, then abscissa quantities. It is customary to plot the dependent variable along the ordinate and the independent variable along the abscissa.

Illustration 12-2
Engineers use principles of graphics in many phases of their work. In this picture, two engineers are investigating methods of detecting satellites by use of a polar chart display.

Figure 12-6 A pictograph (data comparative in nature).

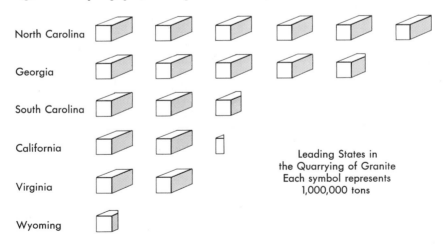

North Carolina

Georgia

South Carolina

California

Virginia

Wyoming

Leading States in
the Quarrying of Granite
Each symbol represents
1,000,000 tons

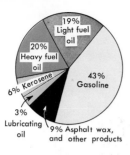

Approximate yield of products
obtained during the refining of
petroleum

Figure 12-7 A circle graph (data expressed as parts of a whole).

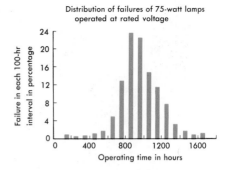

Figure 12-8 A vertical bar graph (a family of individual sets of data).

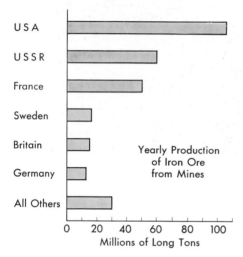

Yearly Production
of Iron Ore
from Mines

Figure 12-9 A horizontal bar graph (numerical data).

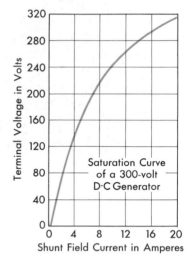

Figure 12-10 A line graph used for display purposes.

4. Make a trial computation to select the scale on each axis.

$$\text{Scale} = \frac{\text{Range in the Variable}}{\text{Scale Length Available}}$$

5. The scale must be suitable for the paper used. For graph paper having 20 divisions per inch, scale divisions of 1, 2, 5, 10, or a multiple of these numbers are desirable for ease of plotting and reading. Do not use a scale that will require awkward fractions in the smallest calibration on the paper. The scale should be consistent with the precision of the data. If the numbers are very large or very small, they may be written as a number times ten to a power; for example $(3.22)(10)^{-5}$, or $(7.50)(10)^{6}$.

6. It is desirable to show zero as the beginning of the ordinate and abscissa quantities unless this would compress the curve unnecessarily. The origin is usually placed in the lower left corner except in cases where both positive and negative

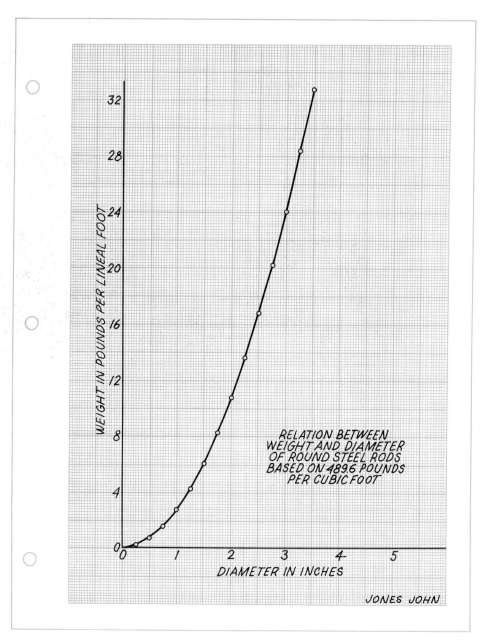

Figure 12-11

values of a function are to be plotted. In such cases the origin should be located so all desired values can be shown.

7. Printed rectangular coordinate paper is not normally available with sufficient margins to accommodate the axes and the description of the quantities plotted. Therefore the axes should be set in far enough from the edge of the paper to allow for lettering. The sheet may be turned so that the abscissa is along either the short or long side of the paper. If the graph is prepared for a report, the holes in the paper should be either to the left or at the top of the sheet.

Illustration 12-3
Well-prepared charts and graphs serve an important function in clarifying the intent of technical presentations.

8. Lettering usually is three squares, or approximately $\frac{3}{20}$ in. high. Either vertical or slant lettering may be used.

9. The ordinate and abscissa variables together with their respective units of measure should be labeled. For example: WEIGHT IN POUNDS.

10. The plotted points are fine, tiny dots in pencil. After the points are located, draw a circle, not more than $\frac{1}{16}$ in. in diameter, around each point. Where multiple curves are plotted on one sheet, the points for each curve may be identified by using distinctive identification symbols such as squares, triangles, diamonds, or other simple geometric figures. Distinctive line work such as solid line, dashed line, or long dash-short dash also may be used to aid identification.

11. Graphs may be drawn for theoretical relationships, empirical relationships, or measured relationships. Curves of theoretical relationships will not normally have point designations. Empirical relationships should form smooth curves or straight lines, depending upon the form of the mathematical expression used. Datum points in measured relationships, not supported by mathematical theory or empirical relationships, should be connected by straight lines drawn from point to point. Otherwise, the data obtained from measured relationships will be drawn to average the plotted points. For this reason curves showing measured data do not necessarily go from center to center of the points.

12. Much experimentally determined data when plotted will show a dispersion of the points about an average position due to the many variable factors entering

Figure 12-12 An example of a graph displaying data which were subject to considerable variation. Obviously the curves can be only approximately located. Such curves are sometimes referred to as "paintbrush" curves.

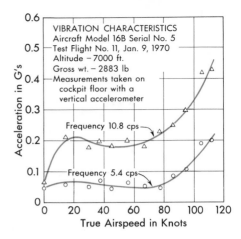

into the measurement. For this condition draw a smooth curve or a straight line, as the data indicate, which as nearly as possible will average the plotted points. A light pencil freehand line will aid in locating the average, but the final line should be mechanically drawn. The example of Figure 12-12 is taken from an actual test to show the dispersion that may occur.

13. In drawing the final curve do not draw the line through the symbols that enclose the plotted points, but rather stop at the perimeter.

14. The title of the graph should include the names of the plotted quantities and should include other descriptive information such as sizes, weights, names of equipment, date that the data were obtained, where data were obtained, serial numbers of apparatus, name of manufacturer of apparatus, and any other information that would help describe the graph.

15. The title should be placed on the sheet where it will not interfere with the curve. The title section of display graphs is usually placed across the top of the sheet. Simple graphs that comprise parts of reports frequently have the title in either the lower right quadrant or the upper left quadrant.

16. The name of the person preparing the graph and the date the graph is plotted should be placed in the lower right hand corner of the sheet.

Problems on graphs

12-8. Plot a graph showing the relation of weight to diameter for round steel rods. Plot values for every quarter-inch to and including $3\frac{1}{2}$ in. in diameter. (See model Figure 12-11).

Weight of round steel rods in pounds per lineal foot (based on 489.6 lb/ft³)

Size, in.	Weight, lb/ft	Size, in.	Weight, lb/ft
$\frac{1}{4}$	0.167	2	10.66
$\frac{1}{2}$	0.668	$2\frac{1}{4}$	13.50
$\frac{3}{4}$	1.50	$2\frac{1}{2}$	16.64
1	2.68	$2\frac{3}{4}$	20.20
$1\frac{1}{4}$	4.17	3	24.00
$1\frac{1}{2}$	6.00	$3\frac{1}{4}$	28.30
$1\frac{3}{4}$	8.18	$3\frac{1}{2}$	32.70

12-9. Plot a graph showing the relation of normal barometric pressure of air to altitude. Plot values up to and including 15,000 ft.

Altitude, feet above sea level	Normal barometric pressure, inches of mercury	Altitude, feet above sea level	Normal barometric pressure, inches of mercury
0	29.95	5000	24.9
500	29.39	6000	24.0
1000	28.86	7000	23.1
1500	28.34	8000	22.2
2000	27.82	9000	21.4
2500	27.32	10000	20.6
3000	26.82	15000	16.9
4000	25.84		

12-10. Plot a graph showing the relation between horsepower transmitted by cold drawn steel shafting and diameter for a speed of 72 rpm based on the formula

$$hp = \frac{D^3 R}{50}$$

where hp = horsepower
D = diameter of shaft, in.
R = rpm of shaft

Calculate and plot values for every inch diameter up to and including 8 in.

12-11. Plot a graph for the following experimental data showing the relation between the period in seconds and the mass of a vibrating spiral spring.

Period in seconds	Mass in grams	Period in seconds	Mass in grams
0.246	10	0.650	70
0.348	20	0.740	90
0.430	30	0.810	110
0.495	40	0.900	130
0.570	50	0.950	150

12-12. Using data in Problem 12-11 plot a graph between period squared and mass on a vibrating spring.

12-13. Plot a graph of the variation of the boiling point of water with pressure.

Boiling point, °C	Pressure, cm of mercury	Boiling point, °C	Pressure, cm of mercury
33	3.8	98	72.9
44	5.3	102	85.8
63	17.2	105	93.7
79	34.0	107	102.2
87	48.1	110	113.5
94	69.1		

12-14. *a.* Plot a graph showing the variation of the following measured values of sliding force with the normal force for a wood block on a horizontal wood surface.

Sliding force in grams	Normal force in grams
100	359
130	462
155	555
185	659
210	765
240	859

b. Determine the slope of the line plotted and compare with the average value of the coefficient of sliding friction obtained from individual readings of normal force and sliding force.

Slope = $\tan \theta$ (where θ is the angle that the line makes with the abscissa axis) $\qquad \tan \theta = \dfrac{y_2 - y_1}{x_2 - x_1}$

12-15. Plot the variation of pressure with volume, using data as obtained from a Boyle's law apparatus.

Pressure, cm of mercury	Volume, cm^3	Pressure, cm of mercury	Volume, cm^3
50.3	23.2	76.8	15.1
52.5	22.4	79.7	14.7
54.5	21.5	82.7	14.1
56.9	20.9	84.2	13.6
59.4	19.6	87.9	13.2
63.0	18.5	90.6	12.8
65.3	17.8	93.5	12.5
67.2	17.3	95.7	12.3
72.6	16.1	101.9	11.4
74.5	15.6		

12-16. Using data in Problem 12-15, plot a graph of the relation between the pressure and the reciprocal of the volume.

12-17. Plot the relation between magnetic flux density in kilolines per square centimeter (B) and magnetizing force in gilberts per centimeter (H) for a specimen of tool steel. This graph will form what is customarily called a *B-H* curve.

B Kilolines per cm^2	H Gilberts per cm	B Kilolines per cm^2	H Gilberts per cm
9.00	27.1	14.66	189.7
11.80	54.2	14.86	216.8
13.02	81.3	14.98	243.9
13.75	108.4	15.23	271.0
14.09	135.5	15.35	298.1
14.22	162.6	15.57	325.2

12-18. The formula for converting temperatures in degrees Fahrenheit to the equivalent reading in degrees Celsius is

$$C° = \tfrac{5}{9}(F° - 32°)$$

Plot a graph so that by taking any given Fahrenheit reading between 0° and 220° and using the graph, the corresponding Celsius reading can be determined.

12-19. Plot a graph showing the relation between drill speed and size of drill for carbon steel drills in brass.

Diameter of drill, in.	Drill speed, rpm	Diameter of drill, in.	Drill speed, rpm
$1/16$	6112	$5/8$	612
$1/8$	3056	$11/16$	555
$3/16$	2036	$3/4$	508
$1/4$	1528	$13/16$	474
$5/16$	1222	$7/8$	438
$3/8$	1018	$15/16$	407
$7/16$	874	1	382
$1/2$	764	$1 1/16$	359
$9/16$	679	$1 1/8$	340

12-20. Plot a graph showing the variation of temperature with electric current through a heating coil, using the following data, which were taken in the laboratory.

Current, amp	Temperature change, °C
0.0	0.0
0.46	0.5
1.05	1.2
1.50	2.0
2.06	5.1
2.20	7.7
2.35	8.8

12-21. The following data were taken in the laboratory for a 16-cp, carbon-filament electric light bulb. Plot a resistance-voltage curve.

Voltage in volts	Resistance in ohms	Voltage in volts	Resistance in ohms
10	169.5	70	114.5
20	140.0	80	113.2
30	129.0	90	112.5
40	121.5	100	111.8
50	117.0	110	111.2
60	113.2		

12-22. The following data were taken in the laboratory for a 60-w, gas-filled, tungsten-filament light bulb. Plot a resistance-voltage curve.

Voltage in volts	Resistance in ohms	Voltage in volts	Resistance in ohms
10	47.5	70	160.2
20	77.5	80	170.0
30	100.3	90	178.3
40	119.0	100	189.0
50	132.6	110	200.1
60	144.2		

12-23. The equation which expresses the variations of electric current with time in an inductive circuit is

$$i = I_0 \epsilon^{(-Rt)/L}$$

where

i is the current in amperes

I_0 is the original steady-state value of current and is a constant

ϵ is the base of the natural system of logarithms and is approximately 2.7183

R is the resistance in ohms in the circuit and is constant

t is the time in seconds measured as the current i varies

L is the inductance in henries and is a constant

Let

$$I_0 = 0.16 \text{ amp}$$
$$R = 1.2 \text{ ohms}$$
$$L = 0.5 \text{ henry}$$

Calculate and plot values of i as t varies from 0 to 0.5 sec.

12-24. Plot the variations of efficiency with load for a $\frac{1}{4}$-hp, 110-v, direct-current electric motor, using the following data taken in the laboratory.

Load output in horsepower	Efficiency in per cent
0	0
0.019	24.0
0.050	42.0
0.084	44.9
0.135	50.7
0.175	56.5
0.195	58.0
0.248	59.1
0.306	58.0
0.326	56.2

Plotting on semilogarithmic graph paper

The preceding discussion has concerned the graphing of data on rectangular coordinate paper. There are cases where the variation of the data is such that it may be desirable to compress the larger values of a variable. To do this, semilogarithmic graph paper may be used. Semilog paper, as it is usually called, is graph paper which has one coordinate ruled in equal increments and the other coordinate ruled in increments which are logarithmically expressed. When plotting on this type of paper, it can be turned so that either the horizontal coordinate or the vertical coordinate will have the logarithmic divisions. Semilog paper is available in either one-cycle, two-cycle, three-cycle, four-cycle, or five-cycle ruling.

A semilog grid is especially useful in the derivation of relationships where it is difficult to analyze the rate of change or trend as depicted on rectangular coordinate paper. Data that will plot as a curve on rectangular coordinate paper may plot as a straight line on semilog paper. In many instances this is desirable because the trends are more easily detected. Where straight lines do not occur on a semilog grid, the rate of change is varying.

The same rules apply for plotting on semilog paper as were given for rectangular coordinate paper, except that the numbering of the logarithmic divisions cannot begin with zero. Each cycle on the paper represents a multiple of ten in value, and the graduations may begin with any power of ten. When reading from a logarithmic graph, interpolations should be made logarithmically rather than arithmetically. An example of data plotted on semilog paper is shown in Figure 12-13.

Plotting on log-log graph paper

Log-log graph paper, as its name indicates, has both coordinate divisions expressed as logarithmic functions. This subdivision of the sheet serves to compress the larger values of the plotted data. In addition, data that plotted as a curve on rectangular coordinate paper may plot as a straight line on log-log paper. For example, the graphs of algebraic equations representing multiplication, division, powers, and roots may be straight lines on log-log paper.

As an example, the plot of the algebraic expression

$$X = Y^2$$

on rectangular coordinate paper is a parabola. However, if its values are plotted on log-log paper, it is equivalent to taking the logarithm of the expression

$$\log X = 2\,(\log Y)$$

This expression has the form of a linear equation having a slope of 2. Thus, a relationship of variable quantities that may be expressed as $X = Y^2$ when plotted on log-log paper will be a straight line with a slope of 2.

Log-log paper may be secured in $8\frac{1}{2}''$ by $11''$ or larger sheets that have one or more cycles for each coordinate direction. The axis lines are drawn on the sheet in a manner similar to the procedure described for plotting on rectangular coordinate paper. However, the beginning values for the axes will never be zero but will always be a power of ten.

An example of data plotted on log-log paper is shown in Figure 12-14.

Plotting on polar graph paper

Polar graphs are sometimes used where a variable quantity is to be examined with respect to various angular positions. The same general principles of plotting apply as were outlined for rectangular plots except that the outer border is marked off in degrees for the independent variable, and either the horizontal or vertical radial line is marked off for the dependent variable.

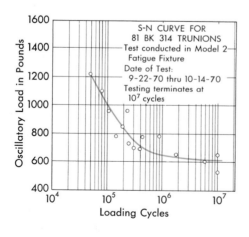

Figure 12-13

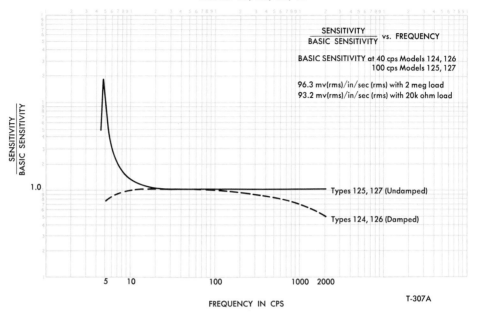

MB MANUFACTURING COMPANY
A Division of Textron Inc.

TYPICAL FREQUENCY RESPONSE — MB VIBRATION PICKUPS
MODELS 124, 125, 126, 127

Figure 12-14

Polar graphs frequently are used to display the light output of luminous sources, the response of microphone pickups, and the behavior of rotating objects at various angular positions. An example of a graph plotted on polar coordinate paper is shown in Figure 12-15.

Determining empirical equations from curves

Experimentally determined data when plotted usually will approximate a straight line or a simple curve. By plotting experimentally determined data, it is frequently possible to obtain a mathematical equation that closely expresses the relations of the variables.

Many equations encountered in engineering work have the form

$$y - k = m(x - h)^n$$

where n may have either positive or negative values. If the exponent n is 1, the equation reduces to the familiar straight-line slope-intercept form. If the value of n is positive, the equation is a parabolic type, but if the value of n is negative, the equation is a hyperbolic type. This expression affords a means of securing empirical equations from experimental data.

If experimental data are to be plotted and an empirical equation is to be determined, it is advisable first to plot the test data on rectangular coordinate paper in order to gain some idea of the shape of the graph. If the locus approximates a straight line, the general equation $y = mx + b$ may be assumed. The Y intercept b and the

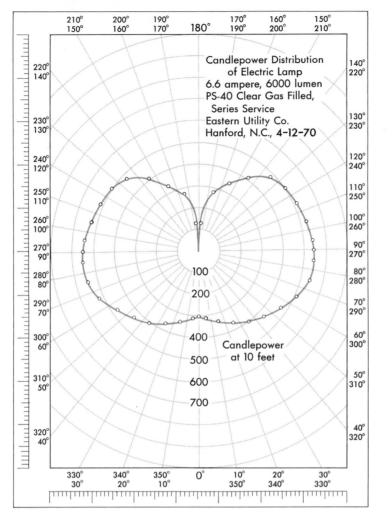

Figure 12-15

slope *m* may be measured by taking a straight line drawn so as to average the plotted points.

Figure 12-16 is a plot of data taken in the laboratory for a test involving the magnitude of frictional forces. A straight line is drawn to average the plotted points, and the slope of the line is found by taking any two points along the line and determining the X component and the Y component between the two points according to the plotted scales. In this example the slope is approximately 65/500, or 0.13. If the line is projected to the Y axis, corresponding to a value of $x = 0$, the Y intercept is seen to correspond approximately to 14 lb. An approximate equation of these data would be $y = 0.13x + 14$.

If a plot of experimental data on rectangular coordinate paper should appear to be approximately parabolic in shape, an empirical equation may be obtained by plotting the datum points on log-log paper. The slope of the line determines the exponent of the independent variable, and the y intercept, when $x = 1$, defines the coefficient of the independent variable. For example, a plot of data taken in the laboratory is shown in Figure 12-17.

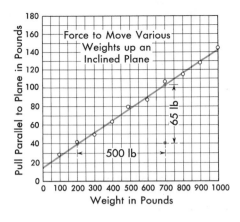

Figure 12-16

A straight line is drawn to average the plotted points. Using a linear scale, measure the X-component and Y-component values for two points on the plotted line. The slope of the graph in Figure 12-17 is 2.2/2.0, or 1.1, and the Y intercept is 23.3. Substituting these values in the basic equation of a parabola gives $y = 23.3(x^{1.1})$ for the approximate equation.

In case the plotted points on log-log paper curve upward as x increases, the expression may approximate the form $y = ax^n + k$. To straighten the curve, try subtracting a constant from the y values. By trial and error, a value of k may be found that will cause the plot to follow a straight line. If this is done, the approximate equation may be determined.

If log-log paper is not available, it is still possible to use rectangular coordinate paper to plot a curve as a straight line. If the data indicate the equation may be of the form $y = ax^n$, we can take the logarithm of the equation and plot logarithmic values for the datum points. For example, if we express $y = ax^n$ in logarithmic form, it will be $\log y = \log a + n \log x$. Let $v = \log y$; $C = \log a$; and $u = \log x$. The straight-line equation will then be

$$v = nu + C$$

Plot the logarithm of the data values on rectangular coordinate paper. Measure the

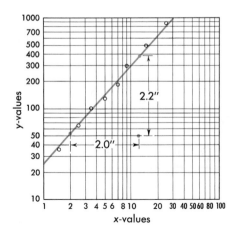

Figure 12-17

slope and the Y intercept. Assume that the slope is measured to be 1.8, using the scales of the plot, and the Y intercept is 0.755. The straight line equation is

$$v = 1.8u + 0.755$$

or $$\log y = 1.8 \log x + 0.755$$

Since $$C = \log a = 0.755$$

then $$a = 5.69$$

The equation then is $$y = \mathbf{5.69}(x^{1.8})$$

There are other methods of determing empirical equations, such as the method of least squares, but a complete discussion of such techniques is beyond the scope of this book. Also, data that plot into curves following harmonic laws or exponential laws are not discussed here.

Nomographs

Nomographs are a pictorial method of solving problems which involve equations of various types. Nomographs consist of scales graduated so that distances are proportional to the variables involved. A simple example would be a single line having graduations corresponding to inches on one side and graduations corresponding to centimeters on the other (see Figure 12-18).

The layout of nomographs is beyond the scope of this book, but since the solution to problems involving repeated readings of process or laboratory data may be obtained readily by use of nomographs, a brief discussion of the types and uses of the charts is presented.

Figure 12-18 is an example of a *functional chart* . Charts of this type are frequently used when two variables are related by a constant coefficient.

An *alignment chart* is another example of a nomograph. A simple form consists of three parallel lines graduated so that a straight line passing through points on two of the graduated lines will intersect the third graduated line at a point that will satisfy the relations between the variables (see Figure 12-19).

Example Given an alignment chart for the equation $x + y = z$. Solve for the value of z when $x = 4$ and $y = 2$.

Solution Lay out a straight line connecting the point on the x scale corresponding to 4 and the point on the y scale corresponding to 2. The intersection of this line with the z scale at 6 is a solution to this problem. Repeating this procedure with

Figure 12-18

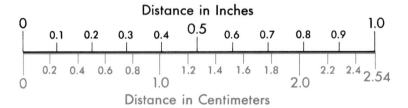

Distance in Inches

Distance in Centimeters

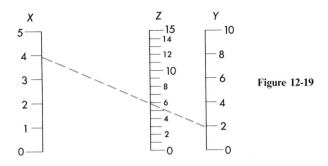

Figure 12-19

other values will enable one to locate the position of the z scale with regard to the x and y scales.

Another form of alignment chart that is of considerable use is the Z chart, so named because the center graduated line runs diagonally. It may be set up to provide a solution to equations of the form $x = (y)(z)$. Other alignment charts may provide solutions to problems having three or four variable quantities by employing multiple interior graduated lines.

Alignment charts are all used in the same manner; that is, a straight line connects two points on the graduated lines and intersects another graduated line, thereby providing a solution to a given problem.

As an example, the nomograph given in Figure 12-20 permits an evaluation of factors concerned with the life of a ball bearing. The straight line drawn across the

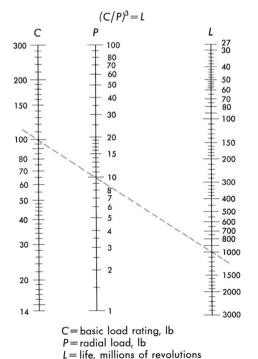

Figure 12-20   Load nomograph.

C = basic load rating, lb
P = radial load, lb
L = life, millions of revolutions

chart shows that for a basic load rating of 100 lb and a radial load of 10 lb, the expected service life of the ball bearing should be a billion revolutions.

Problems

12-25. Plot the values given in Problem 12-8 on semilog paper.
12-26. Plot the values given in Problem 12-11 on semilog paper.
12-27. Plot the values given in Problem 12-15 on semilog paper.
12-28. Plot the values given in Problem 12-23 on semilog paper.
12-29. Plot the values given in Problem 12-8 on log-log paper.
12-30. Plot the values given in Problem 12-10 on log-log paper.
12-31. Plot the values given in Problem 12-15 on log-log-paper.

Determine the slope of the line and give the approximate form of the equation shown by the plot.

12-32. The following data were taken from an acoustical and electrical calibration curve for a Type 1126 microphone. The test was run with an incident sound level of 85 db perpendicular to the face of the microphone.

Frequency, cps	Relative response, db
20	−40
50	−29
100	−19
400	−5
1,000	+1
2,000	+1
3,000	0
6,000	−4
10,000	−11

Plot a graph on semilog paper showing the decibel response with frequency.
12-33. The electrical frequency response of a Type X501 microphone is

Frequency, cps	Relative response, db
20	−40
40	−33
80	−22
100	−18
200	−11
400	−5
600	−2
1,000	+1
2,000	+2
4,000	−1
6,000	−4
10,000	−10

Plot a graph on semilog paper showing the decibel response with frequency.
12-34. According to recommendations of the Thrust Bearing Engineers Committee, bearing loads for bearings lubricated with oil having a viscosity range of 115 to 165 Saybolt sec at 100°F should fall between values:

Speed, rps	Bearing load, lb
10	400
100	170
1,000	74
10,000	32
40,000	20
10	1,700
100	650
1,000	275
10,000	123
40,000	70

Plot graphs of bearing loads against speeds to show the range of acceptable operating speeds.

12-35. The variation of sensitivity of a Model 932 vibration sensing unit with frequency is given below. The basic sensitivity is taken as 96.3 mv (rms) with a 2-MΩ load.

Frequency, cps	Ratio of sensitivity at various frequencies to basic sensitivity
4.0	4.6
4.8	19.0
5.0	11.0
6.0	2.7
7.0	1.9
8.0	1.6
10	1.3
20	1.05
40	1.00
80	0.98
100	0.97
300	0.85
600	0.76
1000	0.66
2000	0.46

Plot sensitivity frequency on three-cycle log-log paper.

12-36. A series of test specimens of a crank arm, part No. 466-1, were tested for the number of cycles needed to produce fatigue failure at various loadings. The results of the tests are

Specimen number	Oscillatory load, lb	Operating cycles to produce failure
1	960	1.1×10^5
2	960	2.2×10^5
3	850	1.5×10^5
4	850	2.4×10^5
5	800	4.2×10^5
6	800	6.0×10^5
7	700	2.4×10^5
8	700	3.1×10^5
9	700	5.1×10^5
10	650	1.8×10^6
11	650	2.6×10^6
12	600	7.7×10^6
13	550	1.0×10^7

Plot a graph of load against operating cycles (*S-N* curve) on semilog paper for the tests on page 279.

12-37. A Weather Bureau report gives the following data on the temperature over a 24-hr period for October 12.

Midnight	47°	2 pm	73°
2 am	46°	4 pm	75°
4 am	44°	6 am	63°
6 am	43°	8 pm	58°
8 am	49°	10 pm	57°
10 am	55°	Midnight	57°
Noon	68°		

Plot the data.

12-38. A test on an acorn-type street lighting unit shows the mean vertical candlepower distribution to be

Midzone angle degrees	Candlepower at 10 ft	Midzone angle degrees	Candlepower at 10 ft
180	0	85	156
175	0	75	1110
165	0	65	1050
155	1.5	55	710
145	3.5	45	575
135	5.5	35	500
125	8.5	25	520
115	13.5	15	470
105	22.0	5	370
95	40.0	0	370

Plot the data. (While data for only half the plot are given, the other half of the plot can be made from symmetry of the light pattern.)

12-39. The candlepower distribution of a 400-w, Type J-H1 flourescent lamp used for street light service was measured with a photometer, and the following data were obtained:

Midzone angle, degrees	Candlepower at 10 ft	Midzone angle, degrees	Candlepower at 10 ft
180	0	75	7700
165	0	72	8600
145	0	65	7100
135	3	55	5300
125	20	45	4300
115	100	35	3500
105	700	25	2700
95	1200	15	2300
85	3000	5	2100
		0	2000

Plot the data. (While data for only half the plot are given, the other half of the plot can be made from symmetry of the light pattern.)

12-40. From data determined by the student, draw a circle chart (pie graph) to show one of the following.

a. Consumption of sulfur by various industries in the United States.

b. Budget allocation of the tax dollar in your state.

c. Chemical composition of bituminous coal.

d. Production of aluminum ingots by various countries.

12-41. Make a bar chart showing the number of men students registered in your school for each of the past ten years.

12-42. Plot the following data and determine an empirical equation for the plotted points:

X:	100	200	300	400	500	600	700	800	900
Y:	0.25	0.38	0.53	0.66	0.79	0.90	1.06	1.17	1.30

12-43. Determine the empirical equation, using the following data which were taken in the laboratory for a test involving accelerated motion:

t:	5	10	20	40	60	80	100
s:	0.93	5.6	32	175	490	989	17,600

12-44. Laboratory data taken on an adjustable time-delay relay show the following values:

Dial Index Settings *D:*	2	4	6	8	10
Seconds Delay Time *T:*	0.124	0.084	0.063	0.026	0.014

Find an empirical equation to express the data.

12-45. The following data were recorded during a laboratory test of a system of gears. Find an empirical equation to express the data.

Applied Force *F:*	11.0	13.0	21.5	26.0	34.0	39.0	41.0	49.0	50.5
Weight Lifted *W:*	135	180	210	345	275	310	340	370	400

12-46. Data taken on a laboratory test involving pressure-volume relations of a gas are as follows:

P:	14.6	17.5	20.9	25.0	29.0	33.6	39.0	45.5
V:	26.4	22.3	19.1	16.3	14.1	12.2	10.5	9.2

Determine an empirical equation for the data.

12-47. Determine an empirical equation to express data given in Problem 12-9.

12-48. Determine an empirical equation that will express data given in Problem 12-11.

12-49. Plot a graph on rectangular coordinate paper of $N = (1.296)^x$ for values of x from -9.0 to $+9.0$ in 0.5 increments.

12-50. Plot a graph on rectangular coordinate paper of the equation $N = (0.813)^x$ for values of x from -9.0 to $+9.0$ in 0.5 increments.

12-51. Using the nomograph of Figure 12-20 what will be the allowable radial load on a ball bearing if the basic load rating is 22 lb and the expected life of the bearing is to be $1.4(10)^8$ revolutions?

12-52. Construct a functional scale about 6 in. long that will relate temperatures in degrees Fahrenheit and degrees Celsius for the range $-40°C$ to $100°C$.

12-53. Construct a functional scale about 10 in. long that will show the relation between the diameter and circumference of a circle for values of diameter from 2 to 9 in.

12-54. The graph of Figure 12-21 has been plotted as a calibration of air flow in a 1-in. duct used in testing bleed air from a turbine engine. If, during a test involving the use of this calibrated duct, the following readings are obtained, compute the pounds per minute of air flowing through the duct. Differential pressure, (ΔP), 6.8 in. of water; Static pressure, P_S), 68.0 lb/in.^{2} gage pressure; Temperature, (T), 421°F; Barometric pressure, (P_B), 29.71 in. of mercury.

12-55. Using the graph in Figure 12-21, compute five points to plot a graph on log-log paper of differential pressure (ordinate), against pounds of air per minute flow (abscissa) for air at a constant temperature of 200°F.

12-56. A heat sink is needed on certain types of electronic apparatus to dissipate the heat evolved in some of the components. A typical heat sink is made of copper or aluminum and has a large surface of fins to promote heat dissipation. The graph

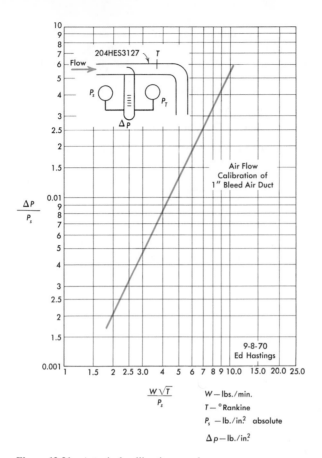

Figure 12-21 A typical calibration graph.

Figure 12-22 Heat sink requirements for a code 8 power supply module using silicon diodes.

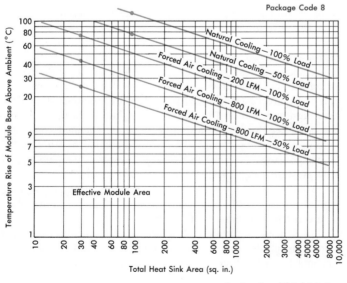

Courtesy Consolidated Avionics

in Figure 12-22 gives the dimensions of a typical heat sink for certain allowable temperature rises for a power supply.

a. If the maximum allowable temperature of a unit mounted on the heat sink is 90°C and the highest ambient temperature expected is 25°C, what area of heat sink will be needed for natural cooling at 100 per cent load?

b. With forced air cooling, the effective area of the module producing the heat is 30 in.² If a forced air flow of 200 linear feet per minute (LFM) is available, what area of heat sink will need to be provided for 100 per cent load conditions?

12-57. Prepare a line chart that will permit converting readings from grams to ounces up to 64 oz and a line chart that will convert readings from pounds to kilograms up to 10 lb.

12-58. The height of a helicopter is to be determined accurately in order to check its altimeter calibration. It is proposed that the helicopter hover over a fixed point at an altitude of approximately 700 ft and that a surveyor's transit be set up some reasonable distance away on level ground and the vertical angle to the helicopter be measured using the transit. The transit vertical angle can be read to ±1′ of angle, and it is desired that the vertical height of the helicopter be determined within ±6 in. Discuss the advantages and disadvantages of this method and give an opinion as to its desirability.

Bibliography

Barry, B. Austin, *Engineering Measurements,* Wiley, New York (1964).

Burr, Irving W., *Engineering Statistics and Quality Control,* McGraw-Hill, New York (1953).

Fogel, Charles M., *Introduction to Engineering Computations,* International, Scranton, Pa. (1960).

French, Thomas E., and Charles J. Vierck, *Graphic Science,* McGraw-Hill, New York (1970).

Spiegel, Murray R., *Theory and Problems of Statistics,* Abelard-Schaum, New York (1961).

13

Digital and
analog computers

The word *computer* frequently brings to mind an image, widely caricatured by cartoonists, of a general-purpose digital computer installation similar to the one shown in Illustration 13-1. This is the type of computer that is most often jokingly associated with credit card foul-ups and the scheduling of early morning college classes. In this chapter we shall learn the real nature and capabilities of this and other, less familiar, types of computer. Our objective here, in contrast to that of other chapters, is not so much to learn specific details of computer programming as it is to learn an approach to problem solving that is applicable to the solution of a wide range of problems using various types of computer. Our hope is to replace the widespread blind faith in the infallibility of computer results as well as un-reasoned fear of computers with a healthy respect for them, based upon an under-standing of their capabilities and limitations.

All students studying this text may not become engineers and fewer yet will specialize in computer technology. However, none of us can escape the impact of computers in nearly every aspect of our life. The introductory article in the reference by Taviss is particularly recommended for reading to serve as a springboard for a study of the social implications of computers, while the succeeding articles in the reference discuss specific nonengineering applications.

Illustration 13-1 (*opposite, top*)
A large general-purpose digital computer installation.

Illustration 13-2 (*opposite, bottom*)
A flight director computer with the cover removed to show the circuitry.

284

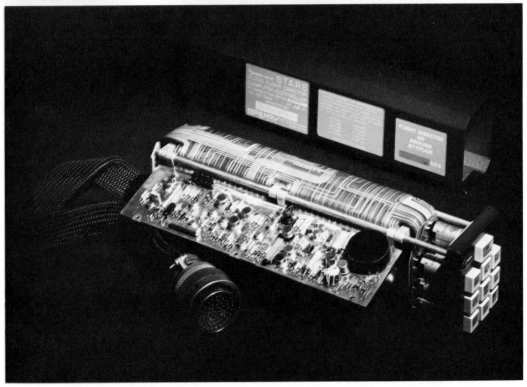

Engineers use computers primarily in two ways. One way is as tools to aid them in analysis and design, along with other tools such as the slide rule and the various drafting instruments. Computers employed in this manner are called *general-purpose* machines, because they can be used readily for solving many different types of problems. Another use for a computer is as a component of a larger system, that is, as part of the end product itself. Such computers are usually referred to as *special-purpose* machines, because they are designed to be quite efficient at some particular task, but they are not readily adaptable to other tasks. This is done, of course, in order to save space, weight, cost, and processing time. Special-purpose computers are used in such engineering activities as in chemical factories to control processes, at electric power plants to assure the stabilization of voltage and frequency, and in aircraft to assist the pilot in flying a desired path. A special-purpose computer for the latter function, known as a flight director, is shown in Illustration 13-2.

In addition to being classified as general- or special-purpose, computers are also categorized as analog, digital, or hybrid.

Analog computers are made to operate by manipulating the magnitude of some physical quantity. The quantity being manipulated represents the number being processed. Data can have any values within the range of the machine; moreover, the values usually can change continuously with time if desired. In a slide rule, which is an example of an elementary analog computer, the physical quantity manipulated is length, whose manipulation represents multiplication or division. In most analog computers, the physical quantity manipulated is voltage. Light intensity and air pressure are also physical quantities that can be manipulated in some analog computers. With analog computers, the accuracy obtainable depends critically upon the accuracy of the component parts; a slide rule that has been dropped on the floor, for example, not only works less smoothly but may also indicate less accurate answers.

Digital computers operate with data that can have only discrete values, that is, values that have been chosen from a limited, predetermined set of distinct values. (Since the set may be made arbitrarily large, perhaps having tens of billions of values, this is not a severe restriction for many purposes.) One of the simplest examples of a digital computer is the ordinary adding machine. Although closely machined parts in an adding machine promote quiet operation and long life, the accuracy of the answer does not depend upon the accuracy of the parts.

Hybrid computers are partly analog and partly digital, using the best features of each type to suit the problem at hand. One disadvantage of the hybrid computer is the necessity for the computer to convert data between analog and digital formats.

In the succeeding sections we shall explore each of these classifications in more detail, always with due consideration to a proper application of the computer and a meaningful interpretation of the results.

Analog computers

To appreciate how the general-purpose analog computer operates, we must first become acquainted with the concept of the *differential equation*. A full understanding of this topic and of the operation of analog computers is well beyond the scope of this text. However, some general knowledge of how the engineer uses this type of computer is important.

Differential equations

In every branch of science and engineering it has been found that the behavior of things can best be described mathematically by equations that represent the *rate* at which certain quantities change. For example, the *rate* at which a constant mass changes velocity is given by Newton's Law (page 242) to be proportional to the applied force and inversely proportional to the mass. We can write this as

$$\dot{v} = a = \frac{F}{M}$$

where the dot above the v means "rate of change, or *derivative,* with respect to time." Other differential equations may describe such activities as the growth of a colony of bacteria, the bouncing of a golf ball, the rate of a chemical reaction, or the motion of charge in an electrical circuit. If one knows the value of a derivative (rate of change) of some quantity, the process itself can be determined by a process of mathematics called *integration.*

General-purpose (and many special-purpose) analog computers consist of components that can perform the following operations:

- Addition of two or more variables.
- Changing the sign of a variable.
- Multiplication of a variable by a constant.
- Supplying a constant.
- Integrating a variable (finding a new quantity whose derivative is the original variable).

The usefulness of the general-purpose analog computer results from the availability of relatively simple devices to perform the necessary mathematical operations nearly instantaneously on quantities that are themselves continuously changing in magnitude. Specifically, the *integrator* makes it possible to solve differential equations, which is by far the most important task of analog computers. Examples of conventional symbols used to represent common elements of analog computers are shown in Figure 13-1. In addition to these mathematical operations, some analog computers can also multiply, divide, take square roots, compare two values, find absolute values, and take sines, cosines, and other functions.

Solving differential equations with an analog computer

To illustrate how an analog computer can be used to solve differential equations, consider the following example. Pretend that you are having a party tonight, and that as soon as you get home from class you must put several cans of cold drinks in the refrigerator to cool. You wish to run a simulation of the process so that you will know when to start serving. (There's nothing worse than warm soda.) The cans have been sitting out and are now at 89°F. Your refrigerator maintains a constant temperature of 33°F. You place a can of soda in the refrigerator at time $t = 0$. Such a system is shown diagrammatically in Figure 13-2.

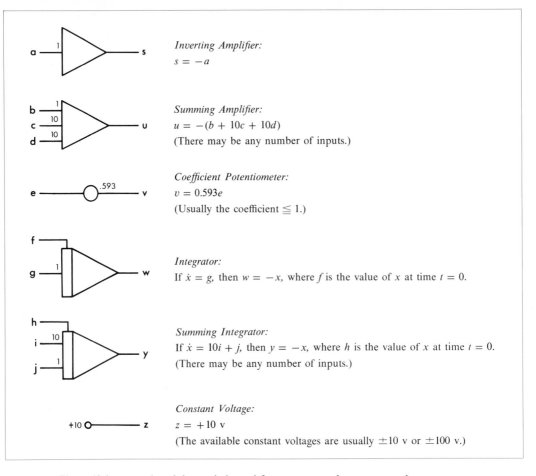

Figure 13-1 Examples of the symbols used for common analog computer elements.

Figure 13-2 System for example problem, showing basic relations obtained from physics. The resulting differential equation, which will be solved by analog computer, is given in the text.

Soda is at temperature T_{soda}. At time $t = 0$, $T_{soda} = 89°F$.

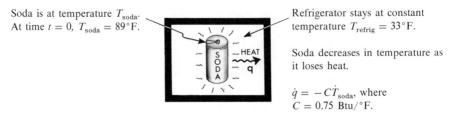

Refrigerator stays at constant temperature $T_{refrig} = 33°F$.

Soda decreases in temperature as it loses heat.

$\dot{q} = -C\dot{T}_{soda}$, where $C = 0.75$ Btu/°F.

Heat transfers from the soda to the refrigerator through thermal resistance R.

$$\dot{q} = \frac{T_{soda} - T_{refrig}}{R}, \text{ where } R = 4000 \text{ °F/(Btu/sec)}.$$

The differential equation describing the temperature of the soda is given as

$$-C\dot{T}_{soda} = \dot{q} = \frac{T_{soda} - T_{refrig}}{R}$$

where C = thermal capacitance of the soda, 0.75 Btu/°F
q = heat energy in Btu
T_{soda} = temperature of the soda in °F
T_{refrig} = temperature of the refrigerator, 33°F
R = thermal resistance between the refrigerator and the soda, 4000 °F/(Btu/sec)

which simplifies mathematically to

$$-\dot{T}_{soda} = \frac{1}{RC}T_{soda} - \frac{1}{RC}T_{refrig}$$

$$= \frac{1}{3000}T_{soda} - \frac{1}{3000}T_{refrig}$$

Assuming that the available computer has a full-scale voltage of ±100 v and using 1 v to represent 1°F, we obtain the circuit of Figure 13-3. This type of diagram is called a *patch diagram*.

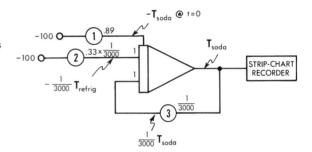

Figure 13-3 Preliminary patch diagram for the example problem. One volt on the computer represents 1°F.

To draw this patch diagram, we began with the differential equation in a form such that the negative[1] of the derivative ($-\dot{T}_{soda}$) was alone on the left side of the equation. Then we drew an integrator (a summing integrator in this case) whose output was the desired unknown quantity (T_{soda}), and we formed the input according to the differential equation. In this case, the input ($1/3000T_{soda} - 1/3000T_{refrig}$) consisted of a constant and a function of the output. The constant term was obtained by reducing the −100 v supply on the computer with Coefficient Potentiometer ("Pot" for short) No. 2. The function of the output was obtained using Pot No. 3. The final step was to obtain the negative of the initial value of T_{soda}, using Pot No. 1 and the −100 v supply.

When the computer simulating the action of the cooling of the soda is started, the voltage labeled T_{soda} will begin to drop from 89 v toward 33 v, just as the actual temperature of the soda in the refrigerator would begin to drop from 89°F toward 33°F. Although the solution obtained on the analog computer will be correct to within the accuracy of the computer, this solution will not be very useful. The computer solution will take several hours, just as the soda will take several hours

[1]The reason for using the negative is that most electronic analog integrators (also applicable for summers) change the polarity of the signal between input and output.

to cool. Fortunately, it is a simple matter to speed up the simulation. It can be shown that the computer can be speeded up by a factor of η simply by multiplying all of the integrator inputs by η. If we set $\eta = 3600$, then 1 sec of computer simulation will represent 3600 sec or 1 hr of time in the refrigerator. The final patch diagram, with the arithmetic carried out, is shown in Figure 13-4. Notice that (usually) coefficient potentiometers can be set no higher than 1.000. Therefore, it was necessary to reduce the setting of Pot No. 3 from the desired value (1.200), for which we compensated by increasing the input gain on the integrator.

Figure 13-4 Final patch diagram for the example problem. One volt on the computer represents 1°F, as before, but the solution has been speeded up so that 1 sec on the computer represents 1 hr in the refrigerator.

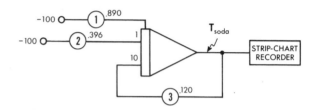

The strip-chart recording that resulted when the computer was operated appears as Figure 13-5.

The process of speeding up or slowing down the computer is called *time scaling*. It is usually necessary to *magnitude scale* as well, in order to keep the voltages within the range of the machine yet not be so small that they become obscured by stray signals and machine imperfections.

Illustration 13-3 shows a fairly large general-purpose analog computer that is capable of solving problems a hundred times as big as the example of the cooling of the soda.

Special-purpose analog computers

Special-purpose analog computers may be used as self-contained machines (*differential analyzers*) to solve differential equations, but often they are used to process signals from a variety of transducers to produce new signals that are used for instrumentation or control. The processes may consist of adding, subtracting, multiplying, dividing, integrating, filtering, comparing, limiting, and so on. The flight

Figure 13-5 Strip-chart recording for the example problem. The tick marks at the bottom of the recording are made by the recorder at 1-sec intervals to serve as a reminder of the paper speed.

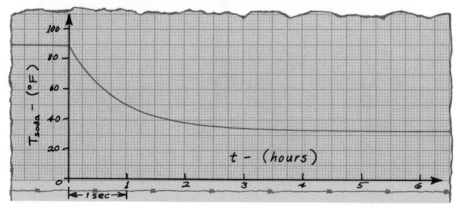

Illustration 13-3
*Photo of a
general-purpose analog
computer.*

director (Illustration 13-2), for instance, receives signals representing aircraft heading, desired heading, roll, pitch, and position relative to various radio beams. It processes these to give signals directing the pilot to roll and pitch the aircraft in the optimum way, taking into account safety factors and the dynamic characteristics of the pilot and aircraft.

Analog computers for special purposes are becoming increasingly common, largely because of the development of small, low-cost *operational amplifiers,* which are the principal components of electronic analog computers.

Digital computers

Although the adding machine is a digital computer in the sense that it calculates with discrete numbers, it lacks two important characteristics that are generally implied when one speaks of digital computers. The first of these characteristics is *automatic sequencing*. This means that the computer will perform operations one after the other without the need for outside intervention. The tremendous speed of electronic computers (hundreds of thousands of operations in a second) would be useless if the computer were forced to stop after each operation to await the next instruction. The second characteristic is the ability of the computer to store inside itself a record of the desired sequence of operations to be performed (called the *program*) before any part of the sequence is started. The advantage of having the entire program stored in advance is that data and intermediate results can be tested; the computer can then transfer control to different parts of the program depending upon the results of the test.

It is necessary, therefore, that the programmer do a very thorough job of planning. He must provide a step-by-step procedure for solving the problem, specifying only those operations that the computer is capable of carrying out. A step-by-step plan for accomplishing any task, whether for a computer or not, is called an *algorithm*. The job of devising an appropriate algorithm can be trickier than it first appears. This point can be emphasized by carrying out the following demonstration.

Place a dozen or so assorted machine screws and other small pieces of hardware on a table, together with a nut and a ruler. Ask someone to sort the hardware into three piles: 2-in. screws that fit the given nut, screws that fit the given nut but only those that are longer than 2 in., and rejects. Most people can accomplish this task in less than 30 sec. Now ask another person to play the role of a computer whose repertoire consists of elementary operations such as picking up a piece, counting, measuring, putting a piece in a given pile, and so on. You and several other persons can now act as programmers who try to tell the "computer" what to do. It is not unusual for the task now to take 15 min! The difference between the two cases is that, in the second case, the people were forced to think in detail about the individual steps that must be taken, and furthermore, that the steps must be completely planned in advance, rather than waiting to "see what happens."

Let us divert the discussion temporarily from the important topic of program planning to consider several other important aspects of digital computers. These will be useful not only in themselves, but also as background material for understanding program planning.

Functional units

The functions of a complete digital computer can be classified into four basic groups: input devices, central processing unit, on-line storage, and output devices. Figure 13-6 is a block diagram outlining these basic functions. In a general way, these functions correspond to the separate pieces of apparatus that comprise a computer.

Figure 13-6   Major functional units of digital computers.

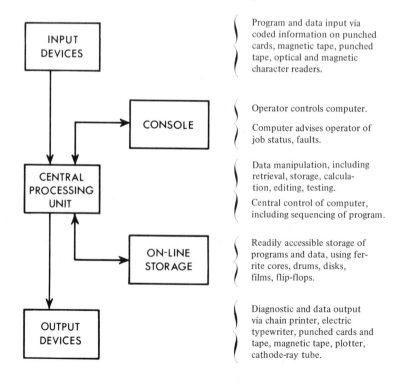

INPUT DEVICES	Program and data input via coded information on punched cards, magnetic tape, punched tape, optical and magnetic character readers.
CONSOLE	Operator controls computer. Computer advises operator of job status, faults.
CENTRAL PROCESSING UNIT	Data manipulation, including retrieval, storage, calculation, editing, testing. Central control of computer, including sequencing of program.
ON-LINE STORAGE	Readily accessible storage of programs and data, using ferrite cores, drums, disks, films, flip-flops.
OUTPUT DEVICES	Diagnostic and data output via chain printer, electric typewriter, punched cards and tape, magnetic tape, plotter, cathode-ray tube.

The most familiar *input device* is the card reader, which uses tiny fingers, brushes, or photocells to detect the presence of holes punched in cards of the DO NOT FOLD, STAPLE, OR MUTILATE variety. Another common device is the magnetic tape reader, which is seen in Illustration 13-1 as an oversized (and very fast and precise) version of the home tape recorder. Very often, data from other input devices are first copied onto magnetic tape, rather than being read directly into the computer, because the greater speed of the tape reader requires less of the expensive computer time. Magnetic character readers are widely used by banks to read checks and other documents. These readers distinguish characters by comparing them with stored patterns for each symbol. The optical character reader works similarly. Sometimes electric typewriters are used, in which case they serve as output devices as well. Other input media are punched paper tape and paper or cards marked in specified areas with graphite pencil (often used for the grading of examinations). Some specialized computer systems obtain data directly from measuring instruments.

The *central processing unit,* or *cpu,* is the nerve center for the entire processing system. It receives information and instructions and executes the actual computational work, including retrieving and storing information. In addition, it coordinates the operation of the system, controlling the input, output, and storage units and sequencing the stored program.

The console works in conjunction with the central processing unit. It is probably the most noticeable part of the system, since it is here that the operator can communicate directly with the computer. The lights, switches, pushbuttons, and electric typewriters are used to turn on the equipment, monitor the operation, and supervise the processing. Beyond impressing the uninitiated, a majority of the flashing lights (that make a computer fun to watch) serve no useful purpose until the computer fails.

Storage or *memory units* are needed to remember data, programs, and intermediate results. If the computer is to be efficient, this storage must be fast and readily accessible. One common device used in storage units is the magnetized core. Such units consist of a flat array of wires forming a grid, with a tiny ring or bead of iron oxide a fraction of a millimeter in diameter that is strung at each intersection of the wires. These beads can be magnetized easily and retain their magnetic state indefinitely. Two other common memory devices are magnetic drums and disks. These consist of an iron oxide coating on a cylinder or set of disks. Small spots on the coating can be magnetized or demagnetized in the same way as recording tape. Information stored on drums and disks is more readily available than that which is stored on tape, just as it is easier to locate a particular passage of music on a phonograph record than on a tape recording. Other storage media include electrostatically charged surfaces, delay lines, and flip-flops.

One *output device* is the high-speed printer. The chain printer is one type of high-speed printer in common use. It consists of a loop (the chain) with raised characters on it which moves continuously in front of the paper. Hammers behind each print position strike the chain against a wide inked ribbon onto the paper just when the desired character passes by. These printers can type over 1000 lines per minute, with 132 characters in each line. A still faster type of high-speed printer forms the characters by squirting tiny jets of ink onto the paper. Other printers use light-sensitive paper. Some computers use electric typewriters, which are much slower than the high-speed printers. Magnetic tape, punched cards, and punched tape are other media.

For some applications, a graphical plot of results is preferable to a tabular presentation. Digital plotters can perform this task, as well as prepare many kinds of engineering and other drawings. The plotter is becoming increasingly valuable as more applications are developed for it. The cathode-ray tube is especially convenient for displaying both drawings and tabular output when a permanent copy is not needed.

As fast as modern input and output devices are, they are still slow when compared with the central processing unit. Much of the developmental work that is being done currently on computers is concerned with (1) ways to keep the cpu busy while input and output are taking place, and (2) ways to obtain faster input and output. The programmer who is planning a program that will use a great amount of input or output should devote considerable thought to this problem.

Talking to the computer

Let us consider the problem of telling the computer what to do. We are not referring here to the mechanical details of punched cards and magnetic tape, but rather to computer languages. When one operates an adding machine or dials a telephone, he probably does not consider that he is using a language since he is merely pushing buttons or turning a dial. But as the computer gets more complex and has more buttons to push and more possible operations, it becomes convenient to think in terms of language. Thus, the people who design and use computers label their pushbuttons with the letters of the alphabet, the numerals, and a few special characters, such as the plus sign and the decimal point, and consider them as forming a language with grammar, syntax, and other notions that have been borrowed from the study of human languages.

Some of the languages used to communicate with computers were designed for the convenience of the computer user; others were designed to reduce the complexity of the computer. During the late 1950's, the development of languages that were convenient for people to use in solving their problems was a major factor in the growth of computer usage. Now, with only a few hours of instruction, one can learn to write simple but useful programs that in former years would have required a computer expert to write. Figure 13-7 shows some examples of computer languages. The most widely used language for engineering and scientific purposes is FOR-TRAN, with its many dialects. ALGOL is also important for technical work; COBOL is used extensively for business applications.

A language that is easy for people to use generally must be translated into machine language before the instructions can be carried out. An *assembler* is a program or device that obtains machine language from another language only slightly more human oriented. An *interpreter*[2] is a program or device that translates from a convenient language to machine language while the program is being carried out, step by step. A *compiler* (also known as a *translator* or *processor*) is a program that translates from a convenient language to machine language (or some intermediate language), the whole program being translated before any work on the problem is begun.

Computer facilities

After one has planned and written his program, how does he go about using the computer? Ordinarily, his program will need to be punched onto cards or paper

---

[2] The name *interpreter* is also used to mean something entirely different, namely, a machine that prints on punched cards the information that has been punched on them, so that it can be read by humans.

tape. As a student, you will get to do this for yourself; as an engineer, probably you will submit it to a keypunch operator. The next step depends upon which of three basic systems is in use at your company or institution.

The *open shop* allows the programmer to run his own programs. This arrangement allows him to secure his results immediately, enabling him to correct program errors or, if there are none, to use the results of the computation for the next stage of his work. For example, an engineer who is designing a filter might use a computer to analyze several proposed designs; depending upon the results, he might be satisfied with one of them, he might modify the design in the direction showing the greatest promise, or he might decide to try another approach altogether.

Computer time is costly, especially for use of the large machines. Such a computer may cost $25 per minute, whether it is solving problems or merely idling while the engineer scratches his head. Moreover, a programmer may damage the computer or waste its time if he is not familiar with the details of running it.

These difficulties are avoided by the *closed shop,* in which many programs are accumulated and then run in a group by trained computer operators. Group or *batch* processing is done under the control of a master program called an *executive* or *operating system,* which keeps the individual programs separated, computes the charges for each job, terminates jobs containing obvious errors or running excessively long, and performs other supervisory tasks. Typically the closed shop allows an engineer two to five runs per day, with the lower number being more realistic. Even if a programming error is readily detected and corrected, several hours will probably elapse before the job can be run again. If the computer is owned by a computer service rather than by the user's own organization, almost surely it will be operated as a closed shop. A disadvantage common to both open and closed shops is that they may not be located physically convenient to the programmer.

An important development of the early 1960's allows the programmer to interact with the computer to an even greater extent than in the typical open shop, avoids

Figure 13-7 Examples of computer languages. In general, the machine-oriented languages are distinctive with each model of computer, whereas the people-oriented languages tend to be standardized.

Machine language	Assembly language	Interpretive language	Compiler language
(distinctive with each machine)	SLEUTH II FAP (largely distinctive with each machine)	PINT 24.2 Floating-Point Interpretive System BASIC (sometimes)	FORTRAN II* FORTRAN IV* BASIC* (usually) ALGOL* COBOL† MAD* GOTRAN* FORTRANSIT* BALGOL* FORTRAN V* PL/1*† JOVIAL SIMSCRIPT LISP

⟵ Machine Orientation
People Orientation ⟶

* Especially suited to general scientific and engineering calculations.
† Especially suited to general business applications.

the cost penalty, and is equivalent to locating the computer close at hand without occupying nearly so much space. This development is called *time sharing*. It may well rank as one of the three most important developments in modern digital computation, along with transistor circuitry and the people-oriented languages.

The principle of time sharing is that, for relatively small problems, the time required by the central processing unit is brief compared with the time for input/output, and it is especially brief when compared with the time spent by the programmer in deciding his next step (precisely the reason that the open shop is often impractical!). In a time-sharing system, numerous input/output stations, or *terminals,* are connected simultaneously to a large computer; the computer works for a few seconds on each user's program *in turn*. At the end of each user's turn, his program and intermediate results are transferred from high-speed core memory to mass storage such as disks or drums. To each user, it appears almost as if he alone had full use of the powerful computer. However, while one user is trying to locate an error, for example, the computer is working on other people's projects rather than sitting idle.

The input/output terminals can be teletypewriters that have been connected by the ordinary dial telephone system to the computer, which may be many miles away, perhaps even in another city. Because teletypewriters are fairly economical and computer charges are based on actual usage, many small companies that cannot justify their own computers now buy time-sharing computation from computer services. Illustration 13-4 depicts a typical time-sharing computer terminal. Later we shall examine an example of a job run on a time-sharing computer, demonstrating the "conversational" interaction between programmer and computer.

Time sharing is not a panacea, however, despite its important advantages. It requires a large, complicated executive system plus a considerable amount of computer time to interface with many terminals simultaneously, interchanging programs and data between mass storage and high-speed memory. These translate into higher cost. Another practical disadvantage is the severely limited size and speed of the teletypewriter for input and output. Since even high-speed card readers and chain

Illustration 13-4
*Time-sharing computer terminals
can be located at any place where a
telephone connection is possible.*

printers are bottlenecks in most systems, the teletypewriter is totally impractical for jobs involving a great amount of data.

A more subtle difficulty is that the very convenience of time sharing may tempt the programmer to devote insufficient effort to planning and checking his program. One should remember that typing is no substitute for thinking!

Number representation and computer repertoire

Digital computers can represent and manipulate information in a number of ways. Information is usually represented by *binary* devices. As the name suggests, binary devices have two and only two states—a hole is punched in a card or it is not, a voltage is high or it is low, a ferrite core is magnetized in one direction or it is magnetized in the other, and so forth. The use of binary devices results simply from the nature of present-day electronic circuits; it is not inherent in computers. (How many states do the devices have in a mechanical adding machine? How many in the stepper switches at an electromechanical dial telephone exchange?) The study of binary numbers is essential to computer designers and advanced programmers, as well as being fun. To the beginning programmer, however, it is more important to know what the binary numbers represent.

A group of binary digits (or *bits,* as they are called) that is treated as a single basic unit of information is called a *word.* Some of the things that a word may represent include an integer, a number in scientific notation (called *floating point* in computer jargon), a logical quantity having as possible values only TRUE and FALSE, and alphabetic characters.

The basic operations that most general-purpose digital computers can perform include the following:

□ Inputting and outputting.
□ Storing and retrieving.
□ Adding, subtracting, multiplying, and dividing (of numerical quantities).
□ Setting and changing the sign (of numerical quantities).
□ Testing the sign (and transferring to different parts of the program depending upon the result).
□ Logical OR, AND, EXCLUSIVE OR, and NOT.
□ Conversion from one form of representation to another.
□ Various operations on the bits of the word (apart from any meaning of the word).
□ Address modification (subscripting).

In general, these operations are performed by means of the physical apparatus that comprises the computer. Beyond this basic list, most operations which one may call upon a computer to perform are built up of combinations of basic operations which have been preprogrammed into the computer, perhaps as part of a compiler. For example, it is possible in FORTRAN to command the computer to find the arc tangent of a number. The computer may accomplish this by carrying out a "power series expansion" using basic operations such as

$$\text{arc tan } \theta = a_1\theta + a_3\theta^3 + a_5\theta^5 + a_7\theta^7$$
$$= \{[(a_7\theta \cdot \theta + a_5)\theta \cdot \theta + a_3]\theta \cdot \theta + a_1\}\theta$$

where $a_1 = 0.9992150$
$a_3 = -0.3211819$
$a_5 = 0.1462766$
$a_7 = -0.0389929$

The list of operations thus available depends considerably upon the language being used and upon the particular installation. To some extent, one can define his own operations.

With the general understanding of computer capabilities and usage that we now have gained, we are ready to resume our study of program planning.

Program planning

Before starting to write any program, the proficient programmer will follow a systematic approach in analyzing the problem and developing its solution. The following steps may appear too obvious to warrant any great attention, but the importance of this logical method cannot be overstressed.

1. *Define the problem.* A hazy understanding of the problem leads to "garbage" for a solution.

2. *Determine the output.* What is the final result of the job supposed to look like in both form and content?

3. *Determine the input.* What information will be needed to produce the desired output?

4. *Determine the method of solution (algorithm).* What operations must be performed to convert the input into output?

5. *Draw a flow chart.* This is a diagrammatic picture of the calculations and decisions which will be required to achieve the solution.

6. *Write the program.* Convert the flow chart into a language that is acceptable to the computer. (This step is called *coding.*)

7. *"Debug" the program.* Programmers have a saying: "Every program contains at least one mistake."

8. *Use the program.* But be careful that its use does not extend beyond the assumptions that were made when the problem was analyzed and that the data are valid. Programmers have another saying: "Garbage in, garbage out."

To repeat, although the steps above may seem obvious, many beginning programmers unfortunately try to approach the computer in a completely illogical and disorganized manner.

Step 5 refers to a very useful tool for the programmer—the *flow chart.* The flow chart is an aid in writing a program because it requires that the programmer follow a methodical, step-by-step description of the problem solution. In addition, it serves as a means of documentation and communication to others. Frequently it is necessary for a person other than the one who wrote the program to make changes or corrections. In such instances, the availability of an accurate flow chart is essential. In fact, the author of the program may need it for his own reference; the clever algorithm whose operation seems so clear today may be incomprehensible in a few months. Figure 13-8 shows a number of widely used flow chart symbols.

Flow charting, like writing, is a rather personal matter and, as no two persons will compose an identical paper about the same subject, so will no two programmers be likely to compose identical flow charts to solve the same problem. The structure of the flow chart and its specific symbols are not nearly so important as that they serve the main purposes of the flow chart.

Flow charts are divided into two general categories: application (or system) charts and program flow charts.

Application charts show how the system is to operate in its environment, with

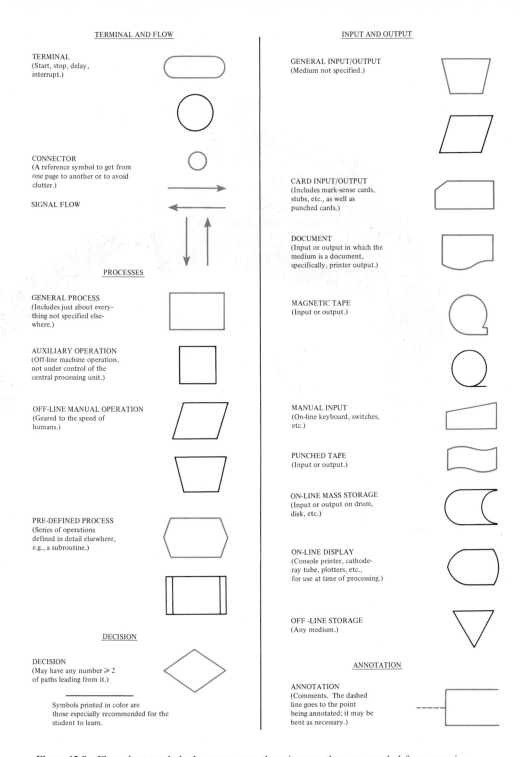

Figure 13-8 Flow chart symbols. In some cases, there is more than one symbol for a meaning.

Illustration 13-5

The preparation of a simple but valid flow chart is not an easy task but certainly one that is essential before one attempts to make use of the digital computer.

the emphasis placed on the documents involved, rather than on the actual machine operations to be performed.

As an example of an application chart, consider the problem of scheduling students in a large school. The desired output consists of two parts: class rosters that show the students who have been scheduled into each class and student schedules that list the courses scheduled for each student. To produce such output, the system will require as input the courses that have been requested by each student and a master file of all the courses that are being offered. The simplified application chart, Figure 13-9, indicates how such a system might operate.

The *program flow chart* is used to describe how the program operates. It shows all of the major steps that the computer will execute to convert the input into output. Just how detailed the flow chart should be depends partially upon the complexity of the program, partially upon the available repertoire, and partially upon the use to which the chart will be put.

To illustrate a program flow chart, consider the following problem. A manufacturer of industrial hardware makes many different parts. He keeps his inventory by punching a card for each part made. These cards contain such information as the part number, color, cost, and price. The plant manager has asked for a program to count the number of green, right- and left-handed wozzles now in stock. Figure 13-10 is a possible flow chart for the program.

Note that the chart has definite starting and stopping points, that it shows the input (inventory cards) and output (wozzle report), and that it shows the decisions which are necessary to perform the count. The symbols RHW, LHW, and TOTW represent the memory locations used to count the right-hand, left-hand, and total number of wozzles. Observe that RHW and LHW are set to zero at the beginning of the program. (Why not TOTW?) This process is called *initialization* and must

Figure 13-9   Application chart for student scheduling.

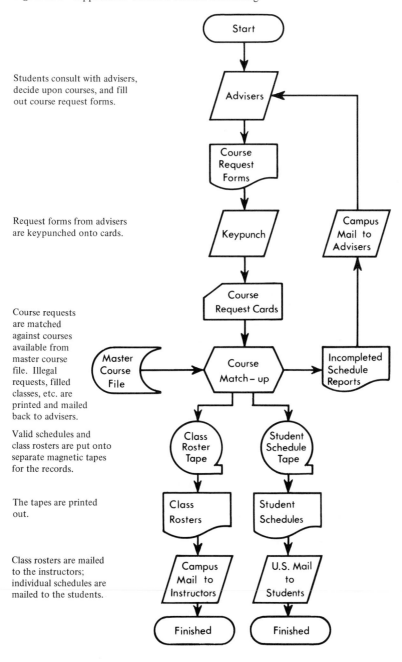

Students consult with advisers, decide upon courses, and fill out course request forms.

Request forms from advisers are keypunched onto cards.

Course requests are matched against courses available from master course file. Illegal requests, filled classes, etc. are printed and mailed back to advisers.

Valid schedules and class rosters are put onto separate magnetic tapes for the records.

The tapes are printed out.

Class rosters are mailed to the instructors; individual schedules are mailed to the students.

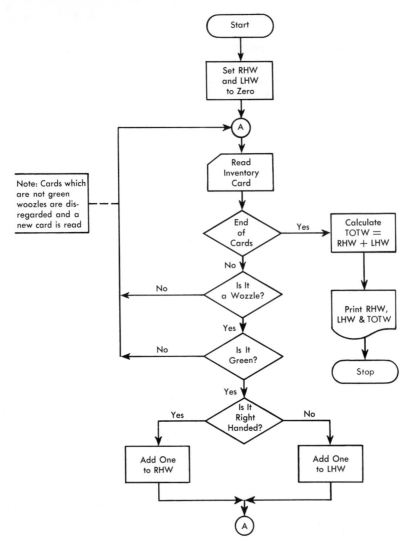

Figure 13-10 Flow chart to count wozzles.

be done to ensure that the locations do not contain numbers left from a previous use of the computer.

Flow charts are the key to successful programming; their value cannot be over-emphasized.

Address modification (subscripting)

The preceding example illustrated two important capabilities of the digital computer—the ability to perform a given set of instructions repetitively and the ability to change the sequence of instructions depending upon the result of some test of the data. In this section we shall consider one other very important way in which the instructions can be modified while the program is running.

Suppose that the computer is to determine the arithmetic mean, $\bar{X}$ (which might be written as XBAR by a programmer), of a set of numbers which already has been stored in the computer (See Chapter 12). For concreteness, let us assume that there are ten numbers. We might assume, further, that these numbers had been stored in memory locations identified as P, Q, R, S, T, U, V, W, X, and Y, and compute the average according to the flow chart of Figure 13-11. Although this program

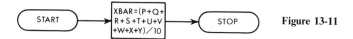

Figure 13-11

segment is both simple and correct, it is not at all general, nor would it be practical if, instead of ten numbers, we had 1000 numbers. We could put the addition of the numbers into a loop, adding one number to the previous sum each time around the loop, if only we had a way to tell the computer to add Q the first time, then R, then S, then T, and so on.

There *is* such a way. It is called *address modification* because the computer can change the "address" of memory locations that are referred to in the instructions. The manner in which this is done in many languages is to define lists or tables (called *arrays*) of variables, all of which have the same basic name but which are distinguished by subscripts. Instead of P, Q, R, . . . , we could refer to P_1, P_2, P_3, ... The subscripts may be variables, allowing them to be the results of any desired calculations. The flow chart for our example thus becomes as shown in Figure 13-12, which is completely general.

Figure 13-12 The notation "$i \leftarrow i + 1$" means that 1 is added to the value of i and the result is stored as i (destroying the original value of i). The notation "$i:N$" means that i is compared with N.

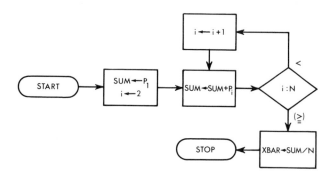

To illustrate the remainder of the programming process and also to demonstrate the "conversational" nature of time-sharing computer systems, let us expand the example by adding provisions for input and output, as shown in Figure 13-13. The complete program and "conversation" with the computer are given in Figure 13-14.

Figure 13-13 Note that the second input command also involves a form of address modification and looping, although the details are beyond the scope of this discussion.

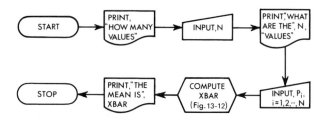

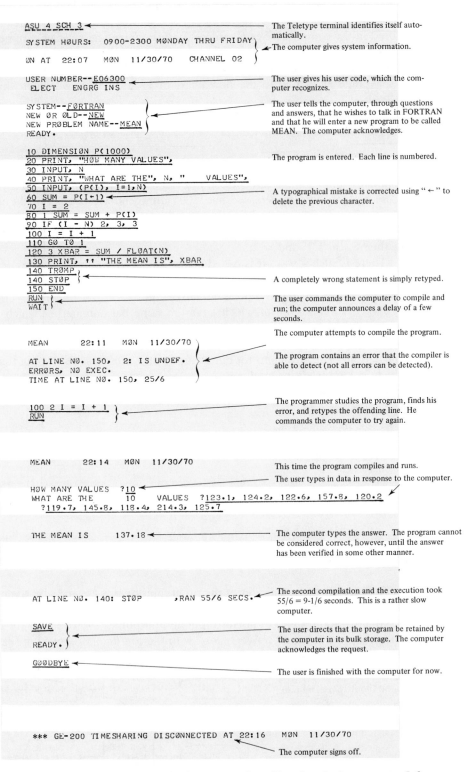

```
ASU 4 SCH 3                                              The Teletype terminal identifies itself auto-
                                                        matically.
SYSTEM HOURS:   0900-2300 MONDAY THRU FRIDAY
                                                        The computer gives system information.
ON AT  22:07   MON  11/30/70    CHANNEL 02

USER NUMBER--E06300                                     The user gives his user code, which the com-
  ELECT   ENGRG INS                                     puter recognizes.

SYSTEM--FORTRAN                                          The user tells the computer, through questions
NEW OR OLD--NEW                                          and answers, that he wishes to talk in FORTRAN
NEW PROBLEM NAME--MEAN                                   and that he will enter a new program to be called
READY.                                                  MEAN. The computer acknowledges.

10 DIMENSION P(1000)
20 PRINT, "HOW MANY VALUES",                            The program is entered.  Each line is numbered.
30 INPUT, N
40 PRINT, "WHAT ARE THE", N, "    VALUES",
50 INPUT, (P(I), I=1,N)
60 SUM = P(I+1)                                         A typographical mistake is corrected using " ← " to
70 I = 2                                                delete the previous character.
80 1 SUM = SUM + P(I)
90 IF (I - N) 2, 3, 3
100 I = I + 1
110 GO TO 1
120 3 XBAR = SUM / FLOAT(N)
130 PRINT, ↑↑ "THE MEAN IS", XBAR
140 TROMP
140 STOP                                                A completely wrong statement is simply retyped.
150 END
RUN                                                     The user commands the computer to compile and
WAIT                                                    run; the computer announces a delay of a few
                                                        seconds.
                                                        The computer attempts to compile the program.
MEAN       22:11    MON  11/30/70

AT LINE NO. 150,   2: IS UNDEF.                          The program contains an error that the compiler is
ERRORS, NO EXEC.                                        able to detect (not all errors can be detected).
TIME AT LINE NO. 150, 25/6

                                                        The programmer studies the program, finds his
100 2 I = I + 1                                          error, and retypes the offending line. He
RUN                                                     commands the computer to try again.


MEAN       22:14    MON  11/30/70
                                                        This time the program compiles and runs.
                                                        The user types in data in response to the computer.
HOW MANY VALUES   ?10
WHAT ARE THE        10     VALUES  ?123.1, 124.2, 122.6, 157.8, 120.2
  ?119.7, 145.8, 118.4, 214.3, 125.7

THE MEAN IS     137.18                                  The computer types the answer. The program cannot
                                                        be considered correct, however, until the answer
                                                        has been verified in some other manner.


                                                        The second compilation and the execution took
AT LINE NO. 140: STOP      ,RAN 55/6 SECS.              55/6 = 9-1/6 seconds. This is a rather slow
                                                        computer.

SAVE                                                    The user directs that the program be retained by
                                                        the computer in its bulk storage. The computer
READY.                                                  acknowledges the request.

GOODBYE                                                 The user is finished with the computer for now.



*** GE-200 TIMESHARING DISCONNECTED AT 22:16   MON  11/30/70
                                                        The computer signs off.
```

Figure 13-14 A Teletype print-out showing conversation with a time-sharing computer. Information entered by the operator is underlined.

Pitfalls in computing

Where can computers and their users go wrong? The answer is: Everywhere, from the original decision to use a computer to the interpretation of the results of a thoroughly debugged program. This section will present a sampling of potential problems, in order to guide the student toward a more meaningful use of the computer.

Many of the problems that can arise apply equally to both analog and digital computation, although some problems are peculiar to a particular type of computer. The first defense against trouble is to ask oneself at every stage of work,

ARE THE RESULTS REASONABLE?

This is not an infallible method (there is none), but often it can save a great amount of time. In our analog computer simulation of the cooling of the soda, for example, we knew that the soda started at 89°F and would eventually cool to (nearly) 33°F. Had our simulation shown any other starting and ending temperatures, we would have recognized it to be wrong. The second defense is to ask oneself, upon correcting a mistake,

DOES THE CORRECTION ACCOUNT
FOR THE OBSERVED DISCREPANCY?

Again, this method is not always feasible, especially when equipment faults are involved. Nevertheless, it does prompt one to avoid the "Eureka[3] syndrome," which is the tendency to assume that when *any* mistake is found, it is the *only* mistake.

Problems affecting both analog and digital computation

1. *Faulty analysis of the problem*. Trouble may result from a limited understanding of the assignment, from an inadequate mathematical model, or from invalid assumptions about the operating conditions of the system being studied. Often a program fails to provide for some logically possible, but unlikely, combination of events. (What will the computer do if Mr. Jones inadvertently pays his bill twice at the Heigh-Pryse Department Store?) Sometimes trouble results from an inadequate range of choices. (A news story told of an honor student who was flunked when a computer was programmed to read only two-digit grades. His score was 100.)

2. *Faulty data*. Poor data may result from measurement errors, from sloppy handling of data (usually poor handwriting!), or from normal variations between the nominal characteristics upon which a design is based and the actual characteristics of a particular component. Another important cause of faulty data that is often neglected is deliberate falsification. (Employees in one company are expected to record how much time they spend on each task, including time for coffee breaks and going to the restroom. Need we comment on the probable validity of the results?)

3. *Limitations of numerical methods*. Whole books[4] have been written on this problem; in this brief discussion, we shall consider two areas of particular concern.

One of these is the subtraction of nearly equal numbers. Suppose, for example, that one number is 10.5, correct to the nearest tenth, and the other number is 10.0, also correct to the nearest tenth. Their difference computationally is equal to 0.5,

---

[3] from the Greek *heúrēka,* "I have found it!"
[4] See, for example, the reference by Golden.

but the actual difference may be as large as 0.6 or as small as 0.4. Thus, the difference between these two numbers, each of which is accurate to within $\frac{1}{2}$ per cent, is accurate only to within 20 per cent! In some cases, the result of a subtraction may be completely worthless.

The second area is sets of equations that are unusually sensitive to changes in some of their constants. Such sets are said to be *ill-conditioned*. As an example, consider the set[5]

$$1.00x + 1.00y = 1$$
$$1.00x + 1.01y = 2$$

The solution is

$$x = -99 \quad \text{and} \quad y = 100$$

A 2 per cent error in one of the original coefficients due to measurement errors, say, changes the equations to

$$1.00x + 1.00y = 1$$
$$1.00x + 0.99y = 2$$

The solution is now

$$x = 101 \quad \text{and} \quad y = -100$$

That is, a change of 0.02 in one of the coefficients has given rise to a change of 200 in each solution. No amount of additional precision in the computation could reduce the range of uncertainty of the solution.

4. *Misinterpretation of results.* Rarely does the computer yield the final answer to a problem. One might really wish to know, for example, that the average current in a certain circuit is 50 ma, but more likely the real problem is, "Can I use a 2N718A transistor here?" The conclusion that the 2N718A is satisfactory may be invalid if there is a 2-amp surge current in the circuit.

5. *Equipment failure.* This occurs more frequently in mechanical equipment, such as input and output devices, than in electronic apparatus. Telephone connections are subject to electrical transients that cause erroneous results.

Problems peculiar to analog computation

1. *Blunders* in scaling, in drawing patch diagrams, in patching, or in setting the various adjustments such as the coefficient potentiometers.

2. *Limited accuracy of computer components.* One of the characteristics of analog computers is that their accuracy depends critically upon their parts.

Problems peculiar to digital computation

1. *Blunders* in preparing the flow chart, in coding the flow chart into computer language, or in keypunching or typing. Some of the most common mistakes are failure to initialize and going around a loop one time too many or too few.

2. *Round-off and truncation errors.* Round-off errors result from the fact that the computer carries out computations only to a finite number of places. Truncation

[5] N. Mendelsohn, "Some Elementary Properties of Ill-Conditioned Matrices and Linear Equations," *The American Mathematical Monthly,* vol. 63, no. 5 (1956), pp. 285–294.

errors occur when an infinite process, such as an "infinite series," is carried out only to a finite number of steps.

The intention of this section has not been to scare the student away from computers, although such a list of problem areas might tend to have that effect. In fact, most of the problems presented are really characteristic of engineering in general. Rather, the intention of this section and of the entire chapter has been to encourage the student to learn to use the computer to serve him well.

Problems

13-1. Your simulation has shown that the soda would take too long to cool in the refrigerator, so you are considering putting it in a special freezer in the chemistry laboratory, which maintains a temperature of $-65°F$. The thermal resistance will be only $2000°F/(Btu/sec)$. Modify the patch diagram of Figure 13-4 to accommodate this case. Will the simulation be correct after the soda reaches the freezing point? Explain.

13-2. A skydiver with mass m equal to 75 kg jumps from an airplane in level flight. He is attracted to the earth by a force (his weight), $w = mg = 735$ N. The air provides viscous damping β of 13.6 N/(m/sec). The man falls with a downward velocity v. You wish to simulate how the velocity v changes with time. The applicable differential equation is

$$\dot{v} = -\frac{\beta}{m}v + \frac{1}{m}w$$

Draw the patch diagram. (Remember that the initial downward velocity is zero.) Assume that the computer has ±100 v full scale.

13-3. Repeat Problem 13-2 for a 7.5-kg box with $\beta = 1.36$ N/(m/sec). This time, however, the airplane is diving when the box is thrown out, so that its initial downward velocity is 10 m/sec.

13-4. Draw a patch diagram to solve the following pair of differential equations. Assume a ±100-v computer.

$$-\dot{x}_1 = x_1 - x_2 - k$$
$$-\dot{x}_2 = -x_1 + 2x_2$$

where $x_1(0) = 10$, $x_2(0) = -30$, and $k = 25$.

13-5. Draw a patch diagram to solve the following pair of differential equations, assuming full-scale voltage is ±10 v:

$$\dot{v}_1 = -v_1 + 2v_2 + 9$$
$$\dot{v}_2 = -v_1 - 5v_2$$

where $v_1(0) = -2.75$, $v_2(0) = 9.9$.

13-6. The box of Problem 13-3 also has a horizontal component of velocity, h. The horizontal value of β is 4.2 N/(m/sec). The airplane was traveling at 40 m/sec when the box was thrown out. Assume a ±100-v computer. The differential equation is

$$\dot{h} = -\frac{\beta}{m}h$$

Draw the patch diagram. Now time scale the problem so that the computer operates at only 0.2 the actual speed.

13-7. Carry out the demonstration described on page 292 involving the pile of hardware to be sorted.

13-8. Draw a flow chart for Problem 13-7.

13-9. Draw a flow chart of the method to evaluate, in very small steps, the equation

$$y = 2a + \frac{bc}{d}$$

(Neglect input and output—assume that this is part of a larger program.)

13-10. Repeat Problem 13-9 for the equation

$$x = \left(\frac{a + b}{c + d}\right) a^2$$

13-11. Draw a flow chart to evaluate the series expansion for the arc tangent given on page 297, using the first equation. Repeat, using the second equation. Which do you think is better?

13-12. Draw a flow chart of the method you would use to calculate ϵ^x using the expansion

$$\epsilon^x = 1 + x + \frac{x^2}{2!} + \frac{x^3}{3!} + \cdots + \frac{x^7}{7!}$$

Use a method similar to that of Problem 13-11, second part.

13-13. Repeat Problem 13-12 using looping.

13-14. Draw a flow chart for a program to calculate the miles per gallon used by an automobile. Input data to be read in for each gasoline stop will be (1) the indicated miles on the odometer, and (2) the number of gallons required to fill the tank. (Note that the first stop will *not* give an answer.)

13-15. Pick a simple process such as changing the tire on an automobile, and draw a flow chart to illustrate how it is done.

13-16. Draw a flow chart of a program to calculate the volume of the solid shown in Figure 13-15. Include provisions for input and output. (Note: You need not use the extremely basic steps in this and succeeding problems.)

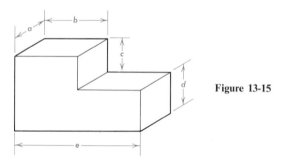

Figure 13-15

13-17. Draw a flow chart to (*a*) read 100 numbers, (*b*) count how many of them are positive, (*c*) find the sum of the positive numbers only, and (*d*) print the number of positive numbers and their sum.

13-18. Given the flow chart of Figure 13-16, and given that the data are 3, 8, and 1, what number will be printed?

Figure 13-16

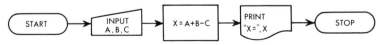

13-19. Given the flow chart of Figure 13-17, and given that the data are 1, 2, 3, 4, what numbers will be printed?

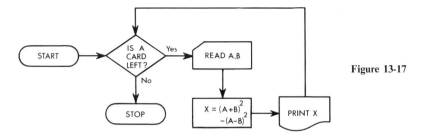

Figure 13-17

13-20. Draw a flow chart to (a) read in three numbers, x_1, x_2, and x_3; (b) set x equal to the middle value of the three numbers; (c) print the three numbers and x.

13-21. The Outer Globbonian Department of Rocketry and Fireworks has commissioned you to draw the flow chart of a program to plot the flight of its missiles. They will give you the initial value, V_0, initial angle of inclination, α, and a set of time values, t, as shown in Figure 13-18. The program should calculate and print the values of

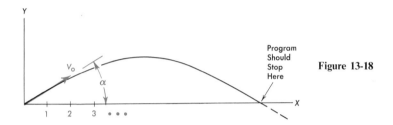

Figure 13-18

the height, y, and the range, x, for each value of time, t. The program should stop when the calculated height is less than zero. Outer Globbonia is flat and has no air so you may use the formulas

$$y = (V_0 \sin \alpha)t - \tfrac{1}{2}gt^2$$
$$x = (V_0 \cos \alpha)t$$

Assume that the computer can take the sine and cosine of α. Use 32 ft/sec² for g.

Bibliography

Golden, James T., *FORTRAN IV Programming and Computing*, Prentice-Hall, Englewood Cliffs, N.J. (1965).

Korn, Granino A., and Theresa M. Korn, *Electronic Analog and Hybrid Computers*, McGraw-Hill, New York (1964).

McCracken, Daniel D., *A Guide to FORTRAN IV Programming*, Wiley, New York (1965).

Peterson, Gerald R., *Basic Analog Computation*, Macmillan, New York (1967).

Scientific American, special issue on "Information," September 1966.

Taviss, Irene (ed.), *The Computer Impact*, Prentice-Hall, Englewood Cliffs, N.J. (1970).

Part Five

Graphic tools
of the engineer

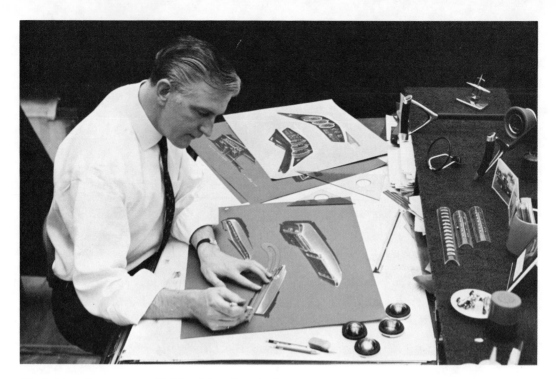

Sketching is an essential tool for the designer.

14

Technical sketching: a medium of communication for the engineer

Since prehistoric times *the sketch* has served as one of man's most effective communication techniques. Although today we know little of the languages that were used by men of primitive societies, the crude sketches they drew have taught us much about their daily routines, food sources, ambitions, and fears. Unlike writing, a pictorial representation needs little translation. As the people of the world have been brought into closer contact with each other, misunderstandings have arisen because of poor communication. Everyone should strive to improve those qualities of self-expression that enable him to communicate with his fellow men—including the ability to sketch. The engineer in particular must be able to communicate his ideas to others rapidly and accurately. The spoken and written word are very important, but neither can replace the sketch. Regardless of educational or linguistic backgrounds engineers can communicate their ideas more clearly to others if they are able to sketch. Therefore, the ability to make a freehand drawing or sketch is an essential skill for every engineer.

Several examples are shown in Figures 14-1 through 14-11 to illustrate how sketches and other graphic forms have been used to communicate ideas.

In addition to communicating with others, a sketch can *stimulate one's own imagination.* This happens because a sketch not only serves to clarify the original idea but frequently suggests additional versions, adaptations, and improvements. The engineer often finds that he is able to organize his thoughts more effectively if he can present his mental impressions in graphic form, whether it be a flow chart summarizing the main points of a presentation or a detailed sketch explaining a complicated mechanism.

The engineer does not need to be an artist, nor does he need to possess unusual talents in drawing. Sketching is a skill that is acquired through practice. One cannot learn to sketch and express himself graphically solely by reading about it, any more

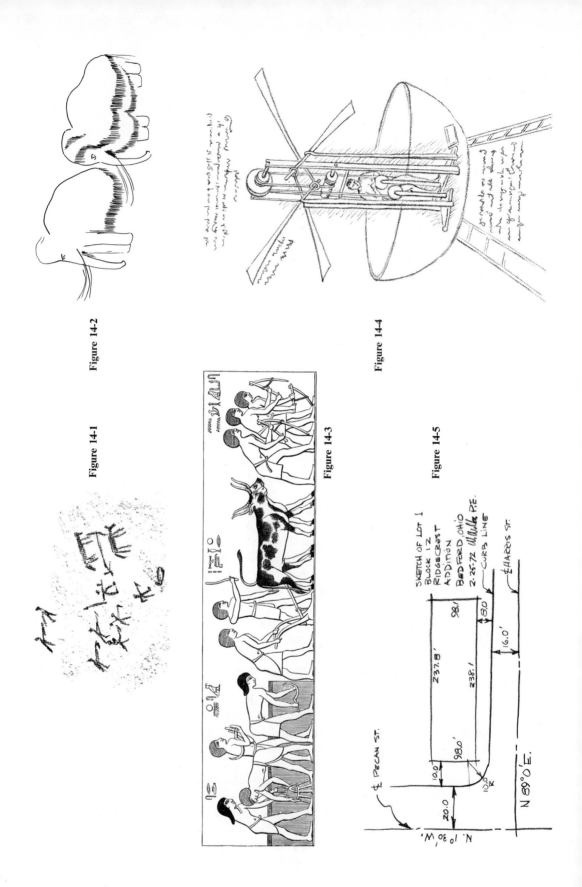

Figure 14-2

Figure 14-1

Figure 14-4

Figure 14-3

Figure 14-5

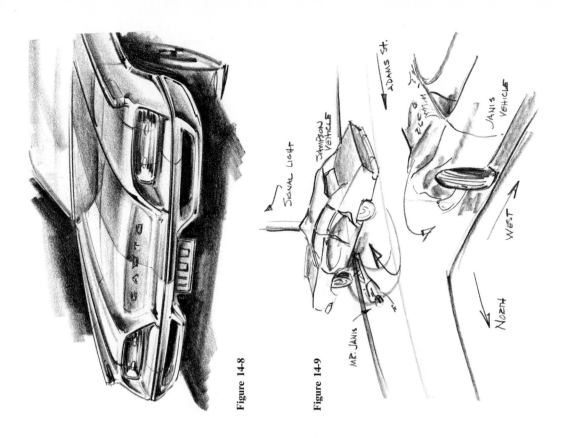

Figure 14-8

Figure 14-9

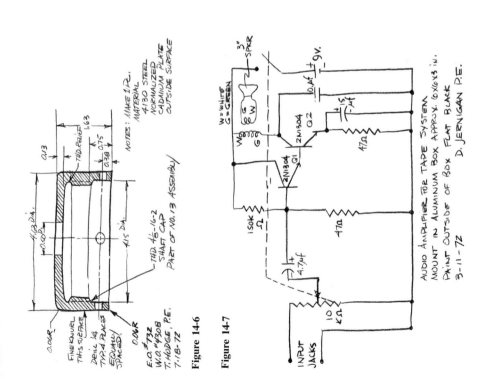

Figure 14-6

Figure 14-7

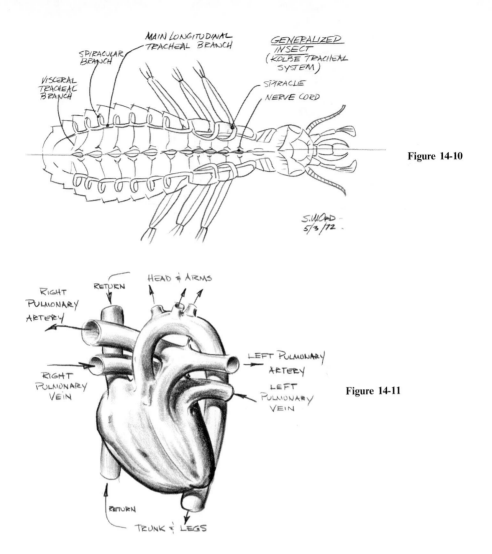

Figure 14-10

Figure 14-11

than one can learn to swim while standing by the pool. Adherence to certain basic principles and procedures will usually produce the best (and certainly the most consistent) results. Consequently, one of the objectives of this chapter is to introduce the most effective principles and procedures of technical sketching.

In learning to sketch, as in learning to swim, a certain amount of preparation is necessary.

The work place

Ideally, sketching should be done in an environment that has a convenient, efficient arrangement of the tools and appropriate materials. However, this may not be possible at times because the engineer may be sitting in an automobile or airplane or perhaps be at a construction site when the need to make a sketch arises. He must be prepared to use the tools at hand and to make the best use of the work space available.

The *ideal* environment includes a desk or table of adequate size. Sketching materials, reference materials, and tools should be conveniently placed. The desk top need not be tilted, but if it is, a shallow box or similar container for pencils and other sketching tools should be provided to prevent them from sliding off the table. A white, neutral light of high intensity is preferred. Fluorescent lights are best because they minimize shadows. A good quality, flexible arm drawing lamp satisfies all of these requirements.

Tools and materials

Of the tools necessary for sketching, the pencil is one of the most important. Any mechanical or wooden pencil with a soft or medium hard lead is acceptable. Professional artists generally prefer a pencil whose "lead" has a high carbon and low clay composition for sketching where no erasures will be made. The pencil point must be sharpened and shaped according to the thickness of line desired. A sharp point will produce a thin line—a dull point, a thicker line. Be careful in sharpening the pencil. If the lead is *too* sharp or pointed, it often breaks when used (Figure 14-12). Lines produced with very sharp points also lack character. Sharpen and shape the pencil point as often as necessary, using any mechanical or electric pencil sharpener that produces a smooth clean tip. A pad of rough paper or sandpaper is useful for "touching up" the pencil point.

The correct choice of paper for sketching is quite important, and a proper selection can aid one's effectiveness and speed. The most desirable paper is a good quality, medium weight translucent vellum. This eliminates the need for most erasing because alterations can be quickly retraced on an overlay. Paper quality and sheet thicknesses are especially important. Thin paper is difficult to use for sketching because it tears easily, Figure 14-13. Smooth or slick paper will not be abrasive enough to give the pencil a "bite" and form a solid, dark line. Where vellum is unavailable, a good quality bond paper is acceptable as long as its surface has a slightly rougher texture than the paper used in this book.

For multiview (orthographic) sketching it is convenient to use a preprinted grid vellum, Figure 14-14. For pictorial sketching, another preprinted grid vellum is available, Figure 14-15. These are especially recommended for beginners.

Figure 14-12

Figure 14-13

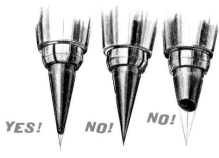

YES!   NO!   NO!

TORN TISSUE

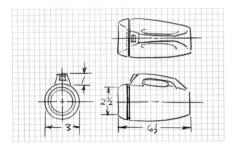

Figure 14-14

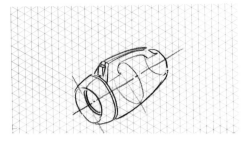

Figure 14-15

Another useful tool for the engineer in sketching is the straightedge. The straightedge can be any smooth-edge object, but a plastic triangle is best. As its name implies, the straightedge aids in drawing straight lines. Properly used it creates a precise, cleanly defined line. Avoid using a straightedge with small indentations or printed marks along its side, such as a scale. Also avoid using any of the rulers with a thin metal edge. These indented and sharp edged tools scrape off small amounts of the pencil lead with each stroke and soon produce smudges on the sketch, Figure 14-16.

Ideally one should not use an eraser in sketching. An important objective is confidence, the confidence to act surely and boldly when putting ideas in graphic form. If one knows that he *can* erase and has an eraser handy, there is a temptation to sketch with light, easily erasable lines. Erasing destroys the paper's surface so that the corrected line on the sketch is poorly defined and has an imprecise appearance. Such techniques produce weak sketches that are unconvincing and devoid of character. That is why it is important to learn to sketch without using an eraser. If the first trial sketch is not satisfactory—make another. This practice usually saves time and builds confidence and proficiency. When one is beginning, it provides more sketching practice. As one is learning to sketch, he must be willing to use a lot of paper and to discard unsuccessful practice efforts without remorse.

There are many *mechanical line guides* available. These guides are as useful for the beginner as they are for the professional designer. Much of the art work that we see in magazines and newspapers was done with mechanical aids. Their value does not come in making it easier to draw but in the time savings and the professional appearance they add to a sketch—even a beginner's sketch.

Most mechanical aids are precisely cut sheets of plastic of selected shapes and sizes. Some of the general-purpose guides are called "French curves," "circle templates," "ellipse guides," "sweeps," and "irregular curves," Figure 14-17.

Another mechanical aid useful in sketching finished curved lines and irregular shapes is the "spline" or adjustable curve. Its advantage lies in its ability to conform to most irregular shapes (except sharp corners) and thus eliminate the need constantly to manipulate the fixed type of guide to curved segments of a line.

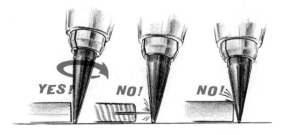

Figure 14-16

Figure 14-17

Figure 14-18

Figure 14-19

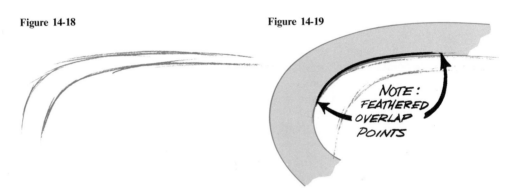

NOTE: FEATHERED OVERLAP POINTS

When using mechanical guides for irregular shapes, it is important first to draw the desired line or shape lightly without using the guide, Figure 14-18. Then select the portion of the guide that fits closely the sketched curve, and draw in the desired line on the final vellum overlay, Figure 14-19.

With circle and ellipse guides one needs only to indicate the center point and orientation of the figure and then trace the appropriate size, Figure 14-20.

After one is proficient in control and proportioning techniques, more effective use can be made of the many mechanical aids available commercially. Other important ingredients necessary to ensure good quality sketches are the intangibles *time* and *the motivation to practice*. Remember—there is no substitute for the desire to learn, in this case the desire to learn to draw.

Fundamental techniques

Let us now consider some fundamental techniques. The hand that holds the pencil can be conditioned to hold steady, to rotate, to control pressure, and even to sense when the lead of the pencil is about to break. The pencil should be held naturally

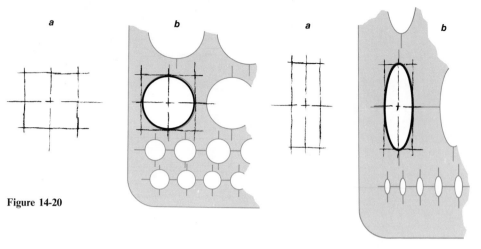

Figure 14-20

and firmly but not cramped. The thumb and fingers should grasp the pencil about an inch and a half from its point in a manner that allows the pencil to be rotated between the fingers as a line is drawn. This produces a line of consistent weight because the pencil point wears evenly. When a guide is used, hold the pencil so that the tapered side of the point is parallel to the vertical edge of the guide. This reduces the amount of lead scraped off by the sharp corner of the guide (Figure 14-16).

When making a sketch, the engineer's arm can serve as a large compass with the point of the elbow (the "funny bone") as the pivot (Figure 14-21). With a pivoting motion, small portions of a large arc can be sketched as short, straight lines. The arm is rather heavy and as such provides the necessary stability for control needed when sketching. For this reason it is recommended that arm motions, and in some cases whole body motions, be used when sketching. In general, the longer the

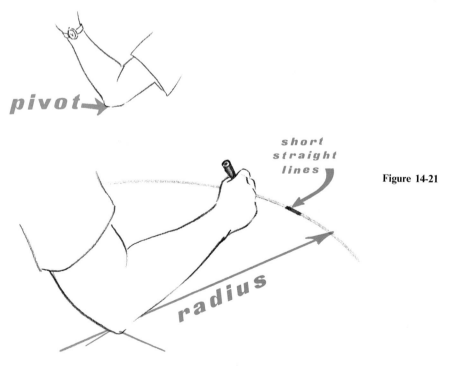

Figure 14-21

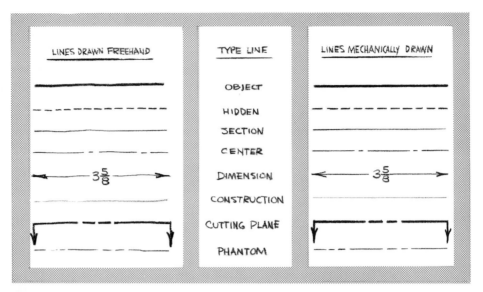

LINES DRAWN FREEHAND	TYPE LINE	LINES MECHANICALLY DRAWN
	OBJECT	
	HIDDEN	
	SECTION	
	CENTER	
$3\frac{5}{8}$	DIMENSION	$3\frac{5}{8}$
	CONSTRUCTION	
	CUTTING PLANE	
	PHANTOM	

Figure 14-22

freehand line being drawn, the larger the stabilizing mass needed to control the line. This technique is similar to that used in many sports where smoothness of body motion is essential to good performance (such as golf, tennis, and baseball). Another benefit derived from using the arm or body as a stabilizing mass is that it promotes body relaxation, which is necessary in sketching.

The quality and precision of sketch linework are not intended to be comparable with instrument-drawn work. Since smoothness and uniformity of the linework are not as necessary as in mechanical drawings, the quality of a line drawn freehand is judged by its *accuracy of direction* and its density of weights, not by its precision. Variations in width and density of lines produce sketches that have a character exhibiting both vitality and interest. Such variations produce visual activity within the sketch by leading the eye from one area to another and by emphasizing important attributes. The rough construction line should be of light weight, that is, a very thin, light line. Dimension lines, center lines, and extension lines should also be light-weight, Figure 14-22. The other lines, however, should be sharp, distinct, and of a heavier weight. The ends of all lines, including dashes, are slightly accented. The visible lines on the sketch, especially those outlining the object, should have the heaviest weight. The contrast among the different line weights should be maintained.

The eye and the brain play an important role in sketching. They are the feedback and control system for the hand and arm. This system is so perfectly constructed and so automatic that very little instruction is required to put it to work. However, avoid getting the eye too close to the sketch. For good control and visual balance the eye should be far enough away to view the sketch as a whole.

Layout

Plan an effective layout—one which arranges the subject of the sketch in a pleasing and logical composition on the paper. Plan the sketch *before* you begin to draw. One of the most useful procedures for planning a sketch is to first make a series of "thumbnail" sketches. These are usually small and are drawn with little attention to detail in a minimum amount of time. In this way a variety of arrangements or layouts can be investigated quickly. That thumbnail sketch which best satisfies the overall requirements will become the basis for the more detailed sketch to follow. Remember, vellum or paper is less expensive than time. Use as many sheets as necessary to achieve the most effective layout. Avoid crowding notes and details as if you had but one sheet of paper. Allow ample paper to surround or frame the sketch because it emphasizes the importance of the work and adds to its professional appearance.

Proportioning

Unlike mechanical drawings, technical sketches are not drawn to an exact scale. It is very important, however, that all width and height relationships be drawn in proportion to those of the object being sketched. The overall size of the sketch is optional and depends upon its intended use, its complexity, and the size of the paper available. In general, small objects are usually sketched oversize while large objects are sketched to some reduced scale.

As has been stated, it is necessary to establish the relative height and width proportions of a sketch. With proper training the eye becomes an excellent proportioning instrument. We might perform a simple experiment to illustrate how effective the eye is as a proportioning instrument. On the line of Figure 14-23, place a mark

Figure 14-23

at the point you estimate to be the midpoint. Do not use a scale or any other measuring device except your eye. Now measure the line and locate the midpoint exactly. How closely did you estimate the midpoint? The proportioning of a line into thirds is more difficult but can be done quite accurately with practice. This is just one of the functions of your eye-brain-hand system *and it becomes more proficient with practice.*

There are several techniques for developing a properly proportioned sketch. One of the more common and successfully used methods is called "scaffolding." "Scaffolding" is very effective for establishing an accurate foundation for a sketch; it is developed in the following manner.

1. Using lightweight lines construct a rectangle which will enclose within its boundaries the overall width and height of the object, Figure 14-24. This rectangle serves in much the same way as the scaffolding used for constructing a building. The lines forming the scaffold are a useful aid during the construction of the sketch. They can be eliminated when the sketch is finished just as construction scaffolding is removed from the site once the job is completed.

2. Subdivide the enclosing rectangle or scaffold into smaller sections representing the major proportions of the object, Figures 14-25 and 14-26. Where objects are symmetrically formed about some axis or plane, the sketch should show this relation, Figure 14-27.

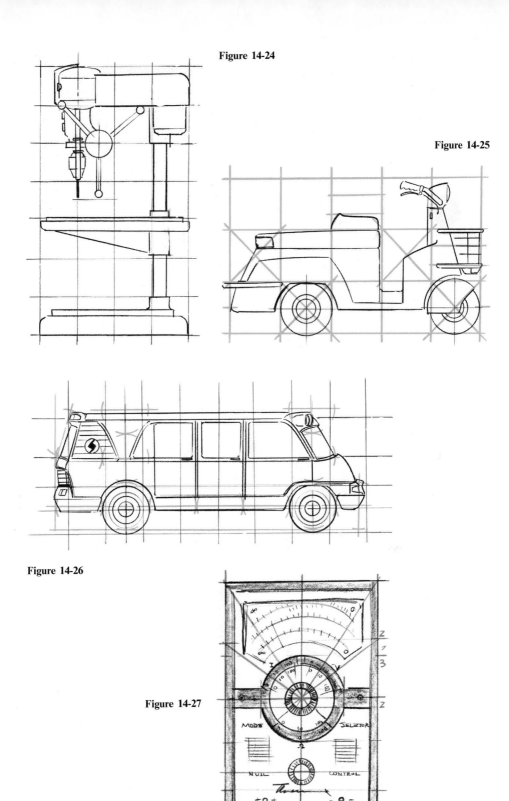

Figure 14-24

Figure 14-25

Figure 14-26

Figure 14-27

3. Sketch other pertinent details such as curves, circular components, and internal lines that will define the final form of the object. After the rough sketch has been developed by the scaffolding technique, Figure 14-28, it is then quickly traced on another vellum sheet, thus eliminating the need for time consuming and messy erasing, Figure 14-29.

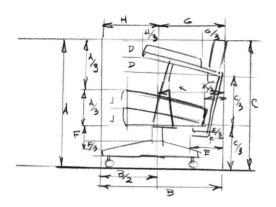

Figure 14-28

Figure 14-29

Figure 14-30

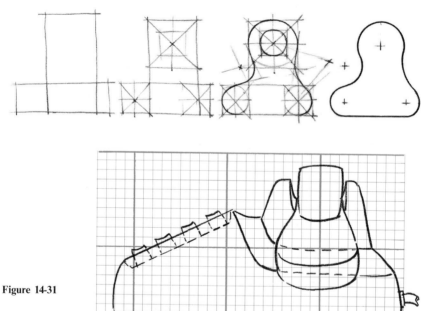

Figure 14-31

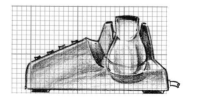

When irregularly shaped objects are sketched, the overall width and height should first be estimated, then the enclosing rectangles are "blocked in," Figure 14–30. As before, one's first effort should be directed to establishing the major proportions of the object, the second to the general sizes and shapes of the curved parts, and finally, to developing and darkening the object lines of the completed sketch.

Frequently it will be desirable to sketch an object in a reduced or enlarged scale from a photograph or drawing. In such instances, ruling a grid across the original picture is helpful. Then the sketch can be made on grid paper in the appropriate proportion to the original. The final sketch can then be made by drawing within and across the squares of the new grid and estimating by eye the relationships in the original photograph as shown by its grid system, Figure 14-31.

Pictures may be selected from magazines or journals whenever they illustrate a point or an idea that one wants to show. Pictures of people, cars, trees, trucks, and equipment may be used—anything which illustrates or amplifies the idea that one wishes to sketch. Such techniques save time and add realism to the sketch. When translucent vellum is used they may be traced directly. Any method which saves time and can produce a more detailed and realistic sketch should be used. There is no reason to make a sketch if a picture is readily available. Photocopy the picture and use it if it is what you have in mind. When it is only a close approximation, such as the handle on an appliance, Figure 14-32, trace the parts that are relevant to your design and then complete the remainder of the sketch from your own imagination, Figure 14-33. This fundamental technique can be mastered if one learns to *think* graphically. *Think in terms of pictures rather than words.*

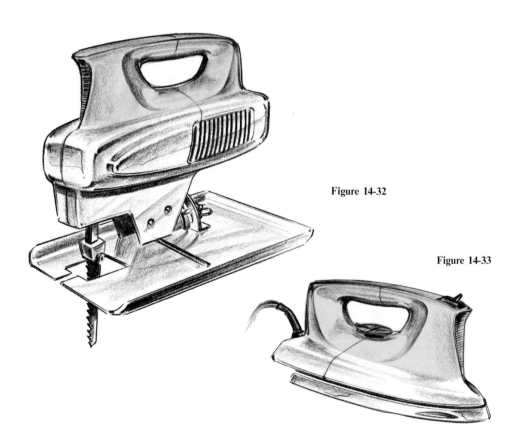

Figure 14-32

Figure 14-33

Arcs, circles, and curves

The engineer must be able to sketch arcs, circles, and curves. Small circles or arcs may be sketched in progressive steps. The scaffold square should be sketched first using very lightweight lines. Then the center lines are sketched through the midpoints of the sides, and arcs are drawn tangent to the sides of the square, Figure 14-34.

Another technique that is often used is to construct a series of radial lines at the point that will be the center of the circle. The radius of the circle is then estimated or measured along each radial line and arcs of the circle are constructed at each of the radius points, Figure 14-35. As many radial lines as desired may be drawn, but the eight lines shown here are generally the most convenient to use.

Segments of circles may be drawn freehand or with a straightedge using the same techniques, Figures 14-36 and 14-37. The scaffolding lines may be used or the radial lines may be used, but it is important that the points of tangency be carefully observed in either case.

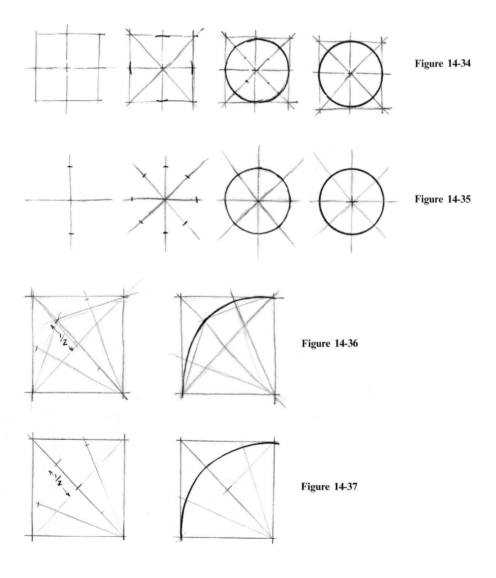

Figure 14-34

Figure 14-35

Figure 14-36

Figure 14-37

Visualization

There are several methods for organizing and presenting visual images. Those most frequently used in sketching are the multiview sketch, the isometric sketch, and the perspective sketch.

The *multiview* sketch is the most familiar method to students of drafting or engineering graphics. In this type of sketch, two, three, or more views of an object are drawn. The line of sight of the viewer is perpendicular to the surface being viewed. The views are sketched as if they were projected on the faces of an imaginary transparent "plastic cube" that surrounds the object, Figure 14-38. If this "plastic cube" were unfolded and laid flat, six views of the object would be seen. In this way one can simultaneously "see" the object from several directions. This type of sketch has the advantage of providing accurate dimensional representations from which a scale model or prototype can be constructed.

Multiview sketching is the most complicated type of drawing to understand. Since the viewer can only concentrate on one view at a time, he must mentally reassemble the object from the various views in order to understand it. This can be particularly difficult for very complex objects, such as an automobile carburetor.

Figure 14-38

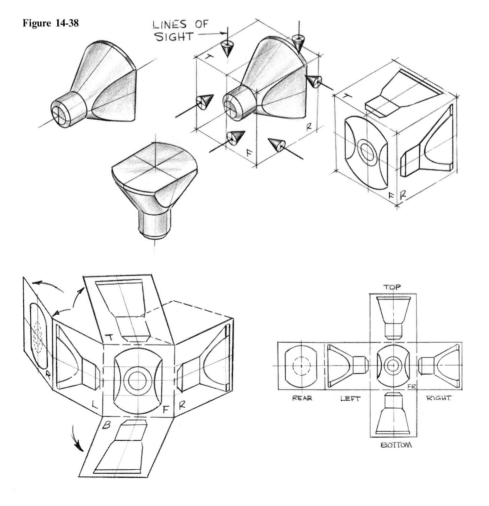

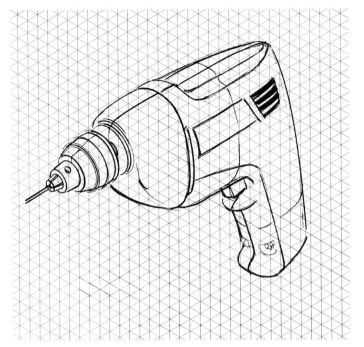

Figure 14-39

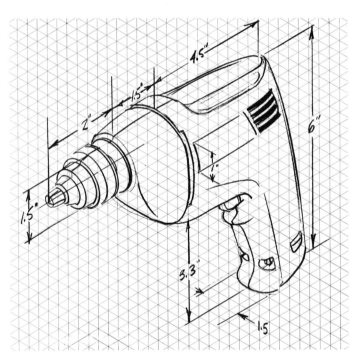

Figure 14-40

The *isometric* sketch, Figure 14-39, is a pictorial method of sketching that has the advantage of simplicity. Isometric sketches also overcome the major difficulty of mental assembly required in the multiview sketch because the object has a visually realistic appearance to the viewer. It permits basic dimensional representation of significant features directly on the sketch, Figure 14-40, or measured from an adjacent scale. The most notable limitation of isometric sketching is the visual

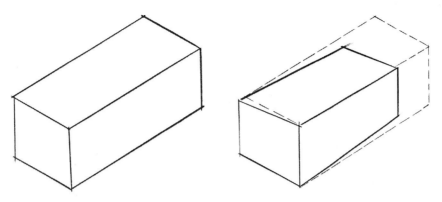

Figure 14-41

distortion that exists because all receding lines are parallel. Thus, isometric sketches give the appearance of perspective sketches but distort the depth perception. This distortion is especially pronounced in objects of considerable depth, Figure 14-41. Another limitation is that the object being sketched has a fixed orientation with respect to the image planes. This often restricts showing important details in the sketch because they are out of view.

The third method, *perspective* sketching, is more difficult to learn, but is generally preferred to the other methods when visual realism is the primary concern. In perspective sketching certain lines are drawn shorter than they actually are, and some parallel lines converge in the distance. Through this technique, known as *foreshortening,* the sketch becomes more realistic; and as a result, it is more easily understood. Another advantage of a perspective sketch, when compared with an isometric sketch, is that the engineer can select the most appropriate view of the object. In the isometric sketch, the object must always be placed at the same angle with respect to the image plane, but in a perspective drawing, the object can be placed at *any* angle, thus providing a means to illustrate particular details. When deciding which of these methods of visualization to use, one should consider the applications and limitations of each. Specific sketching techniques applicable for each method will be discussed separately.

Multiview sketching

Photographs and pictorial drawings serve to produce an illusion of physical reality. They depict a single view as it is seen by an observer, but they are limited in that they cannot always show exactness of detail. This is particularly true where the object is a composite of several components or where details are hidden from view. Therefore a number of views should be sketched and arranged systematically to show the details and dimensions of the object. Such a system of views is produced by *multiview sketching* or *orthographic projection*. Each view is chosen in a direction perpendicular to one of the principal surfaces or one of the sides of the object, Figure 14-42.

It is assumed the observer is an infinite distance from the viewed object, Figure 14-43. In this way the observer will see the size and shape of the object, but only from one direction. Only two of the three principal dimensions (height, width, depth)

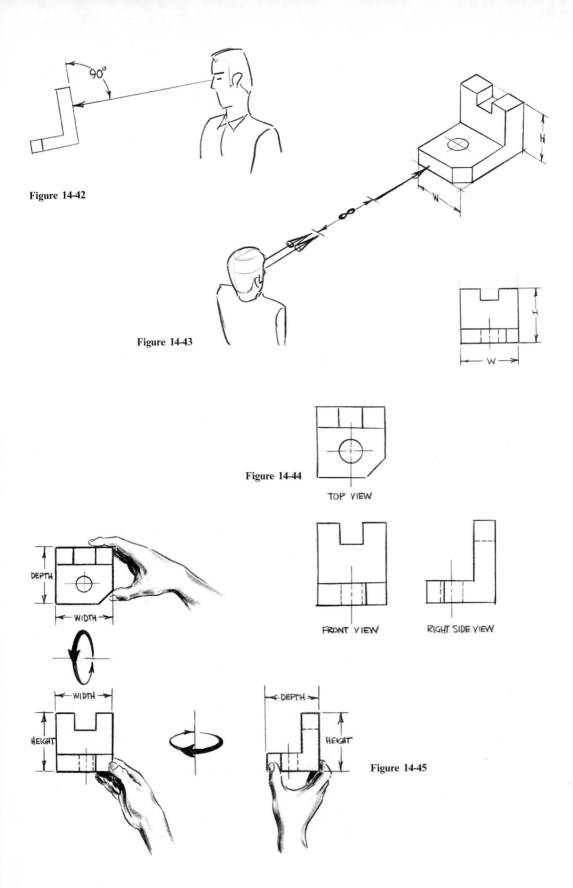

Figure 14-42

Figure 14-43

Figure 14-44

TOP VIEW

FRONT VIEW

RIGHT SIDE VIEW

DEPTH

WIDTH

WIDTH

HEIGHT

DEPTH

HEIGHT

Figure 14-45

can be shown on any one of these views, for example, width and height. If the viewer has a view that shows the width and height dimensions, he cannot judge the depth of the object because he is unable to see it in this orthographic view. In this case, depth is shown by a top, bottom, or side view.

Ordinarily the three views used to describe an object are the front, top, and right- or left-side views, Figure 14-44. They are called *principal views*. The top and right-side views are obtained by revolving the object 90° from the line of sight of the front view. The top view is obtained by rotating the object up and forward toward the observer. The right-side view is obtained by rotating the right side toward the observer, Figure 14-45. This is analogous to flattening the "plastic cube" mentioned earlier. Views of the other sides are obtained in like manner. Customarily, the views are drawn in a standard relationship to one another similar to that shown here.

The selection of views

The engineer should select appropriate views to minimize the number. Careful study should also be given to the silhouette of an object before selecting the views to be sketched. Only those views that are necessary for a clear and complete description should be sketched. The most important view is the one that shows the prominent or characteristic contour of the object. This is usually designated as the front view.

The object shown in Figure 14-46 has three distinctive features that should be completely described by the sketch:

1. The square silhouette top and the rectangular slot in the vertical surface, both of which can be seen from the front view.

2. The hole in the horizontal surface, and the beveled front corner, which are described by the top view.

3. The right angle at the rear, which can be seen from the side.

Upon examination we can see that the left-side, back, and bottom views are unnecessary because they only repeat the information that is contained in the front, top, and right-side views.

Figure 14-46

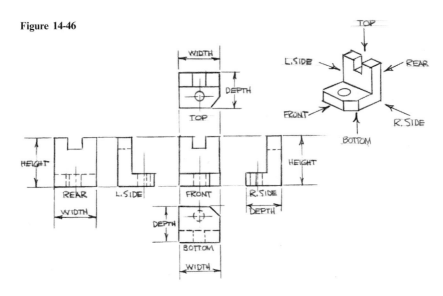

In many instances only two principal views are required, as in Figure 14-47. Also, cylindrical, conical, and pyramidal shapes can be described with two views. This is generally true of any shape that is symmetrical about an axis.

Occasionally, some objects can be adequately described with a single view. When one view is used, supplementary descriptive notes must be added. In Figure 14-48, the view would be incomplete without the note specifying the thickness. In Figure 14-49, the notes are needed to call out the cylindrical shapes of the various portions of the roller.

There are cases when three views will not be adequate, and they must be supplemented with sectional or auxiliary views. The use of these special types of views will be discussed later in the text.

Multiview sketches are most frequently used:

1. Where true shape views are required.
2. Where dimensional notations or tolerance descriptions are required.
3. Where a model or finished part is to be fabricated from the sketch.
4. When angular or oblique surfaces must be described accurately.
5. To precede the preparation of accurate sectional views.
6. When an accurate description of a detail assembly is required.

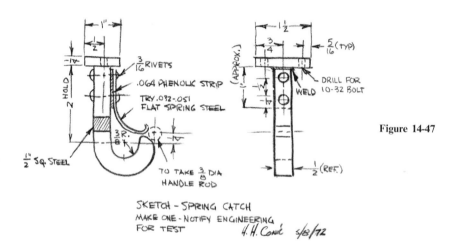

Figure 14-47

Figure 14-48

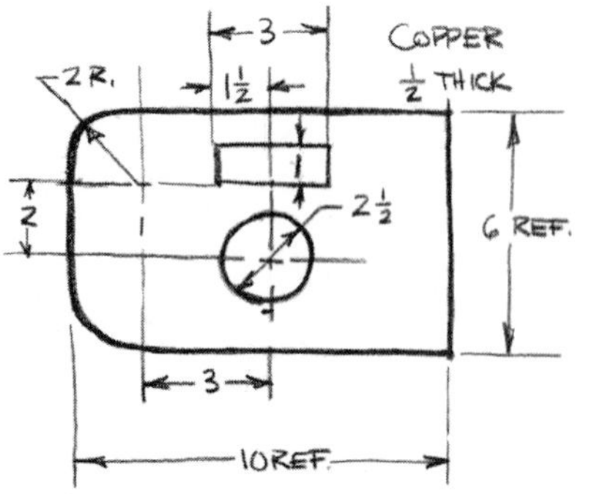

Figure 14-49

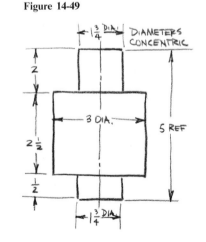

Steps in sketching multiview drawings

First, each space should be blocked in using the "scaffolding" technique mentioned earlier. In Figure 14-50 we see how this should be done in successive steps to prepare the multiview sketches of the support bracket. Note that vertical lines are drawn to separate the view locations and to establish the width of the front and top views. Diagonals are drawn in lightly to serve as locators for the center of the holes. Be certain that the views presented by the sketches are in proper alignment with each other.

Figure 14-50

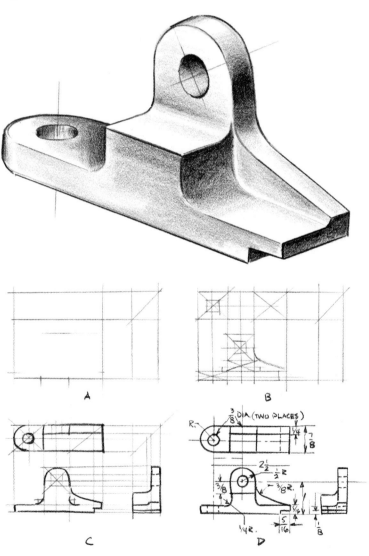

Precedence and representation of lines

Often in a multiview sketch some priority of linework must be established, since two or three lines may appear in identical locations. Visible lines are necessary to establish the physical features of the object and they take precedence over all other lines. A solid line could cover a hidden line, but not vice versa.

The following order of preference (of lines) is recommended:

1. Solid visible lines. (Figure 14-51)

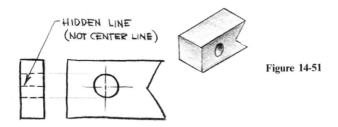

Figure 14-51

2. Hidden lines. (Figure 14-52)

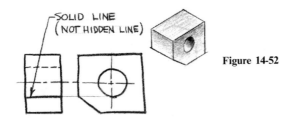

Figure 14-52

3. Center lines.
4. Cutting plane lines.
5. Dimension and extension lines.
6. Crosshatch lines.

Visible lines or hidden lines can be used to show (1) the intersection of two surfaces, (2) an edge view of a surface, or (3) a contour view of a curved surface.

There are certain conventional practices that should be observed when sketching visible and hidden lines:

Figure 14-53

1. When a hidden line forms a continuation of a visible line, there must be a clear separation of their intersection, Figure 14-53.

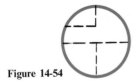

Figure 14-54

2. Intersecting hidden lines should form perpendicular corners as in the letters "L" and "T," Figure 14-54.

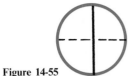

Figure 14-55

3. A hidden line should not intersect a visible line, Figure 14-55.

Figure 14-56

4. Parallel hidden lines should alternate the spaces between the dashes, Figure 14-56.

Figure 14-57

5. When hidden lines join at a point, the dashes should touch, as in the case at the bottom of a drilled hole, Figure 14-57.

Center lines are used to indicate axes of symmetry of round objects, centers of holes, or of arcs. The symbol "₵" is sometimes used to designate the centerline and the center of a circle or the radius of an arc is designated with a cross made of short dashes +. For symmetrical views or portions of views the center lines should be among the first lines drawn. The center line is made up of very light thin lines with alternating short and long dashes and always extends slightly beyond the outline of the object or feature to which it applies.

Dimensioning procedures

The dimensioning of a sketch will do much to clarify it in the mind of the viewer. Adequate space should be planned around the sketch to accommodate proper dimensioning. Regardless of the method of visualization used, these dimensioning rules should be followed:

1. Locate each dimension on the view which shows the detail most clearly.
2. Show only necessary dimensions. Do not repeat the same dimension on more than one other view.
3. Arrange all dimensions, dimension lines, and leaders so as to avoid crowding, interference, and confusion with the lines describing the object.
4. Avoid dimensioning between surfaces and centerlines or hidden lines.
5. Use a consistent system of spacing and layout of the dimensions.
6. Use correct dimensioning symbols and terminology.
7. Locate round shapes by their centerlines.

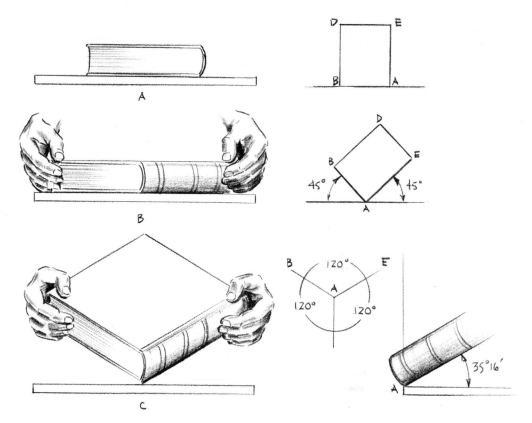

Figure 14-58

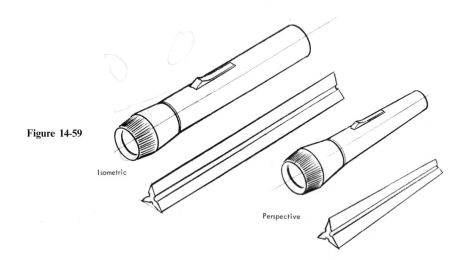

Figure 14-59

Isometric

Perspective

Isometric sketching

The isometric sketch provides a pictorial representation of an object which is more realistic and understandable than the multiview sketch. It permits the viewer with one visual image to see the height, length, and depth dimensions of an object in true length. This overcomes two of the limitations of multiview drawings: the difficult requirement of assembling a mental composite view, and the necessity of drawing many views of the object.

In multiview sketching, the line of sight of the viewer is always perpendicular to one of the sides of the transparent "plastic box." In isometric sketching, the box is rotated until its front face makes a 45° angle with respect to the image plane, Figure 14-58, and then tipped up to 35°16'. As is the case in multiview drawing, the transparent box is assumed to be an infinite distance from the viewer. The front corner of the box will appear as a vertical line. The two receding lines representing the bottom edges, and those lines parallel to them, will appear to be at angles of approximately 30° to the horizontal. Since the box is assumed to be seen from an infinite distance, the lines of sight to the object are parallel. This assumption simplifies the drawing but distorts the resulting image of the object in two directions: by creating the illusion that the receding lines are spreading apart, Figure 14-59, and by foreshortening the true lengths in the top surface.

The use of preprinted *isometric paper* is recommended as a sketching aid, particularly as a reference background under the sketching paper.

The steps for making an isometric sketch are as follows.

Step 1 Establish the *x*, *y*, *z* isometric axes at angles of 120° to each other with the *y* axis being vertical, Figure 14-60.

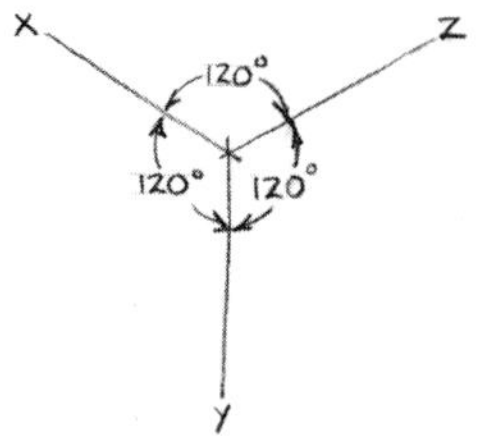

Figure 14-60

Step 2 Construct a scaffolding box just large enough to enclose the object with the *y* isometric axis being the front corner of the box, Figure 14-61.

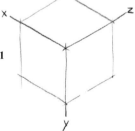

Figure 14-61

Step 3 Place the object to be drawn in the scaffolding box. Surfaces and edges parallel to the *xy* and *yz* planes should be sketched in their respective places within the scaffold, Figure 14-62.

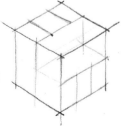

Figure 14-62

Step 4 Angular surfaces or edges should be sketched by first locating their endpoints and then connecting them, Figure 14-63.

Figure 14-63

Step 5 Sketch in the holes and arcs as ellipses or partial ellipses; sketch noncircular arcs by plotting points, Figure 14-64.

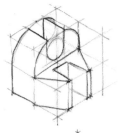

Figure 14-64

Step 6 Trace the object lines of the finished sketch, Figure 14-65.

Figure 14-65

Note: Hidden lines are normally omitted.

Circles viewed obliquely as in isometric and perspective sketches appear as ellipses. To represent a circle, first draw an isometric square (rhombus). Construct the rhombus such that the sides approximate the length of the diameter of the true circle. The ellipse is formed by sketching arcs which are tangent to the midpoints of the sides of the rhombus. When drawing an ellipse in an isometric box, always locate the minor axis parallel and the major axis perpendicular to the axis of the circle which the ellipse represents, Figure 14-66. It is possible to use a 30° ellipse guide for quick construction of isometric circles. If one is not available, the *four-center ellipse method* produces a good approximation.

Four-center ellipse method

The four-center ellipse method of sketching an ellipse produces an *approximate ellipse* and is effective for most sketching requirements.

Figure 14-66

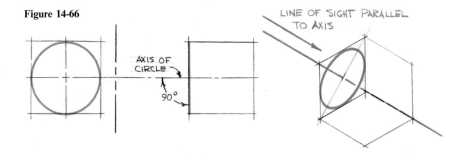

Step 1 Sketch a rhombus whose sides are equal to the diameter of the true circle that is to be represented; sketch the diagonal between the two apexes farthest apart, Figure 14-67.

Figure 14-67

Step 2 Estimate the midpoints of each side of the rhombus, and connect the midpoints of the sides with the rhombus apexes on the opposite side, Figure 14-68.

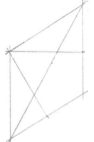

Figure 14-68

Step 3 The two intersections of the bisectors will serve as centers from which circular arcs can be sketched between the two apexes farthest apart, Figure 14-69.

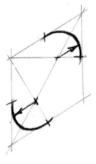

Figure 14-69

Step 4 Complete the ellipse by sketching the two remaining circular arcs, whose radii extend from apex to midpoints, Figure 14-70.

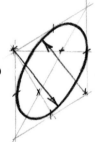

Figure 14-70

Step 5 Erase the construction lines or retrace the ellipse on clean paper and darken the outline of the ellipse, Figure 14-71.

Figure 14-71

14: Technical sketching: a medium of communication for the engineer **339**

Samples of isometric applications are shown in Figures 14-72 through 14-74.

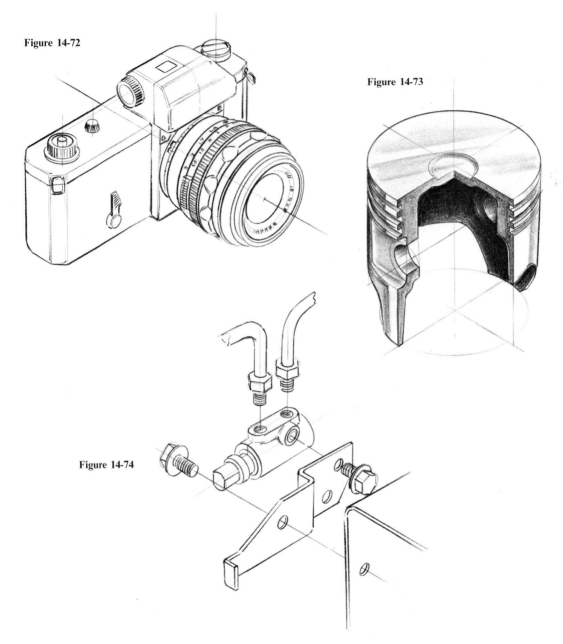

Figure 14-72

Figure 14-73

Figure 14-74

Perspective sketching

Perspective sketching differs from isometric sketching in that the viewer is a finite distance from the object, rather than an infinite distance, and there is no fixed viewing position. The *perspective* view provides a close approximation to a photograph, Figure 14-75. It is a difficult technique to learn. In addition to line technique, special attention must be given to making objects appear proportionately smaller as their

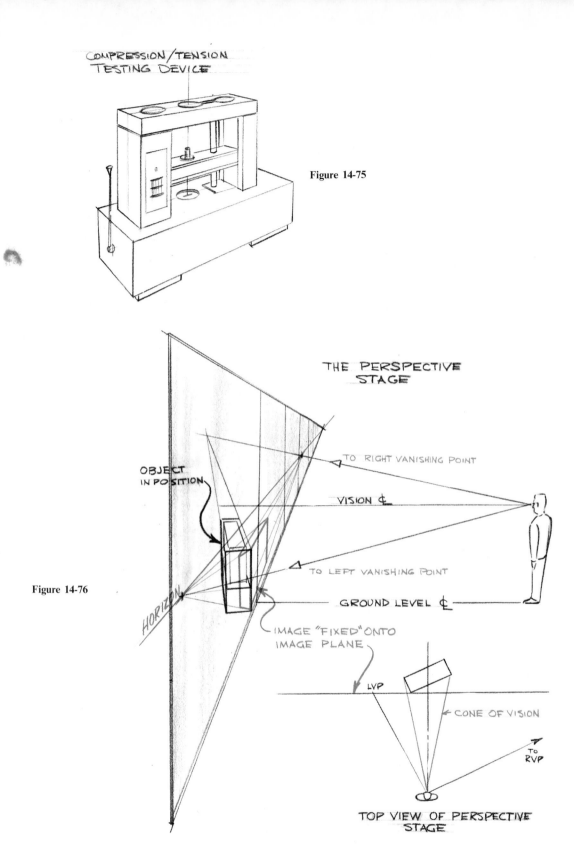

COMPRESSION/TENSION TESTING DEVICE

Figure 14-75

THE PERSPECTIVE STAGE

OBJECT IN POSITION

TO RIGHT VANISHING POINT

VISION ℄

TO LEFT VANISHING POINT

GROUND LEVEL ℄

HORIZON

Figure 14-76

IMAGE "FIXED" ONTO IMAGE PLANE

LVP

CONE OF VISION

TO RVP

TOP VIEW OF PERSPECTIVE STAGE

Illustration 14-1

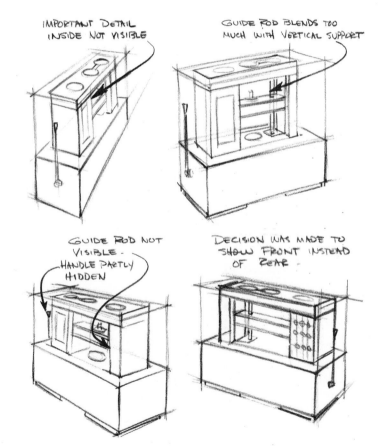

SHADOW ALSO
GOES TO SAME
VANISHING POINT

Figure 14-77

IMPORTANT DETAIL
INSIDE NOT VISIBLE

GUIDE ROD BLENDS TOO
MUCH WITH VERTICAL SUPPORT

Figure 14-78

GUIDE ROD NOT
VISIBLE -
HANDLE PARTLY
HIDDEN

DECISION WAS MADE TO
SHOW FRONT INSTEAD
OF REAR.

distance from the eye increases, to making parallel lines appear to converge as they recede, and to making horizontal lines and planes appear to vanish on the horizon. These considerations are achieved by selective positioning of the object relative to the image plane, by proper location of the horizon, and by designation of appropriate vanishing points on the horizon, Figure 14-76.

An acceptable likeness can be achieved by using a single vanishing point on the horizon, Illustration 14-1 and Figure 14-77. However, two-point perspective sketches, which have two vanishing points, give more realistic results and consequently are more often used. For this reason two-point perspective sketching will be discussed in some detail.

In making a two-point perspective sketch initial consideration should be given to the orientation of the object so that a "scaffolding box" may be constructed that clearly shows the desirable features of the object. Several preliminary sketches of the scaffolding box in varying orientations should be tried to achieve the desired visual presentation, Figure 14-78. After the best orientation has been selected, Figure 14-79, lines are projected along the edges of the box and their intersection with the horizon line establishes the vanishing points, Figure 14-80. The vanishing point is that point on the horizon where parallel lines appear to converge—to vanish. The *center of vision* of the sketch should be located by a centerline. This location is purely arbitrary but in general should be near the visual center of the object being sketched. Once the *center of vision* line has been selected, it is extended vertically until it intersects the edge view of the image plane. Similar vertical projections are made to the image plane from the left and right vanishing points, resulting in intersections "M" and "N." The front edge of the scaffolding box is projected vertically resulting in the location of point "B."

The position of the observer with respect to the image plane, point "O," is determined by the observer's sight lines to the vanishing points "M" and "N" that were projected to the image plane. The observer's lines of sight subtend an internal angle of 90°. The location of the sight lines and point "O" can be found easily by sliding the apex of a 90° triangle down the *center of vision* line until the two sides of the 90° angle intersect the edge view of the image plane at points "M" and "N".

Figure 14-79

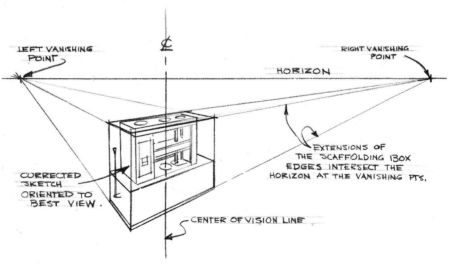

Now construct the orthographic top view of the object with the front corner touching the image plane at point "B" and with sides "AB" and "BD" parallel to observer sight lines "OM" and "ON," respectively. Individual sight lines from the observer, point "O," to each point on the orthographic top view of the object will intersect the image plane. At these intersections, vertical projectors are extended downward to the scaffolding box to locate corresponding points on the object by intersecting the vanishing lines, Figure 14-81. The orthographic side view is drawn and projectors are extended parallel to the horizon line, to the perspective view. Proceeding in this manner, each corner or point on the object can be located within the scaffolding box.

To attain realistic sketches one should select the location of the horizon line

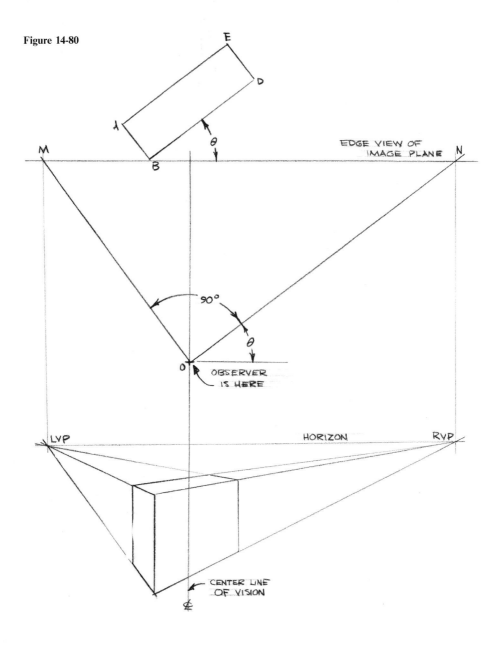

Figure 14-80

carefully so that the object being sketched appears in the position and in the proportion that is expected in real life. The eye level of the observer determines the relative location of the horizon on the sketch because the horizon line *always* passes through the eye level of the observer. Therefore if one were to sketch a view of a refrigerator that is approximately 5 ft high, the horizon line of the sketch should be drawn such that it passes through the refrigerator top, Figure 14-82. Similarly, the observer's sight line to the horizon would pass approximately through the center of a large object such as a bus. Objects that are normally viewed from above, such as typewriters, should be located below the horizon. In the case of small objects that rest on the ground, the horizon would be located approximately 5 ft above the object, as an example, a sidewalk skateboard. Dramatic effects can be obtained by

Figure 14-81

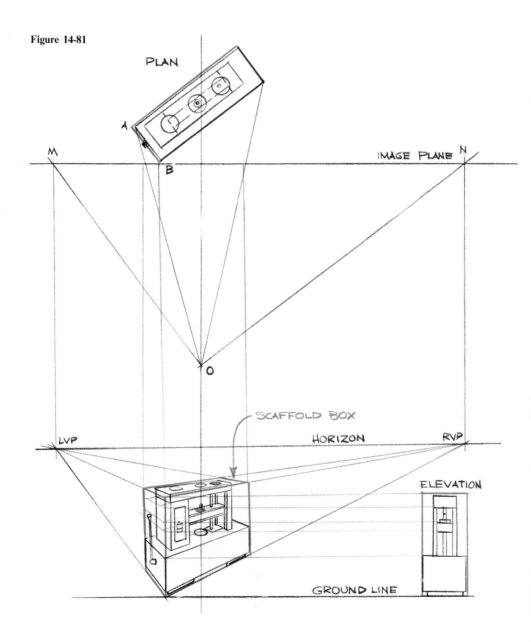

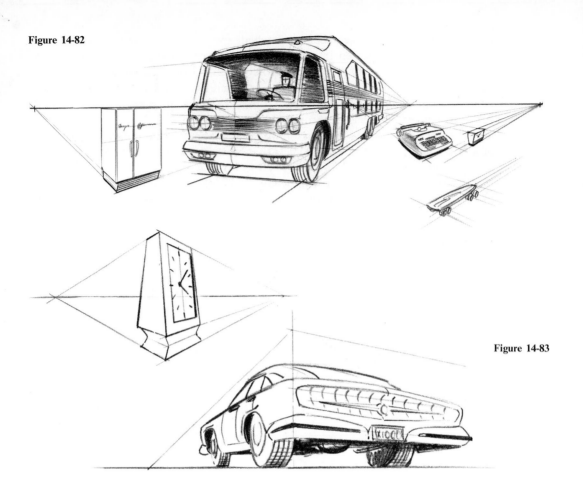

Figure 14-82

Figure 14-83

Figure 14-84

adjusting the eye level of the observer up or down and may enhance the details of a concept, Figure 14-83. Further realism and proportion in sketching can be achieved by adding some familiar object, such as the silhouette of a person, Figure 14-84.

Basic shapes in sketching

One should learn to recognize the presence of four basic shapes which appear again and again: the cylinder, the cube, the cone, and the sphere, Figure 14-85. They are found not only in "man-made" designs but in the structure of living things as well. The construction of some familiar objects using the four basic shapes is shown in Figure 14-86.

Shading

The form of an object determines the way that light is reflected from it. Therefore additional clarity and realism can be achieved by shading. Shading should be practiced on the four basic shapes.

Light originates at a source—the sun, a lamp, and so on, and the light rays radiate outward in all directions from it. These light rays always travel in straight lines,

Figure 14-85

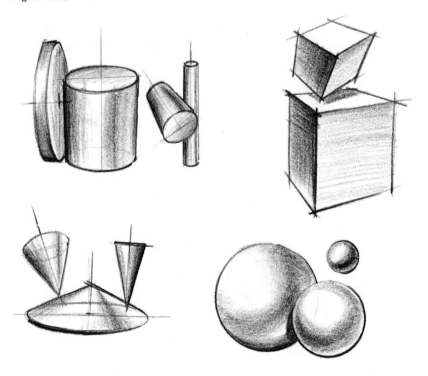

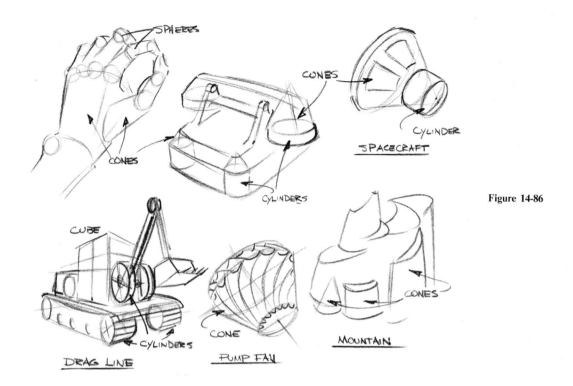

SPHERES

CONES

CONES

CYLINDERS

CONES

SPACECRAFT

CYLINDER

Figure 14-86

CUBE

CYLINDERS

DRAG LINE

CONE

PUMP FAU

CONES

MOUNTAIN

Figure 14-87

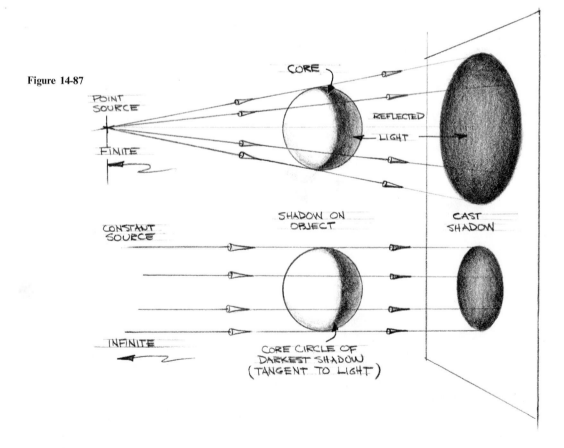

CORE

POINT
SOURCE

FINITE

REFLECTED

LIGHT

CONSTANT
SOURCE

SHADOW ON
OBJECT

CAST
SHADOW

INFINITE

CORE CIRCLE OF
DARKEST SHADOW
(TANGENT TO LIGHT)

348

Figure 14-87. When they are intercepted by an opaque body a shadow is formed. Most objects upon which light strikes will reflect some of the light, depending upon the shape of the object and its surface texture.

When the source of light is undetermined, it is conventional practice to assume that the light comes from a single source at infinity, producing parallel rays falling over the left shoulder of the observer at an angle of approximately 45° to the ground, Figure 14-88. Any spot or surface on the object that intercepts the light perpendicularly will give maximum reflection and this area will appear white, or nearly so, on the sketch. Other surfaces will be shaded depending upon the amount of light that falls upon them. The gradation of shading on the surfaces will give additional emphasis to the depth of the object. The portion of the surface that is closest to the eye but hidden from the light should receive the darkest shading, Figure 14-89.

Figure 14-88

Figure 14-89

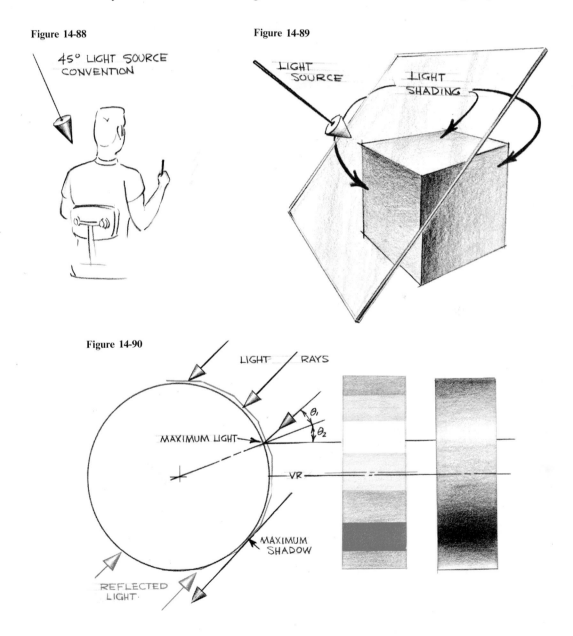

Figure 14-90

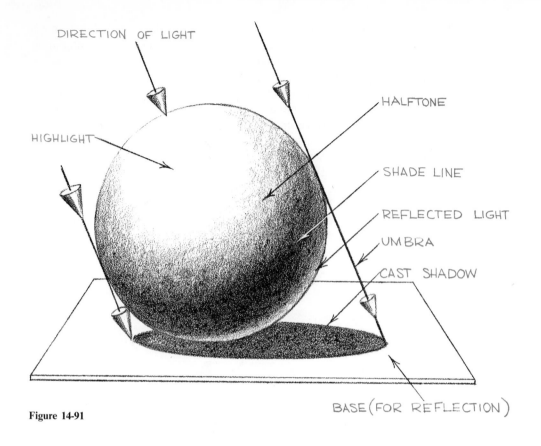

DIRECTION OF LIGHT

HIGHLIGHT

HALFTONE

SHADE LINE

REFLECTED LIGHT

UMBRA

CAST SHADOW

BASE (FOR REFLECTION)

Figure 14-91

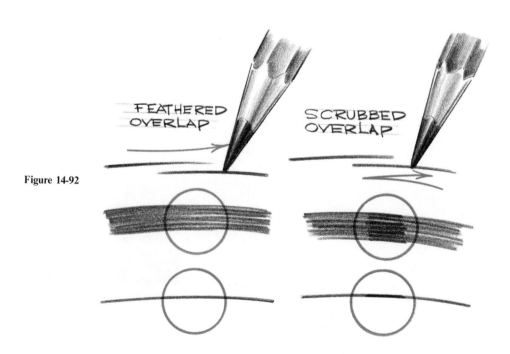

FEATHERED OVERLAP

SCRUBBED OVERLAP

Figure 14-92

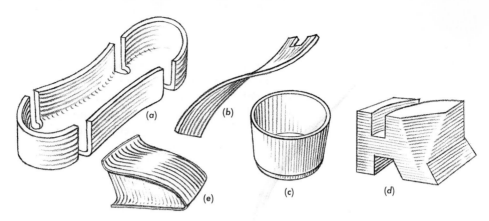

Figure 14-93

As the surface recedes into the distance the shading should become progressively lighter. However, the extreme back edge should be shaded very lightly to indicate the edge of the object. On the side that is exposed to the light source, make the part nearest the observer the lightest and make it darker as it recedes into the distance. No shading on the light side of the object should be as dark as the lightest of the shadows on the surfaces away from the light source.

The surface shading of a cylinder is more difficult than the shading of a cube, but the same principles apply, Figure 14-90. The shading should be darkest at the point where the light rays are tangent to the cylindrical surface. It should be lightest at the point where the light source is reflected directly to the observer.

The surface shading of a sphere should be darkest where the light rays are tangent to the sphere (along the shade line in Figure 14-91) and lightest at the point of incidence of the reflected light source, Figure 14-91. There are many methods to apply shading.

Pencil shading may be applied in two ways, Figure 14-92. For best results use a pencil with a flattened point and lightly cover the entire area that is to receive shading. The darker shades for particular areas are built up to the desired darkness by repeated strokes, being certain that each shade that is developed blends into the next. For shading, begin and end lines with a feather edge—a gentle landing and takeoff of the pencil point on the paper surface. This technique leads to smoother work in all types of sketching.

When one has developed skill in sketching and learned to apply shade and shadows using erasable media, then the eraser becomes a useful tool. It is used to remove small "areas of light" within the dark shaded areas of a sketch.

A second method of shading involves the use of lines of varied weight and spacing, Figure 14-93. No lines are needed for the very light areas. This simple and effective technique is particularly useful where speed is a factor or where the sketch is drawn from the imagination.

Summary

The ability to sketch is an important skill for the engineer to master. Through this skill he may communicate ideas that would otherwise be difficult, if not impossible, to convey. Sketching should not be considered a mystical talent that one is born with, but rather a skill that is developed through practice and effort.

The proper selection and use of tools, such as pencils, paper, and mechanical guides, will do much to enhance and speed the sketching techniques of the engineer, but care must be exercised in becoming unnecessarily dependent on these aids. Overdependence will stifle the development and confidence of one's freehand sketching skills.

There are a number of procedures that can be used for effective sketching. The multiview technique provides means to convey accurate dimensional relationships and selected views of an object, but is difficult to read if one is interested in a composite or pictorial view.

The isometric sketch overcomes the problem of total pictorial representation that is lacking in the multiview sketch, and retains much of the dimensional accuracy. It creates distortions of the object because of the simplified methods used to construct the view. This results in obtaining views which are limited in orientation and clarity.

The perspective sketch is the most visually accurate representation, but also the most time consuming to draw accurately. It is difficult to master the techniques of perspective sketching, and the detail that is revealed is sometimes less than desirable.

All these methods of visual representation are improved through the application of sketching techniques such as line weight, view selection, shading, and curve construction. Considerable practice and the use of imagination are also essential because sketching, like writing, can be learned.

Sketching exercises

Figure 14-94 Study the front face of each object (see arrow) and sketch an orthographic view of that face.

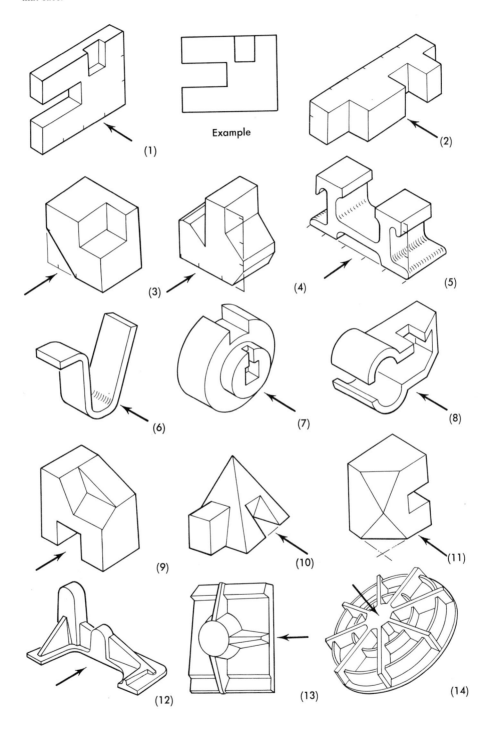

Example

(1)

(2)

(3)

(4)

(5)

(6)

(7)

(8)

(9)

(10)

(11)

(12)

(13)

(14)

Figure 14-95 Sketch the necessary principal orthographic views to describe the objects.

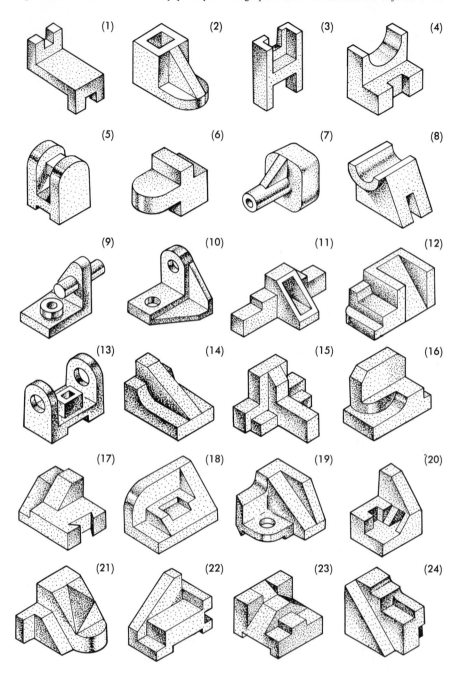

(1)   (2)   (3)   (4)

(5)   (6)   (7)   (8)

(9)   (10)   (11)   (12)

(13)   (14)   (15)   (16)

(17)   (18)   (19)   (20)

(21)   (22)   (23)   (24)

Figure 14-96 Sketch the orthographic views necessary to describe the objects.

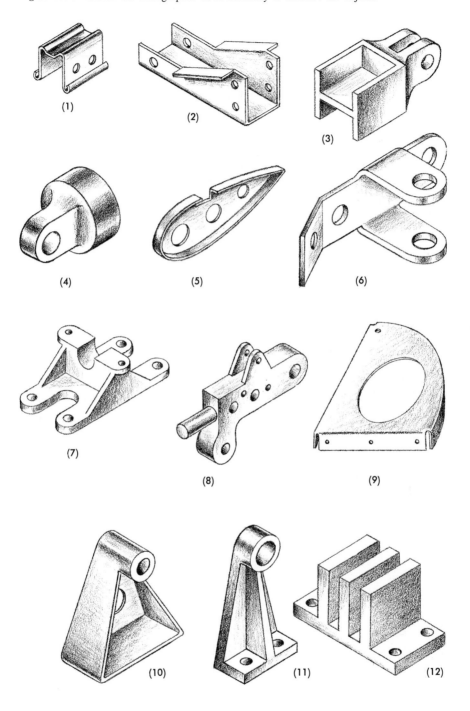

(1)

(2)

(3)

(4)

(5)

(6)

(7)

(8)

(9)

(10)

(11)

(12)

Figure 14-97 Make an isometric sketch of each object.

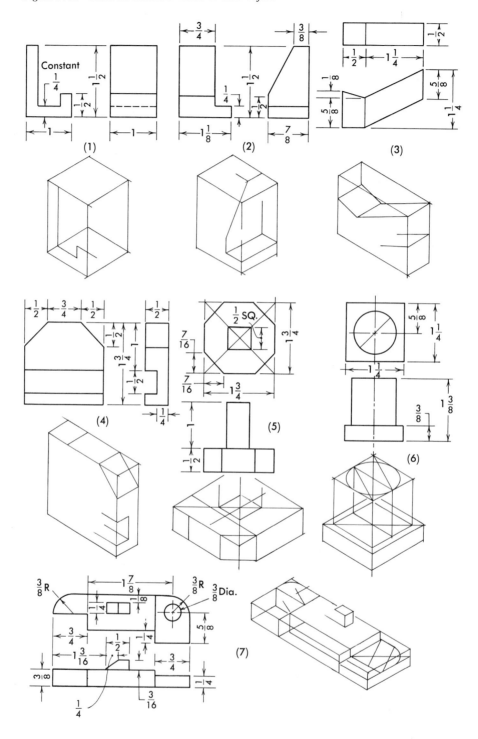

Figure 14-98 Make an isometric sketch of each object.

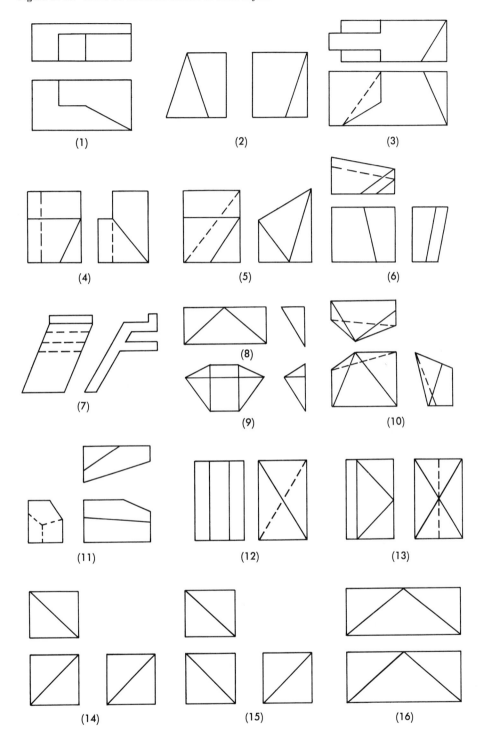

(1) (2) (3)

(4) (5) (6)

(7) (8) (9) (10)

(11) (12) (13)

(14) (15) (16)

Figure 14-99 Make an isometric sketch of each object.

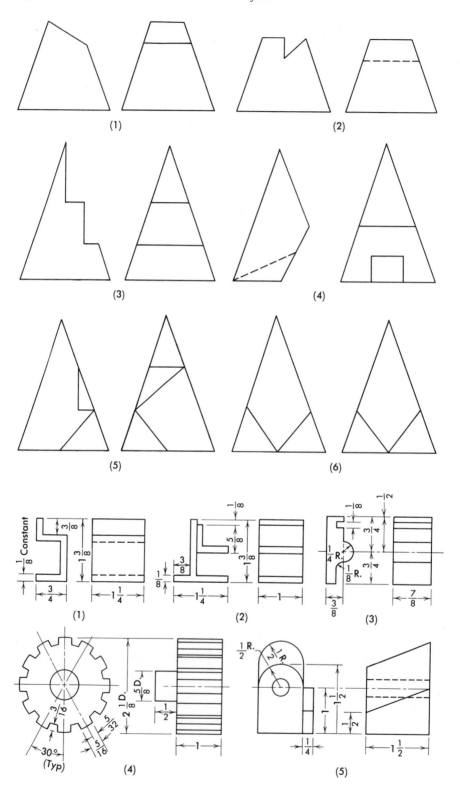

Figure 14-100 Make a one- or two-point perspective sketch of each object.

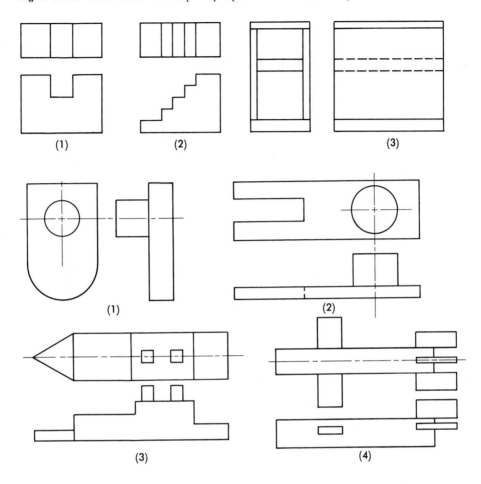

(1)   (2)   (3)

(1)   (2)

(3)   (4)

Figure 14-101 Make sketches from the orthographic views.

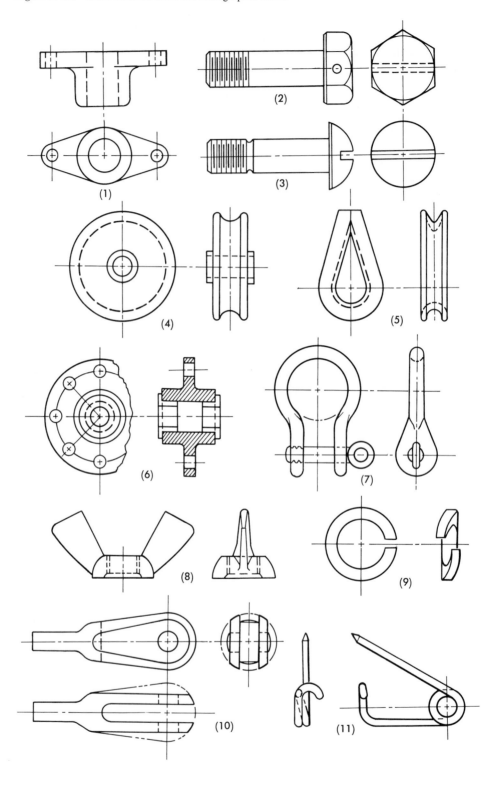

Bibliography

Earle, James H., *Engineering Design Graphics,* Addison-Wesley, Reading, Mass. (1969).

French, Thomas E., and Charles J. Vierck, *Graphic Science and Design,* 3rd ed., McGraw-Hill, New York (1970).

French, Thomas E., and Charles J. Vierck, *Engineering Drawing,* 10th ed., McGraw-Hill, New York (1966).

Giesecke, Frederick E., Alva Mitchell, Henry C. Spencer, Ivan L. Hill, and Robert O. Loving, *Engineering Graphics,* Macmillan, New York (1969).

Giesecke, Frederick E., Alva Mitchell, Henry C. Spencer, and Ivan L. Hill, *Technical Drawing,* 5th ed., Macmillan, New York (1967).

Hammond, Robert H., Carson P. Buck, William B. Rogers, Gerald W. Walsh, Jr., and Hugh P. Ackert, *Engineering Graphics,* 2nd ed., Ronald Press, New York (1971).

Hoelscher, Randolph P., Clifford H. Springer, and Jerry S. Dobrovolny, *Graphics for Engineers,* Wiley, New York (1968).

Katz, Hyman H., *Technical Sketching and Visualization for Engineers,* Macmillan, New York (1949).

Levens, A. S., *Graphics,* 2nd ed., Wiley, New York (1968).

Luzadder, Warren J., *Basic Graphics,* 2nd ed., Prentice-Hall, Englewood Cliffs, N.J. (1968).

Mochel, Myron G., *Fundamentals of Engineering Graphics,* Prentice-Hall, Englewood Cliffs, N.J. (1960).

Rule, John T., and Steven A. Coons, *Graphics,* McGraw-Hill, New York (1961).

Schneerer, William F., *Programmed Graphics,* McGraw-Hill, New York (1967).

Svensen, Carl Lars, and William Ezra Street, *Engineering Graphics,* Van Nostrand Reinhold, New York (1962).

Wellman, B. Leighton, *Introduction to Graphical Analysis and Design,* McGraw-Hill, New York (1966).

Part Six

Introduction to the design process

The design process begins with the recognition of a human need to be satisfied and ends with the achievement of an acceptable solution. The path in between is tenuous, uncertain, and demanding, and worthy of the highest dedication.

15

The phases of design

Much of the history of man has been influenced by developments in engineering, science, and technology. When progress in these fields was impeded, the culture of the era tended to stagnate and decline; the converse was also true. Although many definitions have been given of "engineering," it is generally agreed that *the basic purpose of the engineering profession is to develop technical devices, services, and systems for the use and benefit of man.* The engineer's design is, in a sense, a bridge across the unknown between the resources available and the needs of mankind (Figure 15-1).

Regardless of his field of specialization or the complexity of the problem, the method by which the engineer does his work is known as the *engineering design process.* This process is a creative and iterative approach to problem solving. It is creative because it brings into being new ideas and combinations of ideas that did not exist before. It is iterative because it brings into play the cyclic process of problem solving, applied over and over again as the scope of a problem becomes more completely defined and better understood.

> . . . the process of design, the process of inventing physical things which display new physical order, organization, form, in response to function.
> —Christopher Alexander, *Notes on the Synthesis of Form*
>
> A scientist can discover a new star but he cannot make one. He would have to ask an engineer to do it for him.
> —Gordon L. Glegg

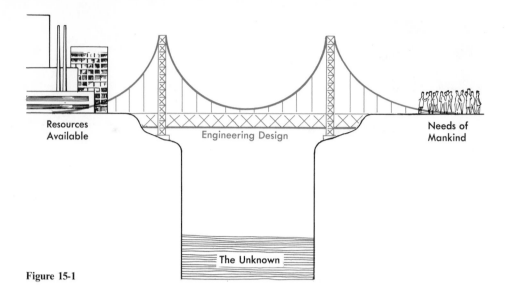

Figure 15-1

Resources Available · Engineering Design · Needs of Mankind · The Unknown

Thus a design engineer must be a creative person—an idea man—and he must be able to try one idea after another without becoming discouraged. In general he learns more from his failures than from his successes, and his final designs usually will be compromises and departures from the "ideal" that he would like to achieve.

A final engineering design usually is the product of the inspired and organized efforts of more than one person. The personalities of good designers vary, but certain characteristics are strikingly similar. Among these will be the following:

1. Technical competence.
2. Understanding of nature.
3. Empathy for the requirements of his fellow men.
4. Active curiosity.
5. Ability to observe with discernment.
6. Initiative.
7. Motivation to design for the pleasure of accomplishment.
8. Confidence.
9. Integrity.
10. Willingness to take a calculated risk and to assume responsibility.
11. Capacity to synthesize.
12. Persistence and sense of purpose.

Certain design precepts and methods can be learned by study, but the ability to design cannot be gained solely by reading or studying. The engineer also must grapple with real problems and apply his knowledge and abilities to finding solutions. Just as an athlete needs rigorous practice, so an engineer needs practice on design problems as he attempts to gain proficiency in his art. Such experience must necessarily be gained over a period of years, but now is a good time to begin acquiring some of the requisite fundamentals.

Phases of engineering design

Most engineering designs go through three distinct phases:

1. The feasibility study.
2. The preliminary design.
3. The detail design.

In general, a design project will proceed through the various phases in the sequence indicated (Figure 15-2). The amount of time spent on any phase is a function of the complexity of the problem and the restrictions placed upon the engineer—time, money, or performance characteristics.

The feasibility study

The feasibility study is concerned with the following:

1. Definition of the elements of the problem.
2. Identification of the factors that limit the scope of the design.
3. Evaluation of the difficulties that can be anticipated as probable in the design process.
4. Consideration of the consequences of the design.

The objectives of the feasibility study are to discover possible solutions and to determine which of these appear to have promise and which are not feasible, and why.

Let us see how this might work in a situation where you, as the chief engineer of an aircraft company, have been asked to diversify the company's product line by designing a small, low-power passenger vehicle for town driving with substantially less pollution than present cars.

What are the elements of the problem; what factors limit its scope? Where and by whom will such vehicles be used? Are they to carry people individually and randomly to and from work, school, shopping areas, or places of amusement like the present car, or are they to be links in a more comprehensive transportation system? Are they to be privately or publicly owned? If privately owned, perhaps the emphasis should be on low cost, simple upkeep, and ease of parking. If publicly owned—a car which a licensed driver can pick up at one parking place and leave at another—then ease of handling, reliable operation, and long life might be the

Figure 15-2

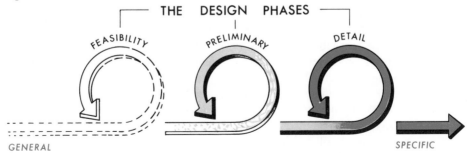

THE DESIGN PHASES

FEASIBILITY   PRELIMINARY   DETAIL

GENERAL   SPECIFIC

major considerations. You will want to know how fast it is to go, how far between fuelings, and how many people it is to carry.

Assume it is decided to design a vehicle for public ownership. What difficulties can be anticipated? Probably the major ones will have to do with people and what they might do. How do you make such a vehicle safe and nearly foolproof? People must be prevented from driving it too far and from abandoning it anywhere except at designated parking places. Provision must be made to redistribute the vehicles if for some reason—a ball game, a sale, a happening—too many people converge on one area. Maintenance and repair will present many problems.

Assuming that such a vehicle can be built and sold to cities, what would be the consequences? Some of the desirable ones are obvious: less traffic, lower air pollution, fewer parking problems, and more efficient vehicle utilization. But what about the uncertainty of finding a car when and where you want it, particularly on a wet, cold night or during the rush hour? The new rules and regulations that would have to be devised? The risk of nonacceptance by the public? These would be some of the early considerations during such a feasibility study.

The ideas and possibilities which are generated in early discussions should be checked for the following:

1. Acceptability in meeting the specifications.
2. Compatibility with known principles of science and engineering.
3. Compatibility with the environment.
4. Compatibility of the properties of the design with other parts of the system.
5. Comparison of the design with other known solutions to the problem.

Each alternative is examined to determine whether or not it can be physically achieved, whether its potential usefulness is commensurate with the costs of making it available, and whether the return on the investment warrants its implementation. The feasibility study is in effect a "pilot" effort whose primary purpose is to seek information pertinent to all possible solutions to the problem. After the information has been collected and evaluated, and after the undesirable design possibilities have been discarded, the engineer still may have several alternatives to consider—all of which may be acceptable.

During the generation of ideas, the engineer has intentionally avoided making any final selection so as to leave his mind open to all possibilities and to give free rein to his thoughts. Now he must reduce this number of ideas to a few—those most likely to be successful, those that will compete for the final solution. How many ideas he keeps will depend on the complexity of ideas and the amount of time and manpower that he can afford to spend during the preliminary design phase. In most design situations the number of ideas remaining at the end of the feasibility study will vary from two to six.

At this point no objective evaluations are available; the discarding of ideas must depend to a large extent upon experience and judgment. There are few substitutes for experience, but there are ways in which judgment can be improved. For example, decision processes based on the theory of probability (see Chapter 19) can be employed effectively. Analog and digital simulations (see Chapter 13) are particularly useful to the engineer in this early comparison of alternatives.

In some instances, it will be more convenient for the engineer to compare the expected performance of the component parts of one design with the counterpart performances of another design. When this is done, he must be very careful to consider if the component parts create the optimum effect in the overall design.

Frequently it is true that a simple combination of seemingly ideal parts will not produce an optimum condition. It is not too difficult to list the advantages and disadvantages of each alternative, but the proper evaluation of such lists may require the wisdom of Solomon.

The consideration of *value* is very important in the early selection process. From whose point of view should a particular alternative be appraised? Performance characteristics that may be advantageous in one situation may be equally disadvantageous in another. As an example, automatic redistribution of cars would increase the efficiency of the public car system and save driver cost. However, such an automatic system would almost surely not be possible on public streets, and the cost of extra rights-of-way may make it prohibitive. How does one select the location and proximity of parking places? How far should people be asked to walk, and how many parking places can be serviced effectively? How does one select the maximum speed of the cars and reconcile the conflicting demands of safety and service? Where danger to human life is a possibility, the measurement of value becomes exceedingly difficult. There is great reluctance to place a "cost" or value on the life of a human being. If the engineer assumes an infinite cost penalty, the design may be impossible, but to ignore this factor would effectively assign a cost factor of zero to a life. The engineer must face his responsibilities with honesty and realism.[1]

Engineers engaged in a feasibility study must be able to project the future effectiveness of the alternative designs. In many cases the preliminary design stage of a product will precede its manufacture by several years. Conditions change with time, and these changes must be anticipated by the engineer. Many companies have become eminently successful because of the accuracy of their projections, whereas others have been forced into bankruptcy.

The preliminary design phase

With alternatives narrowed to a few, the engineer must select the design he wishes to develop in detail. The choice is easy if only one of the proposed designs fulfills all requirements. More often, several of the concepts appear to meet the specifications equally well. The choice then must be made on such factors as economics, novelty, reliability, and the number and severity of unsolved problems.

Since it is difficult to make such comparisons in one's head without introducing personal bias, it is useful to prepare an evaluation table. All the important design criteria are listed, and each is assigned an importance factor. There always will be both positive and negative criteria. Then each design is rated as to how well it meets each criterion. This rating should be done by somebody who is not aware of the value assigned to each importance factor, so that he is not unduly influenced.

Let us apply this procedure to our city transportation problem, and particularly to the selection of the propulsion system. Let us assume that the ordinary automobile engine has already been discarded because it is unable to meet air pollution requirements, and that the choice has narrowed to one of three types of engines: the gas turbine, the electric motor, and the steam engine. We will then enter these as Designs (1), (2), and (3) in a table and assign values to the various positive and negative design criteria (Figure 15-3). For example, the gas turbine and electric motor rate low on "novelty" for they are well developed, but an automobile steam engine could

---

[1] By assigning financial damages to families whose breadwinner has lost his life in an industrial accident, the courts have effectively placed a monetary value on human life. Damages as high as $250,000 have been awarded.

Figure 15-3 Evaluation of propulsion systems. Importance (I) varies from 1 (small importance) to 5 (extreme importance). Rating (R) values are 3 (high), 2 (medium), 1 (low), and 0 (none).

Design criteria	Importance I	Design (1) gas turbine		Design (2) electric		Design (3) steam	
		R	R × I	R	R × I	R	R × I
Positive							
a. Novelty		0		1		3	
b. Practicability		1		3		2	
c. Reliability		2		3		1	
d. Life expectancy		2		2		2	
e. Probability of meeting specifications		2		3		2	
*f. Adaptability to company expertise (research, sales, etc.)		1		1		1	
*g. Suitability to human use							
*h. Other		—	—	—	—	—	—
Total positive score							
Negative							
a. Number and severity of unresolved problems		1		2		3	
b. Production cost		3		1		2	
c. Maintenance cost		1		1		2	
d. Time to perfect		1		1		3	
* Environmental effects		1		0		1	
* Other							
Total negative score		—		—		—	
Net score		—		—		—	

* Such factors may not always be pertinent.

rate high if it used modern thermodynamic principles. On "practicability" the electric motor rates higher than the others, for it requires the least service and provides the easiest and safest way to power a small vehicle. This table is completed to the best ability of the engineer for each of the criteria.

Then the engineer "blanks out" the ratings and assigns "importance" factors to each of the criteria (Figure 15-4). For example, he may rate practicability much higher than novelty.

Finally the ratings and importance factors are multiplied and added, yielding a final rating for the three systems, Figure 15-5, which, in this case, favors the electric motor drive. Although others may come up with different ratings, the method minimizes personal bias.

After selecting the best alternative to pursue, the engineer should make every effort to refine the chosen concept into its most elementary form. Simplicity in design has long been recognized as a hallmark of quality. Simple solutions are the most difficult to achieve, but the engineer should work to this end. He should also learn that such timeless ideas as the lever, the wedge, the inclined plane, the screw, the pulley, and the wheel are still basic ingredients of good design.

In terms of the electric drive vehicle, this means that initially he will strive for a single motor, directly driving the rear wheels, and a battery that can be recharged in each parking area. He may later find that a smaller motor at each wheel is preferable, that a geared-down, high-speed motor is more efficient than a direct-drive motor, or that an on-board electric generator is preferable to a rechargeable battery. He will start with the simplest ideas.

Once the design concept has been selected, the engineer must consider all of the component parts—their sizes, relationships, and materials. In selecting materials, he must consider their strengths, dimensions, and the loads to which they will be exposed. In this sense, he is analogous to the painter who has just chosen his subject and now must select his colors, shapes, and brush strokes and put them together in a pleasing and harmonious arrangement. The engineer, having selected a design concept that fulfills the desired functions, must organize his components to produce a device that is not only pleasing to the eye but is economical to build and operate.

The engineer must make sure that his design does not interfere with or disturb the environment, that it agrees with man and nature. We are especially reminded of these responsibilities when we encounter foul air, polluted streams, and eroded watersheds. Environmental effects are increasingly important criteria in the design of engineering structures, as evidenced by the voluble concern about such projects as the trans-Alaska pipeline, the supersonic jet transport, and facilities for the disposal or reclamation of industrial and human waste. As the earth's natural resources are depleted, the engineer will be under increasing pressure to provide technical assurances that no harm is done to the environment.

Figure 15-4 Evaluation of propulsion systems. Importance (I) varies from 1 (small importance) to 5 (extreme importance). Rating (R) values are 3 (high), 2 (medium), 1 (low), and 0 (none).

Design criteria	Importance I
Positive	
a. Novelty	2
b. Practicability	5
c. Reliability	5
d. Life expectancy	3
e. Probability of meeting specifications	4
*f. Adaptability to company expertise (research, sales, etc.)	3
*g. Suitability to human use	N.A.
*h. Other	
Total positive score	
Negative	
a. Number and severity of unresolved problems	3
b. Production cost	4
c. Maintenance cost	4
d. Time to perfect	4
*Environmental effects	4
*Other	
Total negative score	
Net score	

*Such factors may not always be pertinent.

Figure 15-5 Evaluation of propulsion systems. Importance (I) varies from 1 (small importance) to 5 (extreme importance). Rating (R) values are 3 (high), 2 (medium), 1 (low), and 0 (none).

Design criteria	Importance I	Design (1) gas turbine		Design (2) electric		Design (3) steam	
		R	R × I	R	R × I	R	R × I
Positive							
a. Novelty	2	0	0	1	2	3	6
b. Practicability	5	1	5	3	15	2	10
c. Reliability	5	2	10	3	15	1	5
d. Life expectancy	3	2	6	2	6	2	6
e. Probability of meeting specifications	4	2	8	3	12	2	8
*f. Adaptability to company expertise (research, sales, etc.)	3	1	3	1	3	1	3
*g. Suitability to human use	N.A.						
*h. Other							
Total positive score		—	32	—	53	—	38
Negative							
a. Number and severity of unresolved problems	3	1	3	2	6	3	9
b. Production cost	4	3	12	1	4	2	8
c. Maintenance cost	4	1	4	1	4	2	8
d. Time to perfect	4	1	4	1	4	3	12
* Environmental effects	4	1	4	0	0	1	4
* Other							
Total negative score		—	27	—	18	—	41
Net score			5		35		−3

* Such factors may not always be pertinent.

The designer must consider such factors as heat, noise, light, vibration, acceleration, air supply, and humidity, and their effects upon the physical and mental well-being of the user. For example, while it would be desirable to accelerate to top speed as quickly as possible, there are human comfort limits on acceleration that should not be exceeded. Controls must respond rapidly, have the right "feel," and not tire the driver. The suspension system must be "soft" for a comfortable ride, but stiff enough for good performance on curves. Automatic heating and air conditioning will probably be required in most parts of the country.

By now the picture of the vehicle has become clearer, and the chief engineer can delegate the preliminary design of components to various engineers or designers in his organization. Someone will be working on the drive train, another on the wheels and suspension, a third on the battery. Then there are the speed control systems, the interior layout, and perhaps three or four other components such as access protection, recharging, and systems for redistributing the cars that must be developed.

The detail design phase

Detailed design begins after determination of the overall functions and dimensions of the major members, the forces and allowable deflections of load-carrying members, the speed and power requirements of rotating parts, the pressures and flow rates of moving fluids, the aesthetic proportions, and the needs of the operation—in short, after the principal requirements are determined. The models that were devised during the preliminary selection process should be refined and studied under a considerably wider range of parameters than was possible originally. The designer is interested not only in normal operation, but also in what happens during start-up and shut-down, during malfunctions, and in emergencies. He will study the range of the loads which act on his design and how these loads are transmitted through its parts as stresses and strains. He will look at the effects of temperature, wind, and weather, of vibrations and chemical attack. In short, he will determine the range of operating conditions for each component of the design and for the entire device.

He must have an understanding of the mechanisms of engineering: the levers, linkages, and screw threads that transfer and transform linear and rotating motion; the shafts, gears, belts, and chain drives that transmit power; the electrical power generating systems and their electronic control circuits.

With today's wide range of available materials, shapes, and manufacturing techniques, with the growing array of prefabricated devices and parts, the choices for the design engineer are vast indeed. How should he start? What guidelines are available if he wants to produce the best possible design? It is usually wise to begin investigating that part or component which is thought to be most critical in the overall design—perhaps the one that must withstand the greatest variation of loads or other environmental influences, the one that is likely to be most expensive to make, or the most critical in operation. He may find that operating conditions limit his choices to a few possibilities.

At this stage the designer will encounter many conflicting requirements. One consideration tells him that he needs more power, another that the motor must be smaller and lighter. Springs should be stiff to minimize road clearance; they should be soft to give a comfortable ride. Windows should be large for good visibility, but small for safety and high body strength. The way to resolve this type of conflict is called optimization. It is accomplished by assigning values to all requirements and selecting that design which maximizes (optimizes) the total value.

Materials and stock subassemblies are commercially available in a specific range of sizes. Sheet steel is commonly available in certain thicknesses (gages), electric motors in certain horsepower ratings, and pipe in a limited range of diameters and wall thicknesses. Generally, the engineer should specify commonly available items; only rarely will the design justify the cost of a "special mill run" with off-standard dimensions or specifications. When available sizes are substantially different from the desired optimum size, the engineer may have to revise his optimization procedure.

To illustrate, let us look at the design of a meteorological rocket. At an earlier point in the design process the fuel for this rocket will have been chosen. Let us assume that it is a solid fuel, a material that looks and feels like rubber, burns without air, and when ignited produces high-temperature, high-pressure gases which are expelled through the nozzle to propel the rocket. The rocket consists principally of the payload (the meteorological instruments that are to be carried aloft), the nose cone which houses the instruments, the fuel, the fuel casing, and the nozzle. If we can estimate the weight of the rocket and how high it is to ascend, then we can calculate the requirements.

The most critical design part is the fuel casing, that is, the cylindrical shell which must contain the rocket fuel while it burns. It must be strong enough to withstand the pressure and temperature of the burning fuel, and strong enough to transmit

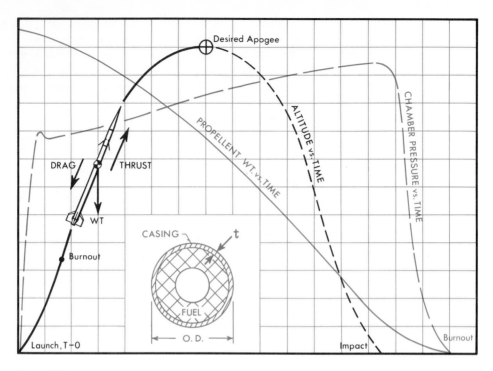

Figure 15-6

the thrust from the nozzle to the nose cone without buckling and without vibrating. The shell must also be light. If the casing weighs more than had been estimated originally, then more fuel will be needed to propel the rocket. More fuel will produce higher pressures and higher temperatures inside the casing. This, in turn, will require a stronger casing and even more weight. This additional weight requires still more fuel, and the spiral continues.

Let us assume we decided to use a high-strength, high-temperature-resistant steel for our casing. Our calculations indicate its wall thickness to be not less than 0.28 in. Our steel catalog tells us this steel is generally available in sheet form only in thicknesses of ¼ and ³⁄₁₆ in. If we use the thicker sheet, the casing weight will increase by 2.7 per cent; then we must recalculate the amount of fuel required, the pressures and stresses in the casing, and consequent changes in the dimensions of the rocket. Will the ¼-in. material withstand the resultant higher stresses? Can we improve its strength by heat treating? If we choose the thinner material, must we provide the casing with extra stiffeners (rings which will reduce the stresses in the casing shell)? In either case, the original design must be altered until the stresses, weights, pressures, and dimensions are satisfactory.

Similar design procedures will be followed in designing the nose cone, the nozzle, and the launching gear for the rocket.

It is important to understand that this example is typical of the design process. Design is not a simple straightforward process but a procedure of *trial and error*

Illustration 15-1   (*opposite*)
The design of a complete system adequate to launch a communications satellite, such as the one pictured above, requires the coordination of the efforts of thousands of technical people and hundreds of separate but related designs.

and compromise until a well-matched combination of components has been found. The more the engineer knows about materials and about ways of reducing or redistributing stresses (in short, the more alternatives he has) the better the structural design is likely to be.

Consider, as another example, that the engineer has been asked to design the gear shift lever for a racing automobile. The gear box has already been designed, so he knows how far the shifting fork (the end that actually moves the gears in the gear box) must travel in all directions. He also knows how much force will be required at the fork under normal and abnormal driving conditions. He will need to refer to anthropometric[2] data to learn how much force the healthy driver can provide forward, backwards, and sideways, and what his reach can be without distracting his eye from the road. With all this information he can choose the location of the ball joint, the fulcrum of the gear shift lever, and the length of each arm of the lever. He may decide to use a straight stick or he may find that a bent lever is more convenient for the driver. Before he finalizes this decision he may build a mock-up and make experiments to determine the most convenient location. Next he must select the material and the cross-sectional shape and area of the lever. Since it is likely to be loaded evenly in all directions, he may find that a circular or a cruciform cross section is most suitable. He must decide between a lever of constant thickness and a lighter, tapered stick (with the greater strength where it is needed—near the joint) which is more costly to manufacture.

Next he will consider the design of the ball joint, which transmits the motion smoothly to the gear box and provides vibration isolation so that the hand of the driver does not shake. It is difficult to find just the right amount of isolation which will retain for the driver the "feel" that is so essential during a race. The engineer needs a complete understanding of lubricated ball joints and proficiency in testing a series of possible designs.

The final component in this design is the handle itself, which should be attractive to look at and comfortable to grip. Here again anthropometric data can tell him much, yet he will be well advised to make several mock-ups and to have them tested for "feel" by experienced drivers.

During the design process, the engineer will have made a series of sketches (somewhat like those in this book) to illustrate to himself the relative position of the parts that he is designing. Now he or his draftsman will use these sketches to make a finished drawing. This will consist of a separate detail drawing for each individually machined item, showing all dimensions, the material from which it is to be made, the type of work to be performed, and the finish to be provided. There also will be subassembly and assembly drawings showing how these parts are to be put together.

The detail design phase will include the completion of an operating physical model or prototype (a model having the correct layout and physical appearance but constructed by custom techniques), which may have been started in an earlier design phase. The first prototype will usually be incomplete and modifications and alterations will be necessary. This is to be expected. Problems previously unanticipated may be identified, undesirable characteristics may be eliminated, and performance under design conditions may be observed for the first time. This part of the design process is always a time of excitement for everyone, especially the engineer.

The final phase of design involves the checking of every detail, every component,

---

[2]*Anthropometry* is the study of human body measurements, especially on a comparative basis.

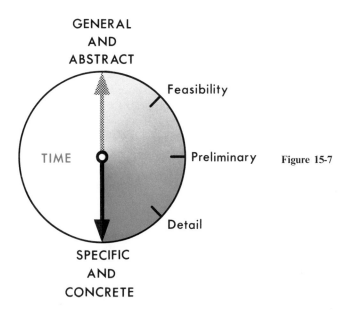

GENERAL
AND
ABSTRACT

Feasibility

TIME

Preliminary

Figure 15-7

Detail

SPECIFIC
AND
CONCRETE

and every subsystem. All must be compatible. Much testing may be necessary to prove theoretical calculations or to discover unsuspected consequences. Assumptions made in the earlier design phases should be reexamined and viewed with suspicion. Are they still valid? Would other assumptions now be more realistic? If so, what changes would be called for in the design?

As one moves through the design phases—from feasibility study to detail design— the tasks to be accomplished become less and less abstract and consequently more closely defined as to their expected functions. (See Figure 15-7.) In the earlier phases, the engineer worked with the design of systems, subsystems, and components. In the detail design phase he also will work with the design of the parts and elementary pieces that will be assembled to form the components.

In the previous phase of engineering design, a large majority of the people involved were engineers. In the detail phase this is not necessarily the case. Many people—metallurgists, chemists, tool designers, detailers, draftsmen, technicians, checkers, estimators, manufacturing and shop personnel—will work together under the direction of engineers. These technically trained support people probably will outnumber the engineers. The engineer who works in this phase of design must be a good manager in addition to his technical responsibilities, and his successes may be measured largely by his ability to bring forth the best efforts of many people.

The engineer should strive to produce a design which is the "obvious" answer to everyone who sees it, *once it is complete.* Such designs, simple and pleasing in appearance, are in a sense as beautiful as any painting, piece of sculpture, or poem, and they are frequently considerably more useful to his well-being.

The planning of engineering projects

In every walk of life, we notice and appreciate evidence of well-planned activities. You may have noticed that good planning involves more than "the assignment of tasks to be performed" although this frequently is the only aspect of planning that is given any attention. Planning in the broad sense must include the enumeration of all the activities and events associated with a project and a recognition and evaluation of their interrelationships and interdependencies. The assignment of tasks to be performed and other aspects of scheduling should follow.

Since "time is money," planning is a very important part of the implementation of any engineering design. Good planning is often the difference between success and failure, and the young engineering student would do well, therefore, to learn some of the fundamental aspects of planning as applied to the implementation of engineering projects.

In 1957 the U.S. Navy was attempting to complete the Polaris Missile System in record time. The estimated time for completion seemed unreasonably long. Through the efforts of an operations research team, a new method of planning and coordinating the many complex parts of the project was finally developed. The overall saving in time for the project amounted to more than 18 months. Since that time a large percentage of engineering projects, particularly those which are complex and time consuming, have used this same planning technique to excellent advantage. It is called PERT (Program Evaluation and Review Technique).

PERT enables the engineer in charge to view the total project as well as to recognize the interrelationships of the component parts of the design. Its utility is

Illustration 15-2
Considerable time and money can be saved by proper scheduling of the various associated activities that must be accomplished to produce a design. The engineers pictured above are discussing the merits of several available alternatives.

not limited to the beginning of the project but rather it continues to provide an accurate measure of progress throughout the work period. Pertinent features of PERT are combined in the following discussion.

How does PERT work?

Basically PERT consists of events (or jobs) and activities arranged into a *time-oriented network* to show the interrelationships and interdependencies that exist. One of the primary objectives of such a network is to identify where bottlenecks may occur that would slow down the process. Once such bottlenecks have been identified, then extra resources such as time and effort can be applied at the appropriate places to make certain that the entire process will not be slowed. The network is also used to portray the events as they occur in the process of accomplishing missions or objectives, together with the activities that necessarily occur to interconnect the events. These relationships will be discussed more fully below.

The network A PERT network is one type of pictorial representation of a project. This network establishes the "precedent relationships" that exist within a project. That is, it identifies those activities which must be completed before other activities are started. It also specifies the time that it takes to complete these activities. This is accomplished by using *events* (points in time) to separate the project *activities*. In other words, project events are connected by activities to form a project network. Progress from one event to another is made by completing the activity which connects them. Let us examine each component of the network in more detail.

Events An event is the *start* or *completion* of a mental or physical task. It does not involve the actual performance of the task. Thus, events are *points in time* which require that action be taken or that decisions be made. Various symbols are used in industry to designate events, such as circles, squares, ellipses, or rectangles. In this book circles, called *nodes,* will be used, Figure 15-8.

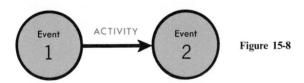

Figure 15-8

Events are joined together to form a project network. It is important that the events be arranged within the network in logical or time sequence from left to right. If this is done, the completion of each event will occupy a discrete and identifiable point in time. An event cannot consume time and it cannot be considered to be completed until all activities leading to it have been completed. After all events have been identified and arranged within the network, they are assigned identification numbers. Since events and activities may be altered during the course of the project, the logical order of the events will not necessarily follow in exact numerical sequence 1, 2, 3, 4, 5, and so on. The event numbers, therefore, serve only for identification purposes. The final or terminal node in the network is usually called the *sink,* while the beginning or initial node is called the *source.* Networks may have varying numbers of sources and sinks.

Activities An activity is the actual performance of a task and, as such, it consumes an increment of time. Activities separate events. An activity cannot begin until all preceding activities have been completed. An arrow is used to represent the time span of an activity, with time flowing from the tail to the point of the arrow, Figure 15-9. In a PERT network an activity may indicate the use of time, manpower,

Activity   **Figure 15-9**

materials, facilities, space, or other resources. A *phantom* activity may also represent waiting time or "interdependencies." A phantom activity, represented by a dashed arrow, Figure 15-10, may be inserted into the network for clarity of the logic,

Phantom
Activity   **Figure 15-10**

although it represents no real physical activity. Waiting time would also be noted in this manner. Remember that:

> *Events* "happen or occur."
> *Activities* are "started or completed."

The case of Mr. Jones getting ready for work each morning can be examined as an example.

Events	**Activities**
1. The alarm rings.	
	A. Jones stirs restlessly.
2. Jones awakens.	
	B. Jones nudges his wife.
	C. Jones lies in bed wishing that he didn't have to go to work.
3. Wife awakens.	
	D. Wife lies in bed wishing that it were Saturday.
4. Jones's wife gets up and begins breakfast.	
Meanwhile	*E.* Wife cooks breakfast.
5. Jones begins morning toilet.	
	F. Jones shaves, bathes, and dresses.
6. The Joneses begin to eat breakfast.	
	G. The Joneses eat part of their breakfast.
7. Jones realizes his bus is about to pass the bus stop.	
	H. Jones jumps up, grabs his briefcase, and runs for the bus.
	I. Wife goes back to bed.
8. Jones boards bus.	
9. Wife falls asleep.	

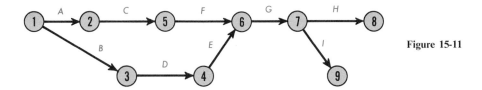

Figure 15-11

His PERT network can now be drawn as shown in Figure 15-11. This is a very elementary example, but it does point up the constituent parts of a PERT network. Note that Jones and his wife must wait until he is dressed (*F*) and the breakfast is cooked (*E*) before they can eat.

In a PERT network each activity should be assigned a specified time for expected accomplishment. The time units chosen should be consistent throughout the network, but the size of the time unit (years, work-weeks, days, hours, etc.) should be selected by the engineer in charge of the project. The time value chosen for each activity should represent the mean (see page 255) of the various times that the activity would take if it were repeated many times.

By using the network of events and activities and by taking into account the times consumed by the various activities, a *critical path* can be established for the project. It is this path that controls the successful completion of the project, and it is important that the engineer be able to isolate it for study. Let us consider the PERT network in Figure 15-12, where the activity times are represented by arabic numbers and are indicated in days. Activities represent the expenditure of time and

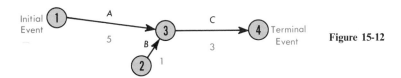

Figure 15-12

effort. For example, activity *A* (from event 1 to event 3) requires 5 days and is likely devoted to planning the project, while activity *B* requires 1 day and may represent the procurement of basic supplies. Event 1 is the beginning of the project and event 4 is the end of the project. The first step in locating the *critical path* is to determine the "earliest" event times (T_E), the "latest" event times (T_L), and the "slack" time ($T_L - T_E$).

Earliest event times (T_E)

The earliest expected time of an event refers to the time, T_E, when an event can be expected to be completed. T_E for an event is calculated by summing all of the activity duration times from the beginning event to the event in question *if the most time-consuming route is chosen*. To avoid confusion, the T_E times of events are usually placed near the network as arabic numbers within rectangular blocks. For reference purposes the beginning of the project is usually considered to be "time zero." In Figure 15-13, T_E for event 3 would be $\boxed{0} + 5 = \boxed{5}$ and T_E for event 4 would be $\boxed{0} + 5 + 3 = \boxed{8}$. However, there are two possible routes to event 4 (*A* + *C*, or *B* + *C*). The *maximum* duration of these event times should be selected as the T_E for event 4. Summing the times we find:

$$\text{By path } A + C: \quad \boxed{0} + 5 + 3 = \boxed{8} \leftarrow \text{Select as } T_E \text{ for event 4}$$
$$\text{By path } B + C: \quad \boxed{0} + 1 + 3 = \boxed{4}$$

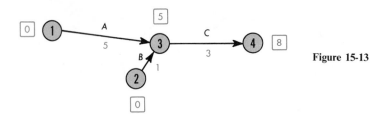

Figure 15-13

Latest event times (T_L)

The latest expected time, T_L, of an event refers to the longest time which can be allowed for an event, assuming that the entire project is kept on schedule. T_L for an event is determined by beginning at the terminal event and working backward through the various event circuits, subtracting the value T_E at each event *assuming the least time-consuming route is chosen*. The resulting values of T_L are recorded as arabic numbers in small ellipses located near the T_E times. Thus, in Figure 15-14, T_L for event 3 would be ⑧ $- 3 =$ ⑤; for event 2, ⑧ $- 3 - 1 =$ ④; and for event 1, ⑧ $- 3 - 5 =$ ⓪.

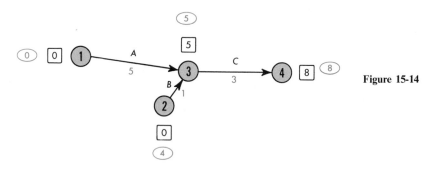

Figure 15-14

Remember that T_L is determined to be the *minimum* of the differences between the succeeding event T_L and the intervening activity times. Also, in calculating T_L values one must always proceed backward through the network—from the point of the arrows to the tail of the arrows.

Slack times

The *slack* time for each event is the difference between the latest event time and the earliest possible time ($T_L - T_E$). Intuitively, one may verify that it is the "extra time that an event can slip" and not affect the scheduled completion time of the project. For example, in Figure 15-14 the slack time for event 2 is ④ $-$ ⓪ $= 4$. For this reason activity B may be started as much as 4 days late and still not cause any overall delay in the minimum project time of 8 days.

The critical path

The *critical path* through a PERT network is a path that is drawn from the initial event of the network to the terminal event by connecting the events of zero slack. The *critical path* is usually emphasized with a very thick line. Color is sometimes used. In the example problem above the *critical path* would be shown connecting events 1–3–4, Figure 15-15. Slack times for each event are indicated as small arabic numbers that are located in triangles adjacent to the events.

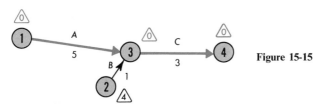

Figure 15-15

Remember that the *critical path* is the path that controls the successful completion of the project. It is also the path that requires the most time to get from the initial event to the terminal event. Any event on the critical path that is delayed will cause the final event to be delayed by the same amount. Conversely, putting an extra effort on noncritical activities will not speed up the project.

Although calculations in this chapter have been done manually, it is conventional practice to program complex networks for solution by digital computer. In this way thousands of activities and events may be considered, and one or more critical paths can be located for further study. Finally, the PERT network should be updated periodically as the work on the project progresses.

The following example will show how a typical PERT diagram is analyzed. It should be noted here, however, that in real-life situations the most difficult task is to identify the precedent relationships that exist and to draw a realistic network of the events and activities. After this is accomplished, following through with a solution technique becomes a relatively routine task.

Example In the PERT network diagram of Figure 15-16, assume that all activity times are given in months and that they exist as indicated on the proper activity branch. Find the earliest times, T_E, the latest times, T_L, and the slack times for each event. Identify the critical path through the network.

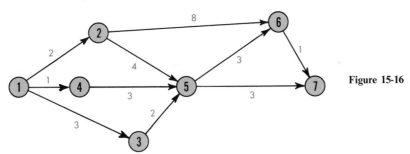

Figure 15-16

Solution: See Figure 15-17.

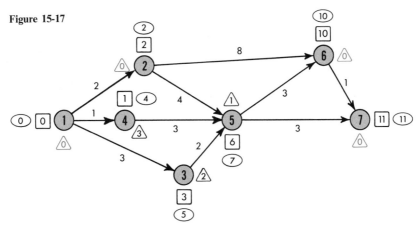

Figure 15-17

It is usually advisable to construct a summary table of the calculations.

Event ○	Path	T_E □	Path	T_L ○	Slack, $T_L - T_E$ △	On critical path
1	—	0	7–6–2–1	0	0	✓
2	1–2	2	7–6–2	2	0	✓
3	1–3	3	7–6–5–3	5	2	
4	1–4	1	7–6–5–4	4	3	
5	1–2–5	6	7–6–5	7	1	
6	1–2–6	10	7–6	10	0	✓
7	1–2–6–7	11	—	11	0	✓

The critical path then is 1–2–6–7, Figure 15-18. This means that as the project is now organized it will take 11 months to complete.

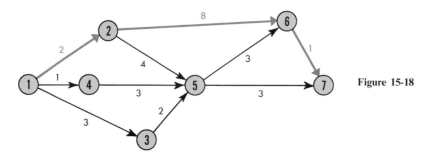

Figure 15-18

Problems

15-1. Consider the network in Figure 15-19. Find T_E, T_L, slack times, and the critical path through the network.

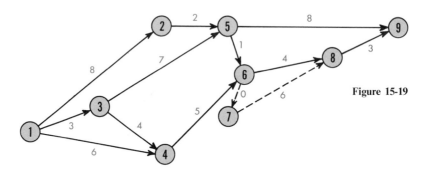

Figure 15-19

15-2. In Figure 15-20, what effect on project length would the following changes have:

Figure 15-20

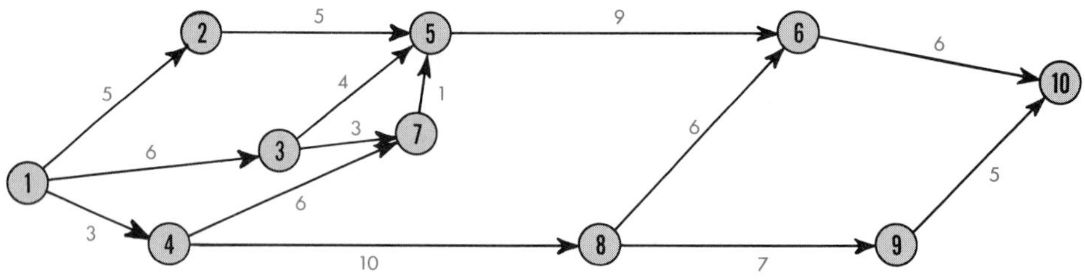

    a. Decrease activity 1–2 to 6 days.

    b. Decrease activity 5–9 to 1 day.

    c. Decrease activity 3–4 to 2 days.

15-3. Explain why "phantom activities" are necessary, and give an example of one.

15-4. Given the following tabular information, determine the PERT network and its critical path.

Activity	Precedent relationships	Time
A	None	5
B	None	3
C	A	1
D	B	4
E	B	3
F	E	7

15-5. For some general process with which you are familiar, construct a PERT network. Be sure to label all events and activities.

15-6. Find the critical path in Figure 15-20 and explain its significance here.

15-7. *a.* Does a decrease in an activity time on the critical path always decrease the project time correspondingly? Why or why not? (Hint: See Problem 15-6.)

    b. Does an increase in an activity time on the critical path always increase the project time correspondingly? Why or why not? (Hint: See Problem 15-4.)

15-8. Given the PERT network in Figure 15-21, when is the earliest possible project completion time?

Figure 15-21

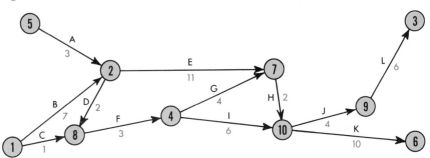

15-9. If you have extra resources to allocate to one activity in Figure 15-21, where would you put those resources and why? How might this affect the expected duration time of the project?

15-10. One thing that a PERT analysis does not consider is the allocation of limited resources (see Problem 15-9). How can this inability affect the usefulness of a PERT analysis?

Design philosophy

Design philosophy is an important factor with many industries, companies, and consulting firms. The aircraft industry, for example, generally would support a design philosophy that includes (*a*) lightweight components, (*b*) safety, (*c*) limited service life, (*d*) a wide range of loading conditions and temperature extremes, and (*e*) concern about vibration and fatigue. The automobile industry, on the other hand, would be more likely to support a design philosophy that stresses (*a*) consumer price consciousness, (*b*) long life with minimum service and maintenance, (*c*) customer appeal, (*d*) safety for the occupants, and (*e*) design for mass production.

Some companies are concerned that their products have a "family-like" image and that a responsiveness to customer appeal be designed into all of their products. In some instances the image is safety, in some efficiency, in some quality. Public relations should be an important factor with all companies, and the engineer should not be insensitive to the effects that his design will have upon the total company image. The appearance of the product is particularly important in consumer-oriented industries. In such cases the engineer must take this into account in all phases of his design.

Any engineering design is but *one* answer to an identified problem. For this reason few designs have withstood the test of time without undergoing substantial revisions. One need but look at the continuous parade of modifications, alterations, changes, and complete redesigns that have taken place within the automobile industry to see how the product of a single industry has been changed thousands and thousands of times. Each change, it was believed at the time, was an improvement over the existing model, even if in appearance only. In some instances this assumption proved to be false, and other modifications were quickly made.

In some situations the pressure for a quick solution has led to the adoption of designs of minimum acceptability. Generally the handicaps and pressures under which the engineer works are of little interest to the customer, who tends to judge the quality of a device or machine by its performance. This emphasis on the product places an additional responsibility upon the shoulders of the engineer to release only those designs which he believes are good designs, those to which he will have no hesitancy in affixing his signature. As a professional person he must be equally aware of his responsibilities to his fellow man and to his employer or client. He must perceive *when he knows,* he must realize *when he does not know,* and he must assume the final responsibility in either case.

An example of the development of an engineering design

There are many well-known engineering designs on the American scene that have, over a period of many years, almost become a "way of life." Although the authors of this text are reluctant to pick any one of these as being superior to another, they are eager that the students who study this text gain an appreciation for the concepts that "good ideas plus good engineering design practice equals success" and "all good engineering designs can be improved." For this reason the story of the developing design of the safety razor is given here.[3]

The idea for the safety razor that the American public knows today was the brainchild of a traveling salesman, King C. Gillette, who on a summer morning in 1895 became irritated and exasperated at his inability to shave with a dull straight

---

[3] Much of the material presented here was made available by and is used with the permission of the Gillette Safety Razor Company, Boston, Massachusetts.

razor. In an instant the idea of a replaceable flat blade secured in a holder for maximum safety was born. In Gillette's own words,

> I saw it all in a moment, and in that same moment many unvoiced questions were asked and answered more with the rapidity of a dream than by the slow process of reasoning. A razor is only a sharp edge and all back of that edge is but a support for that edge. Why do they spend so much material and time in fashioning a backing which has nothing to do with the shaving? Why do they forge a great piece of steel and spend so much labor in hollow grinding it when they could get the same result by putting an edge on a piece of steel that was only thick enough to hold an edge? At that time and in that moment it seemed as though I could see the way the blade could be held in a holder. Then came the idea of sharpening the two opposite edges on the thin piece of steel that was uniform in thickness throughout, thus doubling its service; and following in sequence came the clamping plates for the blade with a handle equally disposed between the two edges of the blade. All this came more in pictures than in thought as though the razor were already a finished thing and held before my eyes. I stood there before that mirror in a trance of joy at what I saw.

Previous to this time, men of wealth and influence of all nationalities frequented barber shops in which the customer was lathered from the community mug and shaved with an unsterilized razor, Illustration 15-3. Such a barber shop shave was a luxury that poor people could not afford, but many men of modest means did

Illustration 15-3
The morning shave in 1568 was not without its difficulties, as shown in the above English woodcut.

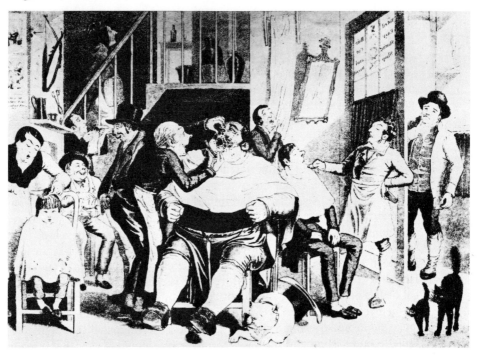

purchase their own straight razors. Ladies of respect would not think of using a razor to remove unsightly hair, although it is reported that such practice was not uncommon for burlesque queens.

Several years previous to the inspirational moment of 1895, King Gillette was talking with a successful inventor friend who advised him:

> King, you are always thinking and inventing something; why don't you try to think of something like the Crown Cork, when used once, it is thrown away, and the customer keeps coming back for more—and with every additional customer you get, you are building a permanent foundation of profit.

Although Gillette often thought of this advice, he never was able to capitalize on it until that moment—holding in his hand a dull razor which was beyond the point of successful stropping and in need of honing—that the idea in his subconscious emerged to reinforce his need for a new and novel solution.

Gillette knew very little about razors and practically nothing about steel, and he could not foresee the trials and frustrations that were to come his way before the "safety razor" was a success. On the same day that he received the inspiration to devise a razor which could use interchangeable and disposable blades, and which were safe to use, Gillette went to a local hardware store and purchased several pieces of brass, some steel ribbon used for clock springs, and some hand tools. Using some rough pencil sketches and the recently purchased hand tools, he fashioned a crude model of his new design, Illustration 15-4. Gillette's invention did not consist primarily in a particular form of blade or design of a blade holder, but in the conception of a blade so cheap as to be discarded when dull. To obtain such a blade he abandoned the forged type and fashioned one of thin steel, so that it might be cut from a strip, avoiding the expense of forging or hollow grinding. Prior to this invention, razor makers produced an expensive blade that was expected to give service as long as possible, even a lifetime, and to be honed and stropped indefinitely. The new idea was a complete reversal of this practice and was a really unique invention.

In his new razor Gillette carried his theory to great completeness. The blade was to be made of relatively thin steel and thereby achieve economy through the saving of both material and labor. It was to have two edges, one on each side, thus giving double shaving service. The adjustment of the blade edge in relation to the guard was to be obtained by flexing the blade so as to bring the edge nearer to or farther from the guard teeth, in order to obtain a finer or coarser cut, Figure 15-22.

However, all was not bright for this new idea. No one but Gillette had any faith in a razor the blades of which were to be used once and then wasted. Such a proposal did not seem to be within the bounds of reason, and even Gillette's friends looked upon it as a joke. Actually he had thought originally that the blades might be made very cheaply from a thin ribbon of steel, but he was, of course, aware that new machines and processes would need to be invented and developed before such "ribbon blades" could be manufactured cheaply. This did not seem to be a likely prospect. For more than five years Gillette clung tenaciously to his razor theories. He made a number of models with minor variations and sought through others to get blades made with shaving qualities. He got very little encouragement either from his helpers and advisers or from the results of his experiments. People who knew most about cutlery and razors in particular were most discouraging. Years later Gillette said, "They told me I was throwing my money away; that a razor was only possible when made from cast steel forged and fashioned under the hammer to give

Illustration 15-4

King Gillette's moment of triumph came when he discovered that his idea could be made to work.

it density so it would take an edge. But I didn't know enough to quit. If I had been technically trained, I would have quit or probably would never have begun." In spite of this discouragement, Gillette did not falter in his faith and persistence.

Faced with an inability to cope with the technical difficulties surrounding his idea, Gillette began to search for others to help him. He associated himself with several men, one of whom—W. E. Nickerson—was a mechanical engineering graduate of the Massachusetts Institute of Technology. The design capability of Nickerson soon became apparent. A notation from the Gillette Safety Razor Company silver jubilee history relates the following:

> . . . after a very urgent plea, he [Nickerson] agreed to turn the problem over in his mind and give a decision within a month. On giving the problem serious thought, he began to see the proper procedure and felt that he could develop the razor into a commercial proposition. Things began to take definite shape in his mind, he could visualize the hardening process and sharpening machines, and definite ideas were developed as to the type of handle necessary to properly hold the blade.
>
> Hardening apparatus and sharpening machines could not be properly designed until the form and size of the blade were known, so the first step was to decide just what the blade and the handle were to be like. Mr. Gillette's models were amply developed to disclose the fundamental ideas, but there was left a wide range of choice in the matter of carrying out these ideas; and furthermore, the commercial success of the razor was sure to

Figure 15-22

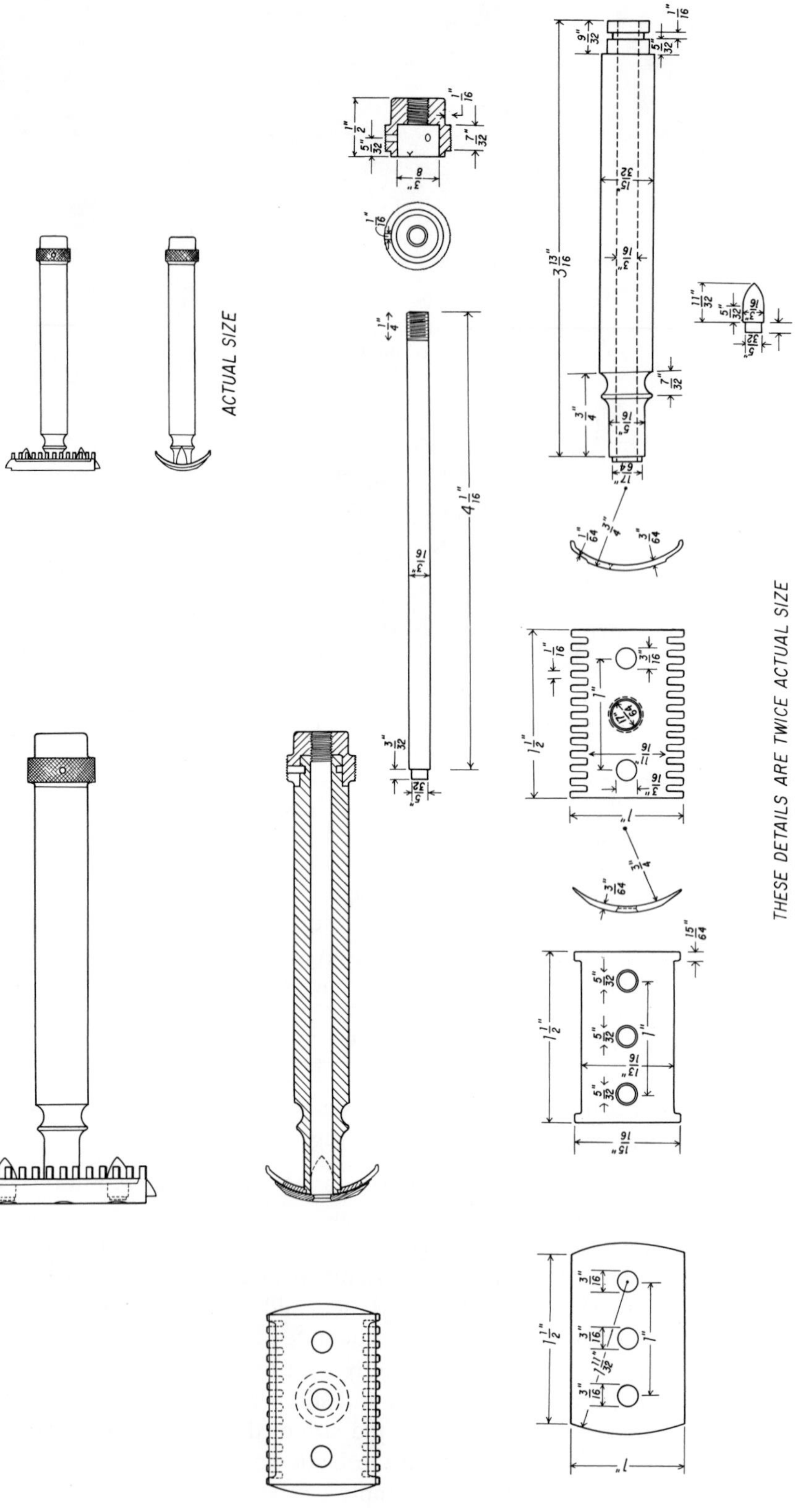

ACTUAL SIZE

THESE DETAILS ARE TWICE ACTUAL SIZE
WORK FROM FIGURES

depend very much upon the judgment used in selecting just the right form and thickness of blade and the best construction in the handle.

Mr. Nickerson's fundamental thought in relation to the remodeled razor was that the handle must have sufficient stability to make possible very great accuracy of adjustment between the edge of the blade and the protecting guard. Here is a point upon which he laid great stress, and which we are constantly endeavoring to drive home today: "No matter how perfect the blade is, you cannot get the best result unless the handle is perfect also." The Gillette handle is made to micrometric dimensions and is an extremely accurate instrument. If damaged or thrown out of alignment, poor shaves are likely to result. This idea of great stability led Mr. Nickerson to design a handle to be "machined" out of solid metal, in contra-distinction to one stamped from relatively thin sheet metal. To this fact much of the Gillette commercial success is due. In fact, it is doubtful if great success could have been achieved without it.

The shape and thickness of the blade were determined as follows: Sheet steel thinner than six one-thousandths of an inch appeared to lack sufficient firmness to make a good blade, and a thickness greater than that seemed too difficult to flex readily; so six thousandths was chosen. In the matter of width, one inch was thought to be unnecessarily wide and three-quarters of an inch was found to be too narrow, especially when flexing was considered. Thus seven-eights of an inch was adopted. As to contour, a circle one and three-quarters inches in diameter if symmetrically crossed by two parallel lines seven-eights of an inch apart give chords corresponding to the cutting edges, one and one-half inches long, which was thought to be the right length for the edges. The rounded ends to the blade form thus produced strengthened the blade along the center where holes were to be and gave the blade its well-known and pleasing shape. After twenty-five years of use nothing has transpired to cause regret that some other shape was not selected. These early decisions were of the utmost importance and almost seemed inspired.

On September 9, 1901, Mr. Nickerson sent a report of his findings and recommendations to Mr. Heilborn of which the following is an exact copy:

Boston, Mass., Sept. 9, 1901.

Jacob Heilborn, Esq.,
Boston, Mass.

Dear Sir:

I have had your proposition, in regard to the manufacture of the Gillette Safety Razor, under consideration for rather more than a month and desire to report as follows:

It is my confident opinion that not only can a successful razor be made on the principles of the Gillette patent, but that if the blades are made by proper methods a result in advance of anything known can be reached. On the other hand, to put out these razors with blades of other than the finest quality of temper and edge would be disastrous to their reputation and to their successful introduction.

With an almost unlimited market, and with such inducements as are offered by this razor, in the way of cheapness of manufacture and of convenience and effectiveness in use, I can see no reason why it cannot easily compete for popular favor with anything in its line ever put before the public.

I wish to reiterate that in my opinion the success of the razor depends very largely, if not almost wholly, on the production at a low price of a substantially perfect blade. This blade must possess an edge that shall, at least, be equal of any rival on the market, and should combine extreme keenness with a hardness and toughness sufficient to stand using a number of times without much deterioration.

For the past month I have been giving much thought to the subject of manufacturing these blades, and I now feel justified in offering to undertake the construction of machines and apparatus to that end. I am confident that I have grasped the situation and can guarantee, as far as such a thing can be guaranteed, a successful outcome. Your knowledge of my long experience with inventions and machine building will, perhaps, cause you to attach considerable weight to my opinion in this matter. You are of course aware that special machines will have to be designed and built for putting on the blades that delicate edge which is necessary for easy shaving. The problem is entirely different from that involved in the tempering and grinding of ordinary razors and other keen tools, not only on account of the thinness of the blades, but also on account of the cheapness with which it must be done. I believe that with the machines which I have in mind, an edge can be put upon these blades which will be unapproachable by ordinary hand sharpened razors. The machinery and methods for making the blades will naturally be of a novel character and admit of sound patents, which would become the property of the Company and would be of great advantage in disposing of foreign rights. It is not unlikely that the machines for honing these blades may be adapted for any of the present form of razors and do away with hand honing. I will also add that I have in mind a convenient and simple method of adjusting the position of the blade for different beards.

In reply to your questions as to the probable expense of fitting up to manufacture the razor on a scale suitable for a beginning on a commercial basis, I will make the following approximation:

Drawings for machines for tempering, grinding, honing and
    stropping . . . . $ 100
Patterns for ditto 250
Materials for machines (one each) 300
Cost of building (one each) 700
Special dies and tools 150

Tools for making holders
  { Small turret lathe
    Power punch
    Small plain milling machine 1500
    Sensitive drill
    Bench lathe
    Bench tools, etc.

Foreign patents:
    England, Germany, Belgium, France, Canada,
      Spain, Italy, Austria—about 800
Labor services, etc. 1200
                                             $5000

I have made what seems to me to be fairly liberal but by no means extravagant figures. It may cost considerably less or possibly a little more, but I think the sum given will not come out very far from the truth.

I should recommend that the machines for making the blades be built in some shop already established, and when they are completed, a suitable room be engaged and they and the holder tools set up in it. It is not easy to say just how long it would take to be ready for manufacturing, but if there are no serious delays it is possible that four months might cover it.

In conclusion let me add that so thoroughly am I satisfied that I can perfect machinery described on original lines which will be patentable, that I am ready to accept for my compensation stock in a Company which I understand you propose forming.

> Very truly yours,
> (Signed) Wm. E. Nickerson

Nickerson did design a machine for sharpening the blades and an apparatus for hardening the blades in packs. Thus through the application of fundamental engineering principles a successful new industry was born.

Success was not immediate because two years later, in 1903, when Gillette put his first razor on the market only 51 razors and 168 blades were sold. Barbers, who believed that their business would be ruined if this new fad caught on, were particularly scathing in their reproof. However, the new razor caught on, sales soared, and by 1905 manufacturing operations had to be moved to larger quarters. By 1917 razor sales had risen to over a million a year, and blade sales averaged 150 million a year. As a result of World War I, self-shaving became widespread and returning servicemen carried the habit home with them. While World War I taught thousands of men the self-shaving habit, World War II introduced millions of men to daily shaving practice.

In the 62 years since Gillette razors first went on sale, the company has produced over one half billion razors and over one hundred billion blades. Throughout this period of time, however, many modifications and redesigns have been made, Figures 15-23 and 15-24.

The latest of these designs, the Techmatic Razor with razor band, Figure 15-25, is a complete departure from the blade-changing routine which has been so successfully sold to the American public. Interestingly enough, the idea of shaving with a "ribbon of steel" is a simple adaptation of the original material purchased by King Gillette on that summer day in 1895. It has, however, taken 70 years for engineering design to make possible mass produced "ribbon blades." Other improvements will undoubtedly follow in the years ahead.

Many other American industries have equally exciting engineering histories. In many respects the engineering students of today live in the most challenging period of history ever, and a *good idea*, together with the application of sound engineering design principles, will still produce *success*.

Exercises in design

15-11. Estimate the number of drug stores in the United States. Give reasons for your estimate.

15-12. Estimate the number of gallons of water of the Mississippi River that pass New Orleans every day. Show your analysis.

15-13. In 100 words or less describe how a household water softener works.

Figure 15-23

Year	New Design	Improvements
1932	Gillette Blue Blade	Better shaving edge
1934	One-Piece Razor	Convenience, more exact edge exposure
1938	Thin Gillette Blade	Reduced cost by one half
1947	Blade Dispenser	Blade edges protected, simplified blade changing
1957	Adjustable Safety Razor	Variable cut, ease of adjustment
1960	Super Blue Blade	Longer life, first coated edge, less pull
1963	Stainless Steel Blade	Comfort, coated edge, durability
1963	Lady Gillette Razor	Designed expressly for women
1965	Super Stainless Steel Blade	Better steel, longer life, new coating
1965	Techmatic Razor with Razor Band	Cartridge load, convenience, no blades
1968	Injector-Type Single-Edge Blade	Provides alternative shaving method
1969	Platinum-Plus Double-Edge Blade	Stronger, harder, corrosion-resistant edges
1970	Platinum-Plus Injector Blade	Improved blade for alternative shaving method

Figure 15-24 The adjustable safety razor.

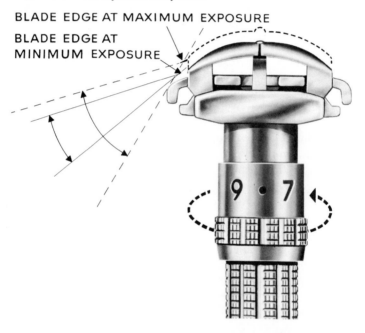

BLADE EDGE AT MAXIMUM EXPOSURE

BLADE EDGE AT
MINIMUM EXPOSURE

15-14. By the use of simple sketches and a brief accompanying explanation, describe the mechanical operation of a household toilet.

15-15. By the use of a diagrammatic sketch show how plumbing in a home might be installed so that hot water is always instantly available when the hot water tap is opened.

15-16. Analyze and discuss the economic problems involved in replacing ground-level railroad tracks with a suspended monorail system for a congested urban area.

15-17. Discuss the feasibility of railroads offering a service whereby your automobile would be carried on a railroad car on the same train on which you are traveling so that you might have your car available for use upon arrival at your destination.

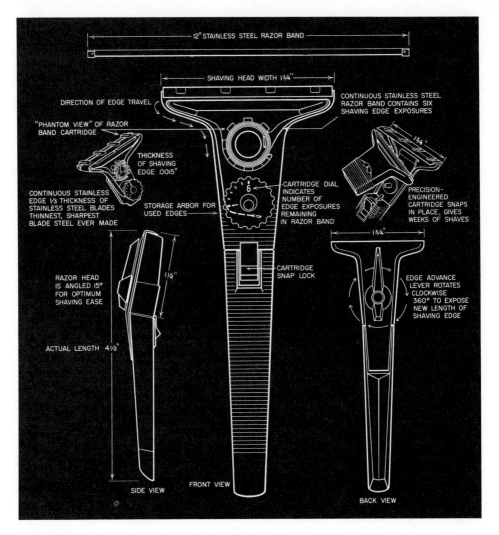

Figure 15-25 The Techmatic Razor with razor band.

15-18. Discuss the desirability of assigning an identifying number to each person as soon as they are born. The number could, for example, be tattooed at some place on the body to serve as a social security number, military number, credit card number, and so forth.

15-19. Using local gas utility rates, electric utility rates, coal costs, fuel oil costs, and wood costs, what would be the comparative cost of heating a five-room house in your home community for a winter season?

15-20. Discuss the advantages and disadvantages of having a channel of television show nothing but market quotations, except for brief commercials, during the time the New York stock market and the Chicago commodity market are open.

15-21. You are called to Alaska to consider the problem of public buildings that are sinking in permafrost due to warm weather. What might you do to solve this problem?

15-22. You are located on an ice cap. Ice and snow are everywhere but no water. Fuel and equipment are available. How can you prepare a well from which water can be pumped?

15-23. Assemble the following items: an ink bottle, a marble, a yardstick, an engineer's scale of triangular cross section, five wooden matches, a pocket knife, a candle, a pencil, and a key. Now, using as few of the objects as possible, balance the yardstick across the top "knife-edge" of the engineer's scale in such manner that soon after being released, and without being touched again, it unbalances itself.

15-24. Explain the operation of the rewind mechanism for the hand cord of a home gasoline lawnmower.

15-25. Devise a new method of feeding passengers on airplanes.

15-26. List the consequences of everyone being able to read everyone else's mind.

15-27. At current market values determine the number of years that would be necessary to regain the loss of money (lost salary plus college expense) if one stayed in college one additional year to obtain a Masters degree in engineering. What would be the number of years necessary to regain the loss by staying three years beyond the bachelor's degree to obtain a doctorate in engineering?

15-28. Estimate the number of policemen in (*a*) New York City, and (*b*) the United States.

15-29. Estimate the number of churches of all faiths in the United States.

15-30. Explain how the following work:
   a. An automobile differential.
   b. A toggle switch.
   c. An automatic cut-off on gasoline pumps.
   d. A sewing machine needle when sewing cloth.
   e. A refrigeration cycle which does not depend upon electricity.

15-31. With six equal-length sticks construct four equilateral triangles.

15-32. Estimate the number of aspirin tablets now available in the United States.

15-33. A cube whose surface area is 6 mi^2 is filled with water. How long will it take to empty this tank using a 1000 gal/min pump?

15-34. From memory sketch (*a*) a bicycle, (*b*) a reel-type lawnmower, (*c*) a coffee pot, (*d*) a salt-water fishing reel, and (*e*) a rifle.

15-35. Make something useful from the following items: a piece of corrugated cardboard 12 in. × 24 in., 6 ft of string, 3 pieces of chalk, 10 rubber bands, a small piece of gummed tape, 3 tongue depressors, 5 paper clips, and 7 toothpicks.

15-36. Propose some way to eliminate the need for bifocal glasses.

15-37. Design a device that can measure to a high degree of accuracy the wall thickness of a long tube whose ends are not accessible.

15-38. Design a man's compact travel kit that can be carried in the inside coat pocket.

15-39. Design a home-type sugar dispenser for a locality where the average rainfall is 100 in./yr.

15-40. Design a new type of men's apparel to be worn around the neck in lieu of a necktie.

15-41. Design a new type of clothespin.

15-42. Design a new fastener for shirts or blouses.

15-43. Design a personal monogram.

15-44. Design a device to aid federal or civil officers in the prevention or suppression of crime.

15-45. Design a highway system and appropriate vehicles for a country where gasoline is not obtainable and where motive power must be supplied external to the vehicle.

15-46. Design an electrical system for a home that does not receive its energy from a power company or a storage battery.

15-47. Design a device for weighing quantities of food for astronauts who are enroute to the moon.

15-48. Design a machine or process to remove Irish potato peelings.

15-49. Design a "black-eyed pea" sheller.

15-50. Design a corn shucker.

15-51. Design a trap to snare mosquitoes alive.

15-52. Design the "ideal" bathroom, including new toilet fixtures.

15-53. Design a toothpaste dispenser.

15-54. Design a woozle.

15-55. Design a device that would enable paralyzed people to read in bed.

15-56. Design a jig-like device that an amateur "do-it-yourself" home workman could use to lay up an acceptably straight brick wall.

15-57. Design a device to retail for less than $10.00 to warn "tailgaters" that they are too close to your automobile.

15-58. Devise a system of warning lights connected to your automobile that will warn drivers in cars following you of the changes in speed of your car.

15-59. You live in a remote community near the Canadian border, and you have a shallow well near your home from which you can get a copious supply of water. Although the water is unfit for drinking or irrigation, its temperature is a constant 64°F. Design a system to use this water to help heat your home.

15-60. Design and build a prototype model of a small spot welder suitable for use by hobby craftsmen. Prepare working sketches and make an economic study of the advisability of producing these units in volume production.

15-61. Design some device that will awaken a deaf person.

15-62. Design a coin-operated hair-cutting machine.

15-63. Design a two-passenger battery powered Urbanmobile for use around the neighborhood, for local shopping center visits, to commute to the railway station, and so on. The rechargeable battery should last for 60 mi on each charge. Provide a complete report on the design, including a market survey and economic study.

15-64. Design some means of visually determining the rate of gasoline consumption (mi/gal) at any time while the vehicle is in operation.

15-65. Design a device to continuously monitor and/or regulate automobile tire pressures.

15-66. Design a novel method of catching and executing mice that will not infringe the patent of any other known system now on the market.

15-67. Design a new toy for children ages 6 to 10.

15-68. Design a device to replace the conventional oarlocks used on all row boats.

15-69. Devise an improved method of garbage disposal for a "new" city that is to be constructed in its entirety next year.

15-70. Design and build a simple device to measure the specific heat of liquids. Use components costing less than $3.00.

15-71. Design for teenagers an educational hobby kit that might foster an interest in engineering.

15-72. Design a portable traffic signal that can be quickly put into operation for emergency use.

15-73. Design an egg breaker for kitchen use.

15-74. Design an automatic dog-food dispenser.

15-75. Design a device to automatically mix body soap in shower water as needed.

15-76. Design an improved keyholder.

15-77. Design a self-measuring and self-mixing epoxy glue container.

15-78. Design an improved means of cleaning automobile windshields.

15-79. Design a noise suppressor for a motorcycle.

15-80. Design a collapsible bicycle.

15-81. Design a tire-chain changer.

15-82. Design a set of improved highway markers.

15-83. Design an automatic oil-level indicator for automobiles.

15-84. Design an underwater means of communication for skin divers.

15-85. Design a means of locating lost golf balls.

15-86. Design a musician's page turner.

15-87. Design an improved violin tuning device.

15-88. Design an attachment to allow a motorcycle to be used on water.

15-89. Design a bedroll heater for use in camping.

15-90. Design a portable device for student use in keypunching computer cards.

15-91. Design an improved writing instrument.

15-92. Design a means of disposing of solid household waste.

15-93. Design a type of building block that can be erected without mortar.

15-94. Design a means for self-cleaning of sinks and toilet bowls.

15-95. Design some means to replace door knobs or door latches.

15-96. Design a simple animal-powered irrigation pump for use in developing nations.

15-97. Design a therapeutic exerciser for use in strengthening weak or undeveloped muscles.

15-98. Design a Morse-code translator that will allow a deaf person to read code received from radio receivers.

15-99. Design an empty-seat locator for use in theaters.

15-100. Design a writing device for use by armless people.

15-101. Design and build an indicator to tell when a steak is cooked as desired.

15-102. Design a device that would effectively eliminate wall outlets and cords for electrical household appliances.

15-103. Design the mechanism by which the rotary motion of a 1-in. diameter shaft can be transferred around a 90° corner and imparted to a ½-in. diameter shaft.

15-104. Design a mechanism by which the vibratory translation of a steel rod can be transferred around a 90° corner and imparted to another steel rod.

15-105. Design a device or system to prevent snow accumulation on the roof of a mountain cabin. Electricity is available, and the owner is absent during the winter.

15-106. Using the parts out of an old spring-wound clock, design and fabricate some useful device.

15-107. Out of popsicle sticks build a pinned-joint structure that will support a load of 50 lb.

15-108. Design a new device to replace the standard wall light switch.

15-109. Design and build a record changer that will flip records as well as change them.

15-110. Design a wheelchair that can lift itself from street level to a level 1 ft higher.

15-111. Design a can opener that can be used to make a continuous cut in the top of a tin can whose top is of irregular shape.

15-112. Design and build for camping purposes a solar still that can produce 1 gallon of pure water per day.

15-113. A ban on the use of firearms in the United States has created the desirability of manufacturing some device suitable for use in hunting small game, such as squirrel and rabbit. The company for which you work has decided to compete for the market of small game hunters who will be seeking some replacement for their guns. You have been assigned the task of developing a blowgun and suitable projectiles for this purpose with the following provisions:

a. The blow tube and five hunting darts must sell for $10.00 or less retail.

b. No poison may be used to paralyze the animal.

c. The technique of loading the blow tube and launching the dart must be simple enough for a 10-year-old boy to learn.

d. The range of 100 ft with hunting accuracy is desirable.

Design and build a prototype tube and projectile. Detail the dimensions, tolerances, material, finish, and capability of the weapon system. Indicate the probable cost of one hunting set of tube and darts when manufactured in lots of 1000, 10,000 100,000, and 1,000,000.

15-114. The company for which you work has decided that altogether too large a percentage of the annual sales depends upon government defense contracts. A decision has been made to diversify and to add product lines that would appeal to individual citizens regardless of current world conditions. After some study it is decided that the manufacture of fishing lures might provide the desired market stability. You are assigned the task of designing a new trout or bass lure under the following conditions:

a. The lure must sell for $3.00 or less retail.

b. The lure should be a design departure from existing lures on the market.

Design and build such a lure. Provide drawings giving dimensions, materials, and finish. Indicate the probable cost per lure when manufactured in lots of 1000, 10,000, and 100,000.

15-115. Few new musical instruments have been invented within the last 100 years. With the availability of modern materials and processes, many novel and innovative designs are now within the realm of possibility. To be marketable over an extended period of time such an instrument should utilize the conventional diatonic scale of eight tones to the octave. It could, therefore, be utilized by symphonies, in ensembles, or as a solo instrument using existing musical compositions. You are the chief engineer for a company whose present objective is to create and market such a new instrument. Design and build a prototype of a new instrument that would be salable. Prepare working drawings of your model together with cost estimates for volume production of the instrument.

15-116. Design some means of communicating with a deaf person who is elsewhere (such as by radio).

15-117. For a bicycle, design an automatic transmission that will change gears according to the force applied.

15-118. Design a "decommercializer" that will automatically cut out all TV commercial sounds for 60 sec.

15-119. Design a solar powered refrigerator.

15-120. Design a small portable means for converting sea water to drinking water.

15-121. Design a fishing lure capable of staying at any preset depth.

15-122. Design an educational toy that may be used to aid small children in learning to read.

15-123. Design some device to help a handicapped person.

15-124. Design a heating and cooling blanket.

15-125. Design an automatic pulse monitoring system for use in hospitals.

15-126. Design a portable solar cooker.

15-127. Design a carbon monoxide detector for automobiles.

15-128. Design a more effective method for prevention and/or removal of snow and ice from military aircraft.

15-129. Design a "practical" vehicle whose operation is based upon the "ground effect" phenomenon.

15-130. Design a neuter (neither male nor female) connector for quick connect and disconnect that can be used on the end of flexible hose to transport liquids.

15-131. Design an electric space heater rated from 10,000 Btu/hr to 50,000 Btu/hr for military use in temporary huts and enclosures.

15-132. There is need for a system whereby one device emplaced in a hazardous area (minefield or other denial area) would interact with another device issued to each soldier, warn him of danger, and send guidance instructions for him to avoid or pass through the area of safety. Design such a system.

15-133. World communication and understanding would be greatly enhanced if there were available a system that would enable rapid translation from a language into a pictorial representation of what was communicated. Such a system would be helpful where there is a need for an exchange of information and where there is no common language between the parties involved. The system would therefore permit parties speaking different languages to rapidly portray in a television-type picture the particular information that they are communicating or exchanging. Identify the problems that would need to be solved to make such a system feasible.

15-134. Various types of objects are in orbit around the earth. The problem of their identification is of concern to the government. Although locating them is not a problem, a suitable method for determining their *mass* has not yet been found. For example, some device might be mounted in an "inspector probe" or fly-by vehicle that could be used to apply a specific thrust to the suspect space object and also measure its resulting acceleration. Design the conceptual features of such a system. What are the apparent difficulties?

15-135. Man has long sought to identify groundwater (beneath the surface) supplies. "Water witching" and other techniques which have been tried have not proved to be reliable. Design an electronic system that would make possible the location of new ground-water supplies.

15-136. Develop some method to rate and/or identify the presence of rust spots when coatings fail to protect metal adequately. Present visual methods are unreliable and variable in results.

15-137. Develop a system whereby diseases of significance could be diagnosed rapidly and accurately.

15-138. Design an instrument that can be mounted on any vehicle and that will measure and record the distance traveled, the time elapsed, and the instantaneous speed of the vehicle when traveling at speeds between 1 and 70 mph.

15-139. Design an instrument that would have the capability of registering degrees of pain.

Bibliography

Alger, John R. M., and Carl V. Hays, *Creative Synthesis in Design,* Prentice-Hall, Englewood Cliffs, N.J. (1964).

Azimow, Morris, *Introduction to Design,* Prentice-Hall, Englewood Cliffs, N.J. (1962).

Buhl, Harold R., *Creative Engineering Design,* Iowa State U. P., Ames (1960).

Conference on Design Methods, London, England, Macmillan, New York (1963).

Dixon, John R., *Design Engineering,* McGraw-Hill, New York (1966).

Eder, Ing. W. E., and W. Gosling, *Mechanical System Design,* Pergamon, New York (1965).

Gibson, John E., *Introduction to Engineering Design,* Holt, Rinehart and Winston, New York (1966).

Hill, Percy H., *The Science of Engineering Design,* Holt, Rinehart and Winston, New York (1970).

Killeffer, D. H., *The Genius of Industrial Research,* Van Nostrand Reinhold, New York (1948).

Krick, Edward V., *An Introduction to Engineering and Engineering Design,* Wiley, New York (1965).

Matousek, Robert, *Engineering Design, A Systematic Approach,* Blackie, London (1963).

Starr, Martin Kenneth, *Product Design and Decision Theory,* Prentice-Hall, Englewood Cliffs, N.J. (1963).

Woodson, Thomas T., *Introduction to Engineering Design,* McGraw-Hill, New York (1966).

16

The engineer—
a creative person

As man counts time, the first act of recorded history was one of creation. When God created man, he endowed him with some of this ability to bring new things into being. Today the ability to think creatively is one of the most important assets that all men possess. The accelerated pace of today's technology emphasizes the need for conscious and directed imagination and creative behavior in the engineer's daily routine. However, this idea is not new.

For centuries primitive man fulfilled his natural needs by using the bounty nature placed about him. Since his choice was limited by terrain, climate, and accessibility, he was forced to choose from his environment those things which he could readily adapt to his needs. His only guide—trial and error—was a stern teacher. He ate whatever stimulated his sense of smell and taste, and he clothed himself and his family in whatever crude materials he could fashion to achieve warmth, comfort, and modesty. His mistakes often bore serious consequences, and he eventually learned that his survival depended upon his ability to think and to act in accordance with a plan. He learned the importance of imaginative reasoning in the improvement of his lot.

In recent years archaeologists have discovered evidence of early civilizations that made hunting weapons and agricultural tools, mastered the use of fire, and improvised fishing equipment from materials at hand—all at an advanced level of complexity. These remains are silent reminders of man's ingenuity. Only his cunning and imagination protected him from his natural enemies. The situation is much the same even today, centuries later. Many believe that in this respect man may not have improved his lot substantially over the centuries. The well-being of our civilization still depends upon how successfully we can mobilize our creative manpower. As a profession, engineering must rise to meet this challenge.

In scientific work the term *creativity* is often used interchangeably with *innovation*. However, the two are not synonymous although they do have some similarities. Both creativity and innovation refer to certain processes within an individual or system. Innovation is the discovery of a new, novel, or unusual idea or product by the application of logic, experience, or artistry. This would include the recombination of things or ideas already known. Creativity is the origination of a concept in response to a human need—a solution that is both satisfying and innovative. It is reserved for those individuals who originate, make, or cause something to come into existence for the first time or those who originate new principles. Innovation, on the other hand, may or may not respond to a human need, and it may or may not be valuable. In effect, creativity is innovation to meet a need.

Creativity is a human endeavor. It presupposes an understanding of human experience and human values, and it is without doubt one of the highest forms of mental activity. In addition to requiring innovation, creative behavior requires a peculiar insight that is set into action by a vivid but purposeful imagination—seemingly the result of a divine inspiration that some often call a "spark of genius." Indeed, the moment of inspiration is somewhat analogous to an electrical capacitor that has "soaked up" an electrical charge and then discharges it in a single instant. To sustain creative thought over a period of time requires a large reservoir of innovations from which to feed. Creative thought may be expressed in such diverse things as a suspension bridge, a musical composition, a poem, a painting, or a new type of machine or process. Problem solving, as such, does not necessarily require creative thought, because many kinds of problems can be solved by careful, discriminating logic.

Imagination is more important than knowledge.
—Albert Einstein

More today than yesterday and more tomorrow than today, the survival of people and their institutions depends upon innovation.
—Jack Morton, *Innovation,* 1969

The age is running mad after innovation. All the business of the world is to be done in a new way. Men are to be hanged in a new way.
—Samuel Johnson, 1777

A given engineer may or may not be a creative thinker, although all engineers should have mastered the basic techniques of problem solving (see Chapter 17). For problem solving, the engineer must be intelligent, well informed, and discerning, so that he can apply the principles of deductive reasoning to the various innovational alternatives when he encounters them.

Every new or original thought may not be a creative thought. A psychotic's hallucinations might well be unique even though they have no intrinsic value. Such thoughts are neither innovational nor creative. Although all creative thinkers must be innovators, it does not necessarily follow that all innovators have to be creative thinkers. Innovation occurs daily, on every hand and in every walk of life. True creative behavior is much rarer and usually requires the fulfillment of some deliberate contemplation.

All persons of normal intelligence possess some ability to think creatively and to engage in imaginative and innovative effort. Unfortunately the vast majority of people are only partially aware of the range of their creative potential. This potential seldom is attained, even if recognized. This is true partially because one's social environment, home life, and education experiences either stimulate or depress the urge to be creative. Even at a very early age, children are often urged to conform to group standards. Any deviations may bring immediate rebuke from the adult in charge. As an example, in the first grade little Johnny may be assigned to color inside the boundaries of his outlined and predrawn horse. He must color his horse brown—because the teacher likes brown horses. Black horses, white horses, green horses or other choices which might occur to Johnny are ruled out. The outline has been predrawn because, in this way, all of the children's work will appear to be reasonably good to the parents on PTA night. No child's work will have the obvious appearance of poor quality or extreme excellence—a very important item to please the majority of parents. Also the teacher will not be embarrassed by horses with horns or wings. And so it goes as Johnny grows up to assume his place in adult life. As a teenager he is considered "different" or an "oddball" unless he always joins in with the majority. As a citizen, he is criticized as "anti-American" unless he affiliates with the political party that is in power at the moment. His neighbors "wonder" about him if he refuses to join a neighborhood drive to "achieve the Community Chest goal." His coworkers believe he is a "threat to our way of life" if he prefers independent action to letting some union speak in his behalf. And on and on we might continue. . . . It is no wonder that many well-informed persons today are creatively sterile, whereas others in former years (like Franklin and Edison) accomplished seemingly impossible results in spite of a poor formal education.

Years ago most American youths were accustomed to using innovative and imaginative design to solve their daily problems. Home life was largely one of rural experience. If tools or materials were not available, they quickly improvised some other scheme to accomplish the desired task. Most people literally "lived by their wits." Often it was not convenient, or even possible, to "go to town" to buy a clamp

---

Creativity is man's most challenging frontier!

A child is highly creative until he starts to school.
—Stanley Czurles, Director of Art Education, New York State College for Teachers

We have as much to learn
about the seas of Earth
as we do about the
Sea of Tranquility

Illustration 16-2 (*opposite*)

or some other standard device. Innovation was, in many cases, "the only way out." A visit to a typical midwestern farm or western ranch today, or to Peace Corps workers overseas, will show that these innovative and creative processes are still at work. However, today most American youths are city or suburb dwellers who do not have many opportunities to solve real physical problems with novel ideas.

A person is not born with either a creative or noncreative mind, although some are fortunate enough to have exceptionally alert minds that literally feed on new experiences. Intellect is essential, but it is not a golden key to success in creative thinking. Intellectual capacity certainly sets the upper limits of one's innovative and creative ability; but nevertheless, motivation and environmental opportunities determine whether or not a person reaches this limit. Surprisingly, students with high I.Q.'s are not necessarily inclined to be creative. Recent studies reveal the fact that over 70 per cent of the most creative students do not rank in the upper 20 per cent of their class on traditional I.Q. measures.[1]

[1] E. Paul Torrance, "Explorations in Creative Thinking in the Early School Years," in Calvin W. Taylor and Frank Barron (eds.), *Scientific Creativity*, Wiley, New York (1963), p. 182.

> An inventor is simply a fellow who doesn't take his education too seriously.
> —Charles F. Kettering
>
> Everybody is ignorant, only in different subjects.
> —Will Rogers

Illustration 16-3
Does the refrigerator light really *go out when the door closes?*

> Creativity is the art of taking a fresh look at old knowledge.
>
> All men are born with a very definite potential for creative activity.
> —John E. Arnold

Everyone has some innovative or creative ability. For the average person, due to inactivity or conformity, this ability has probably been retarded since childhood. If we bind our hand or foot (as was practiced in some parts of the Orient) and do not use it, it soon becomes paralyzed and ineffective. But unlike the hand or foot, which cannot recover full usefulness after long inactivity, the dormant instinct to think creatively may be revived through exercise and stimulated into activity after years of near suspended animation. Thus everyone can benefit from studying the creative and innovative processes and the psychological factors related to them.

Imaginative thinking can be stimulated, and the basic principles of innovative thinking can be mastered. Parnes and Meadow[2] have shown that deliberate education in innovative thinking can significantly increase innovative and creative potential. In reporting this research, Osborn[3] notes that, for an experimental sample of 330 students, the subjects who enrolled in courses in creative problem solving produced 94 per cent more good ideas than subjects who did not get such training. Even if these results are somewhat optimistic, we certainly cannot deny that even a 50 per cent improvement in our own individual creative abilities would be worth achieving. Many organizations—including du Pont, General Electric, Aluminum Company of America, Westinghouse, Aerojet General Corporation, General Motors, and the Armed Forces—believe the fundamental principles of creative thinking and problem solving can be taught, and give their personnel such training. Therefore, all young engineering students should profit from studying the principles used to spark innovative and creative effort.

Development of creative effort

Associated with innovative and creative thought are imagination, curiosity, and intuitive insight. As suggested above, the desire to use these faculties begins at an early age. Thwarting or suppressing this individuality of thought may change a child's personality. It is unfortunate that many of our mental resources are wasted in this way. Creative talent should be sought out, developed, and utilized wherever possible. But doing so is far from easy; although psychologists have described some general attributes and traits of the creative personality, it may be difficult to measure an individual's potential to perform creatively.

[2] Sidney J. Parnes and Arnold Meadow, "Development of Individual Creative Talent," *ibid.*
[3] Alex F. Osborn, *Applied Imagination,* Scribner's, New York (1963), p. xii.

Illustration 16-4 (*opposite*)
The mind can die from inactivity.

Although everyone has some capacity to be innovative and creative, "creative ability" is usually a scarce commodity. It need not be, however, because we can enumerate and measure the influence of the mental attitudes and thought processes that are most conducive to producing innovative and creative effort. Using some of these fundamental processes will certainly return valuable dividends. But first, one must have a proper mental attitude.

An attitude for innovative and creative thought

Unfortunately, there is no *one* set of ideal conditions that will always give the most effective imaginative and creative thought. The best conditions vary with personality and circumstances. However, it is important to approach all problems with an open mind—one as free from restrictions and preconceived limiting conditions as possible. Sentiments such as fear, greed, and hatred must be put aside. Try to approach problem situations with a clear mind that has been stimulated *but not restrained* by past experiences. In general, your thought processes are influenced by *how* and *what* you have already learned, but tradition may hinder rather than help, especially if you have made incorrect or irrelevant assumptions. This is particularly true where certain attitudes, convictions, or feelings have stimulated your emotions excessively. In such instances reasoning tends to be influenced so it will harmonize with these convictions. The engineer must learn to be receptive to new ideas, even though they may depart from conventional practices. He must always seek authenticity and truth, rather than trying to verify preconceived ideas or existing procedures.

The engineer must be *motivated* to use imaginative and innovative thought. Basically most creative persons—whether they are artists, musicians, poets, scientists, or engineers—are motivated to work at a particular task partly because of the

> Reason can answer questions, but imagination has to ask them.

Illustration 16-5
Man's potential habitation of the moon has been a stimulus to his imagination. The concept of a domed city for lunar habitation might be equally useful on this planet.

> Important ideas are those that lie within the allowable scope of nature's laws.

exhilaration, thrill, special satisfaction, pride, and pleasure they get from completing a creative task. It is perhaps natural that man should emulate his Creator in this respect. For, in each case, after creating the heavens and the earth, after adorning the earth with plant and animal life, and again after creating man and woman, God gave expression of His pleasure.

> "And God saw everything that He had made, and behold, it was very good." [4]

But besides the sense of satisfaction that comes from the creative process itself, other factors also stimulate and motivate the engineer toward creative design efforts. These may be classified into two groups.

1. *Basic Motives:* food and preservation, faith, love, aspiration for fame or freedom.
2. *Secondary Motives:* competition, pride, loyalty

Motivation is the power source that drives all engineers forward in their role as problem solvers, innovators, and creators. Some factors and circumstances will reinforce and stimulate natural motive power. Others will weaken and depress motive power. Engineers should be acquainted with both positive and negative motivating factors.

Conditions that stimulate creative thinking

There are a number of conditions and circumstances that stimulate creative thinking. Some of these are general *conditions of circumstance* that are related to individual *personality* and *philosophy* and are apart from any particular or specific action. Other conditions are related to the individual's *state of mind*. In addition, the engineer must have particular personal qualities and attitudes to achieve maximum motivational stimulation.

The engineer must understand both nature and his environment. He must learn to evaluate carefully the results and consequences of his work. Many times it will be easy for him to draw an incorrect, though seemingly obvious, conclusion. The story is told of a young biologist who was investigating the sensitivity of a frog's sensory system. He devised an experimental apparatus with blinking lights and screeching sirens and positioned his frog for testing. He reasoned that the frog would become frightened by the noise and lights and attempt to escape. Beginning with the right rear leg, he carefully severed each leg in turn, and noted how far the frog could jump. When the frog did not move after its fourth leg was severed, he noted the following in his laboratory report:

> All frogs are very sensitive to light and sound. However, at the moment the left foreleg is removed, they become deaf and blind.

[4] Genesis i:31.

We laugh at the young man's foolish statement, but daily we react in a similar manner as time after time we draw incorrect conclusions.

The engineer will devote a lifetime to changing and modifying his environment. His daily work will affect social and economic life. His actions and designs will be reflected in the lives of all people everywhere as their habits and customs change. He must recognize and assume a special responsibility in this regard because *all* of his innovative designs will probably not be used for the *betterment* of his fellow men and for uplifting their culture. He must recognize that the products of his imagination may, in fact, be used in ways that are detrimental to society. Generally his designs are, within themselves, morally neutral. However, it is the use that people make of his designs that become recognized as forces for "good" or "evil." In addition, he must realize that his failures and his successes, all of the fruits of his labor, are always on public display. President Herbert Hoover, himself an engineer, stated these conditions well:

> *Engineering* training deals with the exact sciences. That sort of exactness makes for truth and conscience. It might be good for the world if more men had that sort of mental start in life, even if they did not pursue the profession. But he who would enter these precincts as a life work must have a test taken of his imaginative faculties, for engineering without imagination sinks to a trade.
>
> It is a great profession. There is the fascination of watching a figment of the imagination emerge through the aid of science to a plan on paper. Then it moves to realization in stone or metal or energy. Then it brings jobs and homes to men. Then it elevates the standards of living and adds to the comforts of life. That is the engineer's high privilege.
>
> The great liability of the engineer compared to men of other professions is that his works are out in the open where all can see them. His acts, step by step, are in hard substance. He cannot bury his mistakes in the grave like the doctors. He cannot argue them into thin air or blame the judge like the lawyers. He cannot, like the architect, cover his failures with trees and vines. He cannot, like the politicians, screen his shortcomings by blaming his opponents and hope that the people will forget. The Engineer simply cannot deny that he did it. If his works do not work, he is damned. That is the phantasmagoria that haunts his nights and dogs his days. He comes from the job at the end of the day resolved to calculate it again. He wakes in the morning. All day he shivers at the thought of the bugs which will inevitably appear to jolt its smooth consummation.
>
> On the other hand, unlike the doctor, his is not a life among the weak. Unlike the soldier, destruction is not his purpose. Unlike the lawyer, quarrels are not his daily bread. To the engineer falls the job of clothing the bare bones of science with life, comfort and hope. . . .
>
> The engineer performs many public functions from which he gets only philosophical satisfactions. Most people do not know it, but he is an economic and social force. Every time he discovers a new application of

---

Scientists study the world as it is, engineers create the world that never has been.
—Theodore von Karman

> Our doubts are traitors and make us lose the good we oft might win by fearing
> to attempt.
> —William Shakespeare

science, thereby creating a new industry, providing new jobs, adding to the standards of living, he also disturbs everything that is. New laws and regulations have to be made and new sorts of wickedness curbed. . . . But the engineer himself looks back at the unending stream of goodness which flows from his successes with satisfactions that few professions may know.[5]

No one, regardless of his profession, is likely to be motivated to creative effort unless he has a strong and undiminishing love for his work. With this love, each day's task becomes more than a means of providing a better standard of living. Each successfully accomplished design provides a special satisfaction that comes only to those who have a strong ambition to succeed. The habit of work will become a part of the individual's personality until even his subconscious mind becomes saturated with the problem. These general conditions and circumstances provide very important climates for creative and imaginative thought.

The proper attitudes or states of mind can also contribute much to creative and imaginative thought. To be most effective, a person should certainly have a healthy body and a clear, intelligent mind, although a high I.Q. or a strong physique by no means guarantees innovative or creative ideas. Psychological freedom, in which the mind is unrestricted by past or present evaluations and judgments, is also very important. In fact, where the "fear of being wrong" has been removed, innovative and creative thought usually increases significantly, for groups of engineers working together as well as for individuals.

Significant and imaginative thought processes are usually rare when the conscious mind becomes fatigued or when there is intense emotion (joy, sorrow, or fear). The relationship between *effective creative behavior* and *physiological stress* might be illustrated (Figure 16-1). Each personality would have its own individual pattern or mathematical expression relating these variables.

[5] Herbert Hoover, *Memoirs of Herbert Hoover, Vol. 1, Years of Adventure,* Macmillan, New York (1951), p. 132.

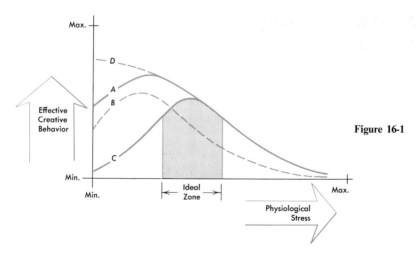

Figure 16-1

The primary curve (*A*) indicates that, when the mind is without tension and the emotions are at rest, there is considerable possibility that imaginative and creative ideas can emerge. As supporting evidence for this conclusion, many creative people testify that their most novel ideas have appeared when they were engaged in such mild mental activities as bathing, listening to a musical concert, walking on the golf course, or riding the subway. Although this is not the usual case, such a situation might be represented by curve *D*. The secondary curves, *B* and *C*, indicate typical alternative paths that two different individuals might show. Thus there is an ideal condition or emotional zone for each individual; for him it is most conducive to creative thought.

Other mental attributes that contribute positively toward creative thought are (*a*) an inquiring and questioning mind, (*b*) abilities to concentrate and communicate, (*c*) ability to accept conflict and tension without becoming frustrated, and (*d*) willingness to consider a new idea *even though it may seem to be in conflict* with previous experience.

In addition, there are personal qualities which are frequently associated with creative individuals. Developing them will enhance the likelihood that the individual will express himself creatively. They are as follows:

1. Intellectual curiosity.
2. Acute powers of observation.
3. Sensitivity to recognize that a problem exists.
4. Directed imagination.
5. Initiative.
6. Originality.
7. Memory.
8. Ability to analyze and synthesize.
9. Intellectual integrity.
10. Ability to think in analogies and images.
11. Intuition.
12. Being articulate in verbal response and alert in mental processes.
13. Patience, determination, and persistence.
14. Understanding of the creative process.

Conditions that depress creative thinking

Just as certain conditions stimulate creative thinking, certain conditions also depress creative thinking and creative behavior. Thus, although the engineer may have high creative potential and intellectual ability to analyze, synthesize, and evaluate, he

---

Observation, not old age, brings wisdom.

Behold the turtle, he makes progress only when his neck is out.
—Dr. James B. Conant, President, Harvard University

---

still may not be creative and innovative. These "road blocks to creative behavior" may be classified into three categories: (*a*) barriers resulting from experience and perception, (*b*) emotional barriers, and (*c*) social and cultural barriers. Each of these will be considered briefly here.

Barriers to creative behavior resulting from experience and perception

A recent experiment vividly illustrates the limitations that can be imposed by habit. This experiment involved a problem-solving situation where two groups were asked to extract a Ping-Pong ball from the bottom of a long, small-diameter pipe standing vertically. When the members of the first group entered the experimental room, they saw assorted objects, including a screwdriver, pliers, string, thumbtacks, and a bucket of dirty water. None of the tools seemed useful, but after some time, about half of the group realized that the Ping-Pong ball could be recovered by pouring water into the pipe until the ball floated to the top.

A second group attacked the same problem. The small articles were displayed again. In this case, however, the container of water was missing. In its place was a dinner table which had been set with china and silverware. On the table were a large pitcher of milk, and a bucket of ice cubes. No one was able to solve the problem because the subjects could not relate the liquid (milk) or "solid water" (ice) used for dining, to the totally different mechanical problem.

This experiment illustrates the danger of blind reliance on *restricted experience* in problem solving. In some instances, one may assume artificial restrictions that limit and bind his thought processes. As an example, consider the puzzle of the trees and the cows (Figure 16-2).

Problem Six cows (shown as circles) are standing in a grove of trees (shown as crosses). Draw three straight *connected* lines *to join* all of the trees without touching any of the cows.

Nothing in the problem statement implies that the lines represent fences or that the three lines must be restricted to the boundaries of the imaginary rectangular plot containing the cows and trees. However, most people automatically restrict themselves within this field and, under these artificial conditions, the problem becomes impossible to solve (Figure 16-3). This puzzle also illustrates the point that, in many instances, workable solutions to a problem are suggested by someone with minimal technical background related *directly* to the problem, but who has a broad fundamental understanding of the principles governing the situation.

Strange as it may seem, it is nevertheless true that the more original and novel an idea is, the more vulnerable it is to criticism. Often the people most apt to prejudge a situation and allow the past experiences to strangle a new idea are the ones whose

Figure 16-2

```
x   x   x   x
x   O   O   x
O   x   O   x
O   O   x   x
```

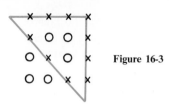

Figure 16-3

analytical abilities have carried them to prior success. Certainly such skills *are essential* for minimum accomplishment in engineering. However, it sometimes seems easier to rely upon a previously successful mathematical model than to consider the problem anew. It may well be that the original conditions have changed. We are all familiar with this tendency to "overconfidence" which sometimes overcomes those who excel in their field. It is particularly evident in athletics, where a less-able person may be the eventual victor because he never recognizes that he is supposed to suffer defeat. The moral: Never prejudge; consider each situation on its own merits.

We are told that a man dying of thirst has little difficulty in seeing a mirage of a lake off in the distance. The image he *is* seeing seems to be affected in large measure by what his mind tells him that he *needs* to see. He is expectant and thirsty, therefore, it is easy for him to see the lake of water. In a sense, then, believing is seeing. The mind's recall of events and experiences also tends to influence one's observation, discernment, and judgment. For example, look at the two arrangements of straight lines (Figures 16-4 and 16-5).

Figure 16-4   Figure 16-5

In Figure 16-4 do the two vertical lines appear equal in length? Probably not. Are the two lines in the Figure 16-5 parallel to each other? "No," you say. Most people will think that these two simple questions are strange indeed. The answers appear obvious in both cases. However, if we tell you that the first is actually a picture of two telephone poles standing in an abandoned field, and that the second is a picture of a railroad track receding into the distance, you might quickly change your answers to "yes" or "maybe." In addition, the brief verbal descriptions that were added have given each picture a quality of depth that you did not recognize originally, demonstrating that we must sharpen our powers of observation, be alert to alternative explanations, and avoid the pitfalls of prejudgment and presumption that so often stifle our thought processes.

Another example might show how prior experience can artificially limit our thinking. Once two medical doctors were riding down the street together when they observed a "head-on" collision ahead. Upon arriving at the scene, they ran to the wrecked automobiles to render aid. After looking into one vehicle, the first physician

> Some things have to be believed to be seen.
> —Ralph Hodgson, *The Skylark and Other Poems* (St. Martin's)

moaned, "My wife and child!" Hearing this exclamation, the second physician pulled out a gun and killed the first physician. What is your analysis of the motive for this murder?

Writers of novels are skillful in maneuvering fiction plots so that the reader makes an invalid assumption. Perhaps you did this in the above example. Did you assume that both physicians were men? If both physicians were men, the story seems confused and no plausible explanation appears possible. However, the familiar triangular plot of secret love and consequential murder quickly unfolds when you realize that the second physician is a young woman.

Other barriers resulting from experience and perception are the following:

1. Limited scope of basic knowledge.
2. Failure to recognize all of the conditions relating to the problem—failure to get all of the facts.
3. Preconception and reliance upon the history of other events.
4. Failure to investigate both the obvious and the trivial.
5. Artificial restriction of the problem.
6. Failure to recognize the *real* problem.
7. Inclusion of extraneous environmental factors.
8. Failure to distinguish between cause and effect.
9. Inability to manipulate the abstract.

Emotional barriers

The graph of effective creative behavior vs. physiological stress (Figure 16-1) illustrates that everyone's creative behavior diminishes to insignificance under high emotional stress. When under emotional strain, one is likely to narrow his field of observation, to make "snap judgments" that are not well thought out, and thus to disregard alternative and more valuable solutions. Overmotivated people are also likely to choose unrealistic and overambitious objectives. Emotional constraints are perhaps more damaging than other types because they can have such lasting influence upon one's personality. The emotional constraint most difficult to cope with is fear—fear of failure, of criticism, of ridicule, of embarrassment, or of loss of employment. The fear of social disapproval can stifle initiative and reduce the flow of imaginative idea. Controlled psychological experiments have shown that groups produce up to 70 per cent more innovative and novel ideas when group members do not *judge and evaluate each other's ideas* until later, thus largely removing the fears of ridicule and criticism. Brainstorming, a technique developed in the advertising business to produce more imaginative ideas, is one type of group effort that receives its stimulus by deferring judgment. Ways to implement this technique will be discussed later.

An inferiority complex, resistance to change from the status quo, and a lack of reward stimulus can also be barriers to creative and innovative thought.

Social and cultural barriers

The history of civilization is essentially the record of man's creative behavior or lack thereof. Ancient cultures rose to great heights in Egypt (2700–1800 B.C.), Greece (600–300 B.C.), and Rome (400 B.C.–A.D. 400), but these civilizations eventually fell because of laxity of purpose, moral decay, and the people's overall lack of initiative.

These conditions frequently arise when complacency, comfort, and luxury become primary objectives. When one must live or die by his wits, so to speak, his mind is stimulated to function more clearly than it would in a sheltered society. Younger generations who *inherit* the advantages of prosperity generally neither know nor appreciate the discipline of work. All these conditions reduce the motivation for creative thought.

Today, America faces a challenge much like those other cultures have faced in ages past. The physical frontiers that inspired our pioneer forefathers are fast disappearing. Fortunately, however, there are new frontiers such as proper use and reuse of natural resources, ecological balance, outer space, ocean exploration, improved human relations and communications, disease eradication, new food and

Illustration 16-6

Illustration 16-7

(Courtesy Pete Cowgill.)

power sources, and waste and pollution elimination, which challenge our best and our maximum effort. These twentieth-century goals are, in many ways, more challenging than the frontier-day obstacles of a few hundred years ago. Even more significant, perhaps, is the fact that these new frontiers cannot be conquered successfully by applying known procedures or processes routinely. Individual initiative and motivation must continue to be the keys that unlock new ideas and stimulate creative thought. However, as with other cultures, intellectual decay must inevitably result if we desire security too strongly, choose undirected leisure instead of work, or deviate from our fundamental ideals.

Man is a social being and, as such, he needs the companionship of other men. His emotions, habits, and thoughts are strongly affected by the cultural influences that surround him. At an early age, he learns that his associates disapprove of some of his actions and reward others with accolades and commendation. Such rewards may motivate him to make supreme efforts to gain recognition, but condemnation may make him afraid of deviating from his comrades' "group opinion" and thus stifle his creative and imaginative thought.

Overconformity to a group seems especially unfortunate since a group or a committee as a discrete entity cannot, as such, produce creative thoughts. Creative thoughts come *only* from the minds of individuals. However, a committee or group

> Daring ideas are like chessmen moved forward; they may be beaten, but they may start a winning game.
> —Goethe
>
> The probability is that tomorrow will not be an extrapolation of today.
> —Ernest C. Arbuckle

Illustration 16-8   (*opposite*)

"Nothing can withstand the power of the mind. Barriers, enormous masses of matter, the remotest recesses are conquered; all things succumb; the very heaven itself is laid open."
—Marcus Manilus, ca. 40 B.C.

can very definitely possess a unique personality that has strengths, weaknesses, and abilities—just as is the case for an individual. This fact does not discredit the accomplishments of teams, where the team members stimulate each other to produce novel and imaginative ideas. Not uncommonly, one team member's inspired idea will set off a chain reaction of ideas from other team members, whose subconscious memories have been awakened and stimulated into action. Team action is particularly effective in producing a large *volume* of ideas or getting a moderate course of action based on a *consensus*. Remember that hundreds of thousands of statues have been erected around the world . . . all to honor individuals. But so far, not one has been raised to honor a committee. It has been said, perhaps too harshly, that a committee never accomplishes anything unless it has three members; one of whom is always absent and one of whom is always ill. Winston Churchill is said to have once remarked that a committee was the organized result of a group of the incompetent who have been appointed by the uninformed to accomplish the unnecessary. Although his statement brings a smile to the lips of anyone who has served on very many committees, we must recognize that Churchill's own life showed there is no substitute for bold, imaginative, individual thought.

Cultural restraints may be intangible, but they are very real. For example, someone assigned to reduce hunger in India might logically begin by looking at the availability of edible and nourishing foodstuffs in India. He would soon discover that India has a higher ratio of cows to people than any other country. Many of these cows could be slaughtered to provide enough bouillon, or clear meat broth, to sustain millions of people. Yet Indian culture, reinforced by the country's predominant religion, considers the cow a sacred animal that must not be harmed—certainly not killed and made into steaks and bouillon cubes.

In modern society most people are reluctant to accept change. Generally they are either indifferent or negative to proposed ideas. This is why creative people like Leonardo da Vinci, Copernicus, Galileo, and Mozart never lived to see mankind accept the products of their imaginations. Modern civilizations have frequently been no more charitable to those who dared challenge contemporary mores. For example, John Kay was assaulted by weavers who feared his flying shuttle would destroy their

---

If you want to kill an idea, assign it to a committee for study.

. . . every idea is the product of a single brain.
—Bishop Richard Cumberland

Society is never prepared to receive any invention. Every new thing is resisted, and it takes years for the inventor to get people to listen to him and years more before it can be introduced.
—Thomas Alva Edison

> We do not have to teach people to be creative; we just have to quit interfering with their being creative.
> —Ross L. Mooney
>
> *BEWARE!* Don't become victimized by habit.

means of livelihood; farmers scoffed at Charles Newbold's iron plow and insisted it would contaminate the soil; and the medical profession censured Dr. Horace Wells for using "gas" when extracting teeth.[6]

In more recent times, when the motel was first proposed as a new concept in innkeeping, the idea was greeted with scorn by leading hotel executives. However, the test of time has shown the immense value of the idea. Because of this built-in resistance to change, many new developments must necessarily originate outside of the specialized area of endeavor.

Cultural blocks to creative behavior are not always as obvious as in these situations. For example, few of us would doubt the validity of a statement if we read it in a school textbook or in the daily newspaper. Under other circumstances, however, the same people might greet the same statement with considerable debate, for example, if it appears to be the casual observation of a friend or associate with equal or lower social or intellectual standing. Yesterday everyone admired the young person who showed initiative in thinking for himself. Unfortunately, today we may not. Too often teachers, parents, and friends value the young person's ability to adapt himself to associates' dictates and his willingness to think and act in accordance with crowd sentiments above everything else. These social constraints tend to stifle and suppress our desire and ability to think independently and imaginatively and to behave creatively.

All of these constraints therefore are detrimental to creative thought processes.

The stimulation of ideas

The engineer, as a professional man, must have keen analytical skill and the ability to synthesize. Without it he would be as handicapped as a boat without a rudder. His education must, necessarily, concentrate on this important part of the engineer's development. Both the engineer and his client must have confidence that his design calculations are both pertinent and accurate. However, an engineer who cannot produce a continuous flow of imaginative ideas is analogous to a boat without an engine. On the one hand, he may wander aimlessly, stumbling over his errors. But on the other hand, he may never get started at all. Therefore, engineering education must consider procedures for stimulating ideas. Certain of these procedures will work satisfactorily in one situation, yet at other times, different methods may be needed.

It is highly desirable for the engineer to maintain the proper mental attitude toward the problem under study. High emotional stress, preconceived ideas based upon habit, or overemphasis on some assumed evaluation of an idea's ultimate

[6]Alex F. Osborn, *Applied Imagination,* Scribner's, New York (1963), p. 54.

value—all these are particularly damaging in the initial stages of idea development. Freedom of thought is essential. If it is restricted, intentionally or not, it makes little difference, the results are the same—reduced imaginative effort. Ancient history reveals that, before 300 B.C. societies allowed the individual considerable freedom; artisans worked to enhance their own well-being rather than to expand the dominion of some ruler, king, or god-king. Inventions, like the ax, the wheel, the plow, sailboats, writing, irrigation, the arch, pottery, spinning, and metallurgy, are all examples of new ideas that appeared in this *free* environment. By about 1000 B.C. artisans found themselves working primarily to enhance the power of the ruler or king. Under these conditions, they produced considerably fewer new ideas.

Customs may also block imaginative thought. For example, archaeologists now believe that the pyramid-shaped structures built to protect Egyptian tombs were originally oblong buildings with sun-dried brick walls. Since rain deteriorated these walls, the Egyptians learned to slope the walls inward at the top, thus improving drainage and increasing durability. This custom persisted some 2000 years later, long after stone had replaced the primitive clay bricks. Even though the outside walls no longer needed to be sloped for protection against erosion, *custom* dictated that they should slope inward at the top.

Other examples have emphasized that the people who have imaginative ideas are the ones who "see with their minds" as well as their eyes. Many times we will think of an idea that seems particularly exciting and innovative. When such a thought occurs, the substance of the idea should be recorded immediately so that it will not be lost. The engineer always should have a small notebook or card that can be carried easily in a shirt or coat pocket and a pencil or pen. He must be continually sensitive to impressions and to their significance. It is said that Galileo was walking about a cathedral one day when he noticed a large lamp swinging from side to side. From this observation he conceived his idea of the pendulum. There are similar possibilities for imaginative thought today; perhaps even more than in the ancient past.

Chapter 17 describes in some detail the several methods that are used in industry to deliberately stimulate ideas.

General principles

The engineer who masters the fundamental principles of mathematics and science is able to understand the laws of nature. If this were the total requirement, the task of the engineer would be simplified. However, he never operates in a free environment where he is limited only by the laws of nature. The engineer always must

Those who dream by day are cognizant of many things which escape those who dream only by night.
—Edgar Allen Poe

"The horror of that moment," the king went on "I shall never, never forget!"
"You will, though," the queen said, "if you don't make a memorandum of it."
—Lewis Carroll

Illustration 16-9
This picture of a sound pattern can be interpreted in various imaginative ways. What images can you discern?

(Photograph by Philip Leonian)

endeavor to bridge between the "desires of man" and the "realities of nature." He must work both with nature and with people. Because of these practical considerations he is limited by artificial or man-made restrictions such as time, money, or personal preference. These restrictions necessitate compromises on the part of the engineer. Such is the nature of the real world, and the engineer must live and make his livelihood in it.

The engineer may be able to produce a novel solution that is seemingly desirable and economically justified, but it does not follow that his fellow man will always accept or implement it. People of all civilizations have resisted change; today's world is no exception. Although he will not suffer being thrown into jail, being whipped, shot, hanged, or burned at the stake as he might have been years ago, the engineer with a radical idea may find that he is ignored, demoted, transferred to another part of the company, or even fired. Such is life in the real world.

It is important for the young engineer to recognize the importance of being able to sell his idea. Some suggestions to keep in mind are the following:

1. People resist change. The status quo is comfortable and familiar. Any alterations or modifications to existing patterns must be "sold" to those who have the authority to approve decisions of change.

2. Never belittle a current practice or procedure in order to enhance the position of your own idea. Remember that your superior may have been responsible for implementing the technique that is now in use. Give him an opportunity to help you refine any improvement. If the idea is successful, there will be honor for all.

3. Present your design in a professional manner. Do not use sloppy sketches and poorly prepared commentary. Rather, take pride in your work. *Remember that its worth may be judged solely upon its clarity and appearance.*

4. Be prepared for all types of criticism. Try to think up as many reasons as you can why your idea *should not* be adopted. Prepare an answer for each objection.

5. Do not boast. It is better to minimize the overall effect of your idea and let others sell its virtue as a major contribution.

6. Do not become discouraged if you fail to sell your idea immediately. Time frequently acts as ointment to injured pride.

Since God created man in His own image, it is only natural for man to express himself in creative ways. The history of civilization is a history of man's creative efforts through the centuries. Man alone possesses the capacity for creative thought, and everyone has some capability for creative thinking. Remember that the real world is not always predictable, and that the art of compromise is in many cases the difference between success and failure. Remember also that creative behavior is a function of the individual personality rather than of organization, luck, or happenstance. For this reason, it is important to understand the characteristics of the creative person and to develop the attributes basic to imaginative and creative thought.

The mind is not a vessel to be filled but a fire to be kindled.
—Plutarch

It takes courage to be creative. Just as soon as you have a new idea, you are a minority of one.
—E. Paul Torrance

Disciplined thinking focuses inspiration rather than constricts it.

It is better to wear out than to rust out.
—Bishop Richard Cumberland

Exercises in creative thinking

16-1. How can engineering help solve some of the major world problems?

16-2. Discuss some of the inventions that have contributed to the success of man's first lunar exploration.

16-3. Write a paragraph entitled "Fiction Today, Engineering Tomorrow."

16-4. Propose a method and describe the general features of a value system whereby we could replace the use of money.

16-5. List five problems that might now confront the city officials of your home town. Propose at least three solutions for each of these problems.

16-6. Cut out five humorous cartoons from magazines. Recaption each cartoon such that the story told is completely changed. Attach a typed copy of your own caption underneath the original caption for each cartoon.

16-7. Propose a title and theme for five new television programs.

16-8. The following series of five words are related such that each word has a meaningful association with the word adjacent to it. Supply the missing words.

Example	girl	*blond*	*hair*	*oil*	rich
a. astronaut					engineer
b. pollution					automobile
c. college					textbook
d. football					radio
e. food					trumpet

16-9. Suggest several "highly desirable" alterations that would encourage personal travel by rail.

16-10. What are five ways in which you might accumulate a crowd of 100 people at the corner of Main Street and Central at 6 a.m. on Saturday?

16-11. "As inevitable as night after day"—using the word "inevitable", contrive six similar figures of speech. "As inevitable as . . . ."

16-12. Name five waste products, and suggest ways in which these products may be reclaimed for useful purposes.

16-13. Recall the last time that you lost your temper. Describe those things accomplished and those things lost by this display of emotion. Develop a strategy to regain that which was lost.

16-14. You have just been named president of the college or university that you now attend List your first ten official actions.

16-15. Describe the best original idea that you have ever had. Why has it (not) been adopted?

16-16. Discuss an idea that has been accepted within the past ten years but which originally was ridiculed.

16-17. Describe some design that you believe defies improvement.

16-18. Describe how one of the following might be used to start a fire: (*a*) scout knife, (*b*) baseball, (*c*) pocket watch, (*d*) turnip, (*e*) light bulb.

16-19. At night you can hear a mouse gnawing wood inside your bedroom wall. Noise does not seem to encourage him to leave. Describe how you will get rid of him.

16-20. Write a jingle using each of these words: cow, scholar, lass, nimble.

16-21. You are interviewing young engineering graduates to work on a project under your direction. What three questions would you ask each one in order to evaluate his creative ability?

16-22. Describe the most annoying habit of your girlfriend (boyfriend). Suggest three ways in which you might tactfully get this person to alter that habit for the better.

16-23. Suggest five designs that are direct results of ideas that have been stimulated by each of the five senses.

16-24. "A man's mother is his misfortune; his wife is his own fault." *The London Spectator.* Write three similar epigrams on boy-girl relations.

16-25. Put a blob of ink on a piece of paper and quickly press another piece of paper against it. Allow it to dry, and then write a paragraph describing "what you see in the resulting smear."

Bibliography

Allen, Myron S., *Morphological Synthesis*, Prentice-Hall, Englewood Cliffs, N.J. (1962).

Anderson, Harold H. (ed.), *Creativity and Its Cultivation*, Harper, New York (1959).

Armstrong, Frank A., *Idea Tracking*, Criterion, New York (1960).

Beveridge, W. I. B., *The Art of Scientific Investigation*, Vintage Books, New York (1957).

Clark, Charles, *Brainstorming*, Doubleday, Garden City, N.Y. (1958).

Crawford, Robert P., *The Techniques of Creative Thinking*, Hawthorn, New York (1954).

Crutchfield, Richard S., "Conformity and Creative Thinking," *Contemporary Approaches to Creative Thinking*, Atherton, New York (1963).

Easton, William H., "Creative Thinking and How to Develop It," *Creative Engineering*, The American Society of Mechanical Engineers, New York (1954).

Flesch, Rudolph, *The Art of Clear Thinking*, Harper, New York (1951).

Ghiselin, Brewster (ed.), *The Creative Process*, University of California Press, Berkeley (1952).

Gordon, William J. J., *Synectics*, Harper, New York (1961).

Guilford, J. P., "Creativity," *American Psychologist*, 1950, 5, p. 444–454.

Haefele, John W., *Creativity and Innovation*, Van Nostrand Reinhold, New York (1962).

Hutchinson, E. D., *How to Think Creatively*, (rev. ed.), Abington-Cokeburg, New York (1949).

Jewkes, John, David Sawers, and Richard Stillerman, *The Sources of Invention*, Macmillan, New York (1961).

Jones, J. Christopher, and D. G. Thornley (eds.), *Conferences on Design Methods*, Macmillan, New York (1963).

Lefford, Arthur, "The Influence of Emotional Subject Matter on Logical Reasoning," *Journal of Psychology*, vol. 34 (April 1946), p. 151.

Osborn, Alex F., *Applied Imagination*, Scribner's, New York (1963).

Parnes, Sidney J., and Harold F. Harding (eds.), *A Sourcebook for Creative Thinking*, Scribner's, New York (1962).

Platt, Washington, and Ross A. Baker, "The Relation of the Scientific Hunch to Research," *Journal of Chemical Education*, vol. 8, no. 10, (1931), p. 1969.

Rossman, Joseph, *The Psychology of the Inventor*, Inventors Pub. Co., Washington, D.C. (1931).

Stein, Morris I., and Shirley J. Heinze, *Creativity and the Individual*, The Free Press of Glencoe, Chicago (1960).

Taylor, Calvin W., and Frank Barron (eds.), *Scientific Creativity*, Wiley, New York (1963).

Taylor, Jack W., *How to Create New Ideas*, Prentice-Hall, Englewood Cliffs, N.J. (1961).

Think, A special Issue: Man's Creative Mind, November-December, 1962.

Tusak, C. D., *Inventors and Inventions*, McGraw-Hill, New York (1957).

Von Fange, Eugene K., *Professional Creativity*, Prentice-Hall, Englewood Cliffs, N.J. (1959).

Whiting, Charles S., *Creative Thinking*, Van Nostrand Reinhold, New York (1958).

17

The engineering design process

To many people engineering design means the making of engineering drawings, putting on paper ideas that have been developed by others, and perhaps supervising the construction of a working model. While engineers should possess the capability to do these things, the process of engineering design includes much more: the *formulation* of problems, the *development* of ideas, their *evaluation* through the use of models and analysis, the *testing* of the models, and the *description* of the design and its function in proposals and reports.

An engineering problem may appear in any size or complexity. It may be so small that an engineer can complete it in one day or so large that it will take a team of engineers many years to complete. It may call for the design of a tiny gear in a big machine, perhaps the whole machine, or an entire plant or process which would include the machine as one of its components. When the design project gets so big that its individual components can no longer be stored in one man's head, then special techniques are required to catalog all of the details and to ensure that the components of the system work harmoniously as a coherent unit. The techniques which have been developed to ensure such coordination are called *systems design*.

Regardless of the complexity of a problem that might arise, the *method* for solving it follows a pattern similar to that represented in Figure 17-1. Each part of this

Perhaps the most valuable result of all education is the ability to make yourself do the thing you have to do, when it ought to be done, whether you like it or not—however early a man's training begins, it is probably the last lesson that he learns thoroughly.
—Thomas Huxley

Figure 17-1   The design process.

"cyclic" process will be described in more detail, but first, two general characteristics of the process should be recognized:

1. Although the process conventionally moves in a circular direction, there is continuous "feedback" within the cycle.
2. The method of solution is a repetitious process that may be continuously refined through any desired number of cycles (Figure 17-2).

The concept of *feedback* is not new. For example, feedback is used by an individual to evaluate the results of actions that have been taken. The eye sees something bright that appears desirable and the brain sends a command to the hand and fingers to grasp it. However, if the bright object is also hot to the touch, the nerves in the

Figure 17-2

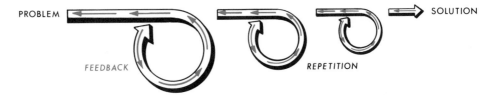

THE ENGINEERING METHOD

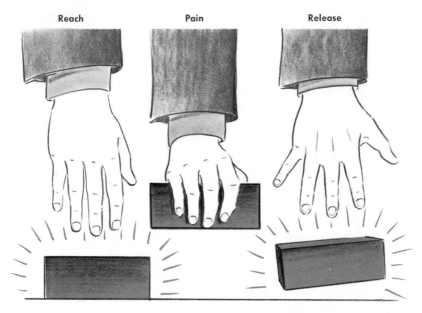

| Reach | Pain | Release |

Figure 17-3

fingers feed back information to the brain with the message that contact with this object will be injurious, and pain is registered to emphasize this fact. The brain reacts to this new information and sends another command to the fingers to release contact with the object. Upon completion of the feedback loop, the fingers release the object (Figure 17-3).

Another example is a thermostat. As part of a heating or cooling system, it is a feedback device. Changing temperature conditions produce a response from the thermostat to alter the heating or cooling rate.

The rate at which one proceeds through the problem solving cycle is a function of many factors, and these factors change with each problem. Considerable time or very little time may be spent at any point within the cycle, depending upon the situation.

Thus the problem solving process is a dynamic and constantly changing process that provides allowances for the individuality and capability of the user.

The *design process* is used in each of the phases of design that were described in Chapter 15. Each phase starts with the identification of the problem and ends with a report. Some parts of the loop are more important in one phase than another. For example, the search for ideas is most important during the feasibility study and the preliminary design phases, as compared to analysis and experimentation, which tend to predominate in the preliminary and detail design phases. The *solution* of one phase often leads directly to the problem formulation for the next phase.

Identification of the problem

One of the biggest surprises that awaits the newly graduated engineer is the discovery that there is a significant difference between the classroom problems that he solved

> The engineer's first problem in any design situation is to discover what the problem really is.

in school and the real-life problems that he is now asked to solve. This is true because problems encountered in real life are poorly defined. The individuals who propose such problems (whether they be commercial clients or the engineer's employer) rarely know or specify exactly what is wanted, and the engineer must decide for himself what information he needs to secure in order to solve the problem. In the classroom he was confronted with well-defined problems, and he usually was given most of the facts necessary to solve them in the problem statements. Now he finds that he has available insufficient data in some areas and an overabundance of data in others. In short, he must first find out what the problem *really* is. In this sense he is no different from the physician who must diagnose an illness or the attorney who must research a case before he appears in court. In fact, problem formulation is one of the most interesting and difficult tasks that the engineer faces. It is a necessary task, for one can arrive at a good and satisfactory solution only if the problem is fully understood. Many poor designs are the result of inadequate problem statements.

The ideal client who hires a designer to solve a problem will know what he wants the designer to accomplish; that is, he knows his problem. He will set up a list of limitations or restrictions that must be observed by the designer. He will know that an *absolute* design rarely exists—a *yes* or *no* type of situation—and that the designer usually has a number of choices available. The client can specify the most appropriate optimization criteria on which the final selection (among these choices) should be based. These criteria might be cost, or reliability, or beauty, or any of a number of other desirable results.

The engineer must determine many other basic components of the problem statement for himself. He must understand not only the task that the design is required to perform but what its range of performance characteristics are, how long it is expected to last in the job, and what demands will be placed on it one year, two years, or five years in the future. He must know the kind of an environment in which the design is to operate. Does it operate continuously or intermittently? Is it subject to high temperatures, or moisture, or corrosive chemicals? Does it create noise or fumes? Does it vibrate? In short, what type of design is best suited for the job.

For example, let us assume that the engineer has been asked by a physician to design a flow meter for blood. What does he need to know before he can begin his design? Of course he should know the quantity of blood flow that will be involved. Does the physician want to measure the flow in a vein, or in an artery? Does he want to measure the flow in the very small blood vessels near the skin or in the major blood vessels leading to and from the heart? Does he want to measure the average flow of blood or the way in which the blood flow varies with every pulse beat? How easy will it be to have access to the blood vessels to be tested? Will it be better to measure the blood flow without entering the vessel itself, or should a device be inserted directly into the vessel? One major problem in inserting any kind of material into the blood stream is a strong tendency to produce blood clots. In case an instrument can be inserted into the vessel, how small must it be so that it does not disturb the flow which it is to measure? How long a section of blood vessel is available, and how does the diameter of the blood vessel vary along its length and during the measurement? These and many more components of the problem statement must be determined by the engineer before an effective solution can be designed.

Another example of the importance and difficulty of problem definition is the urban transportation problem. Designers have proposed bigger and faster subways, monorails, and other technical devices because the problem was assumed to be simply one of transporting people faster from the suburbs into the city. In many cases, it was not questioned whether the problem that they were solving was *really* the problem that needed a solution.

Surely the suburbanite needs a rapid transportation system to get into the city, but the rapid transport train is not enough. He must also have "short haul" devices to take him from the train to his home or to his work with a minimum of walking and delay. Consequently, the typical rapid transit system must be coordinated with a city-wide network of slower and shorter-distance transportation which permit the traveler to exit near his job, wherever it may be. For the suburbanite, speed is not nearly as important as frequent, convenient service, on which he can rely and for which he need not wait.

Urbanites, particularly the poor, who generally live far from the places where they might find work, are also in need of better transportation. For these people, high speed again is not nearly as important as low cost and transportation routes and vehicles that provide access to the job market. Instead of placing emphasis on bigger and faster trains, designers should consider the *wants* and the *needs* of the people they are trying to serve and determine what these wants and needs really are.

How does the engineer find out? How does he define his problem and know that his definition is in fact what is needed? Of course the first step is to find out what is already known. He must study the literature. He must become thoroughly familiar with the problem, with the environments in which it operates, with similar machines or devices built elsewhere, and with peculiarities of the situation and the operators. *He must ask questions.*

It may be, after evaluating the available information, that the engineer will be convinced the problem statement is unsatisfactory—just as today's statement of the transportation problem appears to be unsatisfactory. In that case he may suggest or perform additional studies—studies that involve the formulation of simulation models of the situation and the environment in which the machine is to be built. They may include experiments with these models to show how this environment would react to various solutions of the problem.

The design engineer must work with many types of people. Some will be knowledgeable in engineering—others will not. His design considerations will involve many areas other than engineering, particularly during problem formulation. He must learn to work with physicists and physicians, with artists, architects, and city planners, with economists and sociologists—in short, with all those who may contribute useful information to a problem. He will find that these men have a technical vocabulary different from his. They look at the world through different eyes and approach the solution of problems in a different way. It is important for the engineer to have the experience of working with such people before he accepts a position in industry, and what better opportunity is there than to make their acquaintance during his college years. With the manifold problems that tomorrow's engineer will face—problems that involve human values as well as purely technical values—collaboration between the engineer and other professional people becomes increasingly important.

Collection of information

The amount of technical information available to today's scientists and engineers is prodigious and increasing daily. Two hundred years ago, during the time of Jefferson and Franklin, it was possible for an individual to have a fair grounding in all of the social and physical sciences then known, including geography, history, medicine, physics, and chemistry, and to be an authority in several of these. Since the Industrial Revolution, or about the middle of the last century, the amount of knowledge in all of the sciences has grown at such a rapid rate that no one can keep fully abreast of one major field, let alone more than one. It has been estimated that if a person, trained in speed reading, devoted 20 hours a day, seven days a week to nothing but study of the literature in a relatively specialized field, such as mechanical engineering, he would barely keep up with the current literature. He would not have time to go backwards in time to study what has been published before, or to consider developments in other fields of engineering. How then may one be able to find information that is available, or know what has been done concerning the solution of a particular problem? The answer is twofold: know *where* the information resources are located, and know *how* to retrieve information from a vast resource.

A typical technical library may contain from 10,000 to 200,000 books. It may subscribe to as many as 500 technical and scientific magazines, as well as a large store of technical reports published at irregular intervals by government agencies, universities, research institutes, and industrial organizations. The problem then is principally one of finding the proper books or articles.

Libraries have become quite efficient at cataloging books and major reports in their general catalog file. Usually these catalogs are arranged into three groups, one by author, one by title, and one by subject matter. Although the library catalog is an excellent source of book references, it does not contain any of the thousands of articles in magazines, technical journals, and special reports.

One's direction to these journal articles and special reports is through the reference section in the library. Here the abstract journals and books devoted to collecting and ordering all publications in a particular field are housed. For engineers, two of the most useful of these are the *Engineering Index* and the *Applied Science and Technology Index*. They appear annually and contain short abstracts of most important articles appearing in the engineering field. Articles are organized according to subject headings, so that all articles on a similar subject appear together. By looking under the appropriate heading, the searcher can discover the references of greatest interest to him or related headings where other references might be found. After satisfying himself that he has the correct references, the researcher then goes to the appropriate periodicals to find the full articles. There are many other indexes besides the two mentioned above, some more, some less specialized. Those most important for the engineer are listed at the end of this chapter.

Illustration 17-1
The engineer must be proficient in locating information most pertinent to his design. A good knowledge of library procedures and sources is therefore essential.

As an example, assume that we are concerned with the design of a pipeline to transport solid refuse (garbage) from the center of a large city to a disposal site where it may be processed, incinerated, or buried. Let us follow and observe an engineer making the required library search.

Literature search on "pipelining of refuse"

(The following "capsule narrative" indicates what actually happened during a quick noncomprehensive search conducted in an afternoon at a typical university library, and it is typical of the kind of search that an engineer might make for a brief study.)

Going first to the "subject" section of the catalog file, I could think of only three headings to look under: Refuse, Garbage, and Pipelines. There were eight entries under "Refuse and Refuse Disposal." Some dealt with conveyors and trucking but none with pipelining (not surprisingly since this is not a common way to convey garbage). I copied some of the titles and reference numbers because they might help to give me some idea of the composition and consistency of garbage and of the shredders and other devices used to make refuse more uniform in size and more capable of being transported in a pipeline.

The card under "Garbage" referred me right back to "Refuse and Refuse Disposal," a dead end.

Under "Pipe" there were some 70 entries under 16 different subheadings from "Pipe-Asbestos, Cement" to "Pipe-Welding." I copied the titles and numbers shown in Figure 17-4.

I wasn't satisfied that I had exhausted the subject file but could not think of any other pertinent headings. So I went next to the reference library and sat down in front of the shelf with the *Engineering Index*. The latest complete year was 1968. Looking under the headings like "Pipeline" and

"Refuse Disposal" I paid particular attention to "See also" lists, Figure 17-5, and these eventually led me to a veritable gold mine of references under "Materials Handling." A few of these are shown in Figure 17-6. Notice that two of the most interesting articles are in German. If I find them, I will have to have them translated.

Now that I know some of the best headings, I look through other years' editions of the *Index* and also study other indexes. I can also go back to the subject catalog and look under the headings that have been productive in the *Index,* headings like "Materials Handling," of which I did not think the first time.

In this way, in a short afternoon, one can assemble a reasonably good reference list on any subject one needs to study.

Next I have to obtain copies of those articles that I want to study in their entirety. If I found them as books in the subject catalog, I can ask for them or look for them myself in the stacks. For articles which have appeared in magazines, like the references from the *Engineering Index,* I first have to find out whether these references are available in the library and, if so, I'll find the appropriate order number and borrow them from the library. If they are particularly interesting, I may have the library make me a photostatic copy so that I can have a permanent record of the article.

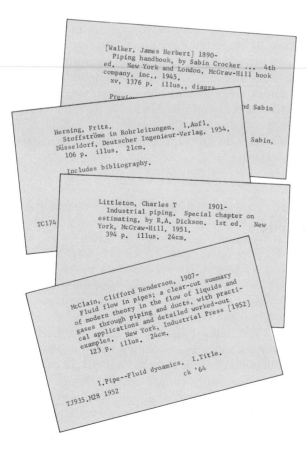

Figure 17-4

REFUSE DISPOSAL

See Also Coal Mines and Mining–Waste Disposal; Coal Preparation–Refuse Disposal; Industrial Wastes.

TRANSPORTATION

See also Air Transportation; City Planning; Coal Transportation; Highway Engineering–Research; Highway Systems–Planning; Industrial Plants–Location; Mines and Mining–Surface Transportation; Motor Bus Transportation; Motor Truck Transportation; Noise–Control; Operations Research; Power Plant Equipment–Transportation; Railroads; Rapid Transit; Street Traffic Control; Traffic Surveys; Vehicles–Ground Effect; Waterway Transportation.

COAL HANDLING

See also Bins; Coal Transportation.

Hydraulic. See also Materials Handling–Pipe Lines; Ore Handling–Hydraulic; Pipe, Plastic.

MATERIALS HANDLING

See also Air Transportation; Aircraft Carriers; Barges; Bins; Bottle Caps; Cableways; Cargo Handling; Cement Handling; Chemicals–Transportation; Coal Handling; Construction Equipment; Containers; Conveyors; Cranes; Elevators; Flour Mills; Food Products–Packaging; Foundry Practice–Cleaning; Freight Handling; Furniture Manufacture–Finishing; Grinding Mills; Hoists; Industrial Engineering; Industrial Trucks; Logging; Machine Tools; Mail Handling; Mines and Mining–Surface Transportation; Nuclear Fuels–Safe Handling; Ore Handling; Packaging; Packaging Machines; Packaging Materials; Production Planning and Control; Rivers–Revetments; Salt–Storage; Scales and Weighing; Silos; Systems Engineering; Transportation; Warehouses.

Figure 17-5 Typical headings from *Engineering Index* for 1968.

If it is important for the searcher to find the very latest work done in his subject, the library will not be of much help. There is a time delay between the performance of a piece of research, its publication, and its appearance in any of the abstract journals. This delay is usually three years or more. The only source for the very latest materials is the expert himself. If one has made an exhaustive literature survey, he has usually found one or more researchers who are specialists and have published extensively in the field under investigation. These people are also the ones who probably can provide the latest technical information in the field. Often these men are happy to share their knowledge with the searcher in the field. However, it is customary to offer them a consultant's remuneration if a substantial amount of their time is required for this service.

Generation of ideas

It is incorrect to use the terms *synthesis, innovation,* and *creativity* interchangeably. They are not synonymous but all are used in the generation of ideas to solve engineering problems. *Synthesis* is the assembly of well-known components and parts to form a solution. *Innovation* is the discovery of a new, novel, or unusual idea or product by applying logic, experience, or artistry. *Creativity* originates an entirely new concept in response to a human need, a solution which is both satisfying and innovative. It presupposes an understanding of human experience and human values.

Problem solving does not necessarily require creative thought. Many kinds of problems can be solved by careful discriminating logic. An electronic computer can be programmed to perform synthesis—and perhaps even a certain degree of innovation—but it cannot create. Creativity is a *human* endeavor.

The engineer who redesigns a radio or improves an automobile engine uses established techniques and components; he synthesizes. Innovators are those who build something new, and who combine different ideas and facts with a purpose. Creativity is one of the rarest and highest forms of human activity. We only call those individuals "creative" who originate, make, or cause to come into existence an entirely new concept or principle. (Patents are mostly the result of clever innovation, rather than creative effort.) If we had to rely on creativity for patents, we would not have the nearly 4 million patents in the United States alone. All engineers must synthesize, some will innovate, but only a very few are able to be truly creative.

Since there is always a great demand for creative and innovative ideas, many attempts have been made to develop procedures for stimulating them. Certain of these procedures will work satisfactorily in one situation, yet at other times different methods may be needed.

There are many methods of stimulating ideas that are used in industry today: (a) the use of checklists and attribute lists, (b) reviewing of properties and alterna-

Figure 17-6 Typical abstracts from *Engineering Index* for 1968.

Research Can Take Guesswork out of Bulk Handling, H.COLIJN. Matl Handling Eng v 23 n 3 Mar 1968 p 105–7. Characteristics of bulk materials include particle size, size consist, abrasiveness, angles of friction, particle shape; bulk handling in mining, primary metals, chemicals, railroading; report of European research at Hanover and Braunschweig.

Konzentrationsprofile beim hydraulischen Transport feinkoerniger Feststoffe, E.KRIEGEL. VDI Zeit-Fortschritt-Berichte pt 13 n 9 Dec 1967 51 p. Concentration profile during hydraulic transport of fine grain solids; dimensionless concentration profiles were calculated for uniform grain mixture and compared to published data; calculated grain distributions were compared with photographic records for coke-water mixture; relationship between profiles and precipitation velocity, suitability of equations for multigrain mixtures, as well as effect of most important physical magnitudes were studied. 11 refs. In German.

Pipeline Flow of Paste Slugs–2, R.A.S.BROWN, E.J.JENSEN. Can J Chem Eng v 46 n 3 June 1968 p 157–61. Pressure gradients and velocities of trains of slugs; measurements were taken in 70-ft long, closed-loop line made from 0.95 in. bore, rigid plastic tubing; flow in line could be switched to maintain continuous movement of train of slugs; tests were made with slugs of 80 to 20 (w/w) coal–water paste which was extruded through 0.775-in. die, and also with slugs which were stabilized by addition of agar to water used for making slugs; oil used as carrier fluid was light mineral oil which was circulated through pipe line loop at velocities ranging from 1.0 to 10.0 fps. 11 refs.

Pipeline Transportation of Solids—Theoretical and Practical Considerations, D.ANDERSON, P.R.PERKINS. ICHCA J v 1 n 10 Oct 1967 p 9–13 (French résumé p 41, 43). For many years it has been known that number of bulk solid materials can be transported by mixing them with suitable liquid and handling them as slurries using conventional pumps, pipes or open channels; as empirical knowledge has accumulated proposed uses of slurry pipelines have greatly increased in size and scope; problems are rapidly being overcome to make solids pipelines serious competitors for transportation of bulk materials.

Considerations in Selection of Pneumatic Conveying System, E.A.VITUNAC. Min Eng v 20 n 5 May 1968 p 83–7. Emerging importance of pneumatic conveying systems for bulk materials is largely due to economic advantages such systems frequently exhibit when compared to alternate methods; basically, there are three types of pneumatic systems—mechanical-pneumatic solids pumps, air slides, and pneumatic systems; choice of pneumatic conveying system should be based on economic, operational and maintenance variables; review of typical industrial systems reveals progress made in recent years in design of systems and their component parts.

Gesetzmaessigkeiten beim hydraulischen und pneumatischen Feststofftransport durch waagerechte Rohre, E.KRIEGEL. Verfahrenstechnik v 2 n 4 Apr 1968 p 170–7. Laws of hydraulic and pneumatic handling of solids in horizontal pipes; these laws are investigated separately because large difference of ratio, density of solids to conveying medium, influences handling mechanism; during pneumatic handling grains hit wall of pipe, while they are carried by forces of flow during hydraulic handling; law of resistance and distribution of solids during hydraulic handling can be determined as concept of turbulent mass exchange in flow of liquid; in case of pneumatic handling only individual explanations can be used; comparison of resistance laws for both types of handling emphasizes fundamental differences. 20 ref. In German.

Optimization of Pipelines Transporting Solids, W.A.HUNT, L.C. HOFFMAN. ASCE—Proc v 94 (J Pipeline Div) n PL1 Oct 1968 paper 6179 p 89–106. Method is presented for optimizing economic model of nonclosed network of pipe lines transporting mixtures of wood chips and water; cost function for single pipe is developed as polynomial expression in terms of concentration of solids and pipe diameter; characteristic response surface generated by this polynomial provides method for reducing pipe diameters; optimization of multiple-pipe networks utilizes cost function of single pipes and requires that continuity of flow of mixture is satisfied at junctions; summaries of numerical examples of three-line network are given; costs of pipe line transport of woodchips are compared with those of truck and rail for existing area.

tives, (c) systematically searching design parameters, (d) brainstorming, and (e) synectics. These methods will be discussed briefly.

Checklists and attribute lists

One of the simplest ways for an individual to originate a number of new ideas in a minimum amount of time is to make use of prepared lists of general questions to apply to the problem under consideration. A typical list of such questions might be the following:

1. In what ways can the idea be improved in quality, performance, and appearance?
2. To what other uses can the idea be put? Can it be modified, enlarged, or minified?
3. Can some other idea be substituted? Can it be combined with another idea?
4. What are the idea's advantages and disadvantages? Can the disadvantages be overcome? Can the advantages be improved?
5. What is the particular scientific basis for the idea? Are there other scientific bases that might work equally well?
6. What are the least desirable features of the idea? The most desirable?

Attribute listing is a technique of idea stimulation that has been most effective in improving tangible things—such as products. It is based upon the assumption that most ideas are merely extensions or combinations of previously recognized observations. Attribute listing involves:

1. Listing the key elements or parts of the product.
2. Listing the main features, qualities, or significant attributes of the product and of each of its key elements or parts.
3. Systematically modifying, changing, or eliminating each feature, quality, or attribute so that the *original purpose* is better satisfied, or perhaps a new need is fulfilled.

With both checklists and attribute lists one must be careful to recognize that these methods are merely "stimulators" and that they are not intended to replace original and intelligent thinking. They are certainly not intended to be used as crutches. Rather, like a wrench which extends the power or leverage of a man's fingers or arm, these ideation tools extend the power and effectiveness of the mind.

Reviewing the properties and alternatives

Another rather common procedure, somewhat similar to attribute listing, is to consider how all of the various properties or qualities of a particular design might be changed, modified, or eliminated. This method lists the modifiable properties such as weight, size, color, odor, taste, shape, and texture. Functions that are desirable for the item's intended use may also be listed: automatic, strong, durable, or light-weight. After developing these lists, the engineer can consider and modify each property or function individually.

Imagine redesigning a lawn mower. The listed properties might include (1) metal, (2) two-cycle, gasoline powered, (3) four wheels, (4) rotary blade, (5) medium weight, (6) manually propelled, (7) chain driven, and (8) green in color. In beginning the design of an improved lawn mower, the engineer might first consider other possibilities for each property. What other materials could be used? Can the engine be improved—what about using electrical power? Should the mower operate automatically? Should the type of blade motion be changed? Questions like these may suggest

> Use logic to decide between alternatives—not to initiate them.

how the design *could* be improved. The properties of lawn mowers have been changed many times, and these changes have presumably made lawn mowers more efficient and easier to use.

Again, besides considering the product's various properties the engineer must question, observe, and associate its functions. Can these functions be modified, rearranged, or combined? Can the product serve other functions or be adapted to other uses? Can we change the shape (magnify or minify parts of the design)? With this type of questioning we can stimulate ideas that will bring design improvements to the product.

Systematic search of design parameters

Frequently it is advisable to investigate alternatives more thoroughly. A systematic search considers all possible combinations of given conditions or design parameters. This type of search is frequently called a "matrix analysis" or a "morphological synthesis" of alternatives.[1,2] Its success in stimulating ideas depends upon the engineer's ability to identify the significant parameters that affect the design. The necessary steps for implementing this type of idea search are the following:

1. **Describe the problem.** This description should be broad and general, so that it will not exclude possible solutions.
2. **Select the major independent-variable conditions** required in combination to describe the characteristics and functions of the problem under consideration.
3. **List the alternate methods** that satisfy each of the independent-variable conditions selected.
4. **Establish a matrix** with each of the independent-variable conditions as one axis of a rectangular array. Where more than three conditions are shown, the display can be presented in parallel columns.[3]

Let us consider a specific example to see how this method can be applied.
1. *Problem Statement:* A continuous source of contaminate-free water is needed.
2. *Independent-Variable Conditions:*
   Energy
   Source
   Process
3. *Methods of Satisfying Each Condition:*
   Types of Energy:
   a. Solar
   b. Electrical
   c. Fossil
   d. Atomic
   e. Mechanical

[1] K. W. Norris, "The Morphological Approach to Engineering Design," in J. Christopher Jones, *Conference on Design Methods,* Macmillan, New York (1963), p. 116.
[2] Myron S. Allen, *Morphological Synthesis,* Prentice-Hall, Englewood Cliffs, N.J. (1962).
[3] Ibid.

Types of Source:
a. Underground
b. Atmosphere
c. Surface supply
Types of Process:
a. Distillation
b. Transport
c. Manufacture
4. *The Matrix* (Figure 17-7)
5. *Combinations*

This particular matrix may be represented as an orderly arrangement of 45 small blocks stacked to form a rectangular parallelepiped. Every block will be labeled with the designations selected previously. Thus, block *X* in our preceding example suggests obtaining pure water by distilling a surface supply with a solar-energy power source, block *Y* means transporting water from an underground source by some mechanical means, and block *Z* recommends manufacturing water from the atmosphere using atomic power. Obviously, some of the blocks represent well-known solutions, and others suggest absurd or impractical possibilities. But, some represent untried combinations that deserve investigation.

Where more than three variables are involved, a method which has been developed by Dr. Myron S. Allen might be implemented:

Step 1   Get the feel of the general problem area. Read all available material concerning the problem, marking or otherwise identifying all ideas that appear to be of any possible significance—without any immediate evaluation. Talk with as many people as possible who are parts of the problem in any way. Take careful notes.

Step 2   Type all of the ideas collected in step one on 2.5″ by 3″ cards, with the 3″ side horizontal.

Step 3   Lay the cards on a table in blocks of 12—three cards wide and four cards high. Leave about one quarter of an inch between individual cards, and one inch between blocks of cards. This arrangement has worked out to be the best of many different plans.

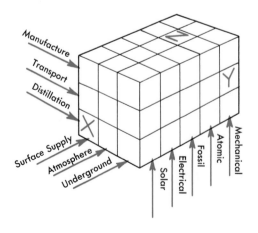

Figure 17-7

> Necessity may be the mother of invention, but imagination is its father.

Step 4   Read the cards over four or five times, as quickly as you can. All of the ideas presented will be retained in your mind permanently, most of them in your subconscious. We shall make intuitive use of these "submerged ideas during the process of setting up the total problem.

Step 5   Go away from the cards for at least half an hour, taking great pains to occupy your conscious mind so completely that it will not be thinking about the cards. Your subconscious mind will continue to work diligently on the problem, and with much higher efficiency than it could if your conscious mind simultaneously is criticizing every new idea proposed by your intuition.

Step 6   Return to the cards and again study them. You will now notice that certain of the cards appear to be friendly to one another—just friendly—and may easily be collected into congenial groups. If you had started with 500 cards you might wind up with from 20 to 30 of these friendly groups. Now write a descriptive title card for each group (use a distinctive color) and place a rubber band around the group.

Step 7   Treating each of the groups of cards now as a single element, continue synthesizing the groups into a still smaller number of groups until you finally come to no more than seven groups. Again write a descriptive card for each of these final groups. These are the fundamental elements of the problem, which are commonly called parameters. (This number seven was not an arbitrary assumption, but is in recognition of the proven psychological fact that seven elements is the maximum that the human mind can consider efficiently at one time in a single group.)

Step 8   Analyze the cards of each parameter into not more than seven subgroups, called components. The original groupings as found in Step 6 will often turn out to be components, but sometimes other arrangements will appear more suitable.

Step 9   Type the parameters, and their components, in columns.

Step 10   Cut the pages up into strips of one parameter each. Then paste the strips on pieces of thin cardboard of the same size as the paper strips. Make a simple device to hold the slides. You are now ready to take a look at the real, the total, problem.[4]

In matrix analysis electronic computers may be used to excellent advantage. After the matrix has been programmed, the computer can print a list of all the alternative combinations. Use of the computer is especially helpful when considering a large number of parameters.

The preceding techniques of stimulating new design concepts are particularly useful for the individual engineer. But often several designers may be searching jointly for imaginative ideas about some particular product. Then it is advantageous to use one of the procedures, "brainstorming" or "synectics."

[4] Myron S. Allen, *Morphological Synthesis,* Prentice-Hall, Englewood Cliffs, N.J. (1962), p. 182.

> Whatever one man is capable of conceiving, other men will be able to achieve.
> —Jules Verne
>
> Originality is just a fresh pair of eyes.
> —W. Wilson

Brainstorming

The term "brainstorming" was coined by Alex F. Osborn[5] to describe an organized group effort aimed at solving a problem. The technique involves compiling all of the ideas which the group can contribute and deferring judgment concerning their worth. This is accomplished (1) by releasing the imagination of the participants from restraints such as fear, conformity, and judgment; and (2) by providing a method to improve and combine ideas the moment an idea has been expressed. Osborn points out that this collaborative group effort does not replace individual ideative effort. Group brainstorming is used solely to supplement individual idea production and works very effectively for finding a large volume of alternative solutions or novel design approaches. It has been particularly useful for stimulating imaginative ideas for new products or product development. It is not recommended where the problem solution will depend primarily on judgment or where the problem is vast, complex, vague, or controversial. A homogeneous "status group" of six to twelve persons seems to be best for stimulating ideas with this method. However, the U.S. Armed Forces have used a hundred or more participants effectively. The typical brainstorming session has only two officials: a chairman and a recorder. The chairman's responsibility is to provide each panel member with a brief statement of the problem, preferably 24 hours prior to the meeting. He should make every effort to describe the problem in clear, concise terms. It should be *specific,* rather than *general,* in nature. Some examples of ideas that satisfy the problem statement may be included with the statement. Before beginning the session, the chairman should review the rules of brainstorming with the panel. These principles, although few, are very important and are summarized as follows:

1. All ideas which come to mind are to be recorded. No idea should be stifled. As Osborn says, "The wilder the idea, the better; it is easier to tame down than to think up." He recommends recording ideas on a chalkboard as they are suggested. Sometimes a tape recorder can be very valuable, especially when panel members suggest several different ideas in rapid succession.

2. Suggested ideas must not be criticized or evaluated. Judgments, whether adverse or laudatory, *must be withheld* until after the brainstorming session, because many ideas which are normally inhibited because of fear of ridicule and criticism are then brought out into the open. In many instances, ideas that would normally have been omitted turn out to be the best ideas.

3. Combine, modify, alter, or add to ideas as they are suggested. Participants should consciously attempt to improve on other people's ideas, as well as contributing their own imaginative ideas. Modifying a previously suggested idea will often lead to other entirely new ideas.

[5] Alex F. Osborn, *Applied Imagination,* Scribner's, New York (1963), p. 151.

4. The group should be encouraged to think up a large quantity of ideas. Research at the State University of New York at Buffalo[6] seems to indicate that when a brainstorming session produces more ideas, it will also produce higher-quality ideas.

The brainstorming chairman must always be alert to keep *evaluations* and *judgments* from creeping into the meeting. The spirit of enthusiasm that will permeate the group meeting is also very important to the success of the brainstorming session. The entire period should be conducted in a free and informal manner. It is most important to maintain, throughout the period, an environment where the group members are not afraid of seeming foolish. Both the speed of producing and recording ideas, and the number of ideas produced, help create this environment. Each panel member should bring to the meeting a list of new ideas that he has generated from the problem statement. These ideas help to get the session started. In general, the entire brainstorming period should not last more than 30 minutes to 1 hour.

The recorder keeps a stenographic account of all ideas presented and after the session, lists them by type of solution without reference to their source. Team members may add ideas to the accumulated list for a 24-hour period. Later, the entire list of ideas should be rigorously evaluated, either by the original brainstorming group or, preferably, by a completely new team. Many of the ideas will be discarded quickly—others after some deliberation. Still others will likely show promise of success or at least suggest how the product can be improved.

Some specialists recommend that the brainstorming team include a few persons who are broadly educated and alert but who are amateurs in the particular topic to be discussed. Thus new points of view usually emerge for later consideration. Usually executives or other people mostly concerned with *evaluation* and *judgment* do not make good panel members. As suggested previously, particular care should be taken to confine the problem statement within a narrow or limited range to ensure that all team members direct their ideas toward a common target. Brainstorming is no substitute for applying the fundamental mathematical and physical principles the engineer has at his command. It should be recognized that the objective of brainstorming is to stimulate ideas—not to effect a complete solution for a given problem.

The person who is capable of producing a large number of ideas per unit of time, other things being equal, has a greater chance of having significant ideas.
—J. P. Guilford

What good is electricity, Madam? What good is a baby?
—Michael Faraday

He that answereth a matter before he heareth it, it is folly and shame unto him.
—Proverbs xviii.13

No idea is so outlandish that it should not be considered with a searching but at the same time with a steady eye.
—Winston Churchill

---

[6]Sidney J. Parnes and Arnold Meadow, "Effects of Brainstorming Instructions on Creative Problem Solving by Trained and Untrained Subjects, *Journal of Educational Psychology,* vol. 50, no. 4 (1959), p. 176.

Dr. William J. J. Gordon[7] has described a somewhat similar method of group therapy for stimulating imaginative ideas, which he calls "synectics."

Synectics

This group effort is particularly useful to the engineer in eliciting a radically new idea or in improving products or developing new products. Unlike brainstorming, this technique does not aim at producing a large number of ideas. Rather, it attempts to bring about one or more solutions to a problem by drawing seemingly unrelated ideas together and forcing them to complement each other. The synectics participant tries to *imagine* himself as the "personality" of the inanimate object: "What would be my reaction *if I were that gear* (or drop of paint, or tank, or electron)?" Thus, familar objects take on strange appearances and actions, and strange concepts often become more comprehensible. A key part of this technique lies in the group leader's ability to make the team members "force-fit" or combine seemingly unrelated ideas into a new and useful solution. This is a difficult and time-consuming process. Synectics emphasizes the conscious, preconscious, and subconscious psychological states that are involved in all creative acts. In beginning, the group chairman leads the members to understand the problem and explore its *broad* aspects. For example, if a synectics group is seeking a better roofing material for traditional structures, the leader might begin a discussion on "coverings." He could also explore how the colors of coverings might enhance the overall efficiency (white in summer, black in winter). This might lead to a discussion of how colors are changed in nature. The group leader could then focus the group on more detailed discussion of how roofing materials could be made to change color automatically to correspond to different light intensities—like the biological action of a chameleon or a flounder. Similarly, the leader might approach the problem of devising a new type of can opener by first leading a group discussion of the word "opening," or he could begin considering a new type of lawn mower by first discussing the word "separation."

In general, synectics recommends viewing problems from various analogous situations. Paint that will not adhere to a surface might be viewed as analogous to water running off a duck's back. The earth's crust might be seen as analogous to the peel of an orange. The problem of enabling army tanks to cross a 40-ft-wide, bottomless crevass might be made analogous to the problem that two ants have in crossing chasms wider than their individual lengths.

Synectics has been used quite successfully in problem solving situations in such diverse fields as military defense, the theater, manufacturing, public administration, and education. Where most members of the brainstorming team are very knowledgeable about the problem field, synectics frequently draws the team members from diverse fields of learning, so that the group spans many areas of knowledge. Philosophers, artists, psychologists, machinists, physicists, geologists, biologists, as well as engineers, might all serve equally well in a synectics group. Synectics assumes that someone who is imaginative but not experienced in that field may produce as many creative ideas as one who *is* experienced in that field. Unlike the expert, the novice can stretch his imagination. He approaches the problem with fewer preconceived ideas or theories, and he is thus freer from binding mental restrictions. (Obviously, this will not be true when the problem requires analysis or evaluation, where

[7] William J. J. Gordon, *Synectics,* Harper, New York (1961).

> A damsel of high lineage and a brow
> May-blossom, and a cheek of apple-blossom
> Hawk-eyes; and lightly her slender nose
> Tip-tilted like the petal of a flower.
> —Tennyson

experience is a vital factor.) There is always present in the synectics conference an expert in the particular problem field. The expert can use his superior technical knowledge to give the team missing facts, or he may even assume the role of "devil's advocate," pointing out the weaknesses of an idea the group is considering. *All* synectics sessions are tape recorded for later review and to provide a permanent record.

Many believe that brainstorming comes to grips with the problem too abruptly while synectics delays too long. However, industry is using both methods successfully today.

Preparation of a model

Psychologists and others who study the workings of the human mind tell us that we can think effectively only about simple problems and small "bits" of information. They tell us that those who master complicated problems do so by reducing them to a series of simple problems which can be solved and synthesized to a final solution. This technique consists of forming a mental picture of the entire problem, and then simplifying and altering this picture until it can be taken apart into manageable components. These components must be simple and similar to concepts with which we are already familiar, to situations that we know. Such mental pictures are called *models*. They are simplified images of real things, or parts of real things—a special picture that permits us to relate it to something already known and to determine its behavior or suitability.

We are all familiar with models of sorts—with maps as models for a road system; with catalogs of merchandise as models of what is offered for sale. We have a model in our mind of the food we eat, the clothes we buy, and of the partner we want to marry.

We will often form judgments and make decisions on the basis of the model, even though the model may not be entirely appropriate. Thus the color of an apple may or may not be a sign of its ripeness, any more than the girl's apple-blossom cheeks and tip-tilted nose are the sign of a desirable girl-friend.

Engineering models are similar to sports diagrams that are composed of circles, squares, triangles, curved and straight lines, and other similar symbols which are used to represent a "play" in a football or basketball game (see Figure 17-8). Such geometrical models are limited because they are two dimensional and do not allow for the strengths, weaknesses, and imaginative decisions of the individual athletes. Their use, however, has proved to be quite valuable in simulating a brief action in the game and to suggest the best strategy for the player should he find himself in a similar situation.

Every football fan understands the value of diagrammed models in preparing for Saturday's "big game."

An *idealized model* may emphasize the whole of the system and minimize its component parts, or it may be designed to represent only some particular part of the system. Its function is to make visualization, analysis, and testing more practical. The engineer must recognize that he is merely limiting the complexity of the problem in order to apply known principles. Often the model may deviate considerably from the true condition; and the engineer must, of necessity, select different models to represent the same real problem. Therefore, the engineer must view his answers with

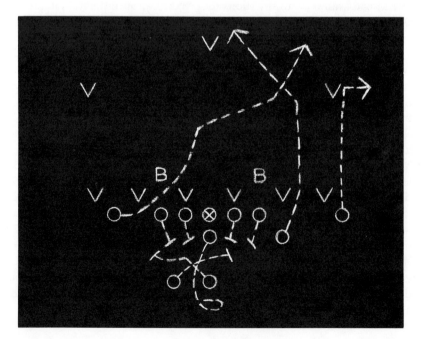

Figure 17-8

Illustration 17-3
Scale models of the design are frequently tested to prove the validity of the engineer's calculations. Instrumentation on the model pictured above is given a final check by two aircraft technicians prior to testing in the Transonic Dynamics Tunnel.

respect to the initial assumptions of the model. If the assumptions were in error, or if their importance was underestimated, then the engineer's analysis will not relate closely with the true conditions. The usefulness of the model to predict future actions must be verified by the engineer. This is accomplished by experimentation and testing. Refinement and verification by experimentation are continued until an acceptable model has been obtained.

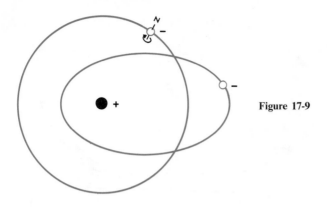

Figure 17-9

Two characteristics, more than many others, determine an engineer's competence. The first is his ability to devise simple, meaningful models; and second is the breadth of his knowledge and experience with examples with which he can compare his models. The simpler his models are, and the more generally applicable, the easier it is to predict the behavior and compute the performance of the design. *Yet models have value only to the engineer who can analyze them.* The beauty and simplicity of a model of the atom, Figure 17-9, will appeal particularly to someone familiar with astronomy. The free-body diagram of a wheelbarrow handle, Figure 17-10, has meaning only to someone who knows how such a diagram can be used to find the strength of the handle.

Aside from models for "things," we can make models of situations, environments, and events. The football or baseball diagram is such a model. Another familiar model of this type is the weather map, Figure 17-11, which depicts high- and low-pressure regions and other weather phenomena traveling across the country. Any meteorologist will tell you that the weather map is a very crude model for predicting weather, but that its simplicity makes the explanation of current weather trends more understandable for the layman. Models of situations and environmental conditions are particularly important in the analysis of large systems because they aid in predicting and analyzing the performance of the system before its actual implementation. Such models have been prepared for economic, military, and political situations and their preparation and testing is a science all its own.

Figure 17-10

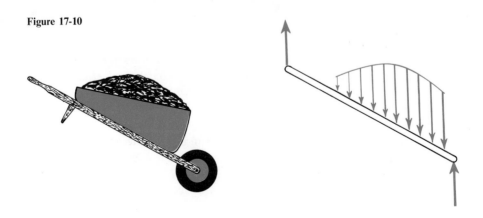

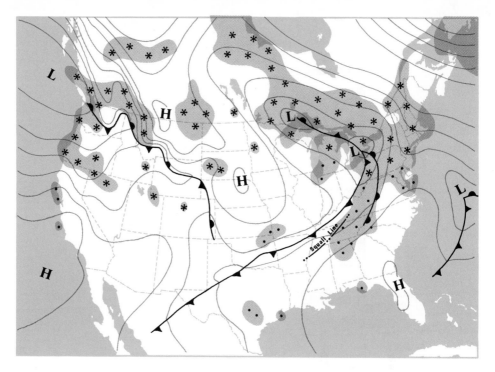

Figure 17-11

Charts and graphs as models

Charts and graphs are convenient ways to illustrate the relationship among several variables. We have all seen charts of the fluctuations of the stock market averages, Figure 17-12, in the newspaper from day to day, or you may have had your father plot your growth on the closet door. In these examples, *time* is one of the variables. The others, in the examples above, are the average value of the stock in dollars

Figure 17-12

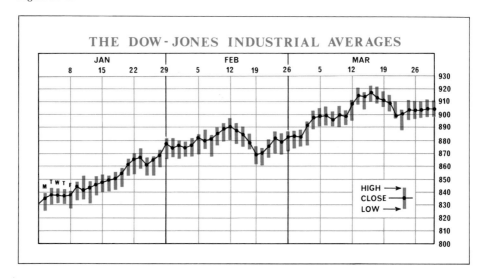

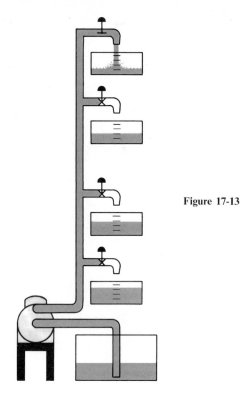

Figure 17-13

and your height in feet and inches, respectively. A chart or graph is not a model but presents facts in a readily understandable manner. *It becomes a model only when used to predict, project, or draw generalized conclusions* about a certain set of conditions. Consider the following example of how facts can be used to develop a chart and a graphical model. An engineer may wish to test a pump and determine how much water it can deliver to different heights, Figure 17-13. Using a stopwatch and calibrated reservoirs at different heights, he measures the amount of water pumped to the different heights in a given time. His test results are plotted as crosses on a chart as shown in Figure 17-14. At this point, the plotted facts are a chart and

Figure 17-14

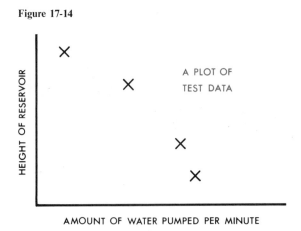

not a model. Only when the engineer makes the assumption that the plotted points represent the typical performance of this or a similar pump under corresponding conditions can the chart be considered to be a graphical model. Once this assumption is made, he can draw a smooth curve throught the points. With this performance curve as a model, the engineer can predict that, if he put additional reservoirs between the actual ones, they would produce results much like those shown by the circles in Figure 17-15. He makes this assumption based on his experience that pumps are likely to behave in a "regular" way. *Now* he is using the graph as an engineering model of the performance of the pump.

The diagram

A model often used by the engineer is the *diagram.* Typical forms of diagrams are the *block diagram,* the *electrical diagram,* and the *free-body diagram.* Some attention should be given to each of these forms.

The *block diagram* is a generalized approach for examining the whole problem, identifying its main components, and describing their relationships and inter-dependencies. This type of diagram is particularly useful in the early stages of design work when representation by mathematical equations would be difficult to accomplish. Illustration 17-4 is an example of a block diagram in which components are drawn as blocks, and the connecting lines between blocks indicate the flow of information in the whole assembly. This type of presentation is widely used to lay out large or complicated systems—particularly those involving servoelectrical and mechanical devices. No attempt is made on the drawing to detail any of the components pictures. They are often referred to as "black boxes"—components whose *function* we know, but whose *details* are not yet designed.

The *energy diagram* is a special form of the block diagram and is used in the study of thermodynamic systems involving mass and energy flow. Some examples of the use of an *energy diagram* are given in Figures 17-16 and 17-17.

The *electrical diagram* is a specialized type of model used in the analysis of electrical problems. This form of *idealized model* represents the existence of particular electrical circuits by utilizing conventional symbols for brevity. These diagrams may be of the most elementary type, or they may be highly complicated and require

Figure 17-15

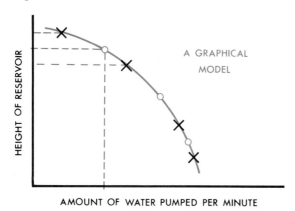

HEIGHT OF RESERVOIR

A GRAPHICAL MODEL

AMOUNT OF WATER PUMPED PER MINUTE

Illustration 17-4
The relation of component parts of a transistorized telemetering system are best shown by means of a block diagram.

many hours of engineering time to prepare. In any case, however, they are representations or models in symbolic language of an electrical assembly.

Figure 17-18 shows an electrical diagram of a photoelectric tube that is arranged to operate a relay. Notice that the diagram details only the essential parts in order to provide for electrical continuity and thus is an idealization that has been selected for purposes of simplification.

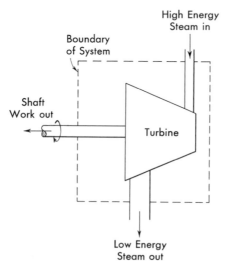

Figure 17-16

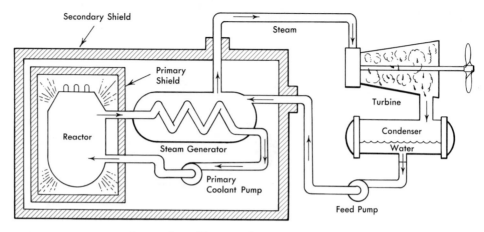

Courtesy: General Dynamics, Electric Boat Division

Figure 17-17 Diagramatic sketch showing how nuclear power can be used to operate a submarine.

The *free-body diagram,* Figure 17-19, is a diagrammatic representation of a physical system which has been removed from all surrounding bodies or systems for purposes of examination and where the equivalent effect of the surrounding bodies is shown as acting on the free body. Such a diagram may be drawn to represent a complex system or any smaller part of it. This form of *idealized model* is most useful in showing the effect of forces that can act upon a system. The free-body diagram will be discussed more fully in Chapter 18.

The scale model

Scale models are used often in various problem solving situations, especially when the system or product is very large and complex or very small and difficult to observe. A *scale model* is a replica, usually three dimensional, of the system, subsystem, or component being studied. It may be constructed to any desired scale relative to the actual design. Such projects as dam or reservoir construction, highway and freeway interchange design, factory layout, and aerodynamic investigations are particularly adaptable to study using scale models.

Scale models are useful for predicting performance because component parts of the model can be moved about to represent changing conditions within the system. Of considerably more usefulness are those scale models which are instrumented and

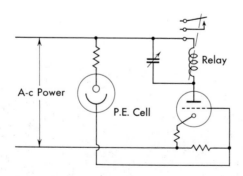

Figure 17-18 A simple photoelectric tube relay circuit.

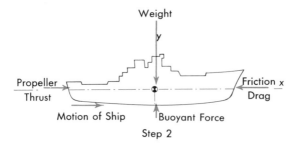

Figure 17-19 Free-body diagram of a ship.

Weight

Propeller
Thrust

Friction x
Drag

Motion of Ship

Buoyant Force

Step 2

subjected to environmental and load conditions that closely resemble reality. In such cases the models are tested and experimental data are recorded by an engineer. From an analysis of these data, predictions of the behavior of the real system can be made.

By using a scale model which can be constructed in a fraction of the time, a final design can be checked for accuracy prior to actual construction. Although scale models often cost many thousands of dollars, they are of relatively minor expense when compared with the total cost of a particular project.

Analog models

Analogs and similes are used to compare something that is unfamiliar to something else that is very familiar. Writers and teachers have found the *simile* to be a very

Illustration 17-5
Exact scale models are valuable aids to the engineer in acquainting others with design and operating parameters. This is particularly true with regard to designs of harbors and transportation systems such as the one pictured here.

effective way to describe an idea. Engineers use analogs in much the same way that teachers use similes. Analogs, however, must provide more than a descriptive picture of what one wants to study; its action should correspond closely with the real thing. It should be *mathematically* similar to it, that is, the same type of mathematical expressions must describe well the action of both systems, the real and the analog.

A vibrating string is an analog of an organ pipe (Figure 17-20) because the sound in an organ pipe behaves quite similarly to the waves traveling along a vibrating string. Under certain assumptions, similar mathematical equations can describe both systems. In other words, we can compare the corresponding actions of the *model* of the organ pipe with a *model* of the vibrating string. It is the *models* that behave exactly alike, *not the real systems*. If these models are "good" models, then, under certain conditions one can perform experiments with the string and draw valid conclusions concerning how the organ pipe would behave. Since one system may be much easier to experiment with than the other, one can work with the easier system and obtain results that are applicable to both.

An example of the use of a very successful analog is the electrical network that forms an analog for complete gas pipeline systems. Using such a model one can predict just what would happen if a lot of gas were suddenly needed at one point along the system. Experiments with the actual pipeline would be very costly and

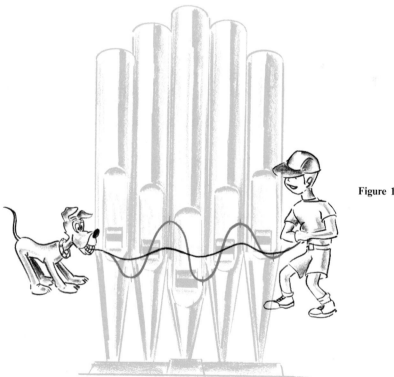

Figure 17-20

might disrupt service. The electrical network analog provides the answers faster, cheaper, and without disturbing anyone.

Analysis

One of the principle purposes of a model is to simplify the problem so that we can calculate the behavior, strength and performance of the design. This is *analysis*.

Analysis is a mental process and, like any useful mental process, requires a store of basic knowledge and the ability to apply that knowledge. Since the amount of knowledge he possesses and his ability to use it are the major measures of a capable engineer, more time is spent at the university in studying analysis than any other subject. Just as one cannot solve a crossword puzzle without a knowledge of words, or make a medical diagnosis without a knowledge of the human body and its functions, so one cannot produce an acceptable engineering design without a basic knowledge of mathematics, physics, and chemistry, and their engineering relatives such as stress analysis, heat transfer, electric network theory, vibration, and so on. Nor can the engineer work effectively without an understanding of how his work effects man and his environment.

Analysis allows the engineer to "experiment on paper." For example, if he is concerned with the behavior of a wheel on a vehicle, his model might be a *rigid, perfectly round* wheel rolling on a *flat, unyielding* surface, Figure 17-21. (Words in italics indicate the assumptions made in the model.)

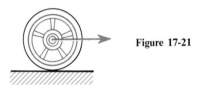

Figure 17-21

The motion of each point on the rim of the model wheel can be expressed by a well-known mathematical relationship called the *cycloid*. By knowing this motion the engineer can calculate the velocity of each point and determine how it varies with time, Figure 17-22. These calculations will enable him to solve for the centrifugal force on the wheel rim and to learn how fast the point makes contact with the ground.

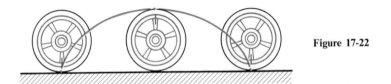

Figure 17-22

This elementary problem illustrates two important restrictions of engineering analysis: First, an equation usually describes only a very limited part of the function of the design, even in the case of a simple design such as a wheel. Second, an equation usually cannot describe *exactly* the action that takes place in the model. For example, we make the assumption that the wheel is perfectly rigid. This implies that it does not deform when it touches the ground. Such an assumption may be reasonably accurate in the case of a steel train wheel rolling on a steel rail, but it is probably a poor assumption to make for the rubber-tired wheels of an automobile.

Just as a carpenter's toolbox may contain several different saws, chisels, and hammers, so the tools of analysis can be divided into several categories such as the following:

Mathematical Tools	Mathematics
	Statistics
	Computer operations
Material Tools	Chemistry
	Materials and metallurgy
Physical Tools	Solid mechanics
	Fluid mechanics
	Electricity
	Thermodynamics
Environmental Tools	Mechanics of man
	Economics
	Social sciences
	Ecological sciences

It is obvious that we cannot describe all of these subjects in this text. Many books have been written about each of them. However some have been discussed earlier and others will be considered in Chapter 18.

Testing

The construction of a model and its analysis are based on assumptions, and these assumptions have to be verified.

One way in which the engineer can accomplish this is by the use of experiments. Experiments do not necessarily require construction of the entire design but only those portions of it that are important for the evaluation of the particular assumption. Components of a design are frequently tested instead of testing the entire design. If, in the design of a pipeline, the strength of the pipe is questionable, the engineer could obtain short sections of the pipe for testing. In the laboratory, liquid of appropriate density and pressure could be pumped through these sections of pipe to simulate the flowing fluid in the line. By measuring how much the pipe expands under the pressure and observing whether the results check the calculations of his model, the engineer can verify if he has selected the proper pipe for his design.

It is important to remember that the value of the experiment is in the checking of the validity of the assumptions, not in checking the accuracy of the algebra. There is no need to run a rigid wheel on a rigid flat surface in order to prove the validity of the cycloidal motion of a point on the rim. If, however, the equation is to show the motion of a rubber-tired vehicle, then it may be well to run a rubber-tired wheel over a rigid surface to see how closely the cycloid does describe the motion of the nonrigid wheel.

For testing one needs a model, a testing facility, and an arrangement of instruments suitable to measure what occurs during the test. Above all, one needs a test plan, just as a traveler needs directions in order to get to a desired destination. There is no sense in beginning a test without an objective and a plan for achieving the results necessary to satisfy that objective.

To test a completed design, the engineer should specify the characteristics that are most important and the instruments to be used for measuring these characteristics. In selecting the instruments the engineer must ask himself the question: "Does it provide the accuracy I need?" There being no such thing as *absolute* accuracy, the engineer must also know the probable error in the measurement. Only if that accuracy is greater than his allowable error is the instrument suitable. He is concerned also with the effect of the measurement on the performance itself. This is very important in the case of small, intricate devices requiring great accuracy. According to Heisenberg[8] we cannot measure any characteristic without affecting the system. (We all know this to be true from our experience in a physician's office. Our pulse rate and blood pressure quite often change as soon as the doctor starts to measure them. Whether this is psychologically or physically conditioned does not really matter; the fact is, the measurement *does* influence the performance.)

The conditions under which tests are to be conducted must be defined; these must include all of the important conditions of the design. A list of characteristics that might be tested include start-up and shut-down conditions, operation under partial and full load,[9] operation under the failure of auxiliary equipment, operator errors, material selection, and many, many others.

There are five frequently used objectives for engineering tests. These objectives determine: (1) quality assurance of materials and subassemblies, (2) performance, (3) life, endurance, and safety, (4) human acceptance, and (5) effects of the environment. Some tests are required on every design and in certain cases all of the tests are needed. In general, when the analysis has been completed a prototype model of the design will be constructed. Usually this model is subjected to all of the necessary tests. Once the prototype has passed the tests and the design has gone into the production stage, each final product may be subjected to selected tests. In this case, the tests are primarily for the purpose of assuring product uniformity and reliability.

Prototype testing generally applies only to products which go into mass production, such as the automobile wheel. When the design is for a "one-of-a-kind" item such as a pipeline, one will make as many tests as possible on raw materials and subassemblies to detect design errors before construction is completed. However, final tests on the complete design still will be necessary *to ensure* its safety and acceptability.

Quality assurance tests

Anyone who has selected wood at a lumber yard knows that the quality of raw material varies substantially from one piece to the next. It is less well known that such variations occur also in other materials, such as metals, ceramics, and polymers. Variation in these materials may be as great as the variation between the pieces of wood at the lumber yard and, just as the lumberman will provide more uniform

[8] Werner Heisenberg [German Physicist, 1901–   ] showed that, since observation must always necessarily affect the event being observed, this interference will lead to a fundamental limit on the accuracy of the observation. *Encyclopedia of Science*, Harper, New York (1967).

[9] Whenever we talk about *load,* we mean this in the general sense to include such things as force, pressure, voltage, vibration, amplitude, temperature, and corrosive effects.

wood at a higher price, so one can get a more uniform steel, aluminum, or plexiglas at a higher price (to pay for preselection by the manufacturer). Typical variations in the strength of metals can be found in engineering handbooks.

The competent designer should account for this type of variation—either by designing the part so that it will perform satisfactorily with the least desirable (weakest) material or by prescribing tests that would ensure that only premium materials be used. Both approaches add to the cost. The conservative design may require more material and more weight; the testing process may require the use of more expensive material, or the extra cost may result from the testing and the discarding of unusable pieces.

Manufacturers, like lumber dealers, have realized the need for uniformity in engineering materials. For this reason, materials with more uniform properties than standard, or with guaranteed minimum properties, are available (at higher prices). For example, one can buy electrical carbon resistors in three ranges: The first grade, indicated by a gold band, varies a maximum of 5 per cent from its indicated value; the second grade (silver band) may vary as much as 10 per cent; and the standard product (no band) may vary as much as 20 per cent. Typically a silver-band resistor will cost twice as much as the standard, and the gold four times as much. Quality assurance includes the checking of dimensions of completed parts (a type of inspection routine in most modern machine shops), tests on the quality of joints between two members whether welded, brazed, soldered, riveted, or glued, and the continuity of electrical circuits.

Performance tests

What has been said about raw materials is also true for components and sub-assemblies which the designer may wish to include in his design. Electric motors, pumps, amplifiers, heat exchangers, pressure vessels, and similar items are designed to certain manufacturing standards. The products will usually be constructed at least as well as the manufacturer claims. However, if the quality of the total design depends critically upon the specifications of a subassembly, then it is best to inspect and test that subassembly separately before it is included in the construction. This is particularly true for one-of-a-kind designs, such as space capsules. Since performance of the capsule is critically dependent upon that of its components, the designer must specify a series of tests that will be made at the manufacturers' plants to assure performance. He may, in fact, personally supervise the testing.

A performance test simply shows whether a design does what it is supposed to do. It measures the skill of the engineer and the validity of the assumptions made in his analyses.

Performance testing generally does not wait until the design is completed. It follows step by step with the design. For example, the heat shield of the space capsule is tested in the supersonic wind tunnel to see if it can withstand the aerodynamic heating for which it was designed; the parachute is tested to see if it supports the capsule at just the right speed; structural members are tested for strength and stiffness; and instruments are checked to show if they indicate what they are supposed to measure.

Performance tests may require special testing apparatus, such as supersonic wind tunnels and space simulation chambers. They always need careful planning and instrumentation to assure that the tests measure what is really needed—a proof of the validity of the design.

Life, endurance, and safety tests

We know that machines, like people, age. One of the most important and most difficult tests to gain meaningful data from are the life tests, tests that tell how long a product will survive in service and whether it can take excessive loads, misoperations, and other punishment without failure. It is rarely possible to carry out life tests accurately, for one seldom has the time to subject the prototype to the same period of aging that the real part will experience in actual service. In some instances, accelerated "life" tests are used. For example, paints and other surface protections may be exposed to the actions of sunlight, wind, rain, snow, or salt-water spray for months or even years. In this way a body of knowledge relating to the "life" of these surface finishes slowly develops, but a final selection by the engineer may be delayed considerably. Therefore these tests must be accelerated and the engineer does so by increasing the load, by applying the load more rapidly, or by subjecting the design to a more severe environment. However, he is never quite sure how accurately these short-term "life" tests *really* represent the effect of the aging conditions and how their results should be interpreted. Usually, this is done (in the case of mechanical tests) by making tests on several specimens, each at a different degree of overload. The length of life of each part tested is then plotted as a function of the applied load, and the resulting curve is extropolated to the maximum load that the part is expected to endure in real life.

If different types of loading are applied to the part, such as pressure, temperature, and vibration, it may be necessary to make separate tests with overloads in each one of these areas to see how they extrapolate to "true life." It may be desirable to use overloads in combination and observe if the combined effect is different from the sum of the effects of the individual loads. Very often two combined loads have a much more serious effect on the part than the arithmetic sum of the separate effects of the two loads. This is called *synergistic behavior.*

We again use the automobile wheel for an example of "life" testing. It is reasonable to assume that a good automobile tire and wheel should survive without failure at least 50,000 mi under normal loads, at speeds of 50 mi/hr. This means that the tire must be tested at that load for at least 1000 hr—a period in excess of 40 days. Such a test may indeed be possible and, in fact, is often performed on new tire designs. The designer will want to know the effects of overload, of speeds higher than 50 mi/hr, of curves, rough roads, under- and overinflation, and of the effect of very high or very low temperatures. It is easy to see that one needs a battery of testing machines to find out all one wants to know within a reasonable period of time.

Even though the test part may pass the predicted life during the test, the test is usually not terminated, but is continued until the part actually fails. This then becomes an endurance test, and it determines the excess life of the part. Since the life of each part is likely to differ, and since not every part can be "life" tested, it is essential to know the excess "life" of the average part. Since there is a statistical variability between parts, the engineer will want to know not only the *average* excess life but also the range of *variation* in this lifetime.

Instead of measuring the endurance of a part under a constant load, the engineer may decide to increase the load until the part fails. This failure load will be higher than the design load if the part is properly designed. The ratio between the failure load and the design load is called the *factor of safety*. Factors of safety may be quite low where parts are very carefully manufactured, where excessive weight is undesirable, or where their failure causes no serious hardship. However, where human life is at stake, factors of safety must be so chosen that no variation in materials or workmanship, or simplified assumption in the designer's calculations, can possibly make the part unsafe and cause failure under normal operating loads.

Because the engineer has the responsibility to see that no one is injured as a consequence of his design, he must also consider the possibility of accidental or thoughtless misoperation of the design. For example, the automobile tire may be underinflated, it may be operated under too heavy a load, at too high a speed, or on a rough road, and yet it should not fail catastrophically.

Human acceptance tests

For a long time the designers of consumer goods have been concerned with the appearance and acceptability of their product to the buyer. It is unfortunate that in many instances they have appealed more often to the buyer's baser instincts, such as pride, greed, and desire for status, rather than to his sense of quality and beauty. Engineers, on the other hand, have been concerned too little with the interaction of their designs with the people who buy or use them. They have often failed to ask themselves whether the physical, mental, and emotional needs and limitations of the human being permit him to operate the machine in the *best* possible way. In the past engineers have all too often assumed that the human body is sufficiently adaptable to operate any kind of control lever or wheel. Although the adaptability of people is truly astonishing, we now know that for maximum efficiency levers and wheels must be carefully designed, that the forces necessary to operate them must be neither too large nor too small, that the operator should be able to "feel" the effect that he is producing, and that the use of the device or design should not tire him physically. A new design, then, should be tested with real people. Such tests usually cannot be performed by an engineer alone, but require the aid of others such as industrial psychologists and/or human factors engineers.

Those who have studied metal processes have found that a man's attention span is short, that he cannot be asked continually to peer at a gage or work piece unless things are "happening" to it. It is also known that warnings are better heeded if they are audible than if they are visual. If they are visual, a bright red light or a blinking light which draws the operator's attention is much better than the movement of a dial to some position that has been marked "unacceptable." In recent years we have learned that our emotional responses play a major part in our daily lives, that whether we are elated or depressed can affect the quality of our work and the attention we give to the instruments we are asked to observe, or the levers we are asked to operate. In turn, our emotions are influenced by color, beauty, or attractive design—in short, by our opinion of the design.

The purpose of acceptability testing is to see whether the design meets the physical, mental, and emotional requirements of the average person for whom it is designed. Since the "average" person can never be found, it is essential that a series of tests be made by and with different people, and that these observations be used to make whatever changes are necessary to make the device as acceptable as possible within the technical and economic constraints.

Environmental tests

The environment is the aggregate of all conditions that surround the design under operating conditions. It may be wind and weather; it may be the soil in which it is buried or the chemicals in which it is immersed; it may be the vacuum of outer space or an intense field of nuclear or electromagnetic radiation. In general, the operating environment is different from the normal environment in the laboratory in which the tests are made. Sometimes the effects of the environment are not important, but more frequently the environment can strongly affect the functioning and life of the part. Therefore environmental testing has become an important part of the final testing of most new products.

We have already mentioned how paints and other surface finishes are exposed to sun, wind, and rain for long periods of time, thereby developing a considerable body of knowledge concerning how such surface finishes behave under both normal and unusual weather conditions. Similarly, an extensive body of knowledge exists on how chemicals deteriorate or "corrode" construction materials. These and other environmental factors are under continuing study. Therefore, unless the engineer is faced with an unusual environment, he can often (but not always) find pertinent information in the literature to predict how a particular environment is going to affect his design.

However, there are many instances where additional tests are needed. Tests are particularly important where two or more environmental effects work together, such as moisture and heat, or chemicals and vibrations. The result of such effects may not be predictable from either of the individual effects acting by themselves. Thus we know that a vibrating environment in a salt-spray atmosphere can cause corrosion fatigue at a rate far higher than that which might have been predicted from either the vibration or the salt water corrosion taken independently.

With the advent of space travel, one of the most intensively studied types of environment is *space*. When away from the earth's atmosphere, a body in space will be in a nearly complete vacuum, but it will be exposed to a variety of types

Illustration 17-6
During the development phase, environmental testing is carried out on all rocket engines, such as the one pictured here.

of radiation and to meteoric dust from which the earth's atmosphere normally protects it. The radiation effects may be severe enough to seriously attack electronic circuits and cause deterioration of transistors and other electronic devices. The meteoric dust, though generally quite fine, travels with speeds of 10,000 to 70,000 mi/hr and has sufficient energy to penetrate some of the strongest materials. Within the last few years some ways have been found to simulate in the laboratory both the high radiation and the presence of meteoric dust, and (on earth) to subject space equipment to these kinds of attack.

The report

Reporting is the process of information transfer. For the engineer the ability to write and speak clearly is most essential, for however good he may be as an analyst or experimenter, if he cannot convey his ideas clearly, concisely, and interestingly to others, then he is like a stranger in a foreign country whose people cannot understand him. The transmittal of information includes writing, drawing, and speaking. Particular attention will be given in this chapter to the preparation of technical papers and to the oral presentation of ideas.

Written reports

There may have been a time when engineers were not required to write reports, that is, when most of them worked with small groups of people and they could let their ideas be known by word of mouth or by circulating an occasional sketch or drawing. These times are gone for all but a very few engineers. Most engineers today work in large organizations. They cannot be "heard" unless their ideas are written down in proposals and their findings are recorded in reports. This does not mean that the spoken word and the drawing or sketch have lost their importance, but rather that they must be supplemented by the written word. Therefore, it is important for the engineer to know how best to communicate his ideas to a reader; how to put his best foot forward with a client whom he may never see, or with the company vice president to whom he will report.

Although the engineer's writing is often directed toward other engineers, occasionally he may be called upon to write for an audience unfamiliar with technical terms. Then he must be able to express his thoughts in terminology that can be understood by an intelligent layman. During the years to come, when engineers must solve the problems of society, such as the urban crisis, air and water pollution, transportation, and so on, the need for cooperation between technical and nontechnical persons becomes increasingly important. The engineer must learn to communicate with people of all types of background, and he must be able to state his views clearly and concisely.

So many books have been written about the art of writing, about grammar, syntax, and style, that it would be presumptuous to try here to summarize them in a few words. However, we would like to quote a few phrases from a small but exceedingly valuable book on style.[10] These authors recommend some 21 rules, among which are the following:

- ☐ Place yourself in the background. Write in a way that draws the reader's attention to the sense and substance of the writing.
- ☐ Write in a way that comes naturally. But do not assume that because you have acted naturally, your product is without flaws.
- ☐ Write with nouns and verbs, not with adjectives and adverbs.
- ☐ Revise and rewrite.
- ☐ Do not overstate, because it causes your reader to lose confidence in your judgment.

If we can assume that we know how to write, how to express our thoughts in words and sentences that are clear to the reader, we still need to know how to organize our ideas. Organization is important to the writer so that his ideas will be presented in a logical sequence and to assure that the important things are included in his writing. Organization is important to the reader so that he can follow the presentation and conclusions of the author easily, so that he need not jump back and forth in his thoughts (a tiring exercise for any reader).

Over the years certain minimum conventions (standards) have been established concerning the writing of engineering reports and proposals, conventions that are not binding but have proven to be useful guidelines for technical writers. Let us look at the typical organization of such a report.

Organization of a technical report

Abstract
Table of Contents
Table of Figures
Acknowledgments
Nomenclature

Introduction

Body of report:
    Analysis
    Design
    Experiments
    Test Results

Discussion
Summary and Conclusions

References
Appendixes

The essential features of the technical report are shown in italics. The other items *may* appear in the report if appropriate.

Although it appears first in the report, the *abstract* is usually the last item to be written. It is a summary of the summary, containing in less than a page a statement of the problem, the way in which it was solved, and the results and conclusions that were drawn from the work. One may well ask, "Why repeat the contents of the report first in the summary and then again in the abstract?" One reason is the variation in the interest of the readers. One man may have only a general interest in the report and is satisfied with a well-written abstract; the second, wanting to go somewhat deeper, may wish to read the summary and conclusions,

---

[10]Strunk, William, Jr., and E. B. White, *The Elements of Style,* Macmillan, New York (1959).

and only a few (those particularly interested in the subject) may be sufficiently interested to read the entire report. Yet, it is important that all of these readers obtain a clear picture of why it was done and what was accomplished. Another reason is the need for some repetition in communication. This attitude is exemplified in the philosophy of the successful southern preacher who, when asked why his sermons were so successful, answered, "Well, first Ah tells 'em what Ah's goin' to tell 'em— then Ah tells 'em,—then Ah tell's 'em what Ah done told 'em."

The *Introduction* tells what the problem is and why it was studied. It will discuss the *background* for the study, the literature that pertains to the subject, the solutions that have been tried before, and why these are not adequate for the present investigation. It is here that the majority of the literature references are mentioned. If there are three or less, it may be adequate to list them in footnotes. However, when there are more than three references, it is common practice to list them together in a reference section at the end of the report.

The *body of the report* may have any of a number of titles and may, in fact, consist of several chapters with different titles. The author has considerable latitude here and he should make use of the titles that appear to him to be appropriate. For example, if the work was essentially analytical in nature, he may wish to entitle the section "Analysis," or he may wish to be more specific and to discuss first the assumptions that were made, then the construction of the model, the pertinent equations, and finally the solution of the equations. If the report contains information on experiments, the writer may wish to discuss the experimental apparatus, the construction of the test model, and the performance and organization of the test. He may then follow it up with a chapter discussing the test results.

The preparation of the body of the report requires considerable judgment. The engineer must provide enough information to give the reader a very clear picture of what was done and to allow him to arrive at the *conclusions* of the report. On the other hand, it is essential that the reader not be bored by unnecessary detail. Many writers find it appropriate to give only the major outline of their work in the body of the report and to relegate all important but minor details to appendixes at the end of the report. This technique gives a report a highly desirable conciseness.

Young engineers often feel impelled to write their reports in the same chronological sequence that the work was accomplished. This is both unnecessary and undesirable, for very rarely does one proceed in a straight line from the beginning to the finish of his work. Rather one detours down side roads and retraces one's steps. If the report follows the same path of procedures, it will be very difficult to follow. It is much more important to present the data in the sequence that the engineer would have used in his work if he had been knowledgeable of all the difficulties and errors in the beginning. The actual chronological sequence of the study is of little interest to anyone but the author.

It is usually expedient to illustrate the body of the report with tables, charts, graphs, sketches, drawings, and photographs. The old adage that "one picture is worth a thousand words" is often true, but care should be taken to avoid unnecessary illustrations.

Since it is customary to limit the body of the report to facts, the *discussion* section permits a review of the author's opinion. It is as if he were able to stand back and look at the work and say why this or that was done, to speculate on why the results are the way they are, and what they might have been if the experiment had been done differently. The discussion sections should anticipate the type of questions the listener would ask and attempt to answer them as forthrightly and honestly as possible.

The *summary and conclusion* is, as the name implies, a concise statement of the work done—including goals, background, analysis, experiment, and a review of the work accomplished. The concise statement of the conclusions reached is most important. For the reader, the conclusions should be the "pot of gold" at the end of the rainbow, the information that will be directly useful to him. Therefore, the development of meaningful conclusions, well stated, is one of the most important parts in writing a report. They should include all that is new and important, and yet they should be so stated that they leave no question in the reader's mind as to what is incontrovertible fact and what is opinion. Wherever possible the writer should make estimates of the accuracy and repeatability of his results. It is often useful to number the conclusions, much as a patent attorney will number the claims in a patent application.

After the conclusions have been written, the author should write the abstract as if it were a summary of the "summary and conclusions" just finished. Only the most important conclusions need be included in the abstract.

A note on the convention for *references*. In most engineering reports, it is now customary to list the last name of the senior author first, followed by his initials, and followed by initials and name of coauthors. The names are then followed by the title of the report and this by the name of the journal in which it was published, or the publisher and year, in case it is a book. Typical references are as follows:

Smith, A. B., and T. D. Jones, "Air Pollution at the North Pole," *J. Arctic Society,* **15**:6 (1964), 317–20.

Beakley, G. C., and H. W. Leach, *Careers in Engineering and Technology,* New York: The Macmillan Company, 1969.

The formal report of a feasibility study may often be in the form of a proposal which suggests how the problem should be pursued. There are many similarities between an engineering report and a proposal, but their purposes are quite different. The report exists to present the results of a study and to present them so clearly and completely that other engineers can use them as stepping stones in the further development of engineering knowledge and use. The proposal, on the other hand, proposes to sell an idea—tries to convince a client or a superior to make funds available for the preliminary design. Thus, while the report is written for a general audience, not necessarily all engineers, the proposal is always written for just one person or organization. A proposal is an attempt to sell an idea. Therefore, what is good advice for the salesman is also good advice for the proposal writer: *try to put yourself in the position of the client.* Find out what his needs and wants are and see to what extent your idea meets these needs. Find out who else competes for the funds which might be used to further your idea and emphasize those special points that make your idea or talents superior to that of others.

There is no general format for the organization of a proposal, but the following order is frequently used.

Typical organization of a technical proposal

Technical Part
    Introduction
    Objectives
    Background
    Method of Approach
    Qualifications

Management Part
    Statement of Work
    Schedule and Reporting
    Cost Estimate
    [Other special paragraphs, i.e.,
        Rights to inventions
        Security provisions
        Time at which work can begin
        Time limit on proposal acceptance]

The proposal is often split into a technical part which discusses the technical aspects and a management part which considers the financial and legal aspects. The first part of the technical portion introduces the reason for the proposed work and clarifies why its solution should be of importance to the potential client. The introduction is followed by a brief statement of the objectives, that is, what the author hopes to be able to achieve by performing the work. This may be followed, if appropriate, by a study of background information, such as the literature surveyed, to indicate that the author is well informed on the subject. Following this, a plan or method of approach is suggested which shows the client that the author has a well-thought-out plan of how he is going to proceed with the work. The method of approach should indicate not only what the author wishes to do, but also what results he expects to obtain from the various portions of his program, what he is going to do if the outcome of the results is as expected, and what if it is not. In conclusion, the technical part of the proposal should include the qualifications of the author or his organization to perform the work.

The management part of the proposal is a precise specification of the work—what it costs and what it entails. This is followed by the schedule for the work, including the time and type of reports to be presented, and by a cost estimate.

Although many young engineers may believe that fancy covers and big words can sell proposals, it is a fact that the most successful proposals are those that convince the reader of the sincerity and expertise of the writer and his ability to accomplish the objective.

Oral communication

Although most engineers like to talk, too few enjoy speaking. Talking is casual, random, and unrehearsed, but speaking requires a plan, an organization, and practice. Public speaking, like writing, is an art of increasing necessity for the successful engineer; an art that he must perfect if he is to succeed in his profession and his society. In his professional life the engineer will be called upon to present his ideas clearly and concisely to his peers, his supervisors, or the board of directors of the company for which he is working. If he has conducted research or development, he may wish to present the results at a meeting of his professional society. As an effective member of civic, social, and religious organizations, he will want to express his opinions clearly and convincingly.

There is an appreciable difference between effective written and spoken words. The reader can proceed as quickly or as slowly as he wishes, or retrace his steps,

Illustration 17-7
The ability to give a technical presentation which is both informative and interesting is a quality that every engineer should endeavor to improve.

and in this way absorb difficult and complicated thoughts. The listener, on the other hand, cannot control the speed of the speaker nor can he retrace his step if he has lost the thread of the conversation. It is important, therefore, for the speaker to retain the interest of his listeners by the conviction of his presentation and by the presentation of a forthright, orderly, and logical sequence of thoughts. The most effective speakers do not try to present more than two or three important ideas in one speech, and they get these ideas across by using clear logic, simple illustrations, and by similes or analogies, knowing that different listeners have different ways of seeing things.

In preparing a speech or oral presentation, first make an outline of the principal ideas that you wish to project. Place them in a logical sequence and prepare your illustrations and similes, but do not attempt to write every word of your speech. Few things are more likely to put an audience to sleep than a speaker who reads his speech. If you tend to be nervous, memorize the first sentence or two, which will get you started, and then use notes only as reminders for the sequence of your talk and to make sure that you have said everything that you wanted to say. Since an audience can best follow simple ideas, it is rarely advisable to present mathematical developments in a speech unless it is to an audience of mathematicians. Nor is it often useful or desirable to delve into the circuitous routes that were used during the development of the idea or the research that is being presented. *The audience is interested in the results and in the usefulness of the results for their own purposes.* All of us are interested primarily in our own life and work, and the better a speaker can convince us that his findings are useful to us, the more successful we believe him to be. Therefore in preparing a speech, first, find out to whom you will be speaking, and then ask yourself what it is that you can give to the audience that is useful to them. What will they remember after you have stopped speaking?

The successful speech, like a successful athletic contest, requires practice and rehearsal. In practicing, use a "sparring partner"—a person not afraid to criticize or interrupt and ask questions when something is not clear. Go over a speech with your "sparring partner" again and again, until you are sure that you could present it even if you lost all of your notes.

Problems

17-1. After reviewing the ecological needs of your home town, state three problems that should be solved.

17-2. Give three examples of *feedback* that existed prior to A.D. 1800.

17-3. Talk to an engineer who is working in design or development in industry. Describe two situations in his work where he has not been able to rely on *theoretical textbook solutions* to solve his problems. Why was he forced to resort to other means to solve the problems?

17-4. Describe an incident where an individual or group abandoned their course of action because it was found that they were spending time working on the wrong problem.

17-5. List the properties of a kitchen electric mixer.

17-6. List the properties of the automobile that you would like to own.

17-7. Make a matrix analysis of the possible solutions to the problem of removing dirt from clothes.

17-8. For ten minutes solo brainstorm the problem of disposal of home wastepaper. List your ideas for solution.

17-9. List five types of models that are routinely used by the average American citizen.

17-10. Diagram the model of the football play that made the longest yardage gain for your team this year.

17-11. Draw an energy system of an ordinary gas-fired hot water heater.

17-12. Draw an energy system representing a simple refrigeration cycle.

17-13. Draw an energy system representing a "perpetual motion" machine.

17-14. Draw an electrical circuit diagram containing two single-pole, double-throw switches in such manner that a single light bulb may be turned on or off at either switch location.

17-15. Arrange three single-pole, single-throw switches in an electrical circuit containing three light bulbs in such a manner that one switch will turn on one of the bulbs, another switch will turn on two of the bulbs, and the third switch will turn on all three bulbs.

17-16. Draw a free-body diagram of the concrete test block that is being crushed in the test machine, Illustration 17-8.

17-17. Draw a free-body diagram of the exercise device that has been designed to help keep astronauts in good physical shape in the weightlessness of space, Illustration 17-9.

17-18. Draw a free-body diagram of the motorcycle, Illustration 17-10.

17-19. Draw a free-body diagram of the electric motor, Illustration 17-11. What is the relationship of the force exerted against the top hook and that exerted against one of the lower hooks?

17-20. Draw a free-body diagram of the nut being tightened, Illustration 17-12.

17-21. Draw a free-body diagram of the boom that is located on the "pipe side" of the tractor, Illustration 17-13.

17-22. Draw a free-body diagram of the forces that are being exerted on the "Phillips head" screwdriver, Illustration 17-14.

17-23. Draw a free-body diagram of the wingless, turbine-powered flying craft, Illustration 17-15.

17-24. Draw a free-body diagram of the horizontal test beam that is being tested, Illustration 17-16.

17-25. Draw a free-body diagram of the four-legged quadruped machine, Illustration 17-17. The right front leg of the unit is controlled by the operator's right arm, its left front leg by his left arm, its right rear leg by his right leg, and its left rear leg by his left leg. This research prototype is 11 ft high and weighs 3000 lb.

17-26. Describe three situations where a scale model would be the most appropriate kind of idealized model to use.

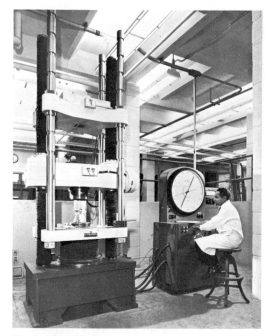

Illustration 17-8

Illustration 17-9

Illustration 17-10

Illustration 17-11

Illustration 17-12

Illustration 17-13

Illustration 17-14

Illustration 17-15

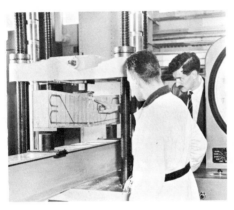

Illustration 17-16

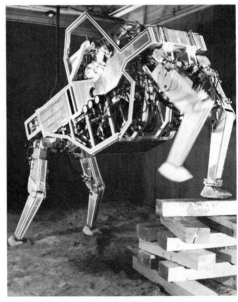

Illustration 17-17

17-27. Give three examples of analogs.

17-28. Describe an example where quality assurance tests were vital to the success of the project.

17-29. Under what conditions are performance tests impractical?

17-30. Why is it necessary for the engineer to consider the synergistic behavior of the materials that he is using?

18

Engineering analysis

Analysis has been described as the engineer's toolbox. This chapter will consider some of the tools within this box which were subdivided in Chapter 17 into mathematical, material, physical, and environmental tools. Nearly 80 per cent of the engineering curriculum is used in learning how to use them. Here we will present only a taste—*we will let you feel the heft of the hammer.*

The mathematical tools

The language of engineering is *mathematics* and to be an effective engineer one must learn to use its language. Although in theory one can describe everything with words of the English language, English is, in fact, cumbersome and frequently ill-adapted to express *precisely* the "physics" of a situation, as can be done with a mathematical equation. Consider, for example, a ball resting on a flat horizontal surface as in Figure 18-1. The force of gravity (W) acts downward and the surface resists upward on the ball (N) so that it does not move. In this case the English language is adequate to describe that the two forces act along the same line and are of equal magnitude. However, consider the same ball resting on an incline against a stop which prevents its moving down the incline, Figure 18-2. Here we must consider the action of three forces: the force of gravity pulling down (W), the normal force from the incline (F_1), and the resisting force from the stop (F_2). Since the ball is not moving, we know that these three forces must somehow balance, and that to do so the magnitudes of the supporting forces will vary depending on the angle of the incline with the horizontal (θ). We can say in general terms that if this angle becomes larger, the

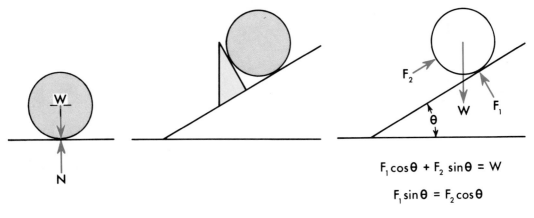

$$F_1 \cos\theta + F_2 \sin\theta = W$$
$$F_1 \sin\theta = F_2 \cos\theta$$

Figure 18-1   Figure 18-2   Figure 18-3

force from the plane (F_1) decreases, and the force on the stop (F_2) increases, but just exactly how they are related to one another would be most difficult to describe using words alone. Yet in mathematical terms the relationship between these forces can be expressed simply and easily, Figure 18-3.

The mathematics of engineering is concerned primarily with two subjects: *the relations between forces and body shapes,* including geometry, trigonometry, and vector analysis, and *the description of things that change*—the realm of calculus.

The ball resting on the incline is an example of the first subject. Others will be found later. To get an idea about the second, let us consider a moving object, such as a car on the road. If a person does not have a speedometer, a simple way to tell how fast he is going is to time himself between mileposts. If, for example, he had measured 72 sec between two posts a mile apart (Figure 18-4), his *average* speed would have been (1 mi/72 secs)(3600 sec/hr) = 50 mi/hr. Knowing the average speed does not tell him if his speed was steady over the mile or if he had driven at varying speeds (Figure 18-5). If there had been a distance marker every one fifth mile, and he had recorded the time at each, his average speed in each fifth of the mile might have looked like the horizontal bars in the second graph, Figure 18-6. This is closer, but still not a good approximation to the actual curve. The only way that this method would give a good speed reading would be to place markers every few feet and record the time interval at each. Such an action would result in the "fine" averaging shown in Figure 18-7. As the time intervals get smaller and smaller the actual local velocity of the car is established more accurately by taking the ratio of a very small distance at that location to the very short time used to traverse it. It is called the *local derivative* of position *with respect to time,* or the *local time rate of change* of position.

Note that we now have an expression of *local* (not average) *velocity* in terms of position and time. Mathematicians have developed methods to compute the resultant velocities once the mathematical expression (formula) or graph of the vehicle location is known. This concept can be extended easily to find the *acceleration*

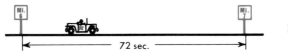

Figure 18-4

72 sec.

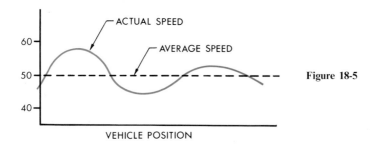

Figure 18-5

VEHICLE POSITION

which engineers need to compute engine torque and power consumption. This type of mathematical solution is known as *calculus* and is a very powerful concept indeed.

The very small items, whose ratio forms the derivative, are often called *differentials,* and the whole process is called *differentiation.* The inverse process—which for example allows one to find the vehicle position if he knows its velocity, is called *integration.*

Derivatives need not always be taken "with respect to time." For example, the amount of heat flowing from the hot to the cold side of a piece of metal that is heated on one side depends upon the *derivative* of temperature *with respect to position,* that is, the ratio dT/dx, Figure 18-8.

Mathematical analysis is rarely if ever able to depict exactly the physical behavior of *real* materials and devices. In fact, even if it were, such exactitude would be of little value to the engineer, since each piece of material differs from all others (even if these differences are only microscopic); and at best one can talk only about *statistical average behavior* and attempt to estimate how much any one sample may vary from this average.

Statistics relates experiment to analysis. It furnishes the numbers used in the analysis and tells how reliable they are. If, for example, a large number of "pull tests" have shown that the average failure load for the samples tested was 100,000 lb, and the failures were distributed as shown in Figure 18-9, then we can expect ten samples in 100 to fail at as low a load as 75,000 lb and 15 to survive a load of 125,000 lb.

The engineer, who can rarely ask that every production item be tested, must decide what kind of failure rate he can tolerate and proceed with his design accordingly. For unimportant items, easily replaced, he may well accept a 1 or 2 per cent failure rate. However, if failure of the part were to endanger human life, he would want to make sure that its *probability* of failure is very low and that it is tested to full load and beyond before it leaves the factory.

The *digital computer* has become an almost indispensible tool for today's engineer. Recognizing this, computer manufacturers have built small office units. These are either independent, and thereby limited in speed and in their capacity to store numbers, or they are connected by telephone or cable to a large-size computer. Some of these large computers work so fast that they can do hundreds of thousands of

Figure 18-6

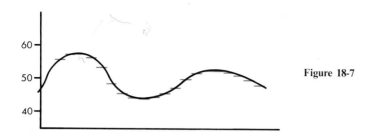

Figure 18-7

computations while the designer's answer is being typed out and before he is ready with his next problem. Therefore several persons can share a single computer—provided that the computer is so constructed that it can keep all of the problems separated. This procedure is called *time sharing*.

But what can a computer do that makes it so valuable to the engineer? Is it some type of ultrafast adding machine or perhaps is it a mysterious device that answers questions that are put to it? It is really neither of these—although it is frequently used for both of these purposes. If one looks beyond the dazzle of flashing lights and whirling tapes, he can identify four primary functions in any modern computer:

1. The ability to store thousands of numbers and to recall them rapidly from storage when needed. The storage is appropriately called *memory*. The memory not only stores the numbers on which the computer operates and the results of its calculations, but also stores the *program* that tells it what kind of calculations to perform. Therefore the same program can be used again and again with different data, without having to repeat the original instructions to the machine.
2. An *arithmetic* center which works much like a desk calculator, primarily by adding (or subtracting) numbers. It can do this so rapidly—an addition may take as little as a few millionths of a second—that even very lengthy calculations are made in an extremely short time.
3. The capability of comparing two numbers and of making a *decision* based upon the outcome. This is one of the most important attributes of the computer. How this works will be demonstrated in the example below.
4. Communication or *input-output* facilities that allow one to "talk" to the computer, to give it instructions, to feed it numbers with which to compute, and to receive its answers in readable form.

Since the computer works only with numbers, the instructions in the program (such as "add number x to number y") must also be translated into appropriate numbers. In the early days of computers, the programmer was required to accomplish

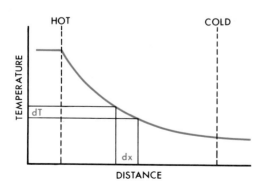

Figure 18-8

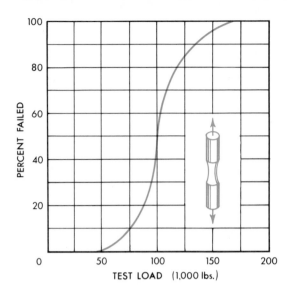

Figure 18-9

these translations himself. To do so he had to know the internal computer language. Today, computers are able to accomplish their own translation, provided that the program is written in a "standard" language. These standard languages are easy to learn because they are written in almost the same way that one would normally express the steps of the program in written English. Among the most frequently used standard languages are FORTRAN, ALGOL, and BASIC.

Let us examine how a typical computer program would work on this problem (reportedly more than 1500 years old).[1]

> According to an Arabic legend, the game of chess was invented by a Brahmian, to show his student, the heir to the throne, that the king is no stronger than his subjects. Invited to name a reward, the Brahmian asked only for grains of rice: one grain on the first square of the chess board, two on the second, four on the third, and so on, always doubling until the sixty-fourth square is reached. Since this request appeared to be modest, it was granted. *Yet all the rice in India could not satisfy this simple request.*

How many grains would there be on each square? How many altogether? Of course one could calculate it easily, *but laboriously.* (Note that the total is one less than twice the amount of the last square.) Here is the computer program (Figure 18-10) that will evaluate the desired result. There are nine *statements,* each one numbered for reference. N stands for the number of the square (from 1 to 64), X for the number of grains of rice on that square. Although the statements beginning with LET look like equations, they are more properly called *assignments,* for we ask the computer to calculate the right-hand side and to *assign* the resultant number to the symbol on the left. For example, in statement 4, the computer adds 1 to the present value of N and then assigns this sum to N. The asterisk (*) is used as the symbol for multiplication. Note the decision statement 3. It tells the computer to compare the present value of N with the number 64. If N is equal to 64, then the program switches to statement 7; if not, it goes on to the next statement in line. When it gets to statement 6, the computer is told to go next to statement 2 and then to proceed accordingly.

The result is shown in Figure 18-11. It took a medium-sized computer 7 sec to

[1] Translated from *Grand Larousse encylopédique,* Librairie Larousse, Paris (1961), vol. 4, p. 321.

```
1 LET  X=N=1
2 PRINT  N,X
3 IF  N=64  THEN  7
4 LET  N=N+1
5 LET  X=2*X
6 GO TO  2
7 LET  X=2*X-1
8 PRINT  "TOTAL=";X
9 STOP
```

Figure 18-10

1	1
2	2
3	4
4	8
5	16
6	32
7	64
8	128
9	256
10	512
11	1024
12	2048
13	4096
14	8192
15	16384
16	32768
17	65536
18	131072
19	262144
20	524288
21	1048576
22	2097152
23	4194304
24	8388608
25	16777216
26	33554432
27	67108864
28	134217728
29	268435456
30	536870912
31	1.07374E+09
32	2.14748E+09
33	4.29497E+09
34	8.58993E+09
35	1.71799E+10
36	3.43597E+10
37	6.87195E+10
38	1.37439E+11
39	2.74878E+11
40	5.49756E+11
41	1.09951E+12
42	2.19902E+12
43	4.39805E+12
44	8.79609E+12
45	1.75922E+13
46	3.51844E+13
47	7.03687E+13
48	1.40737E+14
49	2.81475E+14
50	5.62950E+14
51	1.12590E+15
52	2.25180E+15
53	4.50360E+15
54	9.00720E+15
55	1.80144E+16
56	3.60288E+16
57	7.20576E+16
58	1.44115E+17
59	2.88230E+17
60	5.76461E+17
61	1.15292E+18
62	2.30584E+18
63	4.61169E+18
64	9.22337E+18

TOTAL = 1.84467E+19

Figure 18-11

calculate all of these values, and about 2 min to print them. Note that this particular computer does not keep track of more than nine digits. From square 31 on, the numbers are rounded off and expressed as decimals, with an *exponential* added. For example, square 31 (which should actually be 1,073,741,824) becomes 1.07374×10^9 or, in computer terms, 1.07374E+09.

The material tools

Whatever an engineer builds, whether it be a spaceship, an electronic circuit, or a suspension bridge, he uses materials of construction. Therefore he must know something about material properties and the way that they can be shaped into the forms he needs. Different applications demand different types of properties—high strength and rigidity in one case and suppleness and flexibility in another. There is no universal material. Therefore the engineer uses various metals and polymers, concrete, rubber, wood, ceramics, and special combinations of these.

The most widely used materials for the engineer are the metals. They exhibit strength, toughness, ductility, resistance to both high and low temperatures, and good conductivity of heat and electricity. They can be formed and shaped and joined into a great variety of shapes, and, by suitable treatment, they can be made resistant to most chemical attack. The most important primary metals for the engineer are iron,[2] copper, and aluminum together with auxiliary metals such as nickel, zinc, tin, cobalt, lead, and manganese. During recent years some of the scarcer metals such as titanium, tantalum, vanadium, beryllium, and columbium have gained importance for special applications. Almost without exception metals are not found pure in nature, but as mineral combinations of a metal with such chemical elements as oxygen, sulphur, and carbon in the form of oxides, sulphates, sulphides, and carbonates. The process of separating the metal from the other constituents is called smelting, reducing, or refining. It is usually done either by heating in the presence of other chemicals which have a greater affinity or attractive power for the undesired chemical than the metal has, or by electrolytic methods such as melting or dissolving the original compound in a liquid and applying an electrical current through two electrodes in such a way that the metal portion of the compound is attracted by one of the electrodes and the less desirable chemical by the other. The relatively pure metal resulting from these refining methods is cast into small bars called "pigs" or into larger forms called "ingots," or left molten for further treatment. With the notable exception of copper,[3] the pure metal is rarely useful as an engineering material. Pig iron, for example, is weak and brittle, and pure aluminum is too soft and ductile for most engineering uses. Later we will discuss how the properties of these pure metals can be improved. But first let us consider the demand and supply and the scarcity of minerals.

Until recently, few people have given any thought to the limitation of our supply of minerals—the raw materials which supply our need for metals. Unfortunately we have been using these metals as if the supply were unlimited. Today industry uses 0.55 tons of steel per year for every person in the United States, as opposed

---

[2]Iron is very important since it is the main constituent of steel.

[3]One of the principal uses for copper is as a conductor of electricity. The purer the copper, the higher its electrical conductivity, i.e., the lower its resistance to the flow of electric current.

to 0.35 tons of steel per person in the year 1950 (*the average automobile alone requires 1.5 tons of steel*). The effect of this rate increase is more pronounced when the population increase in the United States (from 150,000,000 to 200,000,000) is considered. Similar increases in use can be demonstrated for most other metals. It is obvious that such a rate of growth cannot be maintained over very many years without using up our mineral resources. In fact, there is already such a shortage of nickel that it has become one of the scarcest and costliest commodities. One answer is to throw less of our used metals away and reuse the maximum amount possible. Already scrap metal is used extensively in the production of new metal, processes are being devised to regain scrap metal from garbage, and aluminum companies are offering a reward for the return of empty beverage cans. Yet all of the reuse of scrap is of little help if populations keep increasing and if the amount of metal used per capita continues to rise.

Metals become most useful to the engineer when they are combined with other metals and elements which give them the qualities of strength and toughness for which they are prized. Metallurgy, the science that deals with the improvement of metal properties, is probably the oldest science known to man. Long before he had fires hot enough to work iron, man combined copper and tin to make bronze, which is stronger than either copper or tin alone. (Brass is an alloy of copper and zinc.) When men learned to use coal rather than wood and obtained a flame hot enough to melt iron, it was probably by accident that he discovered the enormous strength that was added to iron by small additions of carbon. One can well imagine coal dust or a small piece of coal entering into the melt and the surprise of the man when his result turned out to be stronger and tougher than any iron that had been

Illustration 18-1
The work of materials engineers has been of significant importance in the development of new alloys that can withstand very high temperatures.

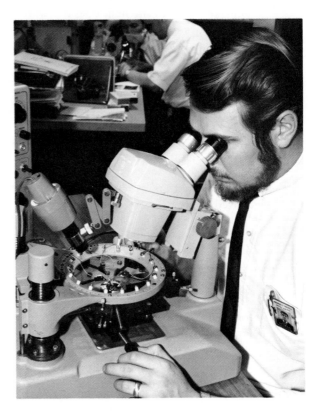

produced before. We know today that very little carbon—usually less than 1 per cent—is needed to make steel out of iron. We also know that additional trace amounts of elements such as silicon and manganese can further improve the strength and other qualities of the steel, and that the methods of heating and cooling are very important in determining what compounds are formed and the properties of the final material. We have also learned that there are elements such as phosphorous and sulphur which, when added to steel, are likely to deteriorate its qualities. Every effort must be made to keep these out of the melt.

Alloys such as bronze or brass are mixtures or "solid solutions" of two metals. Among the most useful of the iron alloys are those made with nickel and chromium, which produce the stainless steels, and the high-strength alloys which usually contain cobalt, manganese, nickel, and other elements. Just as the soft metals tin and copper form a stronger alloy, *bronze,* so do small additions of copper to aluminum form a much stronger alloy which the British call *duralumin.*

There are many manufacturing methods by which metals and alloys can be made into useful engineering products. The oldest method (and still widely used) is sand casting. A pattern or model of the desired shape is made, usually of wood, and this pattern is used to make a tightly compacted sand mold. The mold is made in two parts so that the pattern can be removed without destroying the mold. Liquid metal is then poured into the closed mold and allowed to cool and solidify. A sand mold is not reusable so it is broken up to remove the finished product. The main advantages of cast products are (1) they can be formed in intricate shapes and (2) there is almost no limit to the size of a casting. On the other hand, sand castings tend to have rougher surfaces and to be weaker and more brittle than items that have been produced by other methods. It is difficult to hold dimensions accurately and to make sure that the item does not warp during the cooling process. Finally, sand casting does not lend itself well to the making of mass-produced items. However, in the last 50 years the art of casting has been very much improved, especially by the development of permanent metal molds and other special mold materials which improve accuracy and surface finish. Special metals have been developed which, when cast, are no longer brittle and weak but strong and tough, and continuous casting methods have been developed which do lend themselves to certain mass-production practices. Iron, zinc, and aluminum castings especially have found their way into many engineering applications. The engine block in a car, its transmission housing, and carburetor body (as well as many body trim parts) are all made from castings.

We do not know who first discovered that the toughness of steel could be improved appreciably by hammering when hot, but we do know that for thousands of years swords, horseshoes, and ax heads have been produced by hammering or forging. However, the hand forge of old has now been replaced by huge drop forges, presses, and rolling mills. In the rolling mill the hot steel ingot is squeezed again and again through sets of rollers until it is in the desired form of sheet steel, bar stock, or special shapes such as angle iron or I-beams. Although not strictly the same as forging, the rolling process produces the same working of the material as the forge did and produces the same strength and toughness as was achieved in the forge. Many metals are also successfully formed by cold rolling and pressing.

Castings, forgings, and rolled metal shapes can seldom be used without additional machining. Machining means the controlled removal of material, whether it be in cutting, drilling, or the shaving of material off the surface. Metals are cut either by saw or with an intensely hot pencil-shaped flame. Drilling is done on single- or multispindle drill presses or, if the hole is so big that an ordinary drill press cannot handle it, on boring mills. Surface material is removed on shapers, planers, or milling machines if the workpiece is flat or contoured, and on lathes if it is circular. Planers and lathes normally use stationary cutting tools and have the workpiece move past the cutting tool. In milling machines the cutting tool itself rotates and the piece may or may not remain stationary. The surfaces produced by planing, shaping, milling, and lathe work are usually fairly rough unless considerable effort is spent on the cut. To get very fine surfaces and very accurate dimensions, grinding machines are used, but these are not as useful as the other tools in removing substantial amounts of material. Grinding machines are made for flat as well as cylindrical pieces. To achieve a finish even finer than can be obtained by grinding requires mechanical honing, lapping, and polishing or the use of certain chemical etchants, which can produce a mirror-like surface on metals.

It is the surface of the metal that, like your skin, is in contact with the environment and must be protected against mechanical and chemical attack. Most failures begin at the surface and there are many special techniques to harden and toughen the surface and to make it more resistant to the environment in which it operates. Among the protective techniques are (1) carburizing, cyaniding, and nitriding, in which the surface is hardened chemically, (2) shot-peening, which strengthen the surface mechanically, and (3) galvanizing or plating with chromium, nickel, or cadmium, which protect the surface from corrosion.

Finally, consideration should be given to how metals are joined together. If two pieces of steel are to be joined permanently, the most common method is to weld them together. In welding, the edges which are to meet are heated until almost molten, and are then brought together with or without the use of a flux or filler (additional metal). A proper weld is as strong as the original material. To accomplish this requires considerable experience and ability because heating and cooling in the vicinity of the weld can cause undesirable changes in the material properties. Brazing and soldering are similar to welding in that a continuous joint is produced. However, the base metal is not heated as high as the melting temperature but rather to a temperature only high enough to melt a filler of brass or other nonferrous metal in brazing or a lead-tin mixture in soldering. Brazing and soldering are useful where the strength of the joint is not a prime requirement. They can also be used to join dissimilar materials such as aluminum and steel or brass.

The second most common joining method is by means of mechanical fasteners such as rivets, screws, and bolts. Here holes must be drilled through the parts to be joined. Rivets are usually heated before they are inserted in the hole and then hammered so that they fill the hole completely. As the rivets cool they contract and tighten the joint. Bolts and screws are sometimes preferable because they can be removed easily.

Next to the metals, the most useful engineering materials are found among the rubbers and plastics. Where metals are strong, heavy, and relatively inflexible, the rubbers and plastics are relatively weak, light in weight, and pliable. With the single exception of natural or *hevea* rubber they do not occur in nature and are the product of modern chemistry (even natural rubber must be carefully compounded with other chemicals in order to make a useful material). Metals have a history going back to the beginnings of human history; plastics, however, are primarily an invention of this century.

Rubbers and plastics are long-chain hydrocarbon polymers; that is, they are produced by linking together large numbers of relatively simple molecules called *monomers.* This process is called polymerization. Occasionally a monomer will polymerize with moderate heat (a few hundred degrees Fahrenheit) alone; more often a catalyst[4] is required. The long-chain molecules of a polymer can be visualized as long elastic coiled springs randomly distributed in the polymer. They are interconnected here and there and it is the degree of or number of interconnections that determines the rigidity and strength of the polymer. In rubbers there are few interconnections; in rigid plastics there are many. In some plastics the interconnections can be broken by moderate heat so that the plastic can be reformed by heating. When cooled the links are reestablished. Such plastics are called "thermoplastic." In other plastics the links are permanent and cannot be broken without destroying the material. Such plastics are called "thermosetting."

The most common way of producing plastic parts is by molding. This is substantially the same as casting except that the low temperatures at which plastics can be formed permits the use of very accurately machined metal molds. These can produce plastic parts of exact dimensions and good surface finish and can be used again and again. We are all aware of the innumerable household products and items of modern life which are produced from molded plastics. Though an original mold may be costly, if its price can be distributed over thousands or even hundreds of thousands of parts, the cost of each part may be remarkably low. This is in part why picnic forks, ball-point pens, and pocket combs cost as little as they do.

In recent years some very strong structures have been built by embedding in the plastics strong reinforcing fibers such as glass in the plastic. Although glass may be brittle, it has very great strength, comparable to some of the strongest metals. Thus a whole group of glass fibers held together in a plastic matrix can produce a material of great strength and flexibility.

The idea of combining two different materials and using the good qualities of each to make a superior product is much older than the glass-reinforced plastics. It probably goes back to the use of reinforced concrete, in which the strength of steel and the stiffness of concrete are used to make superior structural members.

Even concrete itself is a mixture of sand, gravel, and cement—each constituent being of relatively little practical importance by itself. Cement, also called Portland cement, is a roasted (calcined) mixture of clay and limestone which combines readily with water to form a rigid, stable solid. Hardened cement is very durable and can resist not only heat, cold, and other variations in climate but also a large number of chemicals. However, it is very brittle and has little physical strength. In concrete, strength is provided by adding the sand and gravel, which are then held together by the cement binder. Concrete, which offers great resistance towards being compressed, offers much less resistance to being pulled apart. Here is where the use of steel reinforcing becomes important. For example, imagine a concrete beam acting as a bridge over a canyon. When a heavy truck travels over this bridge, the beam will be bent downward with the roadway (or top surface of the beam) being pushed together or compressed, and the bottom part of the beam (the part nearest the canyon) being pulled apart in tension. Since concrete is much stronger in compression than in tension, steel reinforcing bars are cast into the bottom part of the beam, which brings its total strength up to that of the top (compression) side.

Typical concrete consists of 13 parts of cement, 33 parts of sand and 46 parts

---

[4] A catalyst may be compared to a marriage broker; its presence is essential for the reaction, but it does not end up in the final product.

of gravel together with 8 parts of water by weight. Since the strength of concrete depends upon how completely the cement and water have reacted, it is important to keep the structure moist for several days after it has been poured if maximum strength is desired.

The cement-water reaction—called *hydration*—develops heat. In most structures this heat is readily dissipated by the surrounding air. However, in large thick sections of concrete, such as dams, special water cooling pipes are often inserted to make sure that this heat can be removed and not cause damage to the structure.

A number of special uses of concrete and cement should also be considered. By adding special chemicals it is possible to make cement harden faster than the usual 12- to 24-hour period. Quick-setting cements are used, for example, in the setting of casings, the metal liners that are put into water or oil wells to prevent collapse of the hole. The cement is pumped into the space between the liner and the soil to prevent earth movement. Consequently a quick-setting cement is essential. Lightweight concrete can be made either by using a lightweight aggregate such as pumice (the hardened lava from volcanic eruption) or by blowing air into the concrete while it is setting. Of course, the strength of lightweight concrete is much less than that of ordinary concrete. Finally, one can spray a cement mixture under pressure out of a nozzle which resembles a small gun. Hence, the material is called "gunnite." It is used to coat tunnels, chemical vessels, swimming pools, and so on, wherever the hardness and chemical resistance of cement is desired and where necessary strength is provided by the backing onto which the gunnite is sprayed.

For extremely high-temperature use (where few of the metals have any strength) refractories or ceramics are used. They resemble cement in that they are generally simple, inorganic chemicals.[5]

Among the most common ceramics are the oxides, nitrides, carbides, and borides of metals such as aluminum, beryllium, titanium, tantalum, and many others. Prior to casting, ceramic compounds usually exist in powder form. They can be shaped into useful engineering products by hot forming and sintering. Here the powder is pressed into a suitable mold; at moderately elevated temperature enough inter-particle bonds are formed to maintain the desired shape. This is then heated to considerably higher temperatures, at which many of the grains fuze to one another and form a dense, strong body that is highly resistant to heat and abrasion. A common ceramic is porcelain, which is made of sand (silicon oxide) and alumina (aluminum oxide). Ceramics are used in the nozzles of rocket engines, in gas turbine combustors, on the nose cones of missiles, in the heat shield for reentry space vehicles, in furnaces, or wherever extremely high temperature resistance is required. Like concrete, ceramics tend to have much greater strength in compression (being pushed together) than in tension (being pulled apart). To increase their strength in tension, engineers have embedded fine metal fibers such as tungsten or boron in the ceramic, with results comparable to glass fiber-reinforced plastics or steel-reinforced concrete. Graphite is usually included among the ceramics because of its high temperature

---

[5] Organic compounds contain carbon and hydrogen and can form very large and complicated molecules, such as the rubbers and plastics mentioned above. They are so called because most living organisms, such as plants, animals, and men, are made of compounds containing carbon and hydrogen. Even petroleum and natural gas, the raw material of today's organic chemical industry, come from long-decayed plants and animals. Inorganic compounds are a combination of other chemical elements. These may contain either carbon or hydrogen, but usually not both. Normally inorganic molecules are smaller and simpler than organic molecules.

resistance. Graphite is pure carbon in a form that permits it to be sintered and worked, like other ceramics. Although not of very high strength, it retains its strength to temperatures even higher than many ceramics. Exposure to oxygen must be avoided at high temperatures.

Glass, prized primarily for its transparency and its resistance to most chemicals, is also one of the strongest materials known to man. Unfortunately, it is also very brittle when exposed to air and moisture. Therefore, its strength can be used only when the glass is protected, when, for example, it is embedded in plastic. Glass fiber-reinforced plastics gain their high strength from thousands of fine glass fibers surrounded and held together by epoxy or other plastics. The production process tends to be costly and lends itself primarily to simple shapes such as pressurized fuel tanks, ship hulls, rocket casings, and sporting goods.

Wood, once one of the most widely used engineering materials, is used very little in industry today, partly because of its scarcity, and partly because as a product of nature its properties vary from batch to batch, thus reducing reliability. The two major categories of woods are softwood and hardwood. Soft woods, such as pines and firs, are relatively plentiful, grow fairly rapidly, and are not too costly. However, their strength is low and they tend to warp easily if not prepared properly; consequently, they are used today primarily for building construction and for the production of paper. Softwood is used in making forms for concrete although metal forms are rapidly replacing wood in large-volume construction. Hardwoods, such as oak, ash, walnut, and other hardwoods from the tropics, have become so scarce and costly that they are used almost exclusively for decorative effects or for the production of beautiful and costly furniture. Their major industrial use is the production of patterns for sand castings. We can expect to see the use of wood to be curtailed more and more as our forests become depleted, and as those that remain are needed more and more for recreation and for the preservation of watersheds.

The physical tools

The engineering curriculum contains more courses in physics and in subjects derived from physics than any of the other pure sciences. *Force, motion, energy,* and *matter*—these are special concerns of the engineer.

Since we can hope to look at only a small selection of the physical tools, let us first consider *mechanics.*

Mechanics is the physical science that describes and predicts the effects of forces acting on material bodies. The condition under study may be one of rest or one

---

Physics: The science that deals with matter and energy in terms of motion and force.
—Random House Dictionary, 1967

Mechanics: The oldest branch of physics, dealing with the state of rest or motion of particles or rigid bodies.
—Harper's Encyclopedia of Science, 1967

---

of motion. There are three specialized branches into which the general field of mechanics may be divided for more specific studies. These are as follows:

1. Mechanics of rigid bodies
   Statics
   Dynamics
2. Mechanics of deformable bodies
3. Mechanics of fluids
   Compressible flow
   Incompressible flow

Our study of mechanics in this chapter will be concerned with an introduction to static mechanics, and to show how the engineering method is applied to a problem solution.

Fundamental concepts and definitions

Concepts used in our study of static mechanics are *force, space,* and *matter.* These concepts are basic and, as a frame of reference, should be accepted on the basis of our general experience. A *force* is the result of the interaction of two or more bodies and in our study here will be considered to be a localized vector quantity. A force may be evolved as the result of physical contact, or it may be developed at some distance—as is the case with magnetic and gravitational forces. *Space* is a region extending in all directions. It is associated with the location or position of a particle or of particles with respect to one another. *Matter* is a substance that occupies space.

A *particle* may be said to be a negligible amount of matter that occupies a single point in space. A *rigid* body is a body that is constructed entirely of particles that do not change their position in space with respect to each other. No body is truly rigid. However, in many situations the deformation, or change in position of the particles, is very small and therefore would have a negligible effect upon the analysis. Such is the assumption in this chapter.

The principles of statics are most easily learned by using *free-body diagrams,* which were discussed briefly in Chapter 17. Here we shall consider in more detail how to draw free-body diagrams and how to use them. Let us start by drawing the free-body diagram of a ship moving in the water, Figure 18-12. It is not necessary that the model of the ship be drawn to scale since the shape of the idealized model is only an imaginary concept.

There are four external forces acting on the model: a forward thrust, which acts at the ship's propeller; a friction drag, which acts so as to retard motion; a buoyant force, which keeps the ship afloat; and the ship's weight, which in simplification may be considered to be acting through the center of gravity of the ship, Figure 18-13.

The symbol ⊗ is used to denote the location of the center of gravity. A coordinate system is very useful for purposes of orientation. The diagram shown would make possible an analysis of the relationships between the weight and buoyant force and between the thrust and drag. However, it would not, for example, be useful for determining the loads on the ship's engine mounts. Another model (free-body diagram) of the engine alone would be required for this purpose.

Another example shows the free-body diagram of a four-wheel drive automobile driving up an incline, Figure 18-14. It is customary to show the model in its true

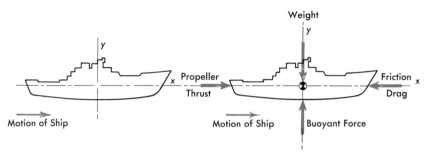

Figure 18-12   **Figure 18-13**

position in space. It would appear awkward and be confusing to draw the automobile in a horizontal position when it is actually going uphill.

General suggestions for drawing free-body diagrams

To aid the student in learning to draw free-body diagrams, the following suggestions are given:

1. Free bodies Be certain that the body is *free* of all surrounding objects. Draw the body so it is *free*. Do not show a supporting surface but rather show only the force vector which replaces that surface. Do not rotate the body from its original position but rather rotate the axes if necessary. Show all forces and label them. Show all needed dimensions and angles.

2. Force components Forces are often best shown in their component forms. When replacing a force by its components, select the most convenient directions for the components. Never show both a force and its components by solid-line vectors; use broken-line vectors for one or the other since the force *and* its components do not occur simultaneously.

3. Weight vectors Show the weight vector as a vertical line with its tail or point at the center of gravity, and place it so that it interferes least with the remainder of the drawing. It should always be drawn vertically.

Figure 18-14

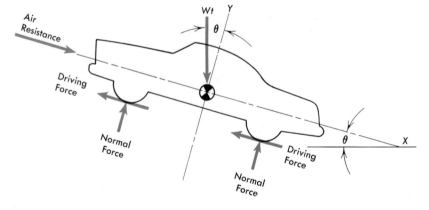

4. Direction of vectors The free-body diagram should represent the facts as nearly as possible. If a pull on the free body occurs, place the tail of the vector at the actual point of application and let the point of the vector be in the true direction of the pull. Likewise, if a push occurs on the free body, the vector should show the true direction, and the point of the arrow should be placed at the point of application. Force vectors on free-body diagrams are not usually drawn to scale but may be drawn proportionate to their respective magnitudes.

5. Free-body diagram of whole structure This should habitually be the first free body examined in the solution of any problem. Many problems cannot be solved without this first consideration. After the free body of the whole structure or complex has been considered, select such members or subassemblies for further free-body diagrams as may lead to a direct solution.

6. Two-force members When a two-force member is in equilibrium, the forces are equal, opposite, and collinear. If the member is in compression, the vectors should point toward each other; if a member is in tension, they should point away from each other.

7. Three-force members When a member is in equilibrium and has only three forces acting on it, the three forces are always concurrent; that is, they go through the same point if they are not parallel. In analyzing a problem involving a three-force member, one should recall that any set of concurrent forces may be replaced by a resultant force. Hence, if a member in equilibrium has forces acting at three points, it is a three-force member regardless of the fact that the force applied at one or more points may be replaced by two or more components.

8. Concurrent force system For a concurrent force system the size, shape, and dimensions of the body can be neglected, and the body can be considered to be a particle.

Example Draw a free body of point *A*, as shown in Figure 18-15.

Solution See Figure 18-16.

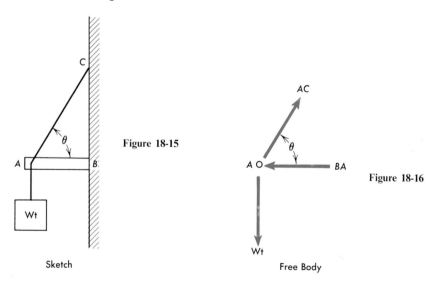

Figure 18-15

Figure 18-16

Sketch

Free Body

Figure 18-17

Situation	Free body	Explanation
A box resting on a plane 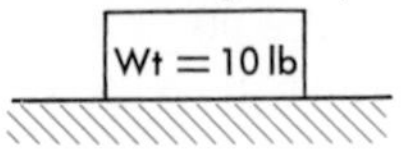 Wt = 10 lb	 10 lb N	The normal force always acts at an angle of 90° with the surfaces in contact. This force N usually is considered to act through the center of gravity of the body.
A weight hanging from a ring 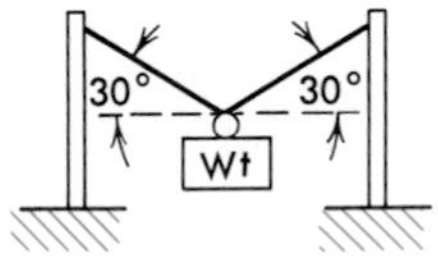 30° 30° Wt	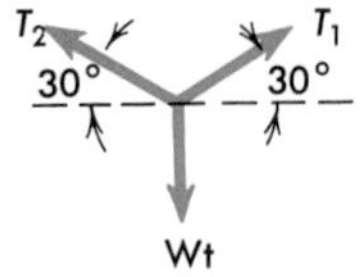 T_2 30° 30° T_1 Wt	Since the ring is of negligible size, it may be considered to be a point. All of the forces would act through this point. The downward force W is balanced by the tensions T_1 and T_2. The numerical sum of these tensions will be greater than the weight. This is true since T_1 is pulling against T_2.
A box on a frictionless surface 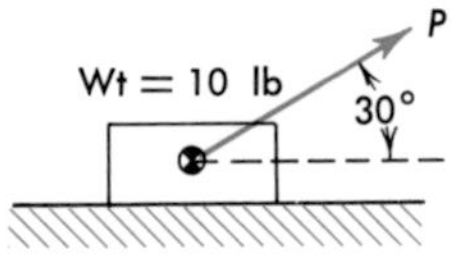 Wt = 10 lb P 30°	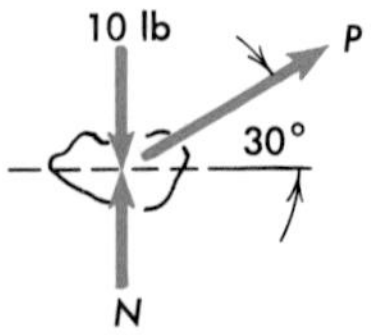 10 lb P 30° N	Some surfaces are considered frictionless although in reality, no surface is frictionless. The force P is an unbalanced force and it will produce an acceleration. The symbol ⊗ denotes the location of the center of gravity of the body.
A small box on a rough surface 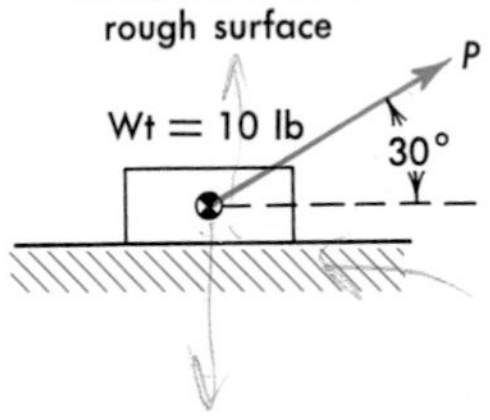 Wt = 10 lb P 30°	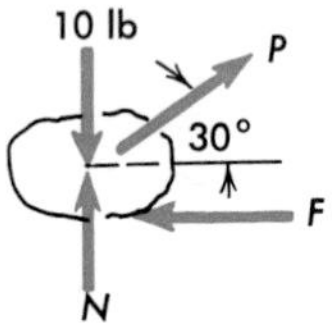 10 lb P 30° F N	The force of friction will always oppose motion or will oppose the tendency to move. For bodies of small size, the *moment effect** of the friction force may be disregarded and the friction and normal forces may be considered to act through the center of gravity of the body.

*See page 497 for an explanation of moments.

Figure 18-18

Situation	Free body	Explanation
A beam resting on fixed supports Load ←8 ft→ 2 ft Wt = 50 lb	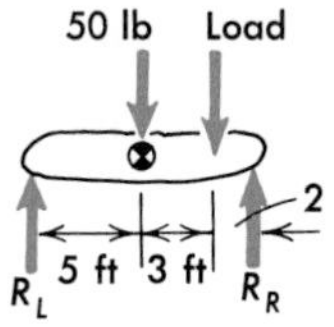 50 lb Load 2 ft R_L 5 ft 3 ft R_R	For a uniform beam, the weight acts at the midpoint of the beam regardless of where the supports are located.
A pivoted beam resting on a roller 100 lb 45° ←12 ft→ Wt = 10 lb	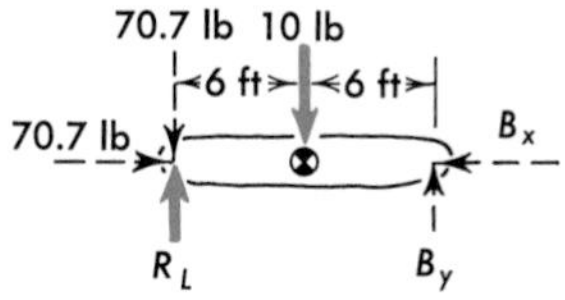 70.7 lb 10 lb ←6 ft→ ←6 ft→ 70.7 lb R_L B_x B_y	Since a roller cannot produce a horizontal reaction, the horizontal component of any force must be counteracted by the horizontal component of the reaction at the pivoted end.
A ladder resting against a frictionless wall 60°	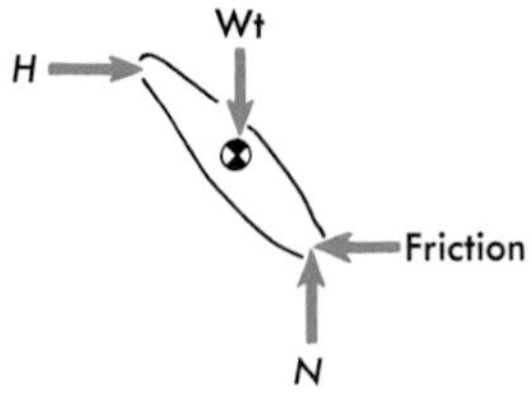 Wt H → ←Friction N	At the upper end of the ladder, the only reaction possible is perpendicular to the wall since the surface is considered to be frictionless.
   Sketch	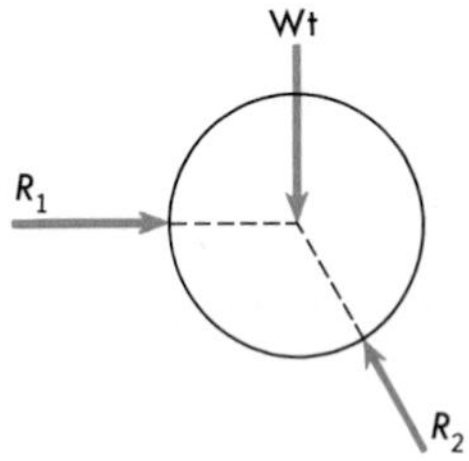 Wt R_1 → R_2 Free body	The reaction between surfaces at rest is perpendicular to the common tangent plane at the point of contact. Thus, if a cylinder rests on a plane, the reaction at the point of contact will pass through the center of the cylinder.
Pulling a barrel over a curb	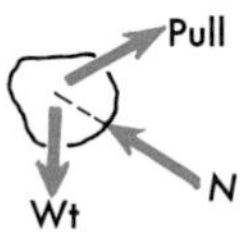 Pull N Wt	All of the forces are acting through the center of the barrel.

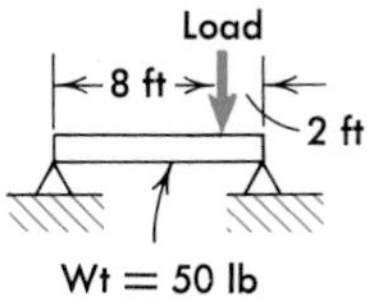

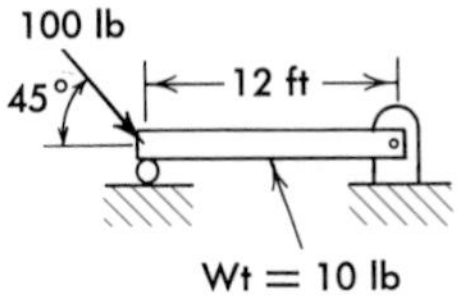

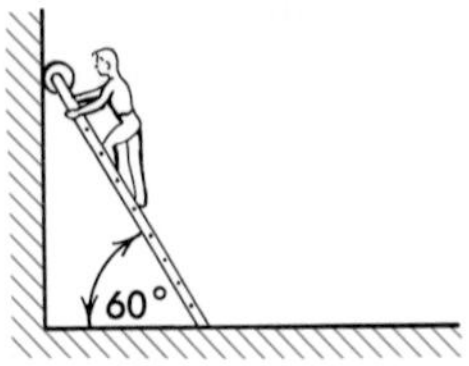

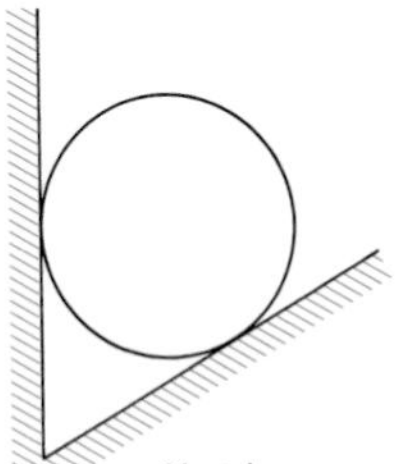

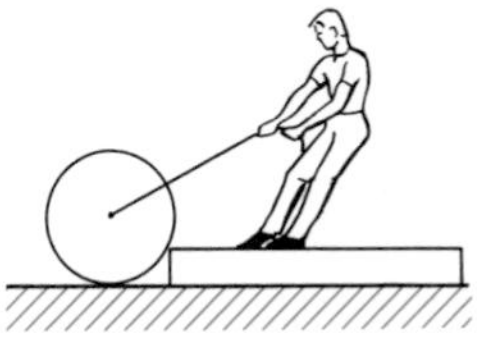

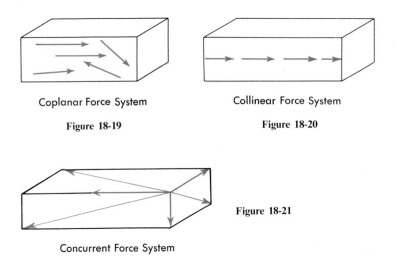

Coplanar Force System

Figure 18-19

Collinear Force System

Figure 18-20

Figure 18-21

Concurrent Force System

In describing free-body diagrams we have talked about force *vectors.* Let us look briefly at vectors and their properties. A *vector* quantity has a *direction* as well as a *magnitude* (in contrast to a *scalar* quantity, which has magnitude only). Examples of vector quantities are force, velocity, and acceleration. Examples of scalar quantities are temperature, volume, time, and energy. Vectors are said to be:

1. Coplanar, when all the vectors lie in the same plane, Figure 18-19.
2. Collinear, when all vectors act along the same line, Figure 18-20.
3. Concurrent, when all the vectors originate or intersect at a single point, Figure 18-21.

Example   A force of 150 lb$_f$ is pulling upward from a point at an angle of 30° with the horizontal, Figure 18-22. The length of the arrow was scaled (using an engineer's scale) to 1 in. equals 100 lb$_f$ and is 1½ in. long acting upward at an angle of 30° with the horizontal. In graphic work the arrow point should not extend completely to the end of the vector, since it is very easy to "overrun" the exact length of the measured line in the drawing of the arrowhead.

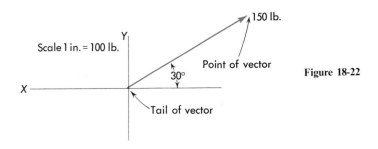

Figure 18-22

In rigid-body mechanics the external effect of a force on a rigid body is independent of the point of application of the force along its line of action. Thus it would be considered immaterial whether a tractor pushed or pulled a box from a given position. The total effect on the box would be the same in either case. This is called the *Principle of Transmissibility* and will be used extensively in this chapter. This may be illustrated as shown in Figure 18-23.

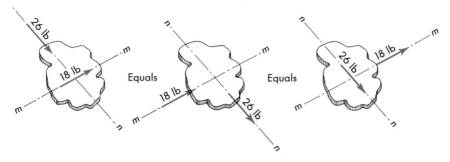

Figure 18-23

Example   In each case the body is being acted upon by forces of 26 lb$_f$ and 18 lb$_f$. The total effect on the body is assumed to be the same for each example, since it is the line of action of a force which is significant, rather than its point of application.

Resolutions of forces

In this initial study of static mechanics we shall deal mainly with concurrent, coplanar force systems. It is sometimes advantageous to combine two such forces into a single equivalent force, which we shall call a *resultant*. The original forces are called *components*.

Example   What single force R pulling at point O will have the same effect as components F_1 and F_2? (Figure 18-24).

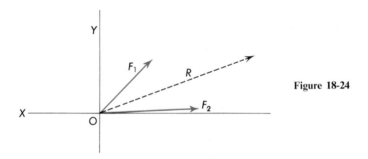

Figure 18-24

There are several methods of combining these two components into a single resultant. Let us examine the *parallelogram method,* the *polygon of forces,* and the *rectangular component method.*

Parallelogram method

1. Choose a suitable scale.
2. Lay out the two coplanar components to scale, pointing away from the point of intersection.
3. Using these two components as sides, construct a parallelogram.
4. Draw the diagonal through the point of intersection.
5. Measure the diagonal (which is the resultant of the two components) for magnitude (with engineer's scale) and direction (with protractor).

Example Solve for the resultant of components F_1 and F_2 if they are separated by angle θ, Figure 18-25.

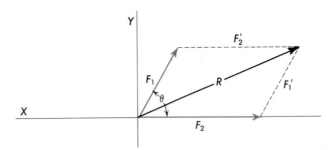

Figure 18-25

Example Two coplanar forces of 30 lb$_f$ and 40 lb$_f$, respectively, are at right angles to each other. Determine the magnitude of the resultant and the angle between the resultant and the 40-lb$_f$ force, Figure 18-26. Lay out the two forces to scale as outlined above. The diagonal is measured to be 50 lb$_f$ and is located at an angle of 36.9° with the 40-lb$_f$ force.

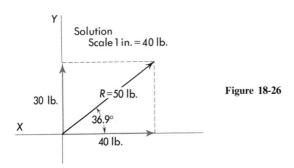

Figure 18-26

Problems

Solve, using the parallelogram method.

18-1. Find the resultant of two concurrent forces of 1939 lb$_f$ and 1220 lb$_f$, respectively, if the angle between them is 20°; if the angle is 130°.

18-2. Find the resultant of two concurrent forces, one 320 lb$_f$ due east and the other 550 lb$_f$ S 30° E.

18-3. Force A is 450 lb$_f$. Force B is 325 lb$_f$ and acts at an angle of 54° with A. The forces are concurrent. What is the amount of the resultant and what angle does it make with force A?

18-4. Find the resultant of two concurrent components, one of 1225 lb$_f$ due west and the other of 1450 lb$_f$ S 30° E.

18-5. A heavy piece of machinery is being moved along a floor with two cables making an angle of 28°30′ with each other. If the pulls are 45,000 and 25,000 lb$_f$, respectively, by what single force could they be replaced, and at what angle would the force act?

18-6. Find the resultant of a velocity of 150 mi/hr due east and a velocity of 280 mph S 70° E. Use a scale of 1 in. equals 20 mi/hr.

18-7. Three ropes are attached to a heavy body. If the first is pulled east by a force of 159 lb$_f$, the second by a force of 75 lb$_f$ 30° east of north, and the third north by a force of 108 lb$_f$, what is the resultant pull exerted on the body?

18-8. Three lines are connected to a missile. One line, having a tension of 1500 lb$_f$, runs due north; a second line, with a tension of 870 lb$_f$, runs S 75° W; a third line, with a tension of 1240 lb$_f$, runs N 58° E. Find the position and direction of a properly placed guy wire to brace the missile.

18-9. A man pulls straight ahead on a test sled with a force of 148 lb$_f$. If this man is replaced by two men, one pulling 36° to his left and the other pulling 20° to his right, what force must each of the new men exert if the sled is to move in the same direction?

18-10. Two men are raising a 100-lb$_f$ container from a reactor by means of two ropes. Find the force each man is exerting on his rope if one rope makes a 15° angle with the vertical and the other makes a 25° angle with the vertical.

Polygon of forces

If two or more forces (or components) are concurrent and coplanar, their resultant can be determined by a faster and more convenient method known as the *polygon of forces.* In order to apply this method, proceed as follows:

1. Select a suitable scale.
2. Lay out one of the components with its correct magnitude and direction. At the tip of this component construct very lightly a small space-coordinate system.
3. From the origin of this new space-coordinate system lay out another component, placing the tail of the second component against the point of the first component.
4. Proceed in like manner until all components are used once (and only once).
5. Draw a vector from the original origin to the tip of the last component. This vector represents the *resultant* of the force system in both magnitude and direction.

Example Solve for the resultant of the vector system shown in Figure 18-27.

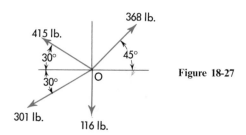

Figure 18-27

Solution See Figure 18-28. Observe that R_1 is the resultant of the 116-lb$_f$ component and the 368-lb$_f$ component, R_2 is the resultant of R_1 and the 415-lb$_f$ component,

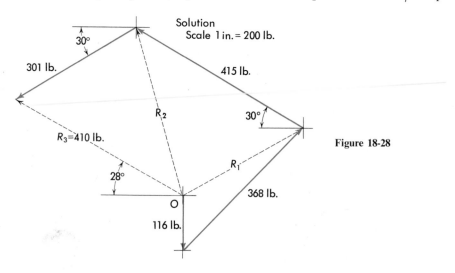

Figure 18-28

and R_3 is the resultant of R_2 and the 301-lb$_f$ component. We see that R_3 (410 lb$_f$ at $\theta = 28°$), then, is the resultant of all the components.

It makes no difference in what sequence the components are placed in series. The resultant will be the same in magnitude and direction. In some cases the vectors cross one another, but this, too, is nothing to cause concern.

Example In Figure 18-29 solve for the resultant, R, and the angle it makes with the X axis.

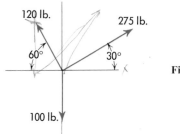

Figure 18-29

Note that in solution A, Figure 18-30, we began with the 120-lb$_f$ component and used components in a counterclockwise direction, while in solution B, Figure 18-31, we began with the 100-lb$_f$ component and worked in a counterclockwise direction.

Scale 1 in. = 200 lb.

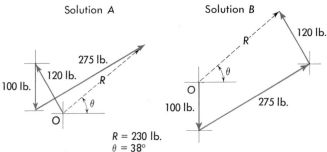

Solution A

$R = 230$ lb.
$\theta = 38°$

Figure 18-30

Solution B

Figure 18-31

Problems

Solve, using the polygon of forces. Find the resultant of each of the following force systems and the angle the resultant makes with force A.

18-11. Forces A and B act 136° apart. $A = 180$ lb$_f$, $B = 325$ lb$_f$.
18-12. Forces A and B act 21° apart. $A = 39.3$ lb$_f$, $B = 41.6$ lb$_f$.
18-13. Forces A, B, and C act 49° apart, with B acting between A and C. $A = 49.3$ lb$_f$, $B = 66.7$ lb$_f$, $C = 35.8$ lb$_f$.
18-14. Find the resultant force which would replace the three forces in Figure 18-32.

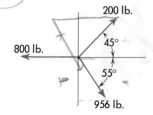

Figure 18-32

18-15. A man weighing 210 lb$_f$ stands at the middle of a wire supported at points 60 ft apart and depresses it 12 ft below the level of the ends. Solve for the tension in the wire due to the man's weight.

18-16. Solve for the magnitude and direction of the resultant of the forces shown in Figure 18-33.

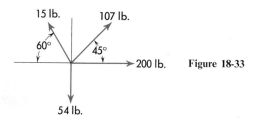

Figure 18-33

18-17. Find the resultant force that would replace the three forces *A*, *B*, and *C* in Figure 18-34.

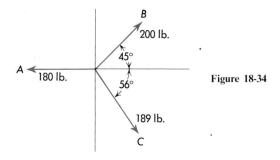

Figure 18-34

18-18. Find the resultant of the four forces shown in Figure 18-35.

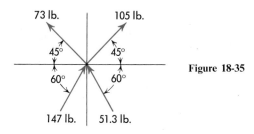

Figure 18-35

18-19. Solve for the resultant of the force systems shown in Figure 18-36.

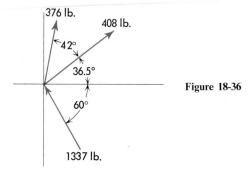

Figure 18-36

18-20. Graphically resolve the force shown in Figure 18-37 into three components, one of which is 10 lb$_f$ acting vertically upward and another 30 lb$_f$ acting horizontally to the left.

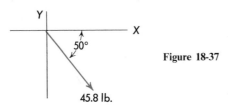

Figure 18-37

18-21. Find the resultant of the force system shown in Figure 18-38, using a scale of 1 in. equals 10 lb$_f$.

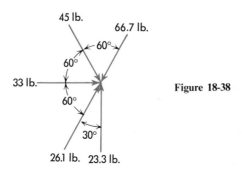

Figure 18-38

Rectangular Components

Graphical solutions, such as the *parallelogram method* and the *polygon of forces,* are useful for estimations where time is a factor. However, where exactitude is important, or when a computer is to be used, a numerical technique is needed. The method most frequently used by engineers is the *rectangular component method.*

As we have seen in the previous methods, vector components can be added together or subtracted—always leaving some resultant value. (This resultant value, of course, may be zero.) Also, any vector or resultant value can be replaced by two or more other vectors that are usually called *components.* If the components are two in number and perpendicular to each other, they are called *rectangular components.* Although it is common practice to use space-coordinate axes that are horizontal and vertical, it is by no means necessary to do so. Any orientation of the axes will produce equivalent results.

Figure 18-39 shows a vector quantity *F*. Figure 18-40 shows *F* with its rectangular components F_x and F_y. Note that the lengths of the components F_x and F_y can be determined numerically by trigonometry. The components F_x and F_y also can be

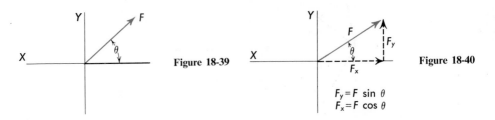

Figure 18-39 **Figure 18-40**

$$F_y = F \sin \theta$$
$$F_x = F \cos \theta$$

resolved into the force F by the polygon of forces. Hence, they may replace the force F in any computation.

Example Let us examine a concurrent coplanar force system, Figure 18-41, and resolve each force into its rectangular components, Figure 18-42. By trigonometry, F_x can be found, using F and the cosine of the angle θ, or $F_x = F \cos \theta °$. In the same manner $F_y = F \sin \theta °$.

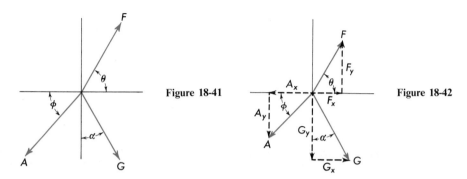

Figure 18-41

Figure 18-42

In order to keep the directions of the vectors better in mind, let us assume that horizontal forces acting to the right are positive and those acting to the left are negative. Also, the forces acting upward may be considered positive and those acting downward negative.

In working such force systems by solving for the rectangular components, a table may be used. When the sums of the horizontal and vertical components have been determined, lay off these values on a new pair of axes to prevent confusion. Solve for the resultant in both magnitude and direction, using the method explained on page 211.

Example Solve for the resultant, R, in Figure 18-43 using the method of rectangular components for the final resolution of the force system.

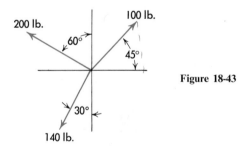

Figure 18-43

Solution See the table on page 496 and Figure 18-44.

Figure 18-44

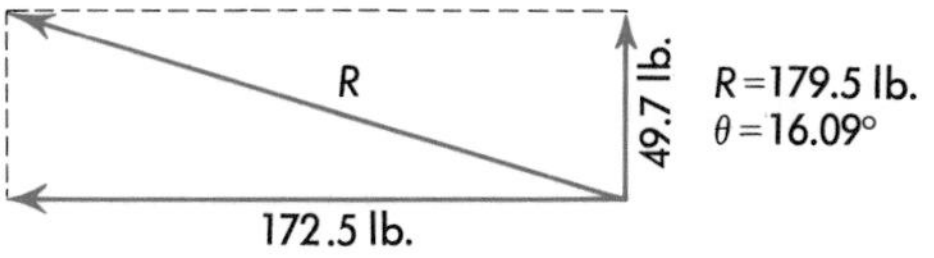

R = 179.5 lb.
θ = 16.09°

172.5 lb.

49.7 lb.

R

Forces	Horizontal component	Horizontal value	Vertical component	Vertical value
100 lb$_f$	100 cos 45° = +70.7 lb$_f$		100 sin 45° = +70.7 lb$_f$	
200 lb$_f$	200 sin 60° = −173.2 lb$_f$		200 cos 60° = +100 lb$_f$	
140 lb$_f$	140 sin 30° = −70.0 lb$_f$		140 cos 30° = −121 lb$_f$	
Total value	Positive	+70.7 lb$_f$	Positive	+170.7 lb$_f$
Total value	Negative	−243.2 lb$_f$	Negative	−121 lb$_f$
Sum	Horizontal	−172.5 lb$_f$	Vertical	+49.7 lb$_f$

Problems

Solve, using rectangular components (analytical method).

18-22. Find the resultant, in amount and direction, of the following concurrent coplanar force system: force A, 180 lb$_f$ acts S 60° W; and force B, 158 lb$_f$, acts S 80° W. Check graphically, using a scale of 1 in. equals 50 lb$_f$.

18-23. Four men are pulling a box. A pulls with a force of 115 lb$_f$, N 20°40′ E; B pulls with a force of 95 lb$_f$ S 64°35′ E; C pulls with a force of 140 lb$_f$ N 40°20′ E; and D pulls with a force of 68 lb$_f$ E. In what direction will the box tend to move?

18-24. Determine the amount and direction of the resultant of the concurrent coplanar force system as follows: force A, 10 lb$_f$, acting N 55° E; force B, 16 lb$_f$, acting due east; force C, 12 lb$_f$, acting S 22° W; force D, 15 lb$_f$, acting due west; force E, 17 lb$_f$, acting N 10° W.

18-25. Find the resultant and the angle the resultant makes with the vertical, using the following data: 10 lb$_f$, N 18° W; 5 lb$_f$, N 75° E; 3 lb$_f$, S 64° E; 7 lb$_f$, S 0° W; 10 lb$_f$, S 50° W.

18-26. Five forces act on an object. The forces are as follows: 130 lb$_f$, 0°; 170 lb$_f$, 90°; 70 lb$_f$, 180°; 20 lb$_f$, 270°; 300 lb$_f$, 150°. The angles are measured counterclockwise with reference to the horizontal through the origin. Determine graphically the amount and direction of the resultant by means of the polygon of forces. Check analytically, using horizontal and vertical components. Calculate the angle that R makes with the horizontal.

18-27. (*a*) In the sketch in Figure 18-45, using rectangular components, find the resultant of these four forces: $A = 100$ lb$_f$, $B = 130$ lb$_f$, $C = 195$ lb$_f$, $D = 138$ lb$_f$. (*b*) Find a resultant force that would replace forces A and B. (*c*) By the polygon of forces, break force A into two components, one of which acts N 10° E and has a magnitude of 65 lb$_f$. Give the magnitude and direction of the second component.

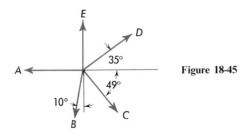

Figure 18-45

18-28. A weight of 1200 lb$_f$ is hung by a cable 23 ft long. What horizontal pull will be necessary to hold the weight 8 ft from a vertical line through the point of support? What will be the tension in the cable?

18-29. A weight of 80 lb$_f$ is suspended by two cords, the tension in AC being 70 lb$_f$ and in BC being 25 lb$_f$, as shown in Figure 18-46. Find the angles α and θ.

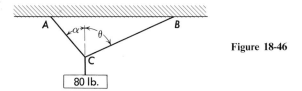

Figure 18-46

Moments

If a force is applied perpendicular to a pivoted beam some distance away from the pivot point, there will be a tendency to cause the beam to turn in either a clockwise or counterclockwise direction (see Figure 18-47). The direction of the tendency will

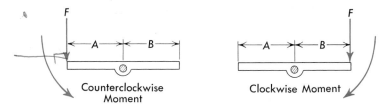

Figure 18-47

depend on the direction of the applied force. This tendency of a force to cause rotation about a given center is called *moment* (see Figure 18-48).

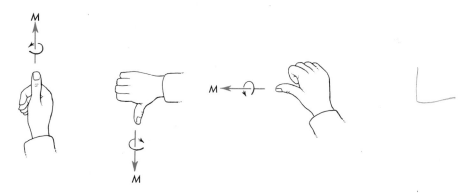

Figure 18-48

The amount of *moment* will depend upon the magnitude of the applied force as well as upon the length of the moment arm. The moment arm is the perpendicular distance from the point of rotation to the applied force. The magnitude of the moment is calculated by multiplying the force by the moment arm.

The sign convention being used in a given problem analysis should be placed on the calculation sheet adjacent to the problem sketch. In this way no confusion will arise in the mind of the reader concerning the sign convention being used. We shall assume that vectors acting to the right have a positive sign, vectors acting upward have a positive sign, and moments directed counterclockwise have a positive sign. To aid in establishing a system of positive sense, the sketch shown in Figure 18-49 will serve as a basis for problem analysis in this text.

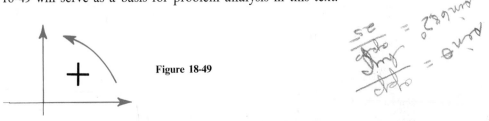

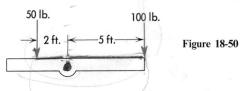

Figure 18-49

Example Solve for the moments in Figure 18-50 that tend to cause turning of the beam about the axle.

$$\text{Counterclockwise moment} = (\;50\;\text{lb})(2\;\text{ft}) = +\,100\;\textbf{lb-ft}$$
$$\text{Clockwise moment} = (100\;\text{lb})(5\;\text{ft}) = -\,500\;\textbf{lb-ft}$$

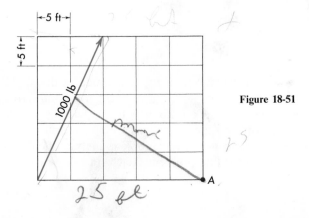

Figure 18-50

Since *moment* is the product of a force and a distance, its units will be the product of force and length units. By convention, moments are usually expressed with the force unit being shown first, as $\text{lb}_f\text{-ft}$, $\text{lb}_f\text{-in.}$, kip-ft (a kip is 1000 lb_f), and so on. This is done because *work* and *energy* also involve the product of distance and force, and the units ft-lb_f, in.-lb_f, and so on are commonly used for this purpose.

The moment of a force about some given center is identical to the sum of the moments of the components of the force about the same center. This principle is commonly called *Varignon's theorem*. In problem analysis it is sometimes more convenient to solve for the sum of the moments of the components of a force rather than the moment of the force itself. However, the problem solutions will be identical.

Example Solve for the total moment of the 1000-lb_f force about point A in Figure 18-51.

Figure 18-51

Solution A Moment of a force as shown in Figure 18-52.

moment = F · momentum
= lb·ft
kip·ft

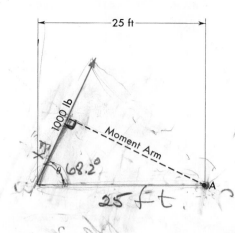

Figure 18-52

$\dfrac{25}{10}$ =

tan θ =

$$\theta = \text{arc tan } \frac{25}{10} = 68.2°$$

Moment arm = 25 sin 68.2°
Total moment = (1000)(25 sin 68.2°)
= 23,200 lb$_f$-ft

23.2 kip·ft

Solution B Moments of components of a force as shown in Figure 18-53.

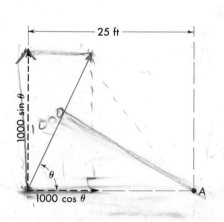

Figure 18-53

$a^2 + b^2 = c^2$
$10^2 + b^2 = 25^2$
$b^2 = 25^2 - 10^2$
$= 625 - 100$
$\sqrt{b} = \sqrt{525}$
$b = 22.9$

Vertical component = 1000 sin 68.2°
Moment arm = 25 ft
and
Horizontal component = 1000 cos 68.2°
and
Moment arm = 0

(Note that the horizontal component passes through the center *A*.)

Total moment = (1000 sin 68.2°)(25) = **23,200 lb$_f$-ft**

Problems

18-30. Solve for the algebraic sum of the moments in pound-feet about *A* when *h* is 20 in. as shown in Figure 18-54.

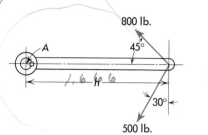

Figure 18-54

18-31. Solve for the algebraic sum of the moments of forces about *A* in Figure 18-55.

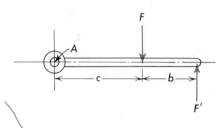

Figure 18-55

18-32. Solve for the algebraic sum of the moments about the center of the axle shown in Figure 18-56.

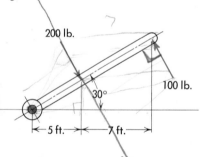

$$\frac{5}{1} = \cos 3 0$$
$$n = 5 \cos 3 0°$$

Figure 18-56

18-33. (*a*) Write an equation for the clockwise moments about the point of application of force *R* in Figure 18-57. (*b*) Write an equation for the counterclockwise moments about the point of application of force *Y*.

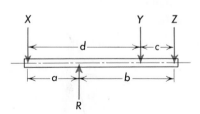

Figure 18-57

18-34. (*a*) Solve for the clockwise moments about *A*, *B*, *C*, *D*, and *E* in Figure 18-58. (*b*)

Solve for the counterclockwise moments about A, B, C, D, and E. (c) Solve for the algebraic sum of the moments about A, B, C, D, and E.

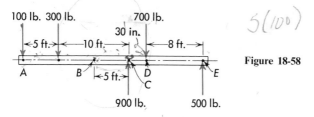

Figure 18-58

18-35. Find the summation of the moments of the forces shown around A in Figure 18-59. Find the moment sum around D.

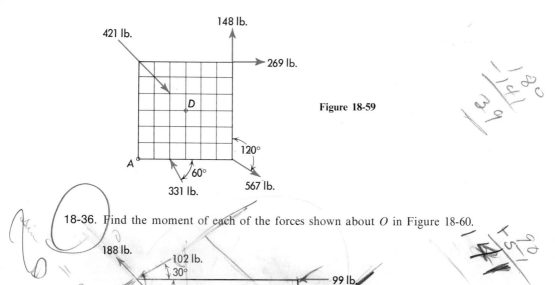

Figure 18-59

18-36. Find the moment of each of the forces shown about O in Figure 18-60.

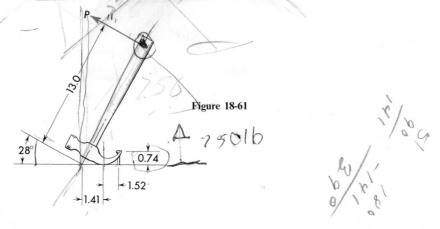

Figure 18-60

18-37. What pull P is required on the handle of a claw hammer to exert a vertical force of 750 lb_f on a nail? Dimensions are shown on Figure 18-61.

Figure 18-61

18-38. On the trapezoidal body shown in Figure 18-62 find the moment of each of the forces about point O.

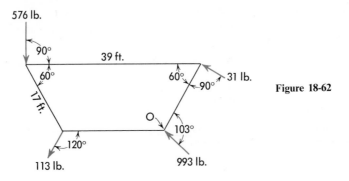

Figure 18-62

18-39. Find the moment of each of the forces shown in Figure 18-63 about the point A.

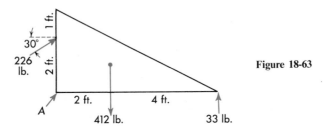

Figure 18-63

Equilibrium

The term *equilibrium* is used to describe the condition of any body when the resultant of all forces acting on the body equals zero. For example, the forces acting upward on a body in equilibrium must be balanced by other forces acting downward on the body. Also, the forces acting horizontally to the right are counteracted by equal forces acting horizontally to the left. Since no unbalance in moment or turning effect can be present when a body is in equilibrium, the sum of the moments of all forces acting on the body must also be zero. The moment center may be located at any convenient place on the body or at any place in space. We may sum up these conditions of equilibrium by the following equations[6]:

$\Sigma F_x = 0$ (the sum of all horizontal forces acting on the body equals zero)
$\Sigma F_y = 0$ (the sum of all vertical forces acting on the body equals zero)
$\Sigma M_o = 0$ (the sum of the moments of all forces acting on the body equals zero)

These equilibrium equations may be used to good advantage in working problems involving beams, trusses, and levers.

Example A beam of negligible weight is supported at each end by a knife-edge. The beam carries a concentrated load of 500 lb$_f$ and one uniformly distributed load

[6]These equations are applicable for two-dimensional problems—or force systems that lie in the plane of this paper.

weighing 100 lb$_f$ per linear foot, as shown in Figure 18-64. Determine the scale readings under the knife-edges.

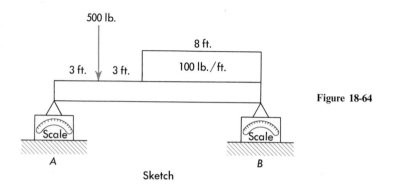

500 lb.

8 ft.

3 ft.   3 ft.   100 lb./ft.

Figure 18-64

Scale

Scale

A

B

Sketch

Solution   The uniformly distributed load is equivalent to a resultant of 8 ft × 100 lb$_f$/ft = 800 lb$_f$ acting at the center of gravity of the uniform-load diagram. Therefore the entire distribution load can be replaced by a concentrated load of 800 lb$_f$ acting at a distance of 10 ft from the left end, as shown in Figure 18-65.

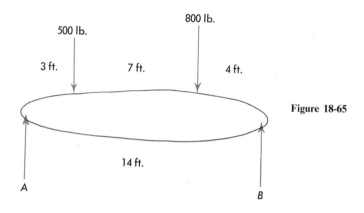

800 lb.

500 lb.

3 ft.   7 ft.   4 ft.

Figure 18-65

14 ft.

A

B

1. Draw a free-body diagram of the beam.
2. Since there are no horizontal forces acting on the free body, $\Sigma F_x = 0$ is satisfied.
3. From $\Sigma F_y = 0$, we know that

$$A + B = 500 \text{ lb}_f + 800 \text{ lb}_f$$
$$= 1300 \text{ lb}_f$$

4. From $\Sigma M_o = 0$, we know that the moments about any point must equal zero. Let us take moments about point A.

$$\Sigma M_A = 0$$
$$(B \text{ lb}_f)(14 \text{ ft}) - (500 \text{ lb}_f)(3 \text{ ft}) - (800 \text{ lb}_f)(10 \text{ ft}) = 0$$
$$B \text{ lb}_f = \frac{1500 \text{ lb}_f\text{-ft} + 8000 \text{ lb}_f\text{-ft}}{14 \text{ ft}}$$
$$= \frac{9500 \text{ lb}_f\text{-ft}}{14 \text{ ft}}$$
$$B = \textbf{679 lb}_f$$

5. From the third step we saw that $A + B = 1300$ lb$_f$. We can now subtract and obtain

$$A = 1300 \text{ lb}_f - 679 \text{ lb}_f = \mathbf{621 \text{ lb}_f}$$

Note The same answer for A could have been obtained by taking moments about B as a moment center.

In this book problems involving trusses, cranes, linkages, bridges, and so on should be considered to be *pin-connected,* which means that the member is free to rotate about the joint. For simplicity, members also are usually considered to be weightless.

By examining each member of the structure separately, internal forces in the various members may be obtained by the conditions of equilibrium.

Example Solve for the tensions in cables *AF* and *ED* and for the reactions at *C* and *R* in Figure 18-66.

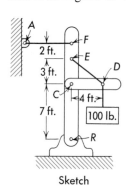

Figure 18-66

Equilibrium Equations

$$\Sigma F_x = 0$$
$$\Sigma F_y = 0$$
$$\Sigma M_o = 0$$

Solution
1. Take moments about point R in free body No. 1, Figure 18-67.

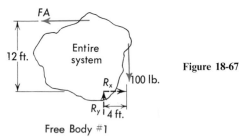

Figure 18-67

Free Body #1

$$\Sigma M_R = 0$$
$$(12 \text{ ft})(FA) - (100 \text{ lb}_f)(4 \text{ ft}) = 0$$
$$FA = \frac{400 \text{ lb}_f\text{-ft}}{12 \text{ ft}} = 33.3 \text{ lb}_f$$

$$\Sigma F_x = 0$$
$$R_x - FA = 0$$
$$R_x = FA = \mathbf{33.3 \text{ lb}_f} \rightarrow$$

2. Take moments about point C in free body No. 2, Figure 18-68.

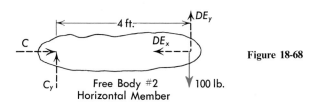

Figure 18-68

$$\Sigma M_c = DE_y\,(4) - 100\,(4) = 0$$
$$DE_y = 100\ \text{lb}_f$$

Therefore
$$DE = \frac{100\ \text{lb}_f}{\sin 36.9°} = \textbf{166.8 lb}_f \nwarrow$$

And free body No. 2
$$\Sigma F_y = 0$$
$$C_y = 100\ \text{lb}_f - 100\ \text{lb}_f$$
$$= \textbf{0}$$

Also free body No. 2
$$\Sigma F_x = 0$$
$$C_x = DE_x = \frac{100\ \text{lb}_f}{\tan 36.9°}$$
$$= \textbf{133.1 lb}_f \rightarrow$$

3. Consider $\Sigma F_y = 0$, using the third free body (vertical member) as shown in Figure 18-69. Remember that in two-force members, such as cable DE, the reactions

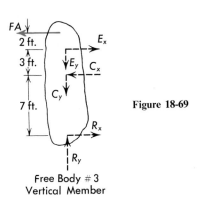

Figure 18-69

at each end will be equal in magnitude but opposite in direction; that is, E_x and E_y are equal to DE_x and DE_y.

$$\Sigma F_y = 0$$
$$R_y - DE_y = 0$$
$$R_y = \textbf{100.0 lb}_f \uparrow$$

The resultant is indicated as before and solved by using the slide rule (see Figure 18-70).

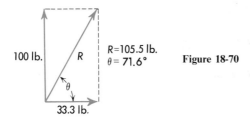

R=105.5 lb.
$\theta = 71.6°$ **Figure 18-70**

Problems

18-40. A horizontal beam 20 ft long weighs 150 lb_f. It is supported at the left end and 4 ft from the right end. It has the following concentrated loads: at the left end, 200 lb_f; 8 ft from the left end, 300 lb_f; at the right end, 400 lb_f. Calculate the reactions at the supports.

18-41. A horizontal beam 8 ft long and weighing 30 lb_f is supported at the left end and 2 ft from the right end. It has the following loads: at the left end, 18 lb_f; 3 ft from the left end, 22 lb_f; at the right end, 15 lb_f. Compute the reactions at the supports.

18-42. A beam 22 ft long weighing 300 lb_f is supporting loads of 700 lb_f 3 ft from the left end and 250 lb_f 7 ft from the right end. One support is at the left end. How far from the right end should the right support be placed so that the reactions at the two supports will be equal?

18-43. A beam 18 ft long is supported at the right end and at a point 5 ft from the left end. It is loaded with a concentrated load of 250 lb_f located 2 ft from the right end and a concentrated load of 450 lb_f located 9 ft from the right end. In addition, it has a uniform load of 20 lb_f per linear foot for its entire length. Find the reactions at the supports.

18-44. A 12-ft beam which weighs 10 lb_f per foot is resting horizontally. The left end of the beam is pinned to a vertical wall. The right end of the beam is supported by a cable that is attached to the vertical wall 6 ft above the left end of the beam. There is a 200-lb_f concentrated load acting vertically downward 3 ft from the right end of the beam. Determine the tension in the cable and the amount and direction of the reaction at the left end of the beam.

18-45. A steel I-beam, weighing 75 lb_f per linear foot and 20 ft long, is supported at its left end and at a point 4 ft from its right end. It carries loads of 10 tons and 6 tons at distances of 5 ft and 17 ft, respectively, from the left end. Find the reactions at the supports.

18-46. A horizontal rod 8 ft long and weighing 12 lb_f has a weight of 15 lb_f hung from the right end, and a weight of 4 lb_f hung from the left end. Where should a single support be located so the rod will balance?

18-47. A uniform board 22 ft long will balance 4.2 ft from one end when a weight of 61 lb_f is hung from this end. How much does the board weigh?

18-48. An iron beam 12.7 ft long weighing 855 lb_f has a load of 229 lb_f at the right end. A support is located 7.2 ft from the load end. (*a*) How much force is required at the opposite end to balance it? (*b*) Disregarding the balancing force, calculate the reactions on the supports if one support is located 7 ft from the left end and the other support is located 4 ft from the right end.

18-49. A horizontal rod 8 ft long and weighing 1.2 lb_f per linear foot has a weight of 15 lb_f hung from the right end, and a weight of 4 lb_f hung from the left end. Where should a single support be located so the rod will balance?

18-50. A 2-ft diameter sphere weighs 56 lb_f, is suspended by a cable, and rests against a vertical wall. If the cable *AB* is 2 ft long, (*a*) calculate the angle the cable will make with the smooth wall, (*b*) solve for the tension in the cable and the reaction at *C* in Figure 18-71. Check results graphically.

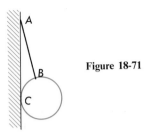

Figure 18-71

18-51. What horizontal pull *P* will be necessary just to start the wheel weighing 1400 lb$_f$ over the 4-in. block in Figure 18-72?

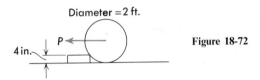

Figure 18-72

18-52. Find the tension in *AB* and the angle θ that *AB* makes with the vertical in Figure 18-73.

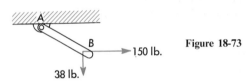

Figure 18-73

18-53. If the tension in the cable *AB* in Figure 18-74, is 196 lb$_f$, how much does the sphere *B* weigh? How much is the reaction of the inclined plane on the sphere?

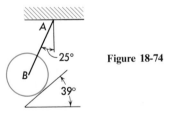

Figure 18-74

18-54. The wheel *B* in Figure 18-75 weighs 175 lb$_f$. Solve for the force in member *AB*, the reaction at *C*, and the horizontal and vertical force components at *A*.

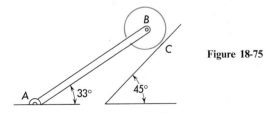

Figure 18-75

18-55. A cylinder weighing 206 lb$_f$ is placed in a smooth trough as shown in Figure 18-76. Find the two supporting forces.

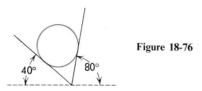

Figure 18-76

18-56. A 796-lb$_f$ load is supported as shown in Figure 18-77. AB equals 8 ft, θ equals 25°. (a) Neglecting the weight of the beam AB, solve analytically for the tension in the

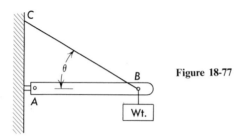

Figure 18-77

cable and the reaction at A. (b) If beam AB is uniform and weighs 12 lb$_f$ per foot, solve for the tension in the cable and the reaction at A.

18-57. Find the tension in AB and the compression in BC in Figure 18-78.

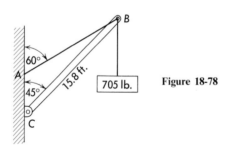

Figure 18-78

18-58. A weight of 1355 lb$_f$ is supported by two ropes making angles of 30° and 45° on opposite sides of the vertical. What is the tension in each rope?

18-59. Forces are applied on a rigid frame as shown in Figure 18-79. Find the reactions at A and B.

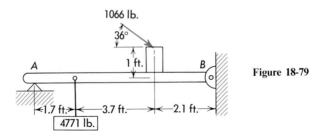

Figure 18-79

18-60. (*a*) What is the tension in *BC* in Figure 18-80? (*b*) What is the amount and direction of the reaction at *A*?

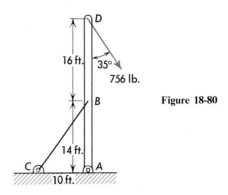

Figure 18-80

18-61. (*a*) Find the tension in *AC* in Figure 18-81. (*b*) Find the amount and direction of the reaction at *B*. $BC = 10$ ft, $BD = 25$ ft.

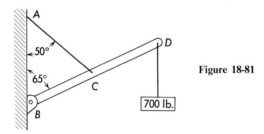

Figure 18-81

18-62. Cylinder No. 1 in Figure 18-82 has a 10-in. diameter and weighs 84 lb_f. Cylinder No. 2 has a 6-in. diameter and weighs 27 lb_f. Find the reactions at *A*, *B*, and *C*. All surfaces are smooth.

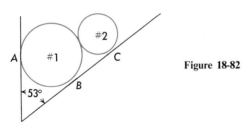

Figure 18-82

18-63. (*a*) Find the force in member *AB* in Figure 18-83 and the reaction at point *E*. (*b*) Find the force in member *CG* and the horizontal and vertical components of the reaction at pin *D*.

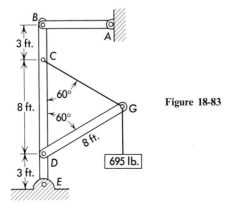

Figure 18-83

18-64. Solve for the reactions at 1, 2, 3, 4, and 5 in Figure 18-84. Weights: $A = 150$ lb$_f$, $B = 100$ lb$_f$, $C = 70$ lb$_f$, $D = 35$ lb$_f$. Diameters: $A = 26$ in., $B = 20$ in., $C = 15$ in., $D = 9$ in. Angle $\theta = 30°$.

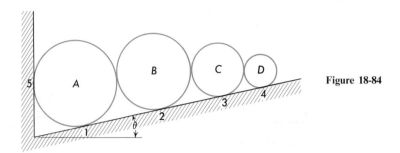

Figure 18-84

18-65. A 15-ft ladder leans against the side of a smooth building in such a position that it makes an angle of 60° with the ground (horizontal). A man weighing 190 lb$_f$ stands on the ladder three fourths of the way up the ladder. The bottom of the ladder is prevented from sliding by the ground. Find the horizontal and vertical components of the reaction at the foot of the ladder and the force between the ladder and the wall.

Bodies in uniform motion

Today the theory of motion and moving things is one of our most important studies. In recent years even governments have become vitally interested in all types of motion—from the motion of atoms to that of satellites and celestial bodies. Moving people, animals, fast-moving commuter trains, sleek automobiles, and jet airplanes are all a routine part of our daily life. Even wars are most decidedly wars of motion.

Motion exists when there is a *change of position* of an object with reference to some other object or plane. For example, a passenger in a jet airliner may be sitting still in the opinion of other passengers, but be in rapid motion with reference to a farmer plowing in the field below. The motion of the airliner may be uniform if it has balanced forces acting on it, or accelerated if jet thrust, air resistance, and gravity do not balance each other.

Sometimes we speak of the motion of a body as *speed*, which refers to its rate of motion. The scientific term *velocity*, which refers to *rate of motion in a given direction*, is sometimes used incorrectly as a synonym for speed. Speed is the term used to designate the magnitude of velocity. Thus speed equals distance divided by time.

Examples $\dfrac{\text{ft}}{\text{sec}}, \dfrac{\text{mi}}{\text{hr}}, \dfrac{\text{cm}}{\text{sec}}, \dfrac{\text{yd}}{\text{hr}}$, etc.

Velocity equals distance divided by time—all expressed in a given direction.

Examples $\dfrac{\text{mi}}{\text{hr}}$ north, $\dfrac{\text{ft}}{\text{sec}}$ 30° east of north.

Illustration 18-2
The study of motion is an interesting pastime for thousands of persons each weekend.

Sir Isaac Newton, an English scientist, was the first to generalize the laws of forces and motions. His findings have been set forth in three laws as follows:

Newton's First Law *A body at rest or in motion will continue either at rest or in motion in the same line and at the same speed unless acted on by some external unbalanced force.*

Common experience tells us that a body at rest, such as a billiard ball, will continue in a state of rest unless some force is applied to move it. Similarly, if the ball is struck and begins to roll, it will continue to roll in a straight line until it strikes, for example, another ball at the end of the table. The velocity with which it strikes the second ball will be reduced somewhat from its beginning velocity. The reduction in velocity is caused by the slight but constant friction between the ball and the table. Automobile wrecks result from this tendency of bodies to continue in the same line. The engine and brakes can act against this tendency and slow the car.

Newton's Second Law *When an external unbalanced force does act on a body, the motion of the body will be changed. The body will be accelerated. This change in motion will be in the direction of the unbalanced force and proportional to it.*

Acceleration is the rate of change of velocity. This is a measurement of how much slower (or faster) a body is traveling now than it was 1 sec ago. The rate at which a body slows down is sometimes called negative acceleration or deceleration. For example: an automobile may start from rest and accelerate to a velocity of 48 mi/hr during an 8 sec period. This means that for every second that the engine acts on the car, there will be an increase in velocity of 6 mi/hr/sec or 8.8 ft/sec/sec. Acceleration is measured as

$$\frac{\text{distance}}{(\text{time})^2} \; ; \; \text{i.e.} \; \frac{\text{ft}}{(\text{sec})^2}, \; \frac{\text{mi}}{(\text{hr})^2}, \; \frac{\text{ft}}{(\text{min})^2}, \; \text{etc.}$$

Newton's Third Law *When any force acts on a body, there is created an equal and opposite reaction.*

Again common experience tells us that the mutual actions of two bodies on each other are always equal. If two men are pulling with equal force against each other on a rope, each will sense the same magnitude of resistance. If one presses the button on an electronic computer with his finger, the finger is also pressed by the button with equal force.

The speed-time diagram

The study of motion becomes rather involved if all of the situations are represented by mathematical equations. Some better understanding can result if one can picture exactly what is taking place. For this reason extensive use will be made of the *speed-time* diagram as a means of pictorially representing the motions described. In addition, this treatment also reduces the amount of memory work normally associated with the various relations.

In motion problems the total distance traveled is represented by the area which lies under the travel line of a speed-time diagram. For example, if an automobile travels at a uniform velocity of 30 mi/hr for 30 min, it will cover a distance of 15 mi.

$$30 \, \frac{\text{mi}}{\text{hr}} \times 30 \, \text{min} \times \frac{1 \, \text{hr}}{60 \, \text{min}} = \textbf{15 mi}$$

This may be shown graphically in Figure 18-85.

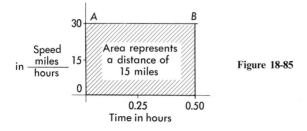

Figure 18-85

If the speed is constant, then the distance traveled may be found by multiplying the ordinate value times the abscissa value. In this case the acceleration is zero as indicated by the straight line A-B.

Therefore, in order to work the above problem, the student need only draw the speed-time diagram and then find the area under the line A-B by simple arithmetic.

Speed-time diagram principles may be summarized as follows:

1. The ordinate of the line at any instant will give the speed at that instant.
2. Abscissa values give the time consumed during travel.
3. The *area* under the travel line of the speed-time diagram gives the distance traveled during the time interval under consideration.
4. The slope of the line at any point gives the acceleration of the body at that point.

Slope may be defined as the *steepness* of a line and can be calculated by dividing the vertical rise by the corresponding horizontal distance.

Example An automobile accelerates uniformly from a speed V_1 to a speed V_2 in time t (Figure 18-86).

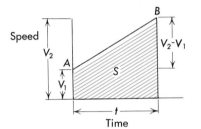

Figure 18-86

A speed-time diagram of the stated problem is drawn. The total distance traveled during time t can be calculated by solving for the area under the line A-B. This area is a trapezoid, and by simple arithemetic,

$$\text{Area} = \tfrac{1}{2}h(b_1 + b_2) \qquad \text{(see page 567)}$$

or
$$S = \tfrac{1}{2}t(V_1 + V_2) \qquad \text{(from speed-time diagram)}$$

The acceleration has been defined as the slope of the travel line. An examination of Figure 18-86 shows that this is also the change in velocity $(V_2 - V_1)$ divided by the time (t) that it took to make the change.

Stated algebraically we have

$$a = \frac{V_2 - V_1}{t} \qquad \text{(slope of travel line)}$$

Example An automobile starts from rest (Figure 18-87) and accelerates uniformly

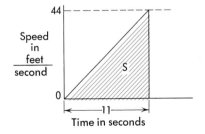

Figure 18-87

to 30 mi/hr in 11 sec. What is its acceleration? What distance was covered during the change in velocity?

$$\left(30 \ \frac{mi}{hr}\right)\left(5280 \ \frac{ft}{mi}\right)\left(\frac{1 \ hr}{3600 \ sec}\right) = 44 \ ft/sec$$

(a)
$$a = \frac{V_2 - V_1}{t} = \frac{44 \ ft/sec - 0}{11 \ sec}$$

$$= 4 \ \frac{ft}{sec \times sec} \quad \text{or} \quad 4 \ \frac{ft}{(sec)^2}$$

(b)
$$S = \tfrac{1}{2}Vt \quad \text{(Area of crosshatched triangle)}$$
$$= \tfrac{1}{2}(44 \ ft/sec)(11 \ sec) = \mathbf{242 \ ft}$$

In some instances the term *average velocity* or *average speed* is used. Average velocity is not necessarily an average of the initial and final velocities. It may be expressed as

$$\text{Average velocity} = \frac{\text{total distance traveled}}{\text{total time during travel}}$$

Example An automobile traveled a total distance of 100 mi at an average speed of 50 mi/hr. During the first 50 mi, the average speed of the automobile was 60 mi/hr. What was the average speed for the last 50 mi?

$$\text{Average speed for trip} = \frac{\text{total distance}}{\text{total time}}$$

$$\text{Total time } (t) = \frac{100 \ mi}{50 \ mi/hr} = \mathbf{2 \ hr}$$

For the first 50 mi:

$$\text{Time} = \frac{50 \ mi}{60 \ mi/hr} = 0.833 \ hr$$

$$\text{Time remaining} = 2 \ hr - 0.833 \ hr = 1.167 \ hr$$

For the last 50 mi:

$$\text{Average speed} = \frac{50 \ mi}{1.167 \ hr} = \mathbf{42.8 \ mi/hr}$$

Many of the situations encountered in linear motion can be solved readily by the use of the speed-time diagram. Some problems involve varied speeds and accelerations during any period under consideration. These changes should be clearly indicated on the speed-time diagram.

Example A train (Figure 18-88) travels 10 mi at a speed of 50 mi/hr and then

Figure 18-88

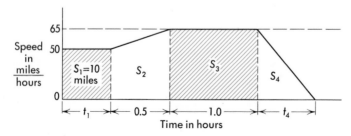

uniformly increases its speed to 65 mi/hr during a 30-min period. The train continues at this speed for 1 hr before being uniformly slowed to a stop with a deceleration of 650 mi/hr/hr. Find (a) stopping time, (b) distance traveled during acceleration, (c) total time, and (d) total distance traveled.

Solution

(a)
$$(a) = \frac{V_2 - V_1}{t} \quad \text{(slope of travel line as train stops)}$$

$$-650 \text{ mi/(hr)}^2 = \frac{0 - 65 \text{ mi/hr}}{t_4 \text{ hr}}$$

$$t_4 = \textbf{0.10 hr}$$

(b)
$$S = \left(\frac{V_1 + V_2}{2}\right) t$$

$$S_2 = \tfrac{1}{2} \times 0.5 \text{ hr } (50 \text{ mi/hr} + 65 \text{ mi/hr})$$
$$= \textbf{28.75 mi}$$

(c)
$$t = \frac{S}{V_{av}}$$

$$t_1 = \frac{10 \text{ mi}}{50 \text{ mi/hr}} = 0.20 \text{ hr}$$

$$\text{Total time} = t_1 + t_2 + t_3 + t_4$$
$$= 0.20 + 0.50 + 1.0 + 0.10$$
$$= \textbf{1.8 hr}$$

(d)
$$S = (V_{av})(t)$$
$$S_3 = 65 \text{ mi/hr} \times 1 \text{ hr} = 65 \text{ mi}$$

$$S = \left(\frac{V_1 + V_2}{2}\right) t$$

$$S_4 = \tfrac{1}{2}(65 \text{ mi/hr} + 0) \, 0.10 \text{ hr}$$

$$= \frac{6.5 \text{ mi}}{2} = 3.25 \text{ mi}$$

$$\text{Total distance} = S_1 + S_2 + S_3 + S_4$$
$$= 10 + 28.78 + 65 + 3.25$$
$$= \textbf{107.03 mi}$$

Problems

18-66. A ball is thrown vertically upward and in due course of time it falls back to the place of beginning. Starting from the time the ball leaves the hand, sketch a speed-time diagram which shows the motion involved. Add such explanation as you may deem necessary.

18-67. A man in a car travels a certain distance at an average speed of 19 mi/hr. After he arrives, he turns around and returns over the same route at an average speed of 13 mi/hr. What was the man's average speed both going and coming?

18-68. An airplane travels from point A to point B and returns, all at an air speed of 200 mi/hr. If a 50-mi/hr wind blows from point A to B during the entire trip, what was the average ground speed?

18-69. A train moves out from a dead stop at the station and in 12 min has uniformly increased its velocity to 60 mi/hr. It travels at this speed for 15 min and then uniformly decelerates to a stop in 1.5 mi. (a) Draw a speed-time diagram to show the entire movement. (*b*) Find the acceleration in the first 12-min period. (*c*) Find the total distance traveled. (*d*) Find the total time consumed.

18-70. A body moving with a constant acceleration of 16 ft/sec/sec passes an observation post with a velocity of 25 ft/sec. (*a*) What will be its velocity in inches per second after 1 min? (*b*) How far will it have gone in 1 min?

18-71. A car having an initial velocity of 15 mi/hr increases its speed uniformly at the rate of 5.5 ft/sec/sec for a distance of 295 ft. (*a*) What will be its final velocity? (*b*) How long will it require to cover this distance?

18-72. A truck passes station *A* with a speed of 10 mi/hr and increases its speed to 45 mi/hr in 1.8 min. At this time its speed becomes constant and remains so for 8 min. The speed is then decreased to zero in 2 min. (*a*) Draw a speed-time diagram for the truck. (*b*) What total distance does the truck travel? (*c*) What is the acceleration in the first 1.8 min? (*d*) What is the deceleration in the last 2 min?

18-73. An automobile is climbing a 20 per cent grade and has an initial velocity of 27 mi/hr and a final velocity of 60 mi/hr. If the time is 38 sec, find (*a*) acceleration in feet per second per second up the grade, (*b*) distance it moves up the grade.

18-74. An automobile traveling at a speed of 16 mi/hr is given a constant acceleration of 90 ft/sec/min. (*a*) What will be its speed at the end of 10 sec? (*b*) How far will the automobile travel in the 10 sec?

18-75. An automobile which has a speed of 80 mi/hr is decelerated at the rate of 20 ft/sec^2 for 5 sec. What is the speed at the end of the 5 sec and how far did the car travel in this time?

18-76. A 3300-lb automobile is traveling up a steep hill whose grade is 22 per cent at a rate of 31 mi/hr when the power is shut off and the car is allowed to coast. Because of the loose gravel on the hill, the car comes to a stop in a distance of 125 ft. After traveling 75 ft, what will be the velocity of the car?

18-77. A car traveling at 45 mi/hr meets a train which is moving 33 mi/hr and the time required for the car to pass the train is 18 sec. What is the length of the train in feet?

18-78. An elevator in a business block goes down at the rate of 9 mi/hr. If the elevator starts from rest and the maximum permissible acceleration is 22 ft/sec/sec, how many feet are required for the elevator to attain maximum speed? Find the time in seconds required to attain this speed.

18-79. A ball is dropped from the top of a tower 86 ft high. Its acceleration is 32.2 ft/sec^2. (*a*) How long does it take it to reach the ground? (*b*) With what velocity does it strike the ground?

18-80. As a train reaches the city limits it reduces its speed uniformly from 60 mi/hr to 18 mi/hr in a distance of $\frac{1}{4}$ mi. It continues at 18 mi/hr for 6 min and as it leaves the city limits it again increases its speed to 40 mi/hr in $2\frac{1}{2}$ min. Find (*a*) the deceleration while the train is slowing down, (*b*) the acceleration during the last $2\frac{1}{2}$ min, (*c*) the total distance traveled.

18-81. The speed of a ship traveling at the rate of 16 knots is uniformly retarded to 5 knots in a distance of 1 statute mile. If the rate of retardation continues constant, (*a*) what time in minutes will be required to bring the ship to rest? (*b*) How many feet will it have traveled from the point where the speed is 16 knots?

18-82. A train and an automobile are passing in opposite directions. When the automobile passes the front of the train, the automobile has a speed of 33 mi/hr and the train has a speed of 26 mi/hr. When the automobile passes the rear of the train the speed of the train is 45 mi/hr and that of the automobile is 20 mi/hr. If the train is 4000 ft long find the time in seconds for the two to pass.

18-83. A train running on a straight level track at 60 mi/hr suddenly detaches its caboose, which decelerates uniformly to a stop. After traveling 2 mi, the engineer notices the accident, and he stops the train uniformly in 50 sec. At the instant the train stops, the caboose stops. What distance in feet did the engineer have to back up in order to hook on to the caboose?

18-84. An automobile crashes into a building. The driver contends that he was not exceeding a 30 mi/hr speed limit when he applied the brakes. If the skid marks of the tires extend for 176 ft and the stopping time was 3 sec, would you agree that the driver was telling the truth?

18-85. A rock is dropped into a well. The sound of impact is heard three sec after the rock is dropped. Sound travels 1100 ft/sec. What was the depth of the well?

18-86. Several small steel balls fall from a tall building at a uniform rate of three every second. After the second ball has fallen for $3\frac{1}{2}$ sec what distance in inches separates it and the ball following it? What distance separates it and the ball preceeding it?

18-87. An automobile is traveling at 35 mi/hr when the driver sees a cow crossing the highway ahead. If 0.9 sec is allowed for reaction time before the brakes take effect, how far away was the cow when the driver first saw her, if the car stopped just as it touched the cow and the time in decelerating was 4 sec?

18-88. An airplane travels from Stephenville to Fort Worth (65 mi) and returns with an overall average ground speed of 196 mi/hr. If there was a 20-mi/hr tailwind on the trip out and a 20-mi/hr headwind on the return trip, what was the air speed of the airplane during the trip? (Assume that the air speed for the trip was constant.)

18-89. An airplane flies from Fort Worth to Amarillo and returns (325 mi each way) at an air speed of 276 mi/hr. If a wind from the northwest (i.e., from Amarillo to Fort Worth) is blowing at 29.6 mi/hr, what is the average ground speed for the return trip? What is the average ground speed for the round trip?

Angular motion

The motion we have just studied was linear motion and was concerned with the movement of a body or particle in straight line travel. Many machines, however, have parts that do not travel in straight-line motion. For example, flywheels, airplane propellers, turbine rotors, motor armatures, and so on all travel in curved paths or with angular motion. For purposes of study here all bodies having angular motion will be considered to be rotating about a fixed center. While rotating about this fixed center there may be a *speeding up* or *slowing down* of the body.

Angular distance (usually designated by some Greek letter such as θ, ϕ, β, etc.) may be measured in degrees, radians, or revolutions. A radian is defined as a central angle subtended by an arc whose length is equal to the radius of the circle.

$$1 \text{ revolution} = 360 \text{ degrees}$$
$$1 \text{ revolution} = 2\pi \text{ radians}$$
$$1 \text{ radian} = 57.3 \text{ degrees}$$

Example: Point A in Figure 18-89 travels through an angular distance θ while moving to position B. $\theta = 120$ degrees, $\theta = 0.333$ revolutions, $\theta = 2.095$ radians.

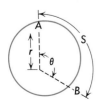

Figure 18-89

Time is measured in the same units as before, that is, seconds, hours, days, and so on. Thus angular velocity, which is an angular distance divided by time, may have such units as radians per second; revolutions per minute, degrees per second, and so on. Angular velocity is usually designated by the Greek letter ω (omega).

Angular acceleration can be found by solving for the slope of the travel line as in linear motion. As in linear motion we must divide the change in angular speed by the time it took to make the change. Problems are worked as before, using the speed-time diagram where applicable. In addition to angular distance being represented by the symbol θ, angular speed, which is θ/t, is usually represented by the symbol ω (omega). Also angular acceleration, represented by α (alpha), is ω/t.

There is a definite relation between angular motion and linear motion. Let us consider a point on the rim of a flywheel. In one revolution the point will travel through an angular distance of 2π radians or a linear distance of $2\pi r$ linear units. All points on a body will travel through the same angular distance during a period of time, but their linear speeds will depend on the radii to the points under consideration. Therefore linear distance is equal to angular distance in radians multiplied by the radius. Linear speed is found by multiplying the angular speed by the radius.

Length of arc:

$$S = r\theta$$

where θ is measured in radians.

Linear speed:

$$V = r\omega$$

where ω is measured in radians per unit of time.

Linear acceleration:

$$a = r\alpha$$

where α is measured in radians per unit of (time)^2.

Example Point A in Figure 18-90 is located on the outside of a flywheel 6 ft in diameter. Point B is located on the inside of the rim 1 ft from point A. If the flywheel travels at 300 rev/min for 10 min, find (a) total angular distance traveled by point B in radians, (b) linear speed of point B in feet per minute, (c) linear distance traveled by point A in miles.

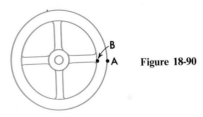

Figure 18-90

Solution Refer to Figure 18-91.

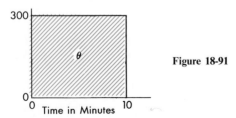

Figure 18-91

a.
$$\theta = (300 \text{ rev/min})(10 \text{ min}) = 3000 \text{ rev}$$
$$= (3000 \text{ rev})(2\pi \text{ rad/rev}) = \textbf{18,900 rad}^{7}$$

b.
$$V = r\omega$$
$$= (2 \text{ ft/rad})[300 \text{ rev/min}(2\pi \text{ rad/rev})] = \textbf{3780 ft/min}$$

c.
$$S = r\theta$$
$$= (3 \text{ ft/rad})(18,900 \text{ rad})$$
$$= 56,700 \text{ ft or } \textbf{10.75 mi}$$

Example The flywheel of a gasoline engine (Figure 18-92) changes its angular velocity from 150 rev/min to 300 rev/min during a 5-min period. Solve (*a*) for the total distance traveled by a point on the rim of the flywheel, and (*b*) the angular acceleration of the point during this change.

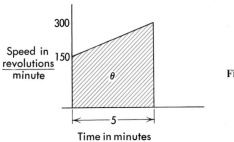

Figure 18-92

Solution

(*a*)
$$\theta = \text{travel during the change}$$
$$= \text{area of the speed-time diagram under the travel line}$$
$$= \left(\frac{\omega_1 + \omega_2}{2}\right)t$$
$$= 5 \text{ min} \left(\frac{150 \text{ rev/min} + 300 \text{ rev/min}}{2}\right)$$
$$= (5 \text{ min})(225 \text{ rev/min})$$
$$= \textbf{1125 rev}$$

(*b*)
$$\alpha = \text{angular acceleration}$$
$$= \text{slope of the travel line}$$
$$= \frac{\omega_2 - \omega_1}{t}$$
$$= \frac{300 \text{ rev/min} - 150 \text{ rev/min}}{5 \text{ min}}$$
$$= \textbf{30 rev/min}^2$$

Problems

18-90. While going around a circular curve of 3000-ft radius, a train slows down from 36 to 13 mi/hr in a distance of 850 ft. Find the angular distance covered in degrees.

18-91. Two pulleys 8 in. and 17 in. in diameter are 10 ft apart on centers and the 17-in. pulley runs 400 rev/min. How many radians per second does the small pulley turn?

[7] *Radian* is a name that is given to a ratio, and it is a sterile value. However, in order to be able to show the name in the answer, it has been carried through this analysis as a name rather than as a unit.

18-92. Given $t = 5$ sec; $\omega_1 = 50$ rev/sec; and $\omega_2 = 15$ rad/sec. Draw a speed-time diagram for the motion involved, calibrating both ordinate and abscissa. Is the angular acceleration positive or negative? Why?

18-93. If an automobile engine is accelerated from 1090 to 4600 rev/min in 3.98 sec, what is the angular acceleration of the crankshaft? What is the distance traversed in feet by a point on the circumference of the 10-in. flywheel?

18-94. Two wheels rolling together without slipping have a velocity ratio of 3 to 1. The driver which is the smaller of the two is 9 in. in diameter, and turns at 50 rev/min. (a) What is the speed in feet per second at a point on the surface of the wheels? (b) What is the angular velocity of the larger wheel? (c) What is the diameter of the larger wheel?

18-95. A belt passes around a 15-in. pulley and a 3-ft pulley. If the 15-in. pulley revolves at the rate of 200 rev/min, (a) what is the angular velocity of the 15-in. pulley in radians per second? (b) What is the angular velocity of the 3-ft pulley in radians per second? (c) What is the speed of the belt in feet per second?

18-96. The flywheel of a gas engine is turning at a speed of 300 rev/min. The diameter of the flywheel is 3.61 ft. What is the linear velocity of an oil drop on the edge of the flywheel?

18-97. A belt passes around an 18-in. shaft and a 4-ft pulley. If the shaft revolves at the rate of 300 rev/min, find (a) the angular velocity of the shaft in radians per second, (b) the angular velocity of the pulley in radians per second, (c) the speed of the belt in feet per second.

18-98. A locomotive, having drive wheels 6 ft in diameter, is traveling at the rate of 58 mi/hr. What are the revolutions per minute of the drive wheels?

18-99. An elevator hoisting drum is decelerating at the rate of 15 rev/min/min. If the drum is brought to rest in 9 min, find (a) the total number of revolutions, (b) the initial speed in radians per second.

18-100. A cylindrical drum $2\frac{1}{2}$ ft in diameter is rotated on its axis by pulling a rope wound around it. If the linear acceleration of a point on the rope is 36.9 ft/sec/sec what will be the angular velocity in (a) revolutions per minute at the end of 6 sec, (b) radians per second? (c) How many turns will it have made during the 6 sec?

18-101. The rotor of a steam turbine is 5 ft $4\frac{3}{4}$ in. in diameter and is turning at the rate of 1850 rev/min when the steam supply is cut off. If it takes the rotor 26 min and 47 sec to come to rest, find (a) the angular deceleration of the shaft in revolutions per minute per second, (b) the angular distance in radians passed through by the shaft before stopping, (c) the average linear velocity of a point on the circumference.

18-102. An engine has a flywheel 49 in. in diameter to which a pulley 16 in. in diameter is attached. The speed of the engine flywheel is 180 rev/min. The engine pulley is connected by a belt to a pump. Assume that the belt does not slip and neglect the thickness of the belt. Find (a) the angular speed of the pulley in revolutions per minute, (b) the angular speed in radians per second. (c) What is the linear speed of the belt in feet per minute? (d) What is the linear speed of a point on the face of the flywheel in feet per minute? (e) If the pump pulley is to turn 105 rev/min, what should be its diameter in feet?

18-103. The flywheel of an engine is 47 in. in diameter and has its speed reduced from 237 rev/min to 176 rev/min in 96 rev. Find (a) the average angular velocity in radians per second, (b) the change in angular velocity in radians per second, (c) the average linear velocity in feet per second, (d) the time in seconds required to make the change in speed.

18-104. A wheel turns at an average speed of 50 rev/sec during a total angular distance of 15,900 rad. During the first 300 rev the average speed of the wheel was 75 rev/sec. During the next 300 rev the average speed of the wheel was 53 rev/sec. Since the overall average speed was 50 rev/sec, what was the average speed during the remainder of the distance traveled?

Work, power, and energy

Many words used in physics and engineering have meanings which differ from their common, nontechnical meanings in everyday use. A word such as *work* is an example of this confusion of meanings, as reference to any dictionary will show. In the common use of the word *work*, it may mean anything from merely a thinking process to the hardest sort of physical exertion. It has required the efforts of science for over 200 years to clear up confusion regarding the use of *work* in technical writings, and the handicap of terms loosely used or misused still is a serious factor in concise scientific notations.

Work is defined for our purposes as the product of a force *F* and a distance *S*, both measured along the same line. From this definition we can see that a force executes work on a body when it acts against a resisting force to produce motion of the body. If there is no motion as a result of an applied force, no work is done.

A person who holds a heavy weight soon gets tired and may feel that he has done hard work. Measured in terms of fatigue, he has done work, but fatigue is not a part of our scientific definition of work. If the distance the weight has moved is zero, the work done is zero. While the ideas advanced regarding work may not agree with the everyday usage of the word *work*, the student is encouraged to accept with an open mind the definition given above, which will be the basis of many definitions of other terms.

The units of work will be the product of a unit of force and a unit of length. For example, in English units a common measure of work is the foot-pound. One foot-pound of work is done when a force of 1 pound is exerted in moving an object through a distance of 1 foot in the direction of the force. In the event that force is not in the same direction that distance is measured, work could be calculated by using the component of force in the same direction as distance is measured.

Example   A constant force of 50 lb acting downward at an angle of 30° with the horizontal moves a box 10 ft across a floor (Figure 18-93). How much work is done?

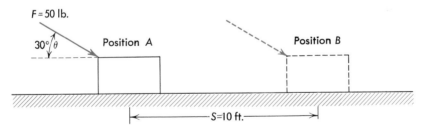

Figure 18-93

In this example, only a portion of the 50-lb force was effective in moving the box from position *A* to position *B*. This effective portion of the 50-lb force was evidently $(50)(\cos 30°) = 43.3$ lb.

The vertical component $(50)(\sin 30°)$ did not produce any motion but served only to press the box against the floor.

Solution
$$\begin{aligned} \text{Work} &= (F\cos\theta)(S) \\ &= (50\ \text{lb}_f)(\cos 30°)(10\ \text{ft}) \\ &= \mathbf{433\ ft\text{-}lb}_f \end{aligned}$$

Example A man carries a precision gage weighing 38.5 lb$_f$ up a flight of stairs that has a rise of 8 in. and a tread of 12 in. He climbs at the rate of two steps per second. How much work is done carrying the gage up a stairway of 31 steps?

Analysis Since we are attempting to find only the work done on the gage, we shall ignore the work done in lifting the man's weight. The work done, then, will be the weight lifted times the vertical height. The length of time to move the gage does not enter into the computation for work.

Solution
$$\text{Vertical height} = \frac{(8)(31)}{12} = 20.65 \text{ ft}$$
$$\begin{aligned}\text{Work} &= (F)(D)\\ &= (38.5)(20.65)\\ &= \textbf{795 ft-lb}_f\end{aligned}$$

Example A cable (Figure 18-94) is pulling a wooden crate of electronic computer parts, which weighs 1380 lb$_f$, up a ramp 30.5 ft long that rises to the second floor

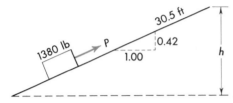

Figure 18-94

of a building at the rate of 0.42 ft vertically per foot horizontally. (*a*) If the cable is pulling parallel to the ramp, what work is done on the crate? (*b*) If the friction force between the crate and the ramp is 120 lb$_f$, what work is done in moving the crate up the ramp?

Analysis (*a*) The work done on the crate is its weight times the vertical distance moved.

(*b*) The work done by the cable is the product of the pull of the cable and the distance through which this pull or force is exerted.

Solution (*a*) The ramp makes an angle of arctan 0.42, or 22.8°, with the horizontal (see Figure 18-94).
$$\begin{aligned}h &= (\sin 22.8°)(30.5)\\ &= 11.82 \text{ ft}\\ \text{Work} &= (F)(h)\\ &= (1380)(11.82)\\ &= \textbf{16,310 ft-lb}_f\end{aligned}$$

(*b*) The pull of the cable is the sum of the friction force and the component of the weight of the crate parallel to the ramp (see Figure 18-95).

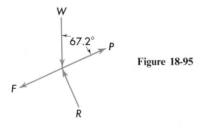

Figure 18-95

$$W_x = (1380)(\sin 22.8°)$$
$$= 535 \text{ lb}_f$$
$$\text{Pull} = \text{friction} + W_x$$
$$= 120 + 535$$
$$= 655 \text{ lb}_f$$
$$\text{Work} = (F)(D)$$
$$= (655)(30.5)$$
$$= \mathbf{19{,}980 \text{ ft-lb}}_f$$

Problems

18-105. It requires a constant horizontal force of 30 lb to move a table on casters that weighs 450 lb. How much work would be done in moving the table 33 ft over a level floor?

18-106. A skip hoist lifts a load of bricks to the third floor of a building under construction. The cable exerts an average pull of 2900 lb for a distance of 25.6 ft. How much work is done in lifting the loaded hoist?

18-107. A man exerts an average force of 30 lb along the handle of a lawn mower. The handle makes an angle of 41° with the ground. How much work is done in moving the lawn mower 100 ft across the lawn?

18-108. An elevated tank in the shape of a cylinder is 13 ft deep and holds 4200 gal. The flat bottom is 30 ft above a ground-level reservoir. How much work is done in filling the tank if the water is pumped in at the bottom of the tank? How much work would be done by the pump if the water is pumped in through a pipe emptying in at the top of the tank?

18-109. A locomotive is pulling a string of 40 box cars, each weighing 45 tons, at a constant speed of 35 mi/hr on a stretch of level track. The frictional resistance of the train is 8 lb/ton weight. How much work is done by the drawbar pull of the engine in moving the train 1 mi?

18-110. A man carries a box weighing 55 lb up a stairway of 17 steps. Each step is 8 in. high and 12 in. wide. How much work does he do in carrying the box up the stairway?

18-111. An automobile engine weighing 550 lb is lifted from the floor to a bench 31 in. high by means of a block and tackle. How much work is done if 10 per cent of the work is used to overcome friction?

18-112. A belt passes over a pulley which is 33 in. in diameter. If the difference in tension on the two sides of the belt is 88 lb and the pulley is turning 530 rev/min, how much work is done per minute by the belt?

18-113. A rope is wrapped around a drum $6\frac{1}{2}$ in. in diameter. A crank handle 14 in. long is connected to the shaft carrying the drum. How much work would be done in lifting a weight of 75 lb a vertical distance of 55 ft? If the length of the crank handle is increased to 20 in. what will be the work done in lifting the weight as before?

18-114. An elevated water storage tank has cylindrical sides and a hemispherical bottom. The tank is 26.8 ft in diameter and the cylindrical part is 36.3 ft high. A pump is located 57.6 ft below the hemispherical bottom. If the tank is filled from the top, what work is necessary to fill it with water? If the hemispherical part of the tank is already filled and water is pumped in from the bottom, how much work is done in filling the cylindrical part of the tank?

18-115. A tractor is towing a loaded wagon weighing 3300 lb over level ground and the average tension in the tow cable is 162 lb. What work is done by the cable in moving the wagon $\frac{1}{4}$ mi?

18-116. A man weighing 188 lb seated in a sling is lifted up the side of a building. If he lifts himself by pulling down on the rope passing over the pulley, how much work does he do in lifting himself 27 ft above the ground? How much work would be done by a group of men standing on the ground and pulling the rope to lift him 27 ft?

Power

It is apparent that no interval of time was mentioned in our previous definition of work. In our modern civilization we frequently are as interested in the time of doing work as we are in getting the work done. For this reason the term *power* is introduced, which is the time rate of doing work.

In symbol form:

$$\text{Power} = \frac{\text{work}}{\text{time}}; \qquad P = \frac{W}{T}$$

or it may be expressed as

$$\text{Power} = (\text{force})(\text{velocity}); \qquad P = FV$$

If a pile of bricks is to be moved from the ground to the third floor of a building, the job may be accomplished by moving one brick at a time, ten bricks at a time, or the whole pile of bricks at once. The work done in any case is the same and is the product of the weight of the pile of bricks and the vertical distance through which the pile is moved. However, the time that will be taken will probably vary in each case, as will the capabilities of the lifting mechanism. In order to obtain an indication of the rate at which work can be done, we use the term *power*, which is a measure of how fast a force can move through a given distance.

The units of power in any system can be found by dividing work units by time units. In the FPS gravitational system, power may be expressed as *foot-pounds per second,* or *foot-pounds per minute.* Since the days of James Watt and his steam engine, the horsepower has been a common unit of power and is numerically equal to 550 ft-lb$_f$/sec or 33,000 ft-lb$_f$/min. Another unit of power frequently used is the watt or kilowatt. There are 746 watts in 1 horsepower (hp).

$$
\begin{aligned}
1 \text{ hp} &= 550 \text{ ft-lb}_f/\text{sec} \\
&= 33{,}000 \text{ ft-lb}_f/\text{min} \\
&= 746 \text{ watts} \\
&= 0.746 \text{ kw}
\end{aligned}
$$

Example A box weighing 1100 lb$_f$ (Figure 18-96) is lifted 15 ft in 3 sec. How much power is necessary?

Analysis
$$\text{Power} = \frac{\text{work}}{\text{time}}$$

Solution

$$\text{Power} = \frac{(1100) \text{ lb}_f \, (15) \text{ ft}}{3 \text{ sec}}$$

$$P = 5500 \, \frac{\text{ft-lb}_f}{\text{sec}}$$

$$\text{Horsepower} = \frac{\text{work in ft-lb}_f}{(\text{time in sec})(550)}$$

$$\text{hp} = \frac{(1100)(15)}{(3)(550)} = \textbf{10 hp}$$

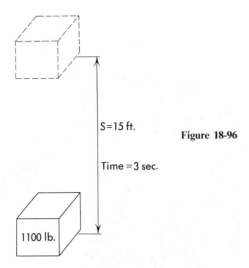

S=15 ft.

Figure 18-96

Time = 3 sec.

1100 lb.

Electric power usually is expressed in watts or kilowatts. A kilowatt is 1000 watts. When electric rates are prepared by utility companies, they customarily base their rates on the kilowatt-hour. Since the kilowatt-hour is the product of power and time, charges for electric services actually are charges for work or energy. When you pay your electric utility bill, you actually are paying for work performed electrically rather than for electric power.

The kilowatt-hour is simply power consumed at the rate of 1 kw for 1 hr.

Example How much will it cost to operate a 150-watt electric light for 2.5 hr when the utility company charges are 6.5 cents per kilowatt-hour.

Analysis Work (or energy) in kwh = (power in kilowatts)(time in hours).

Solution
$$\text{Energy} = \left(\frac{150}{1000}\right)(2.5)$$

$$E = 0.375 \text{ kwh}$$
$$\text{Cost of electric work (or energy)} = (\text{kwh})(\text{cost per kwh})$$
$$= (0.375)(6.5)$$
$$= \textbf{2.33 cents}$$

Efficiency

The efficiency of any machine is expressed as the ratio of work output to the work input, or as a ratio of power output to power input. While efficiency has no units, it is usually expressed as a percentage.

$$\text{Efficiency of a machine} = \frac{\text{work output}}{\text{work input}} = \frac{\text{power output}}{\text{power input}}$$

$$\text{Per cent efficiency} = \frac{\text{work output}}{\text{work input}} (100 \text{ per cent})$$

$$= \frac{\text{power output}}{\text{power input}} (100 \text{ per cent})$$

Illustration 18-3
Prior to this century muscle power reigned supreme throughout the world. In some areas there has been little change, but in others the engineer has brought about its demise as a result of his designs.

Example What is the per cent efficiency of a 12-hp electric motor that requires 9.95 kw of electric power when running at full load?

Analysis The units of power input and power output must both be the same in order to calculate efficiency. We shall convert 12 hp to kilowatts and compute the ratio of power output to power input.

Solution   Power output in kw = (power output in hp)(0.746)

$$= (12)(0.746)$$

$$= 8.95 \text{ kw output}$$

$$\text{Per cent efficiency} = \frac{\text{power output}}{\text{power input}} (100 \text{ per cent})$$

$$= \frac{8.95}{9.95} (100 \text{ per cent})$$

$$= \mathbf{90.0} \text{ per cent efficiency}$$

The result would be the same if the power input in kilowatts had been converted to horsepower, and efficiency had been obtained as a ratio of horsepower output to horsepower input.

The power rating of motors and engines is the maximum output power that they are expected to deliver constantly, unless specifically stated otherwise. The input power will always be greater than the output power. For instance, a 100-hp electric motor can develop 100 hp at its pulley, but more than 100 hp will have to be supplied by the electric power line connected to the motor.

In some situations account must be taken of the efficiency of several machines as we trace the flow of power through them. As an example, let us consider a case in which an electric motor is connected to a pump which is pumping water. The motor obtains its power from electric lines which run through a switchboard. The data are given in Figure 18-97, in which blocks are used to represent parts of the system.

Example   Power supplied to the system, as indicated by electric meters, is 22.1 kw. Find the amount of water delivered by the pump in cubic feet per second.

Analysis   Compute the output power of each part of the system in order, beginning with the switchboard.

Figure 18-97

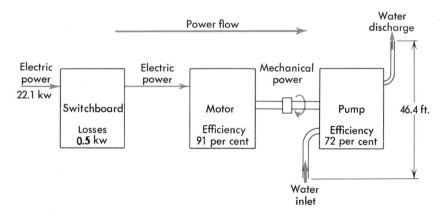

Solution

Power supplied to the motor $= 22.1 - 0.5$

$$= 21.6 \text{ kw} \qquad \text{(This is the power input to the motor.)}$$

Power output of the motor $= (21.6)(0.91)$

$$= 19.66 \text{ kw}$$

If we assume no losses in the coupling between the motor and the pump, the power output of the motor is the same as the power input to the pump.

Power output of the pump $= (19.66)(0.72)$

$$= 14.16 \text{ kw}$$

Converting 14.16 kw to foot-pounds per second:

$$\text{Power} = \frac{(14.16)(550)}{0.746}$$

$$= \mathbf{10,420 \ ft\text{-}lb_f/sec}$$

The amount of water delivered now may be found if we remember that

$$\text{Power} = \frac{\text{work}}{\text{time}}$$

Then

$$\text{Weight of water per unit time} = \frac{10,420}{46.4} \qquad \left[\frac{\text{ft-lb}_f/\text{sec}}{\text{ft}} = \frac{\text{lb}_f}{\text{sec}} \right]$$

$$= 225 \text{ lb}_f \text{ per sec}$$

Converting 225 lb_f/sec to cubic feet per second:

$$\text{Volume of water per second} = \frac{225}{62.4} \qquad \left[\frac{\text{lb}_f/\text{sec}}{\text{lb}_f/\text{ft}^3} \right]$$

$$= \mathbf{3.60 \ ft^3/sec}$$

One additional item of information should be called to the student's attention. We notice that the efficiency of the motor is 91 per cent and the efficiency of the pump is 72 per cent. Considering the overall efficiency of both machines, the input to the motor is 21.6 kw, and the output of the pump is 14.16 kw. The overall efficiency of both machines can be found as follows:

$$\text{Overall efficiency} = \frac{\text{output}}{\text{input}} \ (100 \text{ per cent})$$

$$= \frac{14.16}{21.6} \ (100 \text{ per cent})$$

$$= 65.5 \text{ per cent}$$

The overall efficiency of both machines could also be determined by finding the product of the individual efficiencies:

$$\text{Overall efficiency} = (0.91)(0.72)(100 \text{ per cent})$$

$$= \mathbf{65.5 \ per \ cent}$$

Problems

18-117. An automobile requires 47 hp to maintain a speed of 55 mi/hr. What force is being exerted on it by the engine?

18-118. In a recent experiment a student weighing 168 lb ran from the first floor to the third floor of a building, a vertical distance of 26 ft, in 9 sec. How much horsepower did he develop?

18-119. If a horse can actually develop 1 hp while pulling a loaded wagon at 3.5 mi/hr, what force does he exert on the wagon?

18-120. A car weighing 2900 lb is moving at constant speed up a hill having a slope of 17 per cent. Neglecting friction, how fast will the car be moving when it is developing 25 hp?

18-121. An airplane engine which develops 2000 hp is driving the plane at a speed of 250 mi/hr. What thrust is developed by the propeller?

18-122. An elevator and its load weigh 5300 lb. What will be the maximum upward velocity of the elevator when the driving motor is developing 15 hp?

18-123. A diesel engine runs a pump which pumps 18,000 gal of water per hour into a tank 65 ft above the supply. How many horsepower are required at the pump?

18-124. A bulldozer exerts a force of 7200 lb on its blade while moving 6.5 mi/hr. What horsepower is necessary?

18-125. A car weighing 3900 lb is being towed by another car at a rate of 35 mi/hr. The average force exerted by the tow cable is 200 lb. What horsepower is necessary to tow the car?

18-126. A tank holding 3500 gal of water is to be emptied by a small centrifugal pump. The water is 6 ft deep and is to be pumped to a height of 13.5 ft above the bottom of the tank. The pump is 65 per cent efficient and is driven by a motor which develops $\frac{1}{4}$ hp. How long will it take to empty the tank?

18-127. In a certain industrial plant it was necessary to pump 120,000 gal of water per day an average height of 12 ft. The pump used was 68 per cent efficient and was direct connected to an electric motor having an efficiency of 85 per cent. While running, the motor develops 1 hp. (*a*) How many hours per day would the pump need to run? (*b*) What would be the kilowatt input to the motor? (*c*) Electrical energy costs 3 cents per kilowatt-hour. What will it cost to operate the pump 30 days per month?

18-128. A belt conveyor is used to carry crushed coal into a hopper. The belt carries 13 tons/hr up a 13 per cent slope 45 ft long. The friction losses in the belt and rollers amounts to 22 per cent of the power supplied. How many horsepower are needed to operate the belt?

18-129. A $\frac{1}{2}$-hp electric motor drives a pump that lifts 1200 gal of water each hour to a height of 46 ft. What is the efficiency of the pump? While running, the motor requires 440 watts of power. What is the efficiency of the motor? What is the overall efficiency of the motor-pump combination?

18-130. A pump having an efficiency of 55 per cent is used to pump gasoline. If the pump delivers 50 gal of gasoline per minute through an average height of 38 ft, what horsepower is needed to run the pump?

18-131. A pulley 10 in. in diameter is on the shaft of a motor which is running 1,730 rev/min. If the motor is developing 25 hp, what is the difference in tension on the sides of the belt that passes over the pulley?

18-132. The piston of a steam engine is 12 in. in diameter and moves through a distance of 20 in. each stroke. The average pressure on the piston is 75 lb/in.^{2} and the piston makes 250 power strokes per minute. How much horsepower is developed?

Energy

Another expression much used in mechanics is the term *energy*. The energy of a body is its ability to do work. Energy is measured in terms of work and has the same dimensions and units. Of all the various ways in which energy is produced, such as chemical, electrical, light, heat, sound, and mechanical, the forms in which we shall be concerned are *potential* and *kinetic*.

The potential energy (*PE*) of a body is its ability or capacity to do work because of its position or location.

$$\text{Potential energy } (PE) = (\text{weight})(\text{vertical height})$$

Example   A 100-lb$_f$ box (Figure 18-98) is on a platform 10 ft above the ground. What is its potential energy with respect to the ground?

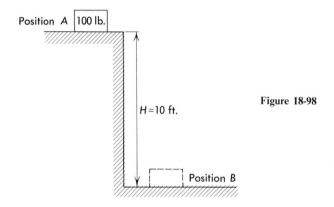

Figure 18-98

To analyze the problem, let us assume the box is initially in position *B*. The work necessary to raise the box to position *A* is (10 ft)(100 lb$_f$) or 1000 ft-lb$_f$. Since energy and work are convertible, the work of lifting the box evidently has gone to increasing its *PE*. The *PE* can then be found as the product of weight and the vertical distance above some reference plane. In this problem:

$$PE = (W)(H)$$
$$= (100 \text{ lb}_f)(10 \text{ ft})$$
$$= 1000 \text{ ft-lb}_f$$

The kinetic energy of a body is its ability to do work because of its motion. The dimensions of kinetic energy must be the dimensions of work. The usual expression for determining *KE* is

$$KE = \frac{(\text{mass})(\text{velocity})^2}{2}$$

The derivation of this expression is as follows: If a force acts on a body that is free to move, the body will accelerate. From Newton's laws this force will produce an acceleration which is proportional to the mass of the body.[8]

$$F = (\text{mass})(\text{acceleration}) = Ma$$

[8]For a discussion of *unit homogeneity* refer to Chapter 11.

If the force is constant and acts through a distance S while the body is accelerating, the work done is $(F)(S)$. Substituting the above value of F in the expression for work:

$$\text{Work} = (Ma)S$$

From the expression of accelerated motion,[9] the velocity acquired by a body starting from rest is $V^2 = 2aS$, or $S = V^2/2a$. Substituting this value of S in the expression for work we get

$$\text{Work} = (Ma)\left(\frac{V^2}{2a}\right) = \frac{MV^2}{2}$$

Since this is the work to give the body a velocity V, the work must have gone into increasing its KE, so

$$KE = \frac{MV^2}{2}$$

The dimensional equation using FPS gravitational units is

$$KE = \left[\frac{lb_f\text{-}sec^2}{ft}\right]\left[\frac{ft}{sec}\right]^2 = ft\text{-}lb_f$$

The units of KE are identical with the units of work. It should be remembered that in the FPS gravitational system of units, the mass of a body in slugs can be calculated by dividing the weight of the body in pounds by the local acceleration of gravity in feet per second per second.

Example A 10-lb_f box (Figure 18-99) is moving with a velocity of 12 ft/sec. What is its kinetic energy?

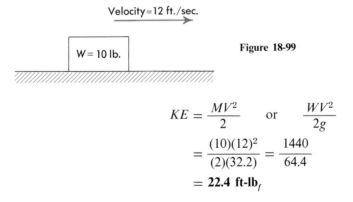

Velocity = 12 ft./sec.

W = 10 lb.

Figure 18-99

$$KE = \frac{MV^2}{2} \quad \text{or} \quad \frac{WV^2}{2g}$$

$$= \frac{(10)(12)^2}{(2)(32.2)} = \frac{1440}{64.4}$$

$$= \textbf{22.4 ft-lb}_f$$

These relations of the equivalence of work and energy can be summed up in what is known as the *Law of Conservation of Energy*. This principle states that energy can neither be created nor destroyed but is only transformed from one kind to another (neglecting mass-energy transformations). As an example, let us take a problem which was previously solved.

The 100-lb_f box in Figure 18-98 when in position A has a PE of 1000 ft-lb_f. Its KE is zero because it is not moving. However, if we push the box to the edge

[9]Refer to page 588.

of the platform so that it falls, we can see that just as the box reaches position B, the height of the box above the ground is zero and its PE is zero. Let us calculate its KE as the box reaches position B. From the expression for motion of a freely falling object starting from rest, the velocity of the box after falling 10 ft will be

$$V^2 = 2gS \qquad\qquad V = \sqrt{664 \frac{ft^2}{sec^2}}$$
$$V^2 = (2)(32.2)(10) \qquad\qquad = 25.4 \ ft/sec$$

Then, solving for the KE of the box as it reaches position B,

$$KE = \frac{MV^2}{2} \quad \text{or} \quad \frac{WV^2}{2g}$$

$$= \frac{(100)(644)}{(2)(32.2)}$$

$$= \textbf{1000 ft-lb}_f$$

which is the same as the potential energy in position A.

Example   A 1000-lb$_f$ pile-driving hammer falls 16 ft onto a pile and drives the pile 3 in. What is the average force exerted?

Analysis   Using the equivalence of energy and work, the energy of the moving hammer was transformed into work by moving the pile $\frac{3}{12}$ ft.

$$KE \ (\text{of hammer}) = \text{work of driving pile}$$

$$KE = \frac{WV^2}{2g}$$

Let $S_1 = 16$ ft and $S_2 = \frac{3}{12}$ ft.

Solution   Since the hammer is assumed to fall freely,

$$V_2^2 - V_1^2 = 2aS$$
$$V^2 = 2gS$$
$$= (2)(32.2)(16)$$
$$= 1030 \ \frac{ft^2}{sec^2}$$

$$KE = \frac{(1000)(1030)}{(2)(32.2)}$$

$$= 16{,}000 \ ft\text{-}lb_f = \text{work of driving the pile}$$

Let FS_2 represent the work of driving the pile. Then

$$16{,}000 = (F)(\tfrac{3}{12})$$

or $F = (16{,}000)(\tfrac{4}{1}) = \textbf{64,000-lb}_f$ average force

It may be seen also in the above example that the PE of the hammer at the beginning of the 16-ft drop is equal to the KE at the end of the travel of the hammer.

Another example of an energy-work conversion is in the use of springs. Using a coil spring as an example, if we compress a coil spring in our hands, we exert a force in order to shorten the spring. This means we have exerted force through

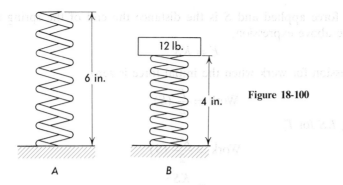

Figure 18-100

a distance and have done work. Also we have stored energy in the spring due to its change in shape. This energy is in the form of potential energy. We know from experience that as the spring is compressed more and more, an increasing amount of force is required. The work done, then, evidently must be the average of the initial and final forces multiplied by the distance the average force has acted.

In diagram A in Figure 18-100, there is no force on the 6-in. spring. As we slowly add weight to the spring, it will shorten. In diagram B the weight has been increased to 12 lb$_f$, and the spring has been compressed until it is only 4 in. long. The applied force, which initially was zero, has been increased to 12 lb$_f$, which is an average force of 6 lb$_f$.

We may take the average force, 6 lb$_f$, times the 2-in. movement of the spring as the work done, rather than take the small change of length due to each increase of force from zero pounds to 12 lb$_f$, and then add all the small increments of work. It can be shown by advanced mathematics that the increment method may be used, but for our purpose we shall use the average force multiplied by the distance the average force will act. The expression for work will then be

Work = (average force)(distance) = energy in the spring

Using the data in Figure 18-100,

$$\text{Work} = (F_{av})(S)$$
$$= \frac{(F_1 + F_2)}{2} (S)$$
$$= \frac{0 + 12 \text{ lb}_f}{2} (2) \text{ in.}$$
$$= \textbf{12 in.-lb}_f$$

In diagrams A and B it is shown that a force of 12 lb$_f$ changes the length of the spring 2 in. A common way of rating springs is by giving the force necessary to change their length a unit distance, such as an inch. In the example used, it will take 6 lb$_f$ to compress the spring 1 in. so we speak of the spring as being a 6-lb$_f$ spring. This value of 6 lb$_f$/in. is called the *force constant* or the *spring rate* of the spring and is substantially independent of the applied force if the elastic limit of the material is not exceeded. If we let K represent the force constant of the spring, then

$$K = \frac{F}{S}$$

where F is the force applied and S is the distance the end of the spring moves. Rearranging the above expression,

$$F = KS$$

In the expression for work when the initial force is zero

$$\text{Work} = \frac{F}{2}(S)$$

Substituting KS for F,

$$\text{Work} = \frac{KS}{2}(S)$$

$$= \frac{KS^2}{2}$$

This shows that we can find the work done on a given spring if we know its force constant and the distance through which a given force has moved it.

Example A spring has a scale (force constant) of 600 lb_f/ft. How much work is done by a force that stretches it 3 in.? What force was acting to stretch the spring 3 in.?

Analysis We must convert our different units of distance into the same units. A distance of 3 in. is $\frac{3}{12}$ or $\frac{1}{4}$ ft.

Solution The work done is

$$\text{Work} = \frac{KS^2}{2}$$

$$= \frac{600\ (lb_f/ft)}{2}(0.25\ ft)^2$$

$$= 300\ lb/ft\ (0.0625\ ft^2)$$

$$= \textbf{18.75 ft-lb}_f$$

The force to stretch the spring 3 in., or 0.25 ft, is found as follows:

$$F = KS$$

$$= (600\ lb_f/ft)(0.25\ ft)$$

$$= \textbf{150 lb}_f$$

Problems

18-133. A car weighing 3800 lb is moving 20 mi/hr. What is its kinetic energy? If the speed is doubled, by how much will the kinetic energy be increased?

18-134. How much potential energy is lost when a cake of ice weighing 300 lb slides down an incline 30 ft long that makes an angle of 25° with the horizontal?

18-135. A box weighing 50 lb starts from rest and slides down an inclined plane with an acceleration of 7 ft/sec/sec. What will be its kinetic energy at the end of the first, second, third, and tenth seconds?

18-136. A train weighing 1100 tons is moving fast enough to possess $(1.5)(10^8)$ ft-lb_f of kinetic energy. What is its speed in miles per hour?

18-137. A car weighing 2600 lb is moving with a speed of 30 mi/hr. What average force is needed to stop it in 62 ft?

18-138. A hammer weighing 1 lb and moving 30 ft/sec strikes a nail and drives it $\frac{3}{4}$ in. into a block of wood. What was the average force exerted on the nail?

18-139. A 22-caliber rifle fires a bullet weighing $\frac{1}{15}$ oz. with a muzzle velocity 1020 ft/sec. The barrel is 26 in. long. Assuming the force on the bullet is constant while it moves down the barrel, what force was exerted on the bullet? What is the kinetic energy of the bullet as it leaves the muzzle?

18-140. A ball weighing 2.5 lb is dropped from the top of a building 125 ft above the ground. After the ball is dropped, how long will it take for the kinetic energy and potential energy to be equal?

18-141. It requires a force of 2.5 lb to stretch a spring 1 in. How much work is done in stretching the spring 3 in.?

18-142. A coil spring has a scale of 70 lb/in. A weight on it has shortened it 2.5 in. and when some more weight is added it is shortened by an additional 0.75 in. What work was done by the added weight?

18-143. The floor of a car is 13.6 in. from level ground when no one is in the car. When several people whose combined weight is 573 lb get in the car, the floor is 11.9 in. from the ground. Assuming that the load was equally distributed to the front and rear wheels, what would be the force constant of the front spring system?

18-144. A weight of 30 lb stretches a spring 0.63 in. What energy is stored in the spring? What is the scale of the spring?

18-145. One end of a screen door spring is fastened to the door 17 in. from the hinge side of the door, and the other end is fastened on the door jamb 2.5 in. from the screen door. It requires a force of 11 oz on the door 32 in. from the hinge side to start the door to open. What is the initial tension in the spring? If the force constant of the spring is 12 lb/in., what force is necessary to open the door through an angle of 65°?

18-146. An iron ball weighing 7.5 lb is dropped on a spring from a height of 10 ft. The spring has a force constant of 70 lb/in. How far is the end of the spring deflected?

The general law of work and energy

A generalization of work and energy relationships may be stated in what is known as the *law of work and energy* and is general enough to apply to almost any problem involving accelerated motion. The law of work and energy may be stated as

$$\begin{bmatrix} \text{The initial} \\ KE \text{ of a} \\ \text{body} \end{bmatrix} + \begin{bmatrix} \text{Work done by} \\ \text{forces tending} \\ \text{to increase the} \\ \text{velocity of the} \\ \text{body} \end{bmatrix} - \begin{bmatrix} \text{Work done by} \\ \text{forces tending} \\ \text{to decrease the} \\ \text{velocity of the} \\ \text{body} \end{bmatrix} = \begin{bmatrix} \text{Final } KE \text{ of} \\ \text{the body} \end{bmatrix}$$

Example A box weighing 200 lb_f is on a plane which makes an angle of 20° with the horizontal, Figure 18-101. A force of 90 lb_f is applied parallel to the plane and

Figure 18-101

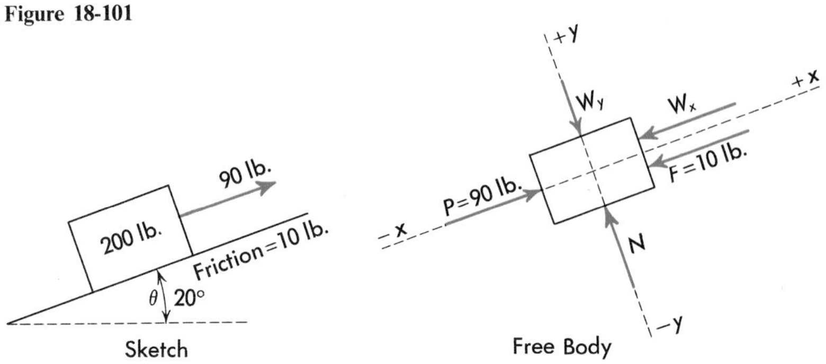

Sketch

Free Body

moves the box up the plane. Friction between the box and the plane is 10 lb$_f$. If the box starts from rest, what will be its velocity at the end of 5 sec?

Let us first solve for the weight components W_x and W_y.

$$\begin{aligned} W_x &= W \sin \theta & W_y &= W \cos \theta \\ &= (200) \sin 20° & &= (200) \cos 20° \\ &= (200)(0.342) & &= (200)(0.94) \\ &= 68.4 \text{ lb}_f & &= 188 \text{ lb}_f \end{aligned}$$

The component W_y is perpendicular to the plane and therefore cannot produce motion along the plane. The work done by the component W_y will be zero. The other forces may produce motion parallel to the plane and must be included in the work and energy law expression.

Taking one term at a time:

Initial kinetic energy $= 0$ (since the body is starting from rest).

Work done by forces tending to increase the velocity. This will be the work done by the 90-lb$_f$ force, as it is the only one that tends to make the body increase its speed up the plane. This work is

$$\text{Work} = (90)(S)$$

Since the numerical value of S is not known, it will have to be included as a letter symbol and solved for later.

Work done by forces tending to decrease the velocity. The component W_x and friction both tend to slow the box as it moves up the plane. The work due to these forces is

$$\begin{aligned} \text{Work} &= (68.4)(S) + (10)(S) \\ &= (78.4)(S) \end{aligned}$$

Final kinetic energy of the box is

$$\begin{aligned} KE &= \frac{MV^2}{2} \quad \text{or} \quad \frac{WV^2}{2g} \\ &= \frac{(200)(V^2)}{(2)(32.2)} \end{aligned}$$

Note that the kinetic energy of the box is found by using all the weight of the box and not just a component of the weight.

Combining all the terms into a single expression, we have

$$0 + (90)(S) - (78.4)(S) = \frac{(200)(V^2)}{(2)(32.2)}$$

$$11.6S = 3.11 \, V^2$$

In the initial statement of the problem, the velocity at the end of 5 sec was required. From the expressions of motion of a body:

$$S = (\text{average velocity})(\text{time}) = \frac{V_1 + V_2}{2}(t)$$

Since the initial velocity V_1 is zero,

$$S = \left(\frac{V_2}{2}\right)(t)$$

and since $t = 5$ sec,

$$S = \left(\frac{V}{2}\right)(5)$$

Substituting for S in the expression $11.6S = 3.11\ V^2$

$$(11.6)\left[\left(\frac{V}{2}\right)(5)\right] = 3.11\ V^2$$

$$29V = 3.11\ V^2$$

$$29 = 3.11\ V$$

$$V = \textbf{9.33 ft/sec}$$

Example A cart and its contents (Figure 18-102) weigh 4260 lb_f. It is sitting on a ramp that makes an angle of 11° with the horizontal. The coefficient of friction between the cart and the ramp is 0.2. What horizontal force will be needed to give the loaded cart an acceleration of 3.70 ft/sec/sec up the ramp?

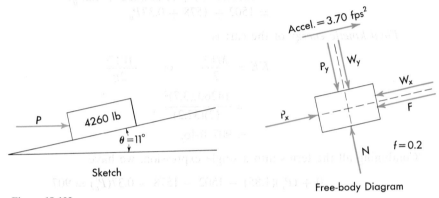

Sketch   Free-body Diagram

Figure 18-102

Analysis Determine the components of forces parallel and perpendicular to the ramp and solve, using the work and energy law.

Solution Solve for the weight components W_x and W_y.

$$
\begin{aligned}
W_x &= W \sin \theta & W_y &= W \cos \theta \\
&= (4260)(\sin 11°) & &= (4260)(\cos 11°) \\
&= (4260)(0.1908) & &= (4260)(0.982) \\
&= 812\ \text{lb} & &= 4190\ \text{lb}
\end{aligned}
$$

From $\Sigma F_y = 0,\ N = W_y + P_y$

and friction force

$$
\begin{aligned}
F &= 0.2N \\
&= 0.2(4260 + P_y) \\
&= 852 + 0.2P_y
\end{aligned}
$$

Since velocities are not given, we should solve for a velocity at some assumed time to provide a value of velocity from which to solve for work and energy relations. Assume that the cart starts from rest and travels for 1 sec.

$$
\begin{aligned}
\text{Velocity} &= at \\
&= (3.7)(1) \\
&= \textbf{3.7 ft/sec}
\end{aligned}
$$

Similarly solve for the distance traveled in 1 sec.

$$S = \tfrac{1}{2}at^2$$
$$= \frac{(3.7)(1^2)}{2}$$
$$= 1.85 \text{ ft}$$

Substitute in each part of the work and energy equation.

The *initial kinetic energy* is zero, since the cart starts from rest.
Work done by forces tending to increase the velocity:

$$\text{Work} = (P_x)(1.85)$$

Since the value of P_x is not known, it will be solved for later.
Work done by forces tending to decrease the velocity:

$$\text{Work} = (W_x)(S) + (F)(S)$$
$$= (812)(1.85) + (1.85)(852 + 0.2P_y)$$
$$= 1502 + 1578 + 0.37P_y$$

Final kinetic energy of the cart is

$$KE = \frac{MV^2}{2} \quad \text{or} \quad \frac{WV^2}{2g}$$
$$= \frac{(4260)(3.7)^2}{(2)(32.2)}$$
$$= 907 \text{ ft-lb}_f$$

Combining all the terms into a single expression, we have

$$0 + (P_x)(1.85) - 1502 - 1578 - 0.37(P_y) = 907$$

To solve for the force P:

$$P_x = P(\cos\theta) \quad \text{and} \quad P_y = P(\sin\theta)$$
$$= P(0.982) \qquad\qquad = P(0.1908)$$

Substituting:

$$P(1.85)(0.982) - P(0.37)(0.1908) = 3987$$
$$P = 2285 \text{ lb}_f$$

Problems

18-147. An electric motor is delivering 18 hp to a water pump. How many gallons of water per minute will be pumped to a height of 32 ft if the efficiency of the motor is 70 per cent and the efficiency of the pump is 55 per cent?

18-148. A bullet weighing 0.065 lb and traveling with a velocity of 1100 ft/sec strikes a large tree. Assuming the bullet meets a constant resistance to motion of 4000 lb, how far will the bullet go into the tree?

18-149. What horsepower motor is necessary to raise a 1200-lb elevator at a constant velocity of 12 ft/sec? (Assume no loss of power in the hoisting cables.) If the motor is 85 per cent efficient, what is the kilowatt input?

18-150. A 3200-lb elevator is raised 40 ft vertically at a constant velocity of 1.6 ft/sec. (a) How much work is done? (b) If the elevator hoist is 90 per cent efficient, what horsepower motor is required to operate the hoist?

18-151. A block weighing 200 lb is setting on an incline that makes an angle of 25° with the horizontal. What force parallel to the incline is necessary to give the block an acceleration of 4 ft/sec² up the incline? Friction amounts to 12 lb.

18-152. How much energy does a 2-lb hammer have, if it is moving 52 ft/sec? How far will it drive a nail into a piece of wood if the nail meets a constant resistance of 3000 lb?

18-153. Water flows into a mine which is 300 ft deep at the rate of 100 ft³/min. What horsepower should be supplied to a pump that is 60 per cent efficient if it is to keep the mine pumped out?

18-154. An electric motor is driving a pump which is delivering 750 gal of water per minute to a height of 83 ft. The motor has an efficiency of 81 per cent and the pump has an efficiency of 73 per cent. What power in kilowatts is supplied to the motor?

18-155. A small boat is powered by a 12-hp outboard motor. At full throttle the speed is 15 mi/hr. Find the resistance to motion of the boat.

18-156. A certain city has a water consumption of 2,500,000 gal per 24-hour day. The average pressure on the discharge side of the pump is 125 lb/in.². If the efficiency of the pump and engine together is 60 per cent, what is the horsepower supplied to the motor driving the pump? If electric current costs 3 cents per kilowatt-hour, how much does the electricity for running the motor cost per month of 30 days?

18-157. A freight train consisting of 60 cars, each weighing 50 tons, starts up a 1.5 per cent grade with an initial speed of 15 mi/hr. The drawbar pull is 90 tons and the train resistance including rolling resistance and air resistance is 15 lb per ton of weight. At the top of the grade the speed is 30 mi/hr. (a) How long is the grade? (b) How much is the work of the drawbar pull? (c) How much work is done against gravity?

18-158. A cylindrical water tank 15 ft high and 10 ft in diameter is filled in 2½ hr by a pump located 30 ft below the bottom of the tank. What horsepower motor is required to operate the pump if the pump is 72 per cent efficient? The water is pumped into the tank through a 4-in. pipe opening into the tank at the top. Neglect friction in the pipe and other friction and head losses.

18-159. A 5-hp electric motor having an efficiency of 80 per cent is directly coupled to a centrifugal pump having an efficiency of 70 per cent. (a) If the pump is delivering 600 gal of water per minute against a head of 18 ft, what horsepower is being supplied by the motor? (b) If the amount of water delivered by the pump is changed so that the motor takes 3.2 kw, what horsepower is the motor putting out at its shaft?

18-160. Water is supplied to a Pelton water wheel from a lake whose surface is 810 ft above the wheel. Water from the lake flows through a conduit and discharges through a nozzle, and 10 per cent of the energy of the flowing water is lost in the conduit and nozzle. When the flow of water is 7.75 ft³/sec, the efficiency of the water wheel is 80.0 per cent. The water wheel drives an electric generator on the same shaft and the generator efficiency is 90.0 per cent. How much electric power in kilowatts is delivered by the generator under the above conditions?

18-161. A certain city has a water consumption of 5,600,000 gal per day of 24 hours, and a pressure gage on the delivery side of the water pump reads 135 lb/in.² pressure. If the efficiency of the pump is 80 per cent, and if the motor is 90 per cent efficient, how many kilowatts of electrical power are supplied to the motor?

18-162. It is desired to install a hydroelectric station on a certain stream. The cross-sectional area of the stream is 800 ft². There is a fall of 48 ft obtainable and the velocity of the stream is 5 mi/hr. What would be the horsepower output assuming an overall efficiency of 75 per cent?

18-163. A wooden box weighing 458 lb starts from rest and slides down a wooden inclined plane with an acceleration of 5.3 ft/sec². What will be its kinetic energy when it reaches a speed of 22 ft/sec?

18-164. A 1.75-ton car coasting at 15 mi/hr comes to the foot of a 2 per cent slope. If it meets a resistance of 12 lb per ton on the slope caused by friction and windage, how far up the slope will it go before it stops?

18-165. A 3400-lb automobile is traveling 63 mi/hr up a 3 per cent grade. The brakes are suddenly applied and the car is brought to a standstill. If the average air resistance is 54 lb and the rolling resistance is 20 lb per ton, what must the braking force be to stop the car in 300 ft?

18-166. A 5-hp motor is operated at full load for 6.3 hr per day, 25 days out of each month. How many kilowatthours will be consumed in a month if the motor is 75 per cent efficient?

18-167. An electric iron requires 550 watts of electric power. How much will it cost to operate the iron for an hour if energy costs 6.0 cents per kilowatt-hour?

18-168. What acceleration will be given an elevator weighing 4650 lb if the pull on the supporting cables is 5300 lb?

18-169. A 3000-lb car is moving with a velocity of 88 ft/sec over level ground. The car is brought to a stop in a distance of 300 ft. Find the braking force. Consider the frictional force to be 50 lb.

Electricity and electronics

The use of electrical machinery and electronic devices has become so much a part of our lives that practically all engineers will work with electricity in some way in their professional role. The applications of electrical phenomena are so widespread that all engineering students should have some basic knowledge of the principles of electricity.

Although the knowledge of electrostatic and magnetic effects has been available for many centuries, the concept that there was any relation between electric charge effects and magnetic effects was not discovered until the last century. An English mathematician, James Clerk Maxwell, was the individual principally responsible for providing a mathematical basis for showing a relationship between electricity and magnetism. His mathematical derivations were based on experimental work done previously by such scientists as Ampère, Volta, Faraday, and Coulomb.

Although we can look back and consider with disdain the difficulties of early experimenters in performing what to us are the most elementary demonstrations of electrical and magnetic phenomena, we must remember that in the days of the early experimenters no one knew even the difference between insulators and conductors. The discovery of the insulating properties of certain materials provided a means for isolating charges and directing their flow. This one discovery, which to us is almost an intuitive concept, was to the early experimenters a major breakthrough in their work. Could it be that 50 years from now, engineers will look back at our present difficulties in grasping concepts of solid-state electronic devices and wonder why we made such a task of attempting to understand the behavior of such obviously elementary phenomena?

The atom

The basis for explaining the behavior of electricity depends on our concept of the atomic structure of matter. Within the atom is presumed to be a system of electrons in orbit surrounding a central nucleus. Some of these electrons in the outer orbit can be transferred to other atoms under the influence of such phenomena as electrical fields, heat, friction, and so on.

Materials differ widely in their tendency to transfer electrons, and all materials can be classified broadly into insulators or conductors as a measure of the ease with which electrons are transferred. For example, if hard rubber is stroked with a woolen cloth, friction will transfer electrons from the cloth to the hard rubber but, since the hard rubber atoms cling tightly to the electrons, little or no movement of the charges can then occur on the surface of the hard rubber.

On the other hand, if a piece of copper is charged, the charges will move readily through the copper by transfer from atom to atom, and, unless insulating structures are provided, the charges usually will dissipate rapidly to other conducting media.

The concept of conductors or insulators then deals not with the production of electrical charges but rather with the relative ease with which charges are transferred.

Since the electrons appear to be moving in orbits, each electron will tend to produce a magnetic field due to its own motion. In almost every material, the orientation of the spins is such that the magnetic effects cancel and the resultant field is substantially zero. However, in the case of iron, nickel, and cobalt, and some of their alloys, the magnetic fields due to the electron spins do not cancel and the atom or molecule does have a definite magnetic pattern, and the material is magnetic.

In a classical experiment conducted by Robert A. Millikan early in the century, the numerical value of the charge on an electron was measured. As a result of this measurement, we find that approximately 6×10^{18} electrons flow through the filament of an ordinary 100-watt 110-volt electric light bulb per second.

Electric currents

If charged particles, usually electrons, move in a conductor, the movement of the charges constitutes what is known as an electric current. Obviously the charges will not move unless there is an excess of charges at one point and a deficiency at another. In the case of a simple electric cell, the tendency of one of the electrode materials to be chemically changed results in an ionization process that will produce a difference in charges on the electrodes. As long as an external path of conducting material exists, the charges flow from one electrode to another in an attempt to equalize the charges. A coulomb is approximately 6.06×10^{18} electrons and a flow of 1 coulomb per second past a given point in an electrical circuit is defined as a current of 1 ampere.

Voltage basically is a measure of the amount of work or energy necessary to move a certain number of charges from one place to another against opposition. A voltage can be present even though the charges actually are not moving. For example, in a certain storage battery, a voltage, representing a state of separation of charges within the battery, exists regardless of whether the circuit is completed so that current can flow. This can be compared to having a pile of rocks on a raised platform. Potential energy due to the rock's elevated position is present even though the rocks are not moving. The usual unit of voltage is the volt—the voltage necessary to cause a current flow of 1 ampere through an opposition of 1 ohm of resistance.

Resistance of flow of an electric current exists because of the difficulty of moving electrons from one atom to another. All materials have some resistance to current flow except that certain metals at temperatures near absolute zero temperature (approximately $-459°F$), appear to have negligible resistance. Commonly used materials having quite low resistances at ordinary temperatures are silver, copper, and aluminum. All metals are good conductors; however, the three mentioned are among the best-conducting materials. Other substances having relatively low resistance are carbon and solutions containing ions. Almost without exception, all other materials are insulators having resistances from thousands to millions of times that of the metals. In some cases, insulators at ordinary temperatures will become fairly good conductors at temperatures of several hundred degrees and upward. Glass and some plastics possess this property of having a markedly lower resistance at elevated temperatures. The unit of resistance is the ohm (Ω) and it is defined legally as the resistance of a column of mercury 1 mm^2 in cross section and 106.3 cm long held at a temperature of 0°C.

Laws and principles

A well-known relation of electrical quantities in a circuit is called Ohm's Law. Stated briefly, it says that in a circuit, the ratio of the voltage to the current is a constant. Of course, like many laws, it must have limiting conditions, the major one being that the temperature of the conductor must remain constant. In symbol form:

$$\frac{V \text{ (voltage)}}{I \text{ (current)}} = R \text{ (resistance)}$$

This means that in a circuit of fixed resistance, if the voltage of the circuit is doubled, the current (flow) will also double.

There are two basic ways in which circuit elements can be connected. These are series and parallel connections. Examples are given in Figure 18-103.

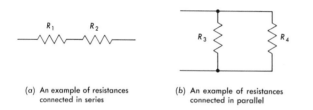

(a) An example of resistances connected in series

(b) An example of resistances connected in parallel

Figure 18-103   Two basic ways in which resistances can be connected.

Series circuit

As an example of an application of Ohm's Law, if a simple series circuit is sketched showing a cell and a resistance with a cell voltage of 28.3 v and a resistance of 2.10 Ω, the current can be computed readily, Figure 18-104.

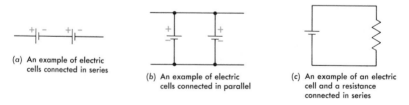

(a) An example of electric cells connected in series

(b) An example of electric cells connected in parallel

(c) An example of an electric cell and a resistance connected in series

Figure 18-104   Series and parallel arrangements of circuit elements.

Solution   First, draw a simple sketch using conventional symbols and label the known quantities. (See Figure 18-105.)

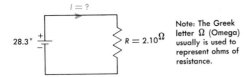

Note: The Greek letter Ω (Omega) usually is used to represent ohms of resistance.

Figure 18-105 A single series circuit using Ohm's Law for solution to obtain unknowns.

Second, solve for the unknown quantities.

Applying Ohm's Law

$$\frac{V}{I} = R$$

$$I = \frac{V \text{ (volts)}}{R \text{ (ohms)}}$$

$$= \frac{28.3}{2.10} = \textbf{13.48 amp}$$

Since this is a closed circuit with no branches, the same current (13.48 amp) is flowing in all parts of the circuit, since it would be unlikely that charges would stack up at some given point. Also, the voltage produced by the cell is assumed to be all used in forcing the current through the resistance. This assumes that the resistance of the cell and of the connecting wires is negligible.

For another example, let us take a circuit where several resistances are connected in series as shown in Figure 18-106.

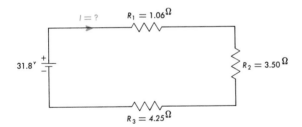

Figure 18-106 Resistances in series.

For this type of circuit, first add all the resistances to get a sum which is the equivalent of all the resistances together. This sum is 8.81 Ω. Then applying Ohm's Law:

$$I = \frac{V \text{ (volts)}}{R \text{ (ohms)}}$$

$$= \frac{31.8}{8.81} = \textbf{3.61 amp}$$

Since the circuit elements are all in series, this same current flows through each element. At this time, we can compute the voltage across each resistance since a part of the total available voltage is used for each.

For Resistance R_1

$$V_1 = IR_1 \text{ v}$$
$$V_1 = (3.61)(1.06) = \textbf{3.77 v}$$

For Resistance R_2

$$V_2 = (3.61)(3.50) = \textbf{12.64 v}$$

For Resistance R_3

$$V_3 = (3.61)(4.25) = \textbf{15.34 v}$$

As a check, the sum of the individual voltages across the resistances, frequently called the voltage drop across the resistance, can be obtained and should be the same as the original cell voltage, within slide rule accuracy.

$$V_1 + V_2 + V_3 = \textbf{31.75 v}$$

Parallel circuits

Figure 18-107 is a sketch of a circuit containing resistances in parallel with the group connected in series with a cell.

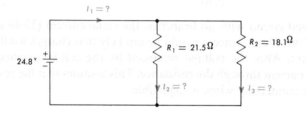

Figure 18-107   A parallel arrangement of resistances.

To solve for the currents in this circuit, first find the value of a single equivalent resistance that can replace the parallel set. This single equivalent can be found by the expression:

$$\frac{1}{R_{\text{equiv}}} = \frac{1}{R_1} + \frac{1}{R_2}$$

or

$$R_{\text{equiv}} = \cfrac{1}{\cfrac{1}{R_1} + \cfrac{1}{R_2}}$$

$$= \cfrac{1}{\cfrac{1}{21.5} + \cfrac{1}{18.1}} = \frac{1}{0.0466 + 0.0553}$$

$$= \frac{1}{0.1019} = \textbf{9.83 } \Omega$$

Using this equivalent resistance:

$$I_1 = \frac{V}{R_{\text{equiv}}}$$

$$= \frac{24.8}{9.83} = \textbf{2.52 amp}$$

Currents I_2 and I_3 can be found in several ways. For instance, since the currents will divide in inverse ratio to the resistances, a current ratio can be determined and since the total current (2.52 amp) is known, the individual currents can be found. A more universal method is to find the current in each resistance by using the *voltage drop* method. Since, in a parallel circuit, the same voltage appears across each resistance, an application of Ohm's Law to each branch will permit a solution for the current.

$$I_2 = \frac{V}{R_1}$$

$$= \frac{24.8}{21.5} = \textbf{1.152 amp}$$

and

$$I_3 = \frac{V}{R_2}$$

$$= \frac{24.8}{18.1} = \textbf{1.370 amp}$$

As a check, $I_2 + I_3$ should add to give the total current out of the cell:

$$I_1 = I_2 + I_3$$
$$= 1.157 + 1.370 = \textbf{2.52 amp}$$

To summarize, for series circuits, the current in all parts is the same and the sum of the voltage drops across the resistances equals the available cell voltage. For parallel circuits, the voltage is the same across each parallel path, and the sum of the currents in each branch or path equals the total current supplied by the cell.

Series-parallel circuits

If a problem involving a series-parallel combination of circuit elements is given, an application of the principles shown above will provide a means of solution.

Example   See Figure 18-108.

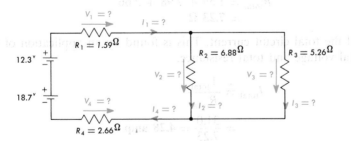

Figure 18-108   A series-parallel arrangement of resistances.

Analysis If the parallel arrangement of resistances R_2 and R_3 can be combined into a single equivalent resistance, the circuit then will be a single series circuit and a method of determining currents or voltages will be available as was used in a previous example.

Solution The equivalent resistance of R_2 and R_3 will be

$$\frac{1}{R_{equiv}} = \frac{1}{R_2} + \frac{1}{R_3}$$

$$= \frac{1}{6.88} + \frac{1}{5.26}$$

$$= 0.1458 + 0.1902$$

$$= 0.3360$$

$$R_{equiv} = \frac{1}{0.3360} = \mathbf{2.98\ \Omega}$$

This means that if the parallel combination were replaced by a single 2.98-Ω resistance, the current and voltage values in the remainder of the circuit would be unchanged. The circuit then can be redrawn substituting R_{equiv} for R_2 and R_3 as shown in Figure 18-109.

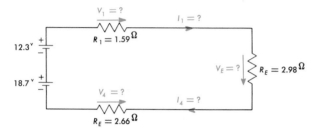

Figure 18-109 The equivalent circuit of Figure 18-108.

First, obtain the total voltage of the electric cells. This is simply the sum of the individual cell voltages.

$$V_{total} = 12.3 + 18.7$$

$$= \mathbf{31.0\ v}$$

Second, find the total circuit resistance. For this circuit, it is the sum of the individual resistances in series.

$$R_{total} = 1.59 + 2.98 + 2.66$$

$$= \mathbf{7.23\ \Omega}$$

Third, find the total circuit current. This is found by an application of Ohm's Law using total voltage and total resistance.

$$I_{total} = \frac{V_{total}}{R_{total}}$$

$$= \frac{31.0}{7.23} = \mathbf{4.28\ amp}$$

Since, in a series circuit, the total current is the same as the current in each part, the current through each resistance also is 4.28 amp. From this, we can obtain the voltage drop across each resistance by applying Ohm's Law only to that part of the circuit:

$$V_1 = I_1 R_1$$

$$= (4.28)(1.59) = \mathbf{6.80\ v}$$

$$V_E = I_1 R_E$$
$$= (4.28)(2.98) = \textbf{12.78 v}$$
$$V_4 = I_1 R_4$$
$$= (4.28)(2.66) = \textbf{11.42 v}$$

As a check, the sum of V_1, V_E, and V_4 should be the same as the available voltage from the cells.

Fourth, referring back to Figure 18-108, we now can solve for the currents I_2 and I_3. Since the voltage across the equivalent resistance was 12.78 v, this will also be the voltage across each member of the parallel set. That is,

$$V_E = V_2 = V_3 = \textbf{12.78 v}$$

The current I_2 and I_3 can be found by applying Ohm's Law only to that part of the circuit.

$$I_2 = \frac{V_2}{R_2}$$
$$= \frac{12.78}{6.88} = \textbf{1.858 amp}$$

and

$$I_3 = \frac{12.78}{5.26} = \textbf{2.43 amp}$$

As a check, $I_2 + I_3$ should equal I_1 or I_4.

More complicated circuits involving delta-wye transformations, applications of Kirchhoff's laws, or network theorems are not discussed here. However, the student may wish to investigate these additional methods of circuit solutions.

Power

Electric power is determined in dc circuits by the product of current and voltage. That is,

$$P = VI$$

where P is the power in watts, V is the voltage in volts, and I is the current in amperes. This expression can be applied to a part of a circuit, but then only the current and voltage in that part can be used.

Example   Refer to Figure 18-108. Suppose it is required to determine the power used in Resistance R_2 and the total power supplied by the battery.

For the resistance R_2 power, use values only for that part.

$$P_R = V_2 I_2 \ \text{(v)(amp)}$$
$$P_R = (12.78)(1.858)$$
$$= \textbf{23.7 watts}$$

For the battery power, use total voltage and current values.

$$P_B = V_B I_1$$
$$= (12.3 + 18.7)(4.28)$$
$$= \textbf{133 watts}$$

By algebra it can be shown that power also can be found by these expressions:

$$P = \frac{V^2}{R} \frac{\text{(volts)}^2}{\text{ohms}}$$

$$= I^2 R$$

In alternating current circuits, power expressions must be modified to account for the possibility of the maximum value of current and the maximum value of voltage not occurring at the same time. This phenomenon usually is referred to as the current leading the voltage or the current lagging the voltage and is caused by the presence of capacitive or inductive components in the circuit. A detailed explanation of these effects is beyond the scope of this discussion, but this leading or lagging effect is a function of time and usually is written as

$$P = VI \cos \theta$$

where P is the power in watts, V is the voltage in volts, I is the current in amperes, and θ is the angle called "phase angle" between a vector representing voltage and one representing current.

The diagram shown in Figure 18-110 is a vector system assumed to rotate counterclockwise and it generates sinusoidal traces on a linear time base. This figure

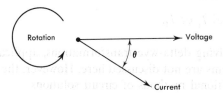

Figure 18-110 Vector representation of voltage and current in an alternating current circuit.

represents current lagging in time behind the voltage. This can be caused by the presence of an inductance, usually a coil producing a magnetic field, in the alternating current circuit.

In making alternating-current power measurements in a circuit having an inductance, the product of a voltmeter reading and an ammeter reading will be different from the reading of a wattmeter by the factor $\cos \theta$. Since the wattmeter reads power, the phase angle, θ, can be found from the meter readings by the expression

$$\cos \theta = \frac{P_{\text{wattmeter}}}{(V_{\text{voltmeter}})(I_{\text{ammeter}})}$$

The expression $\cos \theta$ frequently is referred to as "power factor." It is possible to have a circuit condition of low power factor in which a large current is flowing but which actually involves relatively little actual power. This condition would occur if a very large capacitance or a large inductance having a very low resistance were connected in a circuit.

Measurement of electrical quantities

The most common electrical measurements that are made are measurements of voltage, current, and resistance. Meters that contain a moving element and pointer together with a resistor or resistor network are the common indicating device for most measurements.

Voltmeters A direct-current voltmeter consists usually of a coil of very fine wire suspended but free to rotate in a permanent magnetic field. This is called a D'Arsonval movement. A typical meter contains this movement together with a series resistance of several thousand ohms in series with the coil to limit the flow of current to a few milliamperes. See Figure 18-111. A scale graduated in appropriate units completes the readout assembly. It is not usable on alternating current circuits without additional circuit components.

Figure 18-111 A series resistance and milliammeter combination make up the basic parts of a voltmeter.

An alternating-current voltmeter usually will be one of two kinds. An iron vane type of instrument consists of a stationary coil of wire carrying a current proportional to the impressed voltage to which it is connected. The magnetic field produced by current in the coil reacts with a pivoted iron vane to which a pointer is affixed. The scale over which the pointer moves is graduated in voltage units, Figure 18-112.

A second type of alternating-current voltmeter is made with two coils, one fixed and one moving. When current goes through the coils, a magnetic field is produced in each coil that reacts with each other coil to produce a torque. This is called the electrodynamometer type of instrument.

A D'Arsonval type of movement can be used to measure voltage in ac circuits if a rectifier system is used to convert the ac to dc.

Ammeters A D'Arsonval movement meter can be used to measure direct currents by permitting most of the current to flow through a very low resistance device called

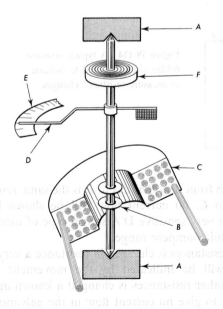

Figure 18-112 Iron vane type of alternating current meter.
A. Pivot bearings
B. Soft iron discs on pivot shaft
C. Cut away section of coil
D. Pointer
E. Scale
F. Controlling Spring
When current flows through the coil, a magnetic field is produced in the coil. The soft iron discs tend to line themselves along the lines of magnetism and the pivot assembly will turn until the controlling spring torque balances the torque due to magnetic effects.

a "shunt," Figure 18-113. When current flows through the shunt, a voltage drop is produced that can be read on a millivoltmeter. Most shunts will have a voltage

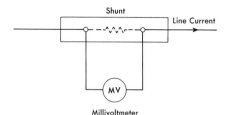

Figure 18-113 A millivoltmeter and a shunt making up an ammeter.

drop of either 50 millivolts (mv) or 100 mv when full rated current flows through them.

An ac ammeter can be made using the iron vane or electrodynamometer type of construction. In addition, for high-frequency current measurements, a hot wire type or a rectifier type of meter is sometimes used. The hot wire type of current-measuring instrument depends on the elongation of a straight wire due to the heat produced by current flowing through the wire. Its scale, like those of most ac meters, is nonlinear and is compressed at its low end.

Wattmeters   A common method of measuring electric power is to use a wattmeter. The usual form of wattmeter employs the dual coil construction of the electro-dynamometer movement. With proper precautions, a wattmeter can be used to measure power either in dc or in ac circuits.

Bridge measurements   A network of components arranged in a diamond shape is referred to as a bridge type of circuit. A typical resistive bridge is shown in Figure 18-114.

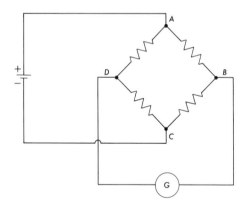

Figure 18-114 A typical resistive bridge circuit as used to indicate or measure resistance changes.

In this circuit, if the resistance path from *A* to *B* and *A* to *D* is the same resistance as the path from *B* to *C* and *D* to *C*, no current flow will be shown by the galvanometer *G*. A galvanometer is a very sensitive D'Arsonval type of movement that will respond to currents in the microampere range.

However, if any one of the four resistances is changed in resistance a very small amount, a current will flow and will be indicated by the movement of the galvanometer pointer. If one of the other resistances is changed a known amount, it is possible to rebalance the bridge to give no current flow in the galvanometer.

This type of circuit measurement is called a "null-method" of measurement, since it depends on balancing a known resistance against an unknown resistance to produce a zero or null deflection of the indicating instrument.

It can be shown that the ratio of resistance at null balances is as follows:

$$\frac{R_{AB}}{R_{AD}} = \frac{R_{BC}}{R_{DC}}$$

If we know the ratio R_{AB} to R_{AD} and know the amount of resistance in ohms of R_{DC}, for example, then an unknown resistance R_{BC} can be computed.

Example The ratio of R_{AB} to R_{AD} is 1 to 10. At bridge balance (null) conditions, the value of R_{DC} is 26.8 Ω. What is the value of R_{BC}?

Solution

$$R_{BC} = R_{DC}\left(\frac{R_{AB}}{R_{AD}}\right)$$

$$= 26.8\left(\frac{10}{1}\right)$$

$$= \mathbf{268}\ \Omega$$

Note that the absolute values of R_{AB} and R_{AD} do not have to be known; only their ratio must be known.

Electron tubes Following the discovery by Edison that electric charges could be transferred from a heated element in an evacuated space to another element in that space, DeForrest developed a device that could amplify electrical currents. The essential parts are shown in Figure 18-115.

In this simplified diagram, a cell or battery at A heats a filament of tungsten that frequently is coated with material such as cesium or thorium. The heat "boils off" electrons from the filament surface and produces a cloud of negatively charged particles around the filament. If the plate is made electrically positive with respect

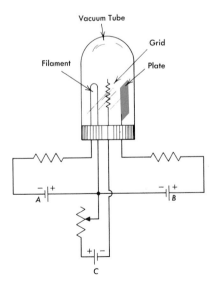

Figure 18-115 The essential parts of a three-element (triode) vacuum tube.

to the filament by the battery *B*, it is possible for the charges to flow through the evacuated space from the filament area to the plate and constitute a current flow. If the positive voltage of the plate is below a certain level or if the polarity is reversed to make the plate negative, no current will flow.

These two elements in an evacuated space constitute a diode and can be used to rectify alternating currents—that is, change the alternating current to pulsating direct current.

If a third electrode is introduced between the filament and plate and is connected so it is negative with respect to the filament, the voltage of this third element, called a "grid," can block the current flow, even though the positively charged plate is attempting to attract electrons. In fact, because the grid is near the filament, a very small change in its voltage will make a large change in the filament-to-plate current flow. This constitutes the amplifying capability of the vacuum tube.

The transistor

Shortly after the close of World War II, an announcement was made of the discovery of a solid-state device requiring no heated filament that could be used as an amplifier. This discovery has in only a few years revolutionized the electronics industry. Although the solid-state diode as a rectifier had been in use for many years, the introduction of another element to permit amplification provided a tremendous opportunity for miniaturizing electronic components. This new device was called a *transistor* and, as it made its appearance almost at the same time that the computer was being developed, it was incorporated into almost all modern computers.

The theory of the transistor is fairly complex, but its action depends essentially on the presence of minute quantities of an "impurity" material such as arsenic in a crystal of pure material such as germanium permitting current to flow in one direction but not in the other. A proper assembly of three sections of negative carrier and positive carrier material permits a small voltage to control a much larger current flow in a manner similar to the way a vacuum tube behaves in a circuit.

The major advantages of the transistor as used in electronic circuits are light weight, small space, low power consumption, and long life. The modern integrated circuit is made possible only by the use of semiconductor techniques, and permits a tiny chip of material to perform the same functions as a vacuum tube type of amplifier which would be thousands of times larger.

A fascinating new world of circuit design has been opened recently with the development of higher-powered transistors, and now they can be used in all but the high current output stages of amplifiers.

Problems

18-170. Using a small compass, verify experimentally the pattern of magnetic lines around a bar magnet or a horseshoe magnet.

18-171. List in order of increasing unit resistance, the ten best metallic conductors. In a word or two, give major advantages and disadvantages of using each as an electric conductor for power circuits.

18-172. Sketch a simple circuit consisting of a crystal microphone, a vacuum tube or transistor used as an amplifier, and a loudspeaker. Explain briefly and concisely its features of operation in terms that might be used for a sales brochure.

18-173. A current of 5.5 ma flows from the filament to the plate of a vacuum tube. What is the approximate number of electrons flowing per second across the space?

18-174. A resistance of 3.65 kΩ is connected in series with 920 Ω. What is the combined resistance? If these two resistors are reconnected so they are in parallel, what will be the equivalent resistance?

18-175. Three resistors having values of 128 Ω, 144 Ω, and 98.2 Ω, respectively, are connected in series. What will be their combined resistance? If these three resistances are reconnected so they are in parallel with each other, what will their equivalent resistance be?

18-176. A current of 75.5 ma flows through a 1.80-kΩ resistance in a circuit containing a vacuum tube. What will be the voltage drop across the resistance? If the current is measured later and is found to have decreased to 48.1 ma, what things could have caused the decrease?

18-177. A circuit is suspected of having damaged insulation at some place in its installation on an aircraft. In order to check the insulation, a battery having a voltage of about 50 v is connected to the ship's metal structure and in series with the suspected circuit using a microammeter having an internal resistance of 100 Ω. If the microammeter reads 7.4 μa, what is the approximate resistance to ground of the circuit?

18-178. A battery having an internal resistance of 0.01 Ω and an open circuit voltage of 27.6 v is connected to a starter on an aircraft. If the starter resistance while not turning is 0.10 Ω and the line resistance of the connecting wires is 0.03 Ω, what maximum current can flow through the starter? What will be the voltage across the starter at the instant of closing the starting circuit?

18-179. Power in watts in a dc electric circuit is defined as the product of current in amperes and voltage in volts. If a 100-watt lamp is connected to a 117-v line, what current will flow through the lamp? If a 40-watt lamp is connected in parallel with the 100-watt lamp, what total current will need to flow in the line supplying both lamps?

18-180. In the circuit of Figure 18-108, if the voltage of the cells is changed to an unknown amount but the current I_1 is measured to be 7.03 amp, what will be the values of V_1, V_2, V_3, V_4, I_2, I_3, I_4, and total cell voltages?

18-181. A dc voltage is to be measured which is known to be about 75 v. A voltmeter is not available, but a dc microammeter having a full scale of 100 μa and a resistance of 100 Ω is on hand. A large quantity of precision resistors is available. What series resistor should be chosen to make the meter show full-scale deflection if 100 v is applied across it with a suitable resistor in series? (This will make the scale "direct reading.")

18-182. A dc shunt is to be made to permit the measurement of starting currents in an automotive starter. The expected current should not exceed 200 amp from a 12-v system. What should be the resistance of the shunt so that a current of 200 amp through it will produce a voltage drop of 50 mv across it?

18-183. A set of instructions accompanying an electrodynamic movement wattmeter says that a wattmeter should always have an ammeter and voltmeter in the circuit when the wattmeter is being used. Why is this desirable?

18-184. A Wheatstone bridge is set up with a ratio of 1:100 in the *AB* and *AD* sections of the bridge (see Figure 18-114). If the galvanometer shows no appreciable deflection when the resistance of *BC* is 157.1 Ω, what will be the resistance of *CD*? If there is a barely discernable deflection of the galvanometer when the resistance of *BC* is changed by ±0.3 Ω, what is the per cent uncertainty of the measurement of *CD*?

18-185. When using a Wheatstone bridge, what things might account for resistance measurements below 1 Ω being subject to considerable uncertainty?

18-186. If a change in plate voltage of 35.0 v in a vacuum tube produces a change in plate current of 2.20 ma and if a corresponding change of grid voltage of 1.7 v will produce the same change in plate current, what is the relative effectiveness of the change in plate voltage to change in grid voltage to produce the same change in each case of plate current? This ratio is known as amplification factor.

18-187. The life of an incandescent lamp varies inversely as the 12th power of the applied voltage. If the rated life of a lamp is 800 hr at 117 v, what would be the expected life if operated continuously at 120 v? What would be the expected life if operated at 110 v?

18-188. If energy cost is 2 cents per kilowatt-hour, what will be the approximate cost of operating a 100-watt lamp an average of 5 hr per day for a month?

18-189. Four strain gages having a resistance of 350.0 Ω each are cemented to a steel bar to measure surface strain. When the bar is strained and the bridge is slightly unbalanced by the strain, a galvanometer having a resistance of 30.5 Ω indicates a current flow of 12.3 μa. What would be the voltage between points B and D (see Figure 18-114) of the Wheatstone bridge network?

18-190. A series circuit is made up using a 10,000-Ω resistance, a 3000-Ω resistance, and an ammeter having a resistance of 720 Ω all connected to a battery. If the ammeter shows a current flow of 3.03 ma, what voltage is supplied by the battery? What voltage drop would exist across the 3000-Ω resistance when this current is flowing?

18-191. A galvanometer used to measure small currents requires a connection to a circuit having an equivalent resistance of 350 Ω in order to help provide proper damping for reading oscillatory currents. If the strain gages making up a Wheatstone bridge to which the galvanometer is connected measure 120 Ω each, what resistance will need to be included in the circuit in order to provide proper matching resistance for the galvanometer?

18-192. A galvanometer used to measure small currents requires a connection to a circuit having an equivalent resistance of 120 Ω in order to help provide proper damping for reading oscillatory currents. If the strain gages making up a Wheatstone bridge to which the galvanometer is connected measure 350 Ω, what resistance will need to be included in the circuit in order to provide proper matching resistance for the galvanometer?

18-193. In the circuit of Fig. 18-108 R_1 is 321 Ω, R_2 is 1080 Ω, R_3 is 844 Ω, R_4 is 112 Ω, and I_1 is 39.5 ma. What will be the amount of the applied battery voltage, voltage V_2, voltage V_3, currents I_2 and I_3, and voltage V_4?

18-194. By applications of Ohm's Law, show by derivation that $P = V^2/R$ and that $P = I^2R$ can be obtained from the expression $P = VI$.

18-195. The heating element of a cookstove is rated at 3000 watts and 220 v. What current will flow when the element is turned on? To how many horsepower would 3000 watts be equivalent?

18-196. If energy costs 2 cents per kilowatt-hour, what would be the approximate cost of operating a 100-watt lamp for 1 hr?

18-197. In a circuit containing a large coil of wire, 60-cycle-per-second alternating current is applied and a wattmeter reads 866 watts at the same time a voltmeter reads 114 v and an ammeter reads 10.1 amp. What is the phase angle in this circuit?

18-198. An electric iron is rated at 660 watts, 110 v. What will be the approximate resistance of the heating element? Is it likely that copper wire is used for the heating element? Describe desirable properties that the heating element conductor should have.

18-199. A lantern type of dry cell has a voltage of 1.58 v when measured with a very-high resistance voltmeter. When a very-low resistance ammeter is connected across it, the current is 28.5 amp. Neglecting effects of the meter resistances on the readings, what is the internal resistance of the dry cell? Could this method be used successfully to measure the internal resistance of a 12-v automotive storage battery? Discuss.

18-200. A microammeter has an internal resistance of 3600 Ω and will show full-scale deflection when a current of 100 μa flows through it. In order to use it as a voltmeter, a high resistance is placed in series with the microammeter to limit the current through it. If it is desired that when connected to a 50-v line the microammeter and series resistor combination will be set to show full-scale deflection of the pointer on the microammeter, what value of series resistance should be used?

Appendixes

APPENDIX I

Logarithms—the mathematical basis for the slide rule

Laws of logarithms

Since a logarithm is an exponent, all the laws of exponents should be reviewed. Let us examine a few of these laws.

Exponential Law I $(a)^m(a)^n = a^{m+n}$

We can put the equation above in statement form, since we know that logarithms are exponents and therefore follow the laws of exponents.

Law I   The logarithm of a product equals the sum of the logarithms of the factors.

Example
$$(5)(7) = ?$$
$$\log_{10}5 + \log_{10}7 = \log_{10} \text{ ans.}$$
$$0.6990 + 0.8451 = \log \text{ ans.}$$
$$1.5441 = \log \text{ ans.}$$
$$\text{Answer} = (3.50)(10)^1$$

This is true because
$$5 = (10)^{0.6990}$$
$$7 = (10)^{0.8451}$$
$$\text{product} = (10)^{0.6990}(10)^{0.8451}$$
$$= (10)^{0.6990+0.8451}$$
$$= (10)^{1.5441}$$
$$= (3.50)(10)^1$$

Exponential Law II $\dfrac{a^m}{a^n} = a^{m-n}$

Putting the equation above in statement form, we obtain the following law.

Law II The logarithm of a quotient equals the logarithm of the dividend minus the logarithm of the divisor.

Example

$$\tfrac{5}{4} = ?$$
$$\log 5 - \log 4 = \log \text{ ans.}$$
$$0.6990 - 0.6021 = \log \text{ ans.}$$
$$0.0969 = \log \text{ ans.}$$
$$\text{Answer} = \mathbf{1.25}$$

Law III The logarithm of the x power of a number equals x times the logarithm of the number.

Example

$$(5)^3 = ?$$
$$3(\log 5) = \log \text{ ans.}$$
$$3(0.6990) = \log \text{ ans.}$$
$$2.0970 = \log \text{ ans.}$$
$$\text{Answer} = \mathbf{(1.25)(10)^2}$$

Law IV The logarithm of the x root of a number equals the logarithm of the number divided by x.

Example

$$\sqrt[3]{3375} = ?$$

$$\frac{\log 3375}{3} = \log \text{ ans.}$$

$$\frac{3.5282}{3} = \log \text{ ans.}$$

$$1.1761 = \log \text{ ans.}$$
$$\text{Answer} = \mathbf{(1.50)(10)^1}$$

Note Law IV is actually a special case of Law III.

In some instances a combination of Law III and Law IV may be used.

Example

$$(0.916)^{3/4.15} = ?$$

$$\frac{(\log 0.916)(3)}{4.15} = \log \text{ ans.}$$

$$\frac{(9.9619 - 10)(3)}{4.15} = \log \text{ ans.}$$

Perform multiplication first:

$$\frac{29.8857 - 30}{4.15} = \log \text{ ans.}$$

To be divided by 4.15, the negative number must be divisible a whole number of times. Therefore, the characteristic (which is -1) is written as $414.0000 - 415$. There are several values which could be chosen, such as 4149.0000 − 4150, which would satisfy the condition that the characteristic be −1. Rewriting and dividing,

$$\frac{414.8857 - 415}{4.15} = \log \text{ ans.}$$

$$99.9725 - 100 = \log \text{ ans.}$$
$$\text{Answer} = \mathbf{(9.39)(10)^{-1}}$$

The cologarithm Many times it is helpful to use the cologarithm of a number rather than the logarithm. The cologarithm of a number is the logarithm of the reciprocal of the number. The cologarithm is also the difference between the logarithm and the logarithm of unity.

Example $\qquad\qquad\qquad \text{colog } 5 = \log \dfrac{1}{5}$

$$= \log 1 - \log 5$$
$$= 0.0000 - 0.6990$$
$$= \mathbf{-0.6990}$$

Since log 5 equals 0.6990, we see that the colog $x = -\log x$. Therefore:

1. The logarithm of the quotient of two numbers equals the logarithm of the dividend plus the cologarithm of the divisor.
2. The logarithm of the product of two numbers equals the logarithm of one number minus the cologarithm of the other number.

Natural logarithms When certain derivations of engineering formulas are made, a term may appear that contains a natural logarithm. For example, the magnetic field intensity near a current-carrying conductor varies with distance from the conductor according to a logarithmic pattern. In advanced texts it may be shown that a natural logarithm function, when plotted, gives an exponential curve whose slope at any point is equal to the ordinate at that point.

In solving problems involving natural logarithms, tables of natural logarithms can be used if they are available, or the natural logarithm, frequently abbreviated as "ln," may be converted to a logarithm to the base 10. To perform this latter operation, an algebraic transformation called *change of logarithmic base* is used. This transformation can be performed as follows:

$$\text{Natural logarithm} = (\text{common log})(\log_\epsilon 10)$$

Since $\log_\epsilon 10 = 2.3026$, we may write:

$$\text{Natural logarithm} = (\text{common log})(2.3026)$$

If natural logarithms are computed, it must be remembered that the mantissa is not independent of the location of the decimal point. Therefore, the same sequence of significant figures does not have the same mantissa, as is the case with common logarithms.

Example Find the natural logarithm of 245.

$$\log_{10} 245 = 2.3892$$
$$\ln 245 = (2.3892)(2.3026)$$
$$= \mathbf{5.5014}$$

Example Find the natural logarithm of 2.45.

$$\log_{10} 245 = 0.3892$$
$$\ln 2.45 = (0.3892)(2.3026)$$
$$= \mathbf{0.8961}$$

The natural logarithm of a number less than 1 is a negative number.

Example Find the natural logarithm of 0.245.

$$\log_{10} 0.245 = 9.3892 - 10$$

Since the logarithm has a negative characteristic, we can solve by first finding the colog and then multiplying by $\log_{\epsilon} 10$.

$$\text{colog}_{10} 0.245 = -0.6108$$
$$\ln 0.245 = (-0.6108)(2.3026)$$
$$= \mathbf{-1.4064}$$

APPENDIX II

Trigonometry

Right triangles

It can be shown by measurements and by formal derivations that for any given size of an angle at A or C, the ratio of the lengths of the sides to each other in a right triangle is a constant regardless of the numerical value of the lengths. In Figure AII-1, the sides of a right triangle are named in reference to the angle under consideration. In the cases, the angle is designated as θ (theta).

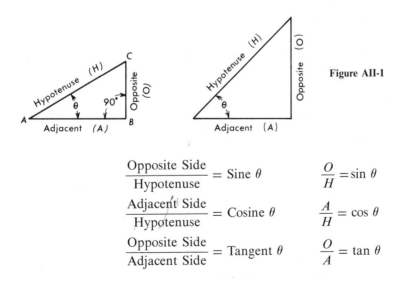

Figure AII-1

$$\frac{\text{Opposite Side}}{\text{Hypotenuse}} = \text{Sine } \theta \qquad \frac{O}{H} = \sin \theta$$

$$\frac{\text{Adjacent Side}}{\text{Hypotenuse}} = \text{Cosine } \theta \qquad \frac{A}{H} = \cos \theta$$

$$\frac{\text{Opposite Side}}{\text{Adjacent Side}} = \text{Tangent } \theta \qquad \frac{O}{A} = \tan \theta$$

$$\frac{\text{Adjacent Side}}{\text{Opposite Side}} = \text{Cotangent } \theta \qquad \frac{A}{O} = \cot \theta$$

$$\frac{\text{Hypotenuse}}{\text{Adjacent Side}} = \text{Secant } \theta \qquad \frac{H}{A} = \sec \theta$$

$$\frac{\text{Hypotenuse}}{\text{Opposite Side}} = \text{Cosecant } \theta \qquad \frac{H}{O} = \csc \theta$$

Methods of solving oblique triangle problems

In order to solve an oblique triangle problem, at least three of the six parts of the triangle must be known, and at least one of the known parts must be a side. In the suggested methods listed below, only the most effective methods are given.

1. Given: two sides and an angle opposite one of them:
   a. Law of sines.
   b. Right triangles.
2. Given: two angles and one side:
   a. Law of sines.
   b. Right triangles.
3. Given: two sides and the included angle:
   a. Law of cosines (answer is usually not dependable to more than three significant figures).
   b. Right triangles.
4. Given: three sides only:
   a. Tangent formula (half-angle solution).
   b. Sine formula (half-angle solution). This formula is not exact if the half-angle is near 90°.
   c. Cosine formula (half-angle solution). This formula is not exact if the half-angle is about 6° or less.
   d. Cosine formula (whole angle solution).
   e. Law of cosines (answer is usually not dependable to more than three significant figures).

Methods for finding areas of oblique triangles

The area of an oblique triangle may be found by any of several methods. Some of the more common methods are given below:

1. Area = $(\frac{1}{2})$(base)(altitude).
2. Area = $\sqrt{(S)(S - AB)(S - BC)(S - AC)}$, where $S = \frac{1}{2}$ perimeter of the triangle.
3. Area = $\frac{1}{2}$ (product of two sides) (sine of the included angle).

Sine law

In any triangle the ratio of the length of a side to the sine of the angle opposite that side is the same as the ratio of any other side to the sine of the angle opposite it. In symbol form (see Figure AII-2):

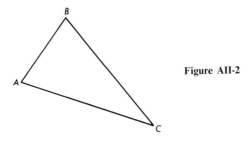

Figure AII-2

$$\frac{AB}{\sin \angle C} = \frac{BC}{\sin \angle A} = \frac{AC}{\sin \angle B}$$

This expression is called the *sine law*. The student is cautioned not to confuse the meanings of sine functions and sine law.

In the event one of the angles of a triangle is larger than 90°, a simple way to obtain the value of the sine of the angle is to subtract the angle from 180° and obtain the sine of this angle to use in the sine law expression.

The sine law can also be used if two sides and an angle of a triangle are known, provided the angle is not the one included between the sides. However, as explained in trigonometry texts, the product of the sine of the angle and the side adjacent must be equal to or less than the side opposite the angle; otherwise no solution is possible.

As an alternate method, the general triangle can be made into right triangles by adding construction lines. This method of using right triangle solutions is as exact as the sine law but usually will take more time than the sine law method.

Cosine law

In an oblique triangle, the square of any side is equal to the sum of the squares of the other two sides minus twice the product of the other two sides times the cosine of the included angle. In symbol form:

$$(AB)^2 = (AC)^2 + (BC)^2 - (2)(AC)(BC)(\cos \angle C)$$

This expression is called the *cosine law* and is useful in many problems, although it may not give an answer to the desired precision since we are adding and subtracting terms that have only three significant figures.

After the side *AB* has been determined, the angles at *A* and *B* can be found by using the law of sines.

In the event that the angle used in the cosine law formula is larger than 90°, subtract the angle from 180°, and determine the cosine of this angle. Remember, however, that the cosine of an angle between 90° and 180° is negative. If the angle used in the formula is larger than 90°, the last term will add to the squared terms.

The problem above can also be solved by using construction lines and making right triangles from the figure (Figure AII-3). To do this, we construct the line BD

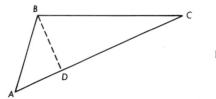

Figure AII-3

perpendicular to AC. This will form two right triangles, ABD and BCD. In triangle BCD, side BD may be found by using BC and the sine of $\angle C$. In a similar manner, by using the cosine of $\angle C$, side DC may be found. From this we can determine side AD in triangle ABD.

Using the tangent function, the angle at A can be found, and AB can be determined by the use of the sine or cosine function or the Pythagorean theorem $(AB)^2 = (BD)^2 + (AD)^2$. The right triangle method, while it may take longer to solve, will in general give a more accurate answer.

Three sides laws

There are a number of formulas derived in trigonometry that will give the angles of an oblique triangle when only three sides are known. The formulas differ considerably in ease of application and precision, especially if logarithms are used. Of all the formulas available, in general the half-angle (tangent) formula is better than others. The formula (half-angle solution) is as follows:

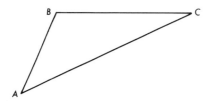

Figure AII-4

$$\tan \tfrac{1}{2} A = \frac{r}{S - BC}$$

where

$$r = \sqrt{\frac{(S - AB)(S - AC)(S - BC)}{S}}$$

and

$$S = \tfrac{1}{2} \text{ perimeter of triangle}$$

Other formulas that may be used are the following:

Sine formula (half-angle solution) $\sin \tfrac{1}{2} A = \sqrt{\dfrac{(S - AC)(S - AB)}{(AC)(AB)}}$

Cosine formula (half-angle solution) $\cos \frac{1}{2} A = \sqrt{\dfrac{(S)(S - BC)}{(AC)(AB)}}$

Cosine formula (whole angle solution) $\cos A = \dfrac{(2S)(S - BC)}{(AB)(AC)} - 1$

In the last formula, the quantity $(2S)(S - BC)/(AB)(AC)$ will usually be between 1 and 2 and can be read to four figures on the slide rule. Subtracting the 1 in the equation will leave the cosine of the angle correct to three figures. The formula has the advantage that it requires fewer operations. Also it is convenient to use if the slide rule is employed in solving problems.

After finding one angle, the remaining angles can be found by successive applications of the law, being careful to use the proper side of the triangle in the formula. The sine law can also be used after one angle is found. In order to have a check on the solution, it is better to solve for all three angles rather than solve for two angles and then subtract their sum from 180°. If each angle is computed separately, their sum should be within the allowable error range of 180°.

As an incidental item in the tangent formula, the constant r is equal to the length of the radius of a circle that can be inscribed in the triangle.

III

Geometric figures

Rectangle

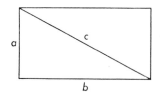

Area = (base)(altitude) = ab
Diagonal = $\sqrt{(\text{altitude})^2 + (\text{base})^2}$
$$C = \sqrt{a^2 + b^2}$$

Right triangle

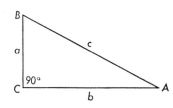

Angle A + angle B = angle C = 90°
Area = ½ (base)(altitude)
Hypotenuse = $\sqrt{(\text{altitude})^2 + (\text{base})^2}$
$$C = \sqrt{a^2 + b^2}$$

Any triangle

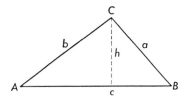

Angles $A + B + C = 180°$
(Altitude h is perpendicular to base c)
Area = ½ (base)(altitude)

Parallelogram

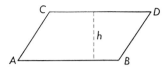

Area = (base)(altitude)
Altitude h is perpendicular to base AB
Angles $A + B + C + D = 360°$

Trapezoid

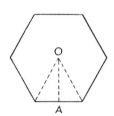

Area = ½ (altitude)(sum of bases)
(Altitude h is perpendicular to sides AB and
CD. Side AB is parallel to side CD.)

Regular polygon

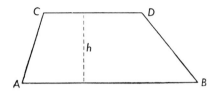

$$\text{Area} = \tfrac{1}{2} \begin{bmatrix} \text{length of} \\ \text{one side} \end{bmatrix} \begin{bmatrix} \text{number} \\ \text{of sides} \end{bmatrix} \begin{bmatrix} \text{distance} \\ OA \text{ to} \\ \text{center} \end{bmatrix}$$

A regular polygon has equal angles and equal
sides and can be inscribed in or circum-
scribed about a circle.

Circle

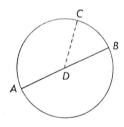

AB = diameter, CD = radius
$$\text{Area} = \pi(\text{radius})^2 = \frac{\pi(\text{diameter})^2}{4}$$
Circumference = π(diameter)
$C = 2\pi(\text{radius})$
$$\frac{\text{arc } BC}{\text{circumference}} = \frac{\text{angle } BDC}{360°}$$
$$1 \text{ radian} = \frac{180°}{\pi} = 57.2958°$$

Sector of a circle

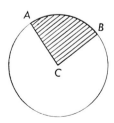

$$\text{Area} = \frac{(\text{arc } AB)(\text{radius})}{2}$$
$$= \pi \frac{(\text{radius})^2(\text{angle } ACB)}{360°}$$
$$= \frac{(\text{radius})^2 \ (\text{angle } ACB \text{ in radians})}{2}$$

Segment of a circle

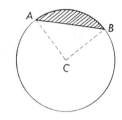

$$\text{Area} = \frac{(\text{radius})^2}{2}\left[\frac{\pi(\measuredangle \, ACB°)}{180} - \sin ACB°\right]$$

$$\text{Area} = \frac{(\text{radius})^2}{2}\left[\measuredangle \, ACB \text{ in radians} - \sin ACB°\right]$$

Area = area of sector ACB − area of triangle ABC

Ellipse

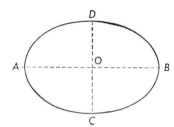

Area = π(long radius OA)(short radius OC)

Area = $\frac{\pi}{4}$ (long diameter AB)(short diameter CD)

Volume and center of gravity equations[1]

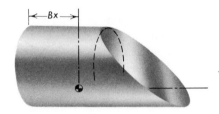

Volume equations are included for all cases. Where the equation for the CG (center of gravity) is not given, you can easily obtain it by looking up the volume and CG equations for portions of the shape and then combining values. For example, for the shape above, use the equations for a cylinder, Figure 1, and a truncated cylinder, Figure 10 (subscripts C and T, respectively, in the equations below). Hence taking moments,

$$B_x = \frac{V_C B_C + V_T(B_T + L_C)}{V_C + V_T}$$

or

$$B_x = \frac{\left(\frac{\pi}{4} D^2 L_C\right)\left(\frac{L_C}{2}\right) + \frac{\pi}{8} D^2 L_T \left(\frac{5}{16}L_T + L_C\right)}{\frac{\pi}{4} D^2 L_C + \frac{\pi}{8} D^2 L_T}$$

$$B_x = \frac{L^2_C + L_T\left(\frac{5}{16}L_T + L_C\right)}{2L_C + L_T}$$

[1] Courtesy of Knoll Atomic Power Laboratory, Schenectady, New York, operated by the General Electric Company for the U.S. Atomic Energy Commission. Reprinted from *Product Engineering*—Copyright owned by McGraw-Hill, New York.

In the equations to follow, angle θ can be either in degrees or in radians.

Thus θ (rad) $= \pi\theta/180$ (deg) $= 0.01745\,\theta$ (deg).

For example, if $\theta = 30$ deg in Case 3, then $\sin\theta = 0.5$ and

$$B = \frac{2R\,(0.5)}{3\,(30)\,(0.01745)} = 0.637R$$

Symbols used are:

B = distance from CG to reference plane,

V = volume,

D and d = diameter,

R and r = radius,

H = height,

L = length.

---

1. Cylinder

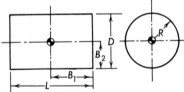

$$V = \frac{\pi}{4}D^2L = 0.7854D^2L \qquad \begin{aligned} B_1 &= L/2 \\ B_2 &= R \end{aligned}$$

Area of cylindrical surface
= (Perimeter of base)(perpendicular height)

---

2. Half cylinder

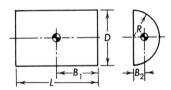

$$V = \frac{\pi}{8}D^2L = 0.3927D^2L$$

$$B_1 = L/2 \qquad B_2 = \frac{4R}{3\pi} = 0.4244R$$

3. Sector of cylinder

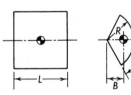

$$V = \theta\,R^2L \qquad B = \frac{2R\sin\theta}{3\theta}$$

4. Segment of cylinder

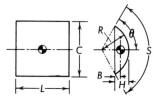

$$V = LR^2 \left(\theta - \frac{1}{2} \sin 2\theta \right)$$
$$V = 0.5L\,[RS - C(R - H)]$$

$$B = \frac{4R \sin^3 \theta}{6\theta - 3 \sin 2\theta}$$

$$S = 2R\theta$$
$$H = R(1 - \cos \theta)$$
$$C = 2R \sin \theta$$

5. Quadrant of cylinder

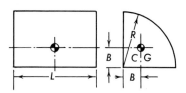

$$V = \frac{\pi}{4} R^2 L = 0.7854R^2 L$$

$$B = \frac{4R}{3\pi} = 0.4244R$$

6. Fillet or spandrel

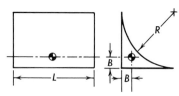

$$V = \left(1 - \frac{\pi}{4} \right) R^2 L = 0.2146R^2 L$$

$$B = \frac{10 - 3\pi}{12 - 3\pi} R = 0.2234R$$

7. Hollow cylinder

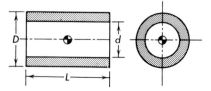

$$V = \frac{\pi L}{4} (D^2 - d^2)$$

CG at center of part

8. Half hollow cylinder

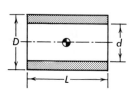

$$V = \frac{\pi L}{8} (D^2 - d^2)$$

$$B = \frac{4}{3\pi} \left[\frac{R^3 - r^3}{R^2 - r^2} \right]$$

9. Sector of hollow cylinder

 10. Truncated cylinder
(with full circle base)

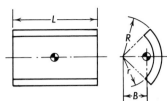

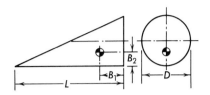

$$V = 0.01745\ (R^2 - r^2)\ \theta L$$

$$B = \frac{38.1972\ (R^3 - r^3)\ \sin\theta}{(R^2 - r^2)\ \theta}$$

$$V = \frac{\pi}{8} D^2 L = 0.3927 D^2 L$$

$$B_1 = 0.3125L$$

$$B_2 = 0.375D$$

 11. Truncated cylinder (with partial circle base)

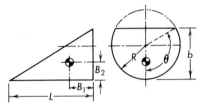

$$b = R\ (1 - \cos\theta)$$

$$V = \frac{R^3 L}{b}\left[\sin\theta - \frac{\sin^3\theta}{3} - \theta\cos\theta\right]$$

$$B_1 = \frac{L\left[\dfrac{\theta\cos^2\theta}{2} - \dfrac{5\sin\theta\cos\theta}{8} + \dfrac{\sin^3\theta\cos\theta}{12} + \dfrac{\theta}{8}\right]}{\left[1 - \cos\theta\right]\left[\sin\theta - \dfrac{\sin^3\theta}{3} - \theta\cos\theta\right]}$$

$$B_2 = \frac{2R\left[-\dfrac{\theta\cos\theta}{2} + \dfrac{\sin\theta}{2} - \dfrac{\theta}{8} + \dfrac{\sin\theta\cos\theta}{8} - N\right]}{\left[\sin\theta - \dfrac{\sin^3\theta}{3} - \theta\cos\theta\right]}$$

$$\text{where } N = \frac{\sin^3\theta}{6} - \frac{\sin^3\theta\cos\theta}{12}$$

12. Oblique cylinder
(or circular hole at oblique angle)

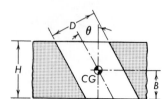

$$V = \frac{\pi}{4} D^2 \frac{H}{\cos \theta} = 0.7854 D^2 H \sec \theta$$

$$B = H/2 \qquad r = \frac{d}{2}$$

13. Bend in cylinder

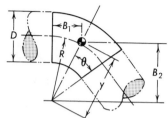

$$V = \frac{\pi^2}{360} D^2 R\theta = 0.0274 D^2 R\theta$$

$$y = R\left[1 + \frac{r^2}{4R^2}\right] \qquad \begin{array}{l} B_1 = y \tan \theta \\ B_2 = y \cot \theta \end{array}$$

14. Curved groove in cylinder

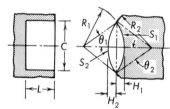

$$\sin \theta_1 = \frac{C}{2R_1} \qquad \sin \theta_2 = \frac{C}{2R_2} \qquad S = 2R\theta$$

$$H_1 = R_1(1 - \cos \theta_1) \qquad H_2 = R_2(1 - \cos \theta_2)$$

$$V = L\left[R_1^2\left(\theta_1 - \frac{1}{2}\theta_1 \sin 2\theta_1\right) + R_2^2\left(\theta_2 - \frac{1}{2}\theta_2 \sin 2\theta_2\right)\right]$$

Compute *CG* of each part separately

15. Slot in cylinder

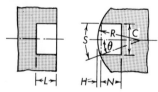

$$H = R(1 - \cos \theta) \qquad \sin \theta = \frac{C}{2R}$$

$$S = 2R\theta$$

$$V = L\left[CN + R^2\left(\theta - \frac{1}{2}\sin 2\theta\right)\right]$$

16. Slot in hollow cylinder

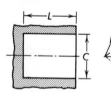

$$S = 2R\theta \qquad \sin \theta = \frac{C}{2R}$$

$$H = R(1 - \cos \theta)$$

$$V = L\left[CN - R^2\left(\theta - \frac{1}{2}\sin 2\theta\right)\right]$$

$$V = L\left\{CN - 0.5\left[RS - C(R - H)\right]\right\}$$

17. Curved groove in hollow cylinder

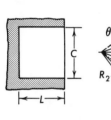

$$\sin \theta_1 = \frac{C}{2R_1} \qquad \sin \theta_2 = \frac{C}{2R_2} \qquad S = 2R\theta$$

$$H_1 = R_1 (1 - \cos \theta_1)$$

$$H_2 = R_2 (1 - \cos \theta_2)$$

$$V = L \left(\left[R_2^2 \left(\theta_2 - \frac{1}{2} \sin 2\theta_2 \right) \right] - \left[R_1^2 \left(\theta_1 - \frac{1}{2} \sin 2\theta_1 \right) \right] \right)$$

$$V = \frac{L}{2} \left(\left[R_2 S_2 - C (R_2 - H_2) \right] - \left[R_1 S_1 - C (R_1 - H_1) \right] \right)$$

18. Slot through hollow cylinder

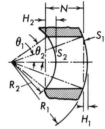

$$\sin \theta_1 = \frac{C}{R_1} \qquad \sin \theta_2 = \frac{C}{R_2}$$

$$S = 2R\theta$$

$$H_1 = R_1 (1 - \cos \theta_1)$$

$$H_2 = R_2 (1 - \cos \theta_2)$$

$$V = L \left(CN + \left[R_1^2 \left(\theta_1 - \frac{1}{2} \sin 2\theta_1 \right) \right] - \left[R_2 \left(\theta_2 - \frac{1}{2} \sin 2\theta_2 \right) \right] \right)$$

$$V = L \left(CN + 0.5 \left[R_1 S_1 - C (R_1 - H_1) \right] - 0.5 \left[R_2 S_2 - C (R_2 - H_2) \right] \right)$$

19. Intersecting cylinder (volume of junction box)	20. Intersecting hollow cylinders (volume of junction box)
$$V = D^3 \left(\frac{\pi}{2} - \frac{2}{3} \right) = 0.9041 D^3$$	$$V = \left(\frac{\pi}{2} - \frac{2}{3} \right) (D^3 - d^3) - \frac{\pi}{2} d^2 (D - d)$$ $$V = 0.9041 (D^3 - d^3) - 1.5708 d^2 (D - d)$$

21. Intersecting parallel cylinders
$(M < R_1)$

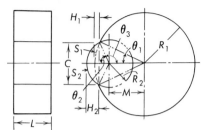

$$\theta_2 = 180° - \theta_3 \qquad \cos\theta_3 = \frac{R_2^2 + M^2 - R_1^2}{2MR_2}$$

$$\cos\theta_1 = \frac{R_1^2 + M^2 - R_2^2}{2MR_1}$$

$$H_1 = R_1(1 - \cos\theta_1)$$
$$S_1 = 2R_1\theta_1$$

$$V = L\left(\pi R_1^2 + \left[R_2^2\left(\theta_2 - \frac{1}{2}\sin 2\theta_2\right)\right] - \left[R_1^2\left(\theta_1 - \frac{1}{2}\sin 2\theta_1\right)\right]\right)$$

---

22. Intersecting parallel cylinders $(M > R_1)$

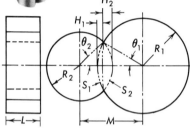

$$H_1 = R_1(1 - \cos\theta_1)$$
$$S_1 = 2R_1\theta_1$$

$$\cos\theta_1 = \frac{R_1^2 + M^2 - R_2^2}{2MR_1}$$

$$V = L\left(\left[\pi(R_1^2 + R_2^2)\right] - \left[R_1^2\left(\theta_1 - \frac{1}{2}\sin 2\theta_1\right)\right] - \left[R_2^2\left(\theta_2 - \frac{1}{2}\sin 2\theta_2\right)\right]\right)$$

---

23. Sphere

$$V = \frac{\pi D^3}{6} = 0.5236D^3$$

Area of surface $= 4\pi(\text{radius})^2 = \pi D^2$

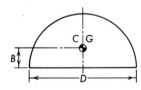

24. Hemisphere

$$V = \frac{\pi D^3}{12} = 0.2618D^3$$

$B = 0.375R$

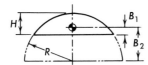 25. Spherical segment

 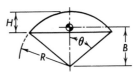 26. Spherical sector

$$V = \pi H^2 \left(R - \frac{H}{3} \right)$$

$$B_1 = \frac{H(4R - H)}{4(3R - H)}$$

$$B_2 = \frac{3(2R - H)^2}{4(3R - H)}$$

$$V = \frac{2\pi}{3} R^2 H = 2.0944 R^2 H$$

$$B = 0.375 (1 + \cos \theta)$$

$$R = 0.375 (2R - H)$$

---

27. Shell of hollow hemisphere

28. Hollow sphere

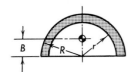

$$V = \frac{2\pi}{3} (R^3 - r^3)$$

$$B = 0.375 \left(\frac{R^4 - r^4}{R^3 - r^3} \right)$$

$$V = \frac{4\pi}{3} (R^3 - r^3)$$

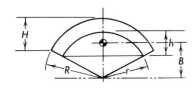

29. Shell of spherical sector

$$V = \frac{2\pi}{3} (R^2 H - r^2 h)$$

$$B = 0.375 \left\{ \frac{[R^2 H (2R - H)] - [r^2 h (2r - h)]}{R^2 H - r^2 h} \right\}$$

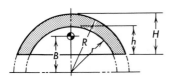

30. Shell of spherical segment

$$V = \pi \left[H^2 \left(R - \frac{H}{3} \right) - h^2 \left(r - \frac{h}{3} \right) \right]$$

$$B = \frac{3}{4} \left[\frac{\left(R - \frac{H}{3} \right) \frac{H^2(2R - H)^2}{3R - H} - \left(r - \frac{h}{3} \right) \frac{h^2(2r - h)^2}{3r - h}}{H^2 \left(R - \frac{H}{3} \right) - h^2 \left(r - \frac{h}{3} \right)} \right]$$

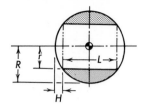

31. Circular hole through sphere

$$V = \pi\left[r^2 L + 2H^2\left(R - \frac{H}{3}\right)\right] \qquad \begin{array}{l} H = R - \sqrt{R^2 - r^2} \\ L = 2(R - H) \end{array}$$

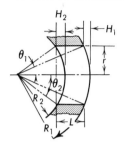

32. Circular hole through hollow sphere

$$V = \pi\left\{r^2 L + H_1\left(R_1 - \frac{H_1}{3}\right) - H_2^2\left(R_2 - \frac{H_2}{3}\right)\right\}$$

$$\sin\theta_1 = r/R_1 \qquad \sin\theta_2 = r/R_2 \qquad H = R(1 - \cos\theta)$$

33. Spherical zone

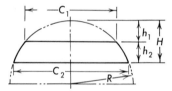

$$V = \pi\left\{\left[H^2\left(R - \frac{H}{3}\right)\right] - \left[h_1^2\left(R - \frac{h_1}{3}\right)\right]\right\}$$

$$V = \frac{\pi h_2}{6}\left[\frac{3}{4}C_1^2 + \frac{3}{4}C_2^2 + h_2^2\right]$$

34. Conical hole through spherical shell

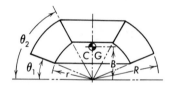

$$V = \frac{2\pi}{3}(R^3 - r^3)(\sin\theta_2 - \sin\theta_1)$$

$$B = \frac{0.375(R^4 - r^4)(\sin\theta_2 + \sin\theta_1)}{R^3 - r^3}$$

35. Torus

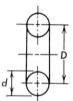

$$V = \frac{1}{4}\pi^2 d^2 D = 2.467 d^2 D$$

36. Hollow torus

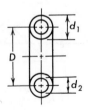

$$V = \frac{1}{4}\pi^2 D(d_1^2 - d_2^2)$$

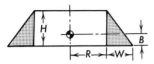 37. Bevel ring

 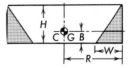 38. Bevel ring

$$V = \pi \left(R + \frac{1}{3} W \right) WH$$

$$B = H \left[\frac{\frac{R}{3} + \frac{W}{12}}{R + \frac{W}{3}} \right]$$

$$B > \frac{H}{3}$$

$$V = \pi \left(R - \frac{1}{3} W \right) WH$$

$$B = H \left[\frac{\frac{R}{3} - \frac{W}{12}}{R - \frac{W}{3}} \right]$$

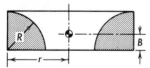 39. Quarter torus

$$B < 0.4244R$$

$$V = \frac{\pi^2 R^2}{2} \left(r + \frac{4R}{3\pi} \right) = 4.9348R^2 \, (r + 0.4244R)$$

$$B = \frac{4R}{3\pi} \left[\frac{r + \frac{3R}{8}}{r + \frac{4R}{3\pi}} \right] = \frac{0.4244Rr + 0.1592R^2}{r + 0.4244R}$$

 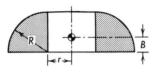 40. Quarter torus

 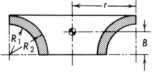 41. Curved shell ring

$$V = \frac{\pi^2 R^2}{2} \left[r - \frac{4R}{3\pi} \right]$$

$$B = \frac{4R}{3\pi} \left[\frac{r - \frac{3R}{8}}{r - \frac{4R}{3\pi}} \right]$$

$$V = 2\pi \left\{ r - \frac{4}{3\pi} \left[\frac{R_2{}^3 - R_1{}^3}{R_2{}^2 - R_1{}^2} \right] \right\} \frac{\pi}{4} \, (R_2{}^2 - R_1{}^2)$$

$$B = \frac{4}{3\pi} \frac{\left[R_2{}^3 \left(r - \frac{3}{8} R_2 \right) - R_1{}^3 \left(r - \frac{3}{8} R_1 \right) \right]}{(R_2{}^2 - R_1{}^2) \left\{ r - \frac{4}{3\pi} \left[\frac{R_2{}^3 - R_1{}^3}{R_2{}^2 - R_1{}^2} \right] \right\}}$$

42. Curved shell ring

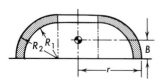

$$V = \frac{\pi^2}{2}\left[r(R_2{}^2 - R_1{}^2) + \frac{4}{3\pi}(R_2{}^3 - R_1{}^3)\right]$$

$$B = \frac{2}{\pi}\left[\frac{\dfrac{2r}{3}(R_2{}^3 - R_1{}^3) + \dfrac{1}{4}(R_2{}^4 - R_1{}^4)}{r(R_2{}^2 - R_1{}^2) + \dfrac{4}{3\pi}(R_2{}^3 - R_1{}^3)}\right]$$

43. Fillet ring

$$V = 2\pi R^2\left[\left(1 - \frac{\pi}{4}\right)r - \frac{R}{6}\right]$$

$$B = R\left[\frac{\left(\dfrac{5}{6} - \dfrac{\pi}{4}\right)r - \dfrac{R}{24}}{\left(1 - \dfrac{\pi}{4}\right)r - \dfrac{R}{6}}\right]$$

44. Fillet ring

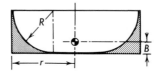

$$V = 2\pi R^2\left[\left(1 - \frac{\pi}{4}\right)r - \left(\frac{5}{6} - \frac{\pi}{4}\right)R\right]$$

$$B = R\left[\frac{\left(\dfrac{5}{6} - \dfrac{\pi}{4}\right)r - \left(\dfrac{19}{24} - \dfrac{\pi}{4}\right)R}{\left(1 - \dfrac{\pi}{4}\right)r - \left(\dfrac{5}{6} - \dfrac{\pi}{4}\right)R}\right]$$

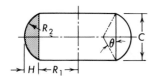

45. Curved-sector ring

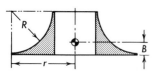

$$V = 2\pi R_2{}^2\left[R_1 + \left(\frac{4\sin 3\theta}{6\theta - 3\sin 2\theta} - \cos\theta\right)R_2\right]\left[\theta - 0.5\sin 2\theta\right]$$

46. Ellipsoidal cylinder

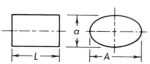

$$V = \frac{\pi}{4}AaL$$

47. Ellipsoid

$$V = \frac{4}{3}\pi ACE$$

48. Paraboloid

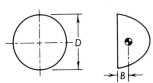

$$V = \frac{\pi}{8} HD^2 \qquad B = \frac{1}{3} H$$

49. Pyramid (with base of any shape)

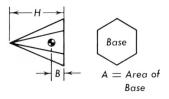

$$A = \text{Area of Base}$$

$$V = \frac{1}{3} AH \qquad B = \frac{1}{4} H$$

---

50. Frustum of pyramid (with base of any shape)

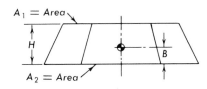

$A_1 = \text{Area}$

$A_2 = \text{Area}$

$$V = \frac{1}{3} H (A_1 + \sqrt{A_1 A_2} + A_2)$$

$$B = \frac{H (A_1 + 2\sqrt{A_1 A_2} + 3A_2)}{4 (A_1 + \sqrt{A_1 A_2} + A_2)}$$

51. Cone

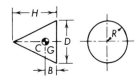

$$V = \frac{\pi}{12} D^2 H \qquad B = \frac{1}{4} H$$

Area of conical surface (right cone) = ½ (circumference of base) × (slant height)

---

52. Frustum of cone

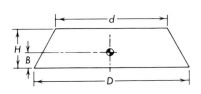

$$V = \frac{\pi}{12} H (D^2 + Dd + d^2)$$

$$B = \frac{H (D^2 + 2Dd + 3d^2)}{4 (D^2 + Dd + d^2)}$$

53. Frustum of hollow cone

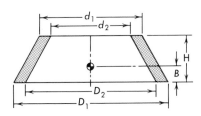

$$V = 0.2618H [(D_1^2 + D_1 d_1 + d_1^2) - (D_2^2 + D_2 d_2 + d_2^2)]$$

54. Hexagon

$$V = \frac{\sqrt{3}}{2} d^2 L$$
$$V = 0.866 d^2 L$$

55. Closely packed helical springs

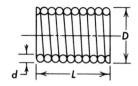

$$V = \frac{\pi^2 dL}{4} (D - d)$$
$$V = 2.4674 (D - d)$$

56. Rectangular prism

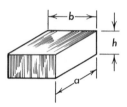

Volume = length × width × height
Volume = area of base × altitude

57. Any prism

(Axis either perpendicular or inclined to base)
Volume = (area of base)(perpendicular height)
Volume = (lateral length)(area of perpendicular cross section)

APPENDIX **IV**

Tables

Weights and measures

Avoirdupois weight

1 grain (avdp)	1 grain 1 grain (troy)
$27^{11}/_{32}$ grains	1 dram
16 drams	1 ounce (oz)
16 ounces	1 pound (lb)
100 pounds	1 hundredweight (cwt)
2000 pounds	1 short ton (T)
2240 pounds	1 long ton

Metric weight

10 milligrams (mg)	1 centigram (cg)
10 centigrams	1 decigram (dg)
10 decigrams	1 gram (g)
10 grams	1 dekagram (Dg)
10 dekagrams	1 hectogram (hg)
10 hectograms	1 kilogram (kg)

Mass and force equivalents

1 gram	0.03527 ounce	980.6 dynes	5 carats
1 kilogram	2.2046 pounds	$(6.852)(10^{-2})$ slug	9.807 newtons
1 metric ton	2205 pounds	10^3 kilograms	35,274 ounces

1 pound	453.6 grams	0.4536 kilogram	4.448 newtons
1 ounce	28.35 grams	0.0625 pound	16 drams
1 newton	10^5 dynes	0.2248 lb_f	0.1020 kilogram
1 dyne	$2.2481(10)^{-6}$ lb_f	$7.233(10)^{-5}$ poundal	

Dry measure

2 pints	1 quart (qt)	67.2 cubic inches (in.^{3})
8 quarts	1 peck	
4 pecks	1 bushel (bu)	

Liquid measure

4 gills		1 pint (pt)	16 fluid ounces	2 cups	28.875 in.^{3}
2 pints		1 quart			
4 quarts		1 gallon (gal)	231 cubic inches		
7.48 gallons		1 cubic foot (ft^3)			
31$\frac{1}{2}$ gallons		1 barrel (bbl)			
1 British Imperial gallon		1.200 U.S. gallons			

Linear measure

1 mil	0.001 inch (in.)		
12 inches	1 foot (ft)	30.48 centimeters	$1.894(10)^{-4}$ mile
3 feet	1 yard (yd)		
5$\frac{1}{2}$ yards	1 rod		
40 rods	1 furlong		
320 rods	1 mile	5280 feet	1760 yards
3 miles	1 league		
6 feet	1 fathom	1.8288 meters	

Linear measure equivalents

6.08 feet	1 fathom	
6080.2 feet	1 nautical mile	
1 nautical mile	1.15 statue mile	1852 meters

Metric linear measure

10 millimeters (mm)	1 centimeter (cm)
10 centimeters	1 decimeter (dm)
10 decimeters	1 meter (m)
10 meters	1 dekameter (Dm)
10 dekameters	1 hectometer (hm)
10 hectometers	1 kilometer (km)

Metric linear equivalents

| 1 centimeter | 0.3937 inch | 10^{-5} kilometer | $6.214(10)^{-6}$ mile |
| 1 meter | 39.37 inches | 1.0936 yards | 3.281 feet |

1 kilometer	0.62137 mile		3281 feet
	(approximately $\frac{5}{8}$ mile)		
1 inch	2.540 centimeters	0.001263 chain	0.02778 yard
1 foot	30.48 centimeters	0.3048 meter	$1.894(10)^{-4}$ mile
1 mile	1.6093 kilometers	80 chains	63,360 inches
1 angstrom	10^{-10} meter	10^5 fermis	$3.937(10)^{-9}$ inch
1 micron (μ)	10^{-6} meter	10^4 angstroms	$3.973(10)^{-5}$ inch
1 fermi	10^{-15} meter	10^{-5} angstrom	$3.937(10)^{-14}$ inch

Area measure

144 square inches (in.^{2})	1 square foot (ft^2)		
9 square feet	1 square yard (yd^2)	0.83613 square meter (m^2)	
$30\frac{1}{4}$ square yards	1 square rod		
160 square rods	1 acre	4840 square yards	43,560 square feet
640 acres	1 square mile	1 section	
2.47 acres	1 hectare (metric)		
0.7854 square mils	1 circular mil	$7.854(10^{-7})$ square inches	
$(10)^{24}$ barns	1 square centimeter (cm)	0.155 square inches	

Volume measure

1728 cubic inches	1 cubic foot (ft^3)	7.481 gallons (U.S.)	28.32 liters
27 cubic feet	1 cubic yard (yd^3)	202.2 gallons (U.S.)	
231 cubic inches	1 standard gallon (U.S.)	3.785 liters	
2150.42 cubic inches	1 standard bushel	9.309 gallons (U.S.)	
144 cubic inches	1 board foot (f.b.m.)		
61.03 cubic inches	1 liter (metric)	0.2642 gallon (U.S.)	1000 cubic centimeters

Time

1 week	7 days	168 hours	10,080 minutes	604,800 seconds
1 mean solar day			1440 minutes	86,400 seconds
1 calendar year	365 days	8760 hours	$5.256(10)^5$ minutes	$3.1536(10)^7$ seconds
1 tropical mean solar year	365.2422 days (basis of modern calendar)			

Temperature

$\triangle 1°$ Celsius (formerly Centigrade) (C) $= \triangle 1°$ Kelvin (K) $= 1.8°$ Fahrenheit (F)
$= 1.8°$ Rankine (R)

$0°C = 273.15°K = 32°F = 491.67°R = 0°R$
$0°K = -273.15°C = -459.67°F$

Electrical

1 coulomb	$1.036(10)^5$ faradays	0.1 abcoulomb	$2.998(10)^9$ statcoulombs
1 ampere		0.1 abampere	$2.998(10)^9$ statcoulombs
1 volt	10^3 millivolts	10^8 abvolts	$3.335(10)^{-3}$ statvolt
1 ohm	10^6 megohms	10^9 abohms	$1.112(10)^{-12}$ statohm
1 farad	10^6 microfarads	10^{-9} abfarads	$8.987(10)^{11}$ statfarads

| 1 henrie | 10^3 millihenries | 10^9 abhenries | $1.112(10)^{-12}$ stathenries |
| 1 tesla | 10^{-4} gauss | | |

Conversion equivalents

1 atmosphere	14.69 pounds per square inch (psi)	406.8 inches of water
	29.92 inches of mercury	1.0133 bars
	$1.01325(10)^6$ dynes/cm^2	
1 British thermal unit	252 calories (gram, at 15°C)	1055 joules
1 British thermal unit	778 foot-pounds (ft-lb)	0.00039 horsepower-hour
1 calorie	0.003968 British thermal unit	
1 cubic inch	16.39 cubic centimeters	0.01639 liters
1 degree	60 minutes	2.90888 radians
1 knot is a speed of 1 nautical mile per hour 1.1508 miles per hour 1.6878 feet per second		
1 slug	32.17398 pounds mass 14.5939 kilograms mass	
1 electron volt (ev)	$1.6021(10)^{-19}$ joule	
1 foot-pound per second	0.001818 horsepower (hp)	
1 horsepower	746 watts 33,000 foot-pounds per minute	
	550 foot-pounds per second	
1 kilowatt	1.34 horsepower	
Hydrostatic water pressure in pounds per square inch = (height in feet)(0.4332)		
1 inch Hg (mercury)	0.491 pound per square inch	
1 joule	1 watt second	0.738 foot-pound 10^7 ergs
	$9.48(10^{-4})$ Btu	10^7 dyne-centimeter 1 newton-meter
1 kilowatt-hour	3413 British thermal unit 1.341 horsepower-hour	
	$3.6(10^6)$ joules	$2.655(10)^6$ foot-pounds
1 radian	57.2958 degrees	10^3 angular mils
1 million electron volts (Mev)	$1.602(10^{-13})$ joule	
1 ton of refrigeration	3517 watts	200 Btu/min $2.88(10)^5$ Btu/day

Coefficients of friction

Average values

Surfaces	Static	Kinetic
Metals on wood	0.4 –0.63	0.35–0.60
Wood on wood	0.3 –0.5	0.25–0.4
Leather on wood	0.38–0.45	0.3 –0.35
Iron on iron (wrought)	0.4 –0.5	0.4 –0.5
Glass on glass	0.23–0.25	0.20–0.25
Leather on glass	0.35–0.38	0.33–0.35
Wood on glass	0.35–0.40	0.28–0.31
Wood on sheet iron	0.43–0.50	0.38–0.45
Leather on sheet iron	0.45–0.50	0.35–0.40
Brass on wrought iron	0.35–0.45	0.30–0.35
Babbitt on steel	0.35–0.40	0.30–0.35
Steel on ice	0.03–0.04	0.03–0.04

The Greek alphabet

A	α	Alpha	N	ν	Nu
B	β	Bēta	Ξ	ξ	Xī
Γ	γ	Gamma	O	o	Omicron
Δ	δ	Delta	Π	π	Pī
E	ϵ	Epsilon	P	ρ	Rhō
Z	ζ	Zēta	Σ	σ	Sigma
H	η	Eta	T	τ	Tau
Θ	θ	Thēta	Υ	υ	Upsilon
I	ι	Iōta	Φ	ϕ	Phī
K	κ	Kappa	X	χ	Chī
Λ	λ	Lambda	Ψ	ψ	Psī
M	μ	Mu	Ω	ω	Omega

Dimensional prefixes

Symbol	Prefix	Multiple
T	tera units	10^{12}
G	giga units	10^{9}
M	mega units	10^{6}
k	kilo units	10^{3}
h	hecto units	10^{2}
da	deca units	10^{1}
	units	10^{0}
d	deci units	10^{-1}
c	centi units	10^{-2}
m	milli units	10^{-3}
μ	micro units	10^{-6}
n	nano units	10^{-9}
p	pico units	10^{-12}
f	femto units	10^{-15}
a	atto units	10^{-18}

Specific gravities and specific weights

Material	Average specific gravity	Average specific weight, lb_f/ft^3	Material	Average specific gravity	Average specific weight, lb_f/ft^3
Acid, sulphuric, 87%	1.80	112	Iron, grey cast	7.10	450
Air, S.T.P.	0.001293	0.0806	Iron, wrought	7.75	480
Alcohol, ethyl	0.790	49			
Aluminum, cast	2.65	165	Kerosene	0.80	50
Asbestos	2.5	153			
Ash, white	0.67	42	Lead	11.34	710
Ashes, cinders	0.68	44	Leather	0.94	59
Asphaltum	1.3	81	Limestone, solid	2.70	168
			Limestone, crushed	1.50	95
Babbitt metal, soft	10.25	625			
Basalt, granite	1.50	96	Mahogany	0.70	44
Brass, cast-rolled	8.50	534	Manganese	7.42	475
Brick, common	1.90	119	Marble	2.70	166
Bronze, 7.9 to 14% S_n	8.1	509	Mercury	13.56	845
			Monel metal, rolled	8.97	555
Cedar, white, red	0.35	22			
Cement, portland, bags	1.44	90	Nickel	8.90	558
Chalk	2.25	140			
Clay, dry	1.00	63	Oak, white	0.77	48
Clay, loose, wet	1.75	110	Oil, lubricating	0.91	57
Coal, anthracite, solid	1.60	95			
Coal, bituminous, solid	1.35	85	Paper	0.92	58
Concrete, gravel, sand	2.3	142	Paraffin	0.90	56
Copper, cast, rolled	8.90	556	Petroleum, crude	0.88	55
Cork	0.24	15	Pine, white	0.43	27
Cotton, flax, hemp	1.48	93	Platinum	21.5	1330
Copper ore	4.2	262			
			Redwood, California	0.42	26
Earth	1.75	105	Rubber	1.25	78
Fir, Douglas	0.50	32	Sand, loose, wet	1.90	120
Flour, loose	0.45	28	Sandstone, solid	2.30	144
			Sea water	1.03	64
Gasoline	0.70	44	Silver	10.5	655
Glass, crown	2.60	161	Steel, structural	7.90	490
Glass, flint	3.30	205	Sulphur	2.00	125
Glycerine	1.25	78	Teak, African	0.99	62
Gold, cast-hammered	19.3	1205	Tin	7.30	456
Granite, solid	2.70	172	Tungsten	19.22	1200
Graphite	1.67	135	Turpentine	0.865	54
Gravel, loose, wet	1.68	105			
			Water, 4°C	1.00	62.4
Hickory	0.77	48	Water, snow, fresh fallen	0.125	8.0
Ice	0.91	57	Zinc	7.14	445

Note: The value for the specific weight of water which is usually used in problem solutions, is 62.4 lb_f/ft^3 or 8.34 lb_f/gal.

Trigonometric functions

$\sin(-\alpha) = -\sin\alpha$

$\cos(-\alpha) = \cos\alpha$

$\tan(-\alpha) = -\tan\alpha$

$\sin^2\alpha = \frac{1}{2} - \frac{1}{2}\cos 2\alpha$

$\cos^2\alpha = \frac{1}{2} + \frac{1}{2}\cos 2\alpha$

$\sin^2\alpha + \cos^2\alpha = 1$

$\sec^2\alpha = 1 + \tan^2\alpha$

$\csc^2\alpha = 1 + \text{ctn}^2\alpha$

$\sin 2\alpha = 2\sin\alpha\cos\alpha$

$\cos 2\alpha = \cos^2\alpha - \sin^2\alpha = 1 - 2\sin^2\alpha = 2\cos^2\alpha - 1$

$\sin\alpha = \alpha - \dfrac{\alpha^3}{3!} + \dfrac{\alpha^5}{5!} - \dfrac{\alpha^7}{7!} + \dfrac{\alpha^9}{9!}\cdots$

$\cos\alpha = 1 - \dfrac{\alpha^2}{2!} + \dfrac{\alpha^4}{4!} - \dfrac{\alpha^6}{6!} + \dfrac{\alpha^8}{8!}\cdots$

$\sin(\alpha \pm \theta) = \sin\alpha\cos\theta \pm \cos\alpha\sin\theta$

$\cos(\alpha \pm \theta) = \cos\alpha\cos\theta \mp \sin\alpha\sin\theta$

Differentials and integrals

$\dfrac{dx^n}{dx} = nx^{n-1}$

$\dfrac{d(uv)}{dx} = U\dfrac{dv}{dx} + V\dfrac{du}{dx}$

$\dfrac{d(u/v)}{dx} = \dfrac{V(du/dx) - U(dv/dx)}{v^2}$

$\displaystyle\int x^n dx = \dfrac{x^{n+1}}{n+1} + C$

$\displaystyle\int u\, dv = uv - \int v\, du$

$\displaystyle\int \dfrac{dx}{x} = \log_\epsilon x + C$

$\displaystyle\int \sin x\, dx = -\cos x + C$

$\displaystyle\int \cos x\, dx = \sin x + C$

$\displaystyle\int \sin^2 x\, dx = \dfrac{x}{2} - \dfrac{\sin 2x}{4} + C$

$\displaystyle\int \cos^2 x\, dx = \dfrac{x}{2} + \dfrac{\sin 2x}{4} + C$

Special-purpose formulas useful in solving uniform motion problems

Legend

V	velocity	V_2	final velocity	S	distance	a acceleration
V_1	initial velocity	V_{av}	average velocity	t	time	

Given	To find	Suggested formulas
V_1, V_2, t	S	$S = \left(\dfrac{V_1 + V_2}{2}\right)t$
V_1, V_2, a	S	$S = \dfrac{V_2^2 - V_1^2}{2a}$
V_1, a, t	S	$S = V_1 t + \dfrac{at^2}{2}$
V_1, V_2	V_{av}	$V_{av} = \dfrac{V_1 + V_2}{2}$
S, t	V_{av}	$V_{av} = \dfrac{S}{t}$
V_2, a, t	V_1	$V_1 = V_2 - at$
V_2, a, S	V_1	$V_1 = \sqrt{V_2^2 - 2aS}$
S, a, t	V_1	$V_1 = \dfrac{S}{t} - \dfrac{at}{2}$
V_1, a, t	V_2	$V_2 = V_1 + at$
V_1, a, S	V_2	$V_2 = \sqrt{V_1^2 + 2aS}$
V_1, S, t	V_2	$V_2 = \dfrac{2S}{t} - V_1$
V_1, V_2, S	t	$t = \dfrac{2S}{V_1 + V_2}$
V_1, a, S	t	$t = \dfrac{-V_1 \pm \sqrt{V_1^2 + 2aS}}{a}$
V_1, V_2, a	t	$t = \dfrac{V_2 - V_1}{a}$
V_1, V_2, t	a	$a = \dfrac{V_2 - V_1}{t}$
V_1, V_2, S	a	$a = \dfrac{V_2^2 - V_1^2}{2S}$
V_1, S, t	a	$a = \dfrac{2S}{t^2} - \dfrac{2V_1}{t}$

Logarithms

Natural Numbers	0	1	2	3	4	5	6	7	8	9	PROPORTIONAL PARTS								
											1	2	3	4	5	6	7	8	9
10	0000	0043	0086	0128	0170	0212	0253	0294	0334	0374	4	8	12	17	21	25	29	33	37
11	0414	0453	0492	0531	0569	0607	0645	0682	0719	0755	4	8	11	15	19	23	26	30	34
12	0792	0828	0864	0899	0934	0969	1004	1038	1072	1106	3	7	10	14	17	21	24	28	31
13	1139	1173	1206	1239	1271	1303	1335	1367	1399	1430	3	6	10	13	16	19	23	26	29
14	1461	1492	1523	1553	1584	1614	1644	1673	1703	1732	3	6	9	12	15	18	21	24	27
15	1761	1790	1818	1847	1875	1903	1931	1959	1987	2014	3	6	8	11	14	17	20	22	25
16	2041	2068	2095	2122	2148	2175	2201	2227	2253	2279	3	5	8	11	13	16	18	21	24
17	2304	2330	2355	2380	2405	2430	2455	2480	2504	2529	2	5	7	10	12	15	17	20	22
18	2553	2577	2601	2625	2648	2672	2695	2718	2742	2765	2	5	7	9	12	14	16	19	21
19	2788	2810	2833	2856	2878	2900	2923	2945	2967	2989	2	4	7	9	11	13	16	18	20
20	3010	3032	3054	3075	3096	3118	3139	3160	3181	3201	2	4	6	8	11	13	15	17	19
21	3222	3243	3263	3284	3304	3324	3345	3365	3385	3404	2	4	6	8	10	12	14	16	18
22	3424	3444	3464	3483	3502	3522	3541	3560	3579	3598	2	4	6	8	10	12	14	15	17
23	3617	3636	3655	3674	3692	3711	3729	3747	3766	3784	2	4	6	7	9	11	13	15	17
24	3802	3820	3838	3856	3874	3892	3909	3927	3945	3962	2	4	5	7	9	11	12	14	16
25	3979	3997	4014	4031	4048	4065	4082	4099	4116	4133	2	3	5	7	9	10	12	14	15
26	4150	4166	4183	4200	4216	4232	4249	4265	4281	4298	2	3	5	7	8	10	11	13	15
27	4314	4330	4346	4362	4378	4393	4409	4425	4440	4456	2	3	5	6	8	9	11	13	14
28	4472	4487	4502	4518	4533	4548	4564	4579	4594	4609	2	3	5	6	8	9	11	12	14
29	4624	4639	4654	4669	4683	4698	4713	4728	4742	4757	1	3	4	6	7	9	10	12	13
30	4771	4786	4800	4814	4829	4843	4857	4871	4886	4900	1	3	4	6	7	9	10	11	13
31	4914	4928	4942	4955	4969	4983	4997	5011	5024	5038	1	3	4	6	7	8	10	11	12
32	5051	5065	5079	5092	5105	5119	5132	5145	5159	5172	1	3	4	5	7	8	9	11	12
33	5185	5198	5211	5224	5237	5250	5263	5276	5289	5302	1	3	4	5	6	8	9	10	12
34	5315	5328	5340	5353	5366	5378	5391	5403	5416	5428	1	3	4	5	6	8	9	10	11
35	5441	5453	5465	5478	5490	5502	5514	5527	5539	5551	1	2	4	5	6	7	9	10	11
36	5563	5575	5587	5599	5611	5623	5635	5647	5658	5670	1	2	4	5	6	7	8	10	11
37	5682	5694	5705	5717	5729	5740	5752	5763	5775	5786	1	2	3	5	6	7	8	9	10
38	5798	5809	5821	5832	5843	5855	5866	5877	5888	5899	1	2	3	5	6	7	8	9	10
39	5911	5922	5933	5944	5955	5966	5977	5988	5999	6010	1	2	3	4	5	7	8	9	10
40	6021	6031	6042	6053	6064	6075	6085	6096	6107	6117	1	2	3	4	5	6	8	9	10
41	6128	6138	6149	6160	6170	6180	6191	6201	6212	6222	1	2	3	4	5	6	7	8	9
42	6232	6243	6253	6263	6274	6284	6294	6304	6314	6325	1	2	3	4	5	6	7	8	9
43	6335	6345	6355	6365	6375	6385	6395	6405	6415	6425	1	2	3	4	5	6	7	8	9
44	6435	6444	6454	6464	6474	6484	6493	6503	6513	6522	1	2	3	4	5	6	7	8	9
45	6532	6542	6551	6561	6571	6580	6590	6599	6609	6618	1	2	3	4	5	6	7	8	9
46	6628	6637	6646	6656	6665	6675	6684	6693	6702	6712	1	2	3	4	5	6	7	7	8
47	6721	6730	6739	6749	6758	6767	6776	6785	6794	6803	1	2	3	4	5	5	6	7	8
48	6812	6821	6830	6839	6848	6857	6866	6875	6884	6893	1	2	3	4	4	5	6	7	8
49	6902	6911	6920	6928	6937	6946	6955	6964	6972	6981	1	2	3	4	4	5	6	7	8
50	6990	6998	7007	7016	7024	7033	7042	7050	7059	7067	1	2	3	3	4	5	6	7	8
51	7076	7084	7093	7101	7110	7118	7126	7135	7143	7152	1	2	3	3	4	5	6	7	8
52	7160	7168	7177	7185	7193	7202	7210	7218	7226	7235	1	2	2	3	4	5	6	7	7
53	7243	7251	7259	7267	7275	7284	7292	7300	7308	7316	1	2	2	3	4	5	6	6	7
54	7324	7332	7340	7348	7356	7364	7372	7380	7388	7396	1	2	2	3	4	5	6	6	7

Logarithms (continued)

Natural Numbers	0	1	2	3	4	5	6	7	8	9	Proportional Parts								
											1	2	3	4	5	6	7	8	9
55	7404	7412	7419	7427	7435	7443	7451	7459	7466	7474	1	2	2	3	4	5	5	6	7
56	7482	7490	7497	7505	7513	7520	7528	7536	7543	7551	1	2	2	3	4	5	5	6	7
57	7559	7566	7574	7582	7589	7597	7604	7612	7619	7627	1	2	2	3	4	5	5	6	7
58	7634	7642	7649	7657	7664	7672	7679	7686	7694	7701	1	1	2	3	4	4	5	6	7
59	7709	7716	7723	7731	7738	7745	7752	7760	7767	7774	1	1	2	3	4	4	5	6	7
60	7782	7789	7796	7803	7810	7818	7825	7832	7839	7846	1	1	2	3	4	4	5	6	6
61	7853	7860	7868	7875	7882	7889	7896	7903	7910	7917	1	1	2	3	4	4	5	6	6
62	7924	7931	7938	7945	7952	7959	7966	7973	7980	7987	1	1	2	3	3	4	5	6	6
63	7993	8000	8007	8014	8021	8028	8035	8041	8048	8055	1	1	2	3	3	4	5	5	6
64	8062	8069	8075	8082	8089	8096	8102	8109	8116	8122	1	1	2	3	3	4	5	5	6
65	8129	8136	8142	8149	8156	8162	8169	8176	8182	8189	1	1	2	3	3	4	5	5	6
66	8195	8202	8209	8215	8222	8228	8235	8241	8248	8254	1	1	2	3	3	4	5	5	6
67	8261	8267	8274	8280	8287	8293	8299	8306	8312	8319	1	1	2	3	3	4	5	5	6
68	8325	8331	8338	8344	8351	8357	8363	8370	8376	8382	1	1	2	3	3	4	4	5	6
69	8388	8395	8401	8407	8414	8420	8426	8432	8439	8445	1	1	2	2	3	4	4	5	6
70	8451	8457	8463	8470	8476	8482	8488	8494	8500	8506	1	1	2	2	3	4	4	5	6
71	8513	8519	8525	8531	8537	8543	8549	8555	8561	8567	1	1	2	2	3	4	4	5	5
72	8573	8579	8585	8591	8597	8603	8609	8615	8621	8627	1	1	2	2	3	4	4	5	5
73	8633	8639	8645	8651	8657	8663	8669	8675	8681	8686	1	1	2	2	3	4	4	5	5
74	8692	8698	8704	8710	8716	8722	8727	8733	8739	8745	1	1	2	2	3	4	4	5	5
75	8751	8756	8762	8768	8774	8779	8785	8791	8797	8802	1	1	2	2	3	3	4	5	5
76	8808	8814	8820	8825	8831	8837	8842	8848	8854	8859	1	1	2	2	3	3	4	5	5
77	8865	8871	8876	8882	8887	8893	8899	8904	8910	8915	1	1	2	2	3	3	4	4	5
78	8921	8927	8932	8938	8943	8949	8954	8960	8965	8971	1	1	2	2	3	3	4	4	5
79	8976	8982	8987	8993	8998	9004	9009	9015	9020	9026	1	1	2	2	3	3	4	4	5
80	9031	9036	9042	9047	9053	9058	9063	9069	9074	9079	1	1	2	2	3	3	4	4	5
81	9085	9090	9096	9101	9106	9112	9117	9122	9128	9133	1	1	2	2	3	3	4	4	5
82	9138	9143	9149	9154	9159	9165	9170	9175	9180	9186	1	1	2	2	3	3	4	4	5
83	9191	9196	9201	9206	9212	9217	9222	9227	9232	9238	1	1	2	2	3	3	4	4	5
84	9243	9248	9253	9258	9263	9269	9274	9279	9284	9289	1	1	2	2	3	3	4	4	5
85	9294	9299	9304	9309	9315	9320	9325	9330	9335	9340	1	1	2	2	3	3	4	4	5
86	9345	9350	9355	9360	9365	9370	9375	9380	9385	9390	1	1	2	2	3	3	4	4	5
87	9395	9400	9405	9410	9415	9420	9425	9430	9435	9440	0	1	1	2	2	3	3	4	4
88	9445	9450	9455	9460	9465	9469	9474	9479	9484	9489	0	1	1	2	2	3	3	4	4
89	9494	9499	9504	9509	9513	9518	9523	9528	9533	9538	0	1	1	2	2	3	3	4	4
90	9542	9547	9552	9557	9562	9566	9571	9576	9581	9586	0	1	1	2	2	3	3	4	4
91	9590	9595	9600	9605	9609	9614	9619	9624	9628	9633	0	1	1	2	2	3	3	4	4
92	9638	9643	9647	9652	9657	9661	9666	9671	9675	9680	0	1	1	2	2	3	3	4	4
93	9685	9689	9694	9699	9703	9708	9713	9717	9722	9727	0	1	1	2	2	3	3	4	4
94	9731	9736	9741	9745	9750	9754	9759	9763	9768	9773	0	1	1	2	2	3	3	4	4
95	9777	9782	9786	9791	9795	9800	9805	9809	9814	9818	0	1	1	2	2	3	3	4	4
96	9823	9827	9832	9836	9841	9845	9850	9854	9859	9863	0	1	1	2	2	3	3	4	4
97	9868	9872	9877	9881	9886	9890	9894	9899	9903	9908	0	1	1	2	2	3	3	4	4
98	9912	9917	9921	9926	9930	9934	9939	9943	9948	9952	0	1	1	2	2	3	3	4	4
99	9956	9961	9965	9969	9974	9978	9983	9987	9991	9996	0	1	1	2	2	3	3	3	4

Trigonometric functions

Angle θ Degrees Radians		$\cos \theta$	$\sin \theta$	$\tan \theta$	$\sec \theta$	$\csc \theta$	$\cot \theta$		
0° 00′	.0000	1.0000	.0000	.0000	1.000	No value	No value	1.5708	90° 00′
10	029	000	029	029	000	343.8	343.8	679	50
20	058	000	058	058	000	171.9	171.9	650	40
30	087	1.0000	087	087	000	114.6	114.6	621	30
40	116	.9999	116	116	000	85.95	85.94	592	20
50	145	999	145	145	000	68.76	68.75	563	10
1° 00′	.0175	.9998	.0175	.0175	1.000	57.30	57.29	1.5533	89° 00′
10	204	998	204	204	000	49.11	49.10	504	50
20	233	997	233	233	000	42.98	42.96	475	40
30	262	997	262	262	000	38.20	38.19	446	30
40	291	996	291	291	000	34.38	34.37	417	20
50	320	995	320	320	001	31.26	31.24	388	10
2° 00′	.0349	.9994	.0349	.0349	1.001	28.65	28.64	1.5359	88° 00′
10	378	993	378	378	001	26.45	26.43	330	50
20	407	992	407	407	001	24.56	24.54	301	40
30	436	990	436	437	001	22.93	22.90	272	30
40	465	989	465	466	001	21.49	21.47	243	20
50	495	988	494	495	001	20.23	20.21	213	10
3° 00′	.0524	.9986	.0523	.0524	1.001	19.11	19.08	1.5184	87° 00′
10	553	985	552	553	002	18.10	18.07	155	50
20	582	983	581	582	002	17.20	17.17	126	40
30	611	981	610	612	002	16.38	16.35	097	30
40	640	980	640	641	002	15.64	15.60	068	20
50	669	978	669	670	002	14.96	14.92	039	10
4° 00′	.0698	.9976	.0698	.0699	1.002	14.34	14.30	1.5010	86° 00′
10	727	974	727	729	003	13.76	13.73	981	50
20	765	971	756	758	003	13.23	13.20	952	40
30	785	969	785	787	003	12.75	12.71	923	30
40	814	967	814	816	003	12.29	12.25	893	20
50	844	964	843	846	004	11.87	11.83	864	10
5° 00′	.0873	.9962	.0872	.0875	1.004	11.47	11.43	1.4835	85° 00′
10	902	959	901	904	004	11.10	11.06	806	50
20	931	957	929	934	004	10.76	10.71	777	40
30	960	954	958	963	005	10.43	10.39	748	30
40	.0989	951	.0987	.0992	005	10.13	10.08	719	20
50	.1018	948	.1016	.1022	005	9.839	9.788	690	10
6° 00′	.1047	.9945	.1045	.1051	1.006	9.567	9.514	1.4661	84° 00′
10	076	942	074	080	006	9.309	9.255	632	50
20	105	939	103	110	006	9.065	9.010	603	40
30	134	936	132	139	006	8.834	8.777	573	30
40	164	932	161	169	007	8.614	8.556	544	20
50	193	929	190	198	007	8.405	8.345	515	10
7° 00′	.1222	.9925	.1219	.1228	1.008	8.206	8.144	1.4486	83° 00′
10	251	922	248	257	008	8.016	7.953	457	50
20	280	918	276	287	008	7.834	7.770	428	40
30	309	914	305	317	009	7.661	7.596	399	30
40	338	911	334	346	009	7.496	7.429	370	20
50	367	907	363	376	009	7.337	7.269	341	10
8° 00′	.1396	.9903	.1392	.1405	1.010	7.185	7.115	1.4312	82° 00′
		$\sin \theta$	$\cos \theta$	$\cot \theta$	$\csc \theta$	$\sec \theta$	$\tan \theta$	Radians Degrees Angle θ	

Trigonometric functions (continued)

Angle θ Degrees	Angle θ Radians	cos θ	sin θ	tan θ	sec θ	csc θ	cot θ		
8° 00′	.1396	.9903	.1392	.1405	1.010	7.185	7.115	1.4312	82° 00′
10	425	899	421	435	010	7.040	6.968	283	50
20	454	894	449	465	011	6.900	827	254	40
30	484	890	478	495	011	765	691	224	30
40	513	886	507	524	012	636	561	195	20
50	542	881	536	554	012	512	435	166	10
9° 00′	.1571	.9877	.1564	.1584	1.012	6.392	6.314	1.4137	81° 00′
10	600	872	593	614	013	277	197	108	50
20	629	868	622	644	013	166	6.084	079	40
30	658	863	650	673	014	6.059	5.976	050	30
40	687	858	679	703	014	5.955	871	1.4021	20
50	716	853	708	733	015	855	769	1.3992	10
10° 00′	.1745	.9848	.1736	.1763	1.015	5.759	5.671	1.3963	80° 00′
10	774	843	765	793	016	665	576	934	50
20	804	838	794	823	016	575	485	904	40
30	833	833	822	853	017	487	396	875	30
40	862	827	851	883	018	403	309	846	20
50	891	822	880	914	018	320	226	817	10
11° 00′	.1920	.9816	.1908	.1944	1.019	5.241	5.145	1.3788	79° 00′
10	949	811	937	.1974	019	164	5.066	759	50
20	.1978	805	965	.2004	020	089	4.989	730	40
30	.2007	799	.1994	035	020	5.016	915	701	30
40	036	793	.2022	065	021	4.945	843	672	20
50	065	787	051	095	022	876	773	643	10
12° 00′	.2094	.9781	.2079	.2126	1.022	4.810	4.705	1.3614	78° 00′
10	123	775	108	156	023	745	638	584	50
20	153	769	136	186	024	682	574	555	40
30	182	763	164	217	024	620	511	526	30
40	211	757	193	247	025	560	449	497	20
50	240	750	221	278	026	502	390	468	10
13° 00′	.2269	.9744	.2250	.2309	1.026	4.445	4.331	1.3439	77° 00′
10	298	737	278	339	027	390	275	410	50
20	327	730	306	370	028	336	219	381	40
30	356	724	334	401	028	284	165	352	30
40	385	717	363	432	029	232	113	323	20
50	414	710	391	462	030	182	061	294	10
14° 00′	.2443	.9703	.2419	.2493	1.031	4.134	4.011	1.3265	76° 00′
10	473	696	447	524	031	086	3.962	235	50
20	502	689	476	555	032	4.039	914	206	40
30	531	681	504	586	033	3.994	867	177	30
40	560	674	532	617	034	950	821	148	20
50	589	667	560	648	034	906	776	119	10
15° 00′	.2618	.9659	.2588	.2679	1.035	3.864	3.732	1.3090	75° 00′
10	647	652	616	711	036	822	689	061	50
20	676	644	644	742	037	782	647	032	40
30	705	636	672	773	038	742	606	1.3003	30
40	734	628	700	805	039	703	566	1.2974	20
50	763	621	728	836	039	665	526	945	10
16° 00′	.2793	.9613	.2756	.2867	1.040	3.628	3.487	1.2915	74° 00′

		sin θ	cos θ	cot θ	csc θ	sec θ	tan θ	Radians	Degrees
								Angle θ	

Trigonometric functions (continued)

Angle Degrees	Radians	cos θ	sin θ	tan θ	sec θ	csc θ	cot θ		
16° 00′	.2793	.9613	.2756	.2867	1.040	3.628	3.487	1.2915	74° 00′
10	822	605	784	899	041	592	450	886	50
20	851	596	812	931	042	556	412	857	40
30	880	588	840	962	043	521	376	828	30
40	909	580	868	.2944	044	487	340	799	20
50	938	572	896	.3026	045	453	305	770	10
17° 00′	.2967	.9563	.2924	.3057	1.046	3.420	3.271	1.2741	73° 00′
10	.2996	555	952	089	047	388	237	712	50
20	.3025	546	.2979	121	048	357	204	683	40
30	054	537	.3007	153	048	326	172	654	30
40	083	528	035	185	049	295	140	625	20
50	113	520	062	217	050	265	108	595	10
18° 00′	.3142	.9511	.3090	.3249	1.051	3.236	3.078	1.2566	72° 00′
10	171	502	118	281	052	207	047	537	50
20	200	492	145	314	053	179	3.018	508	40
30	229	483	173	346	054	152	2.989	479	30
40	258	474	201	378	056	124	960	450	20
50	287	465	228	411	057	098	932	421	10
19° 00′	.3316	.9455	.3256	.3443	1.058	3.072	2.904	1.2392	71° 00′
10	345	446	283	476	059	046	877	363	50
20	374	436	311	508	060	3.021	850	334	40
30	403	426	338	541	061	2.996	824	305	30
40	432	417	365	574	062	971	798	275	20
50	462	407	393	607	063	947	773	246	10
20° 00′	.3491	.9397	.3420	.3640	.1064	2.924	2.747	1.2217	70° 00′
10	520	387	448	673	065	901	723	188	50
20	549	377	475	706	066	878	699	159	40
30	578	367	502	739	068	855	675	130	30
40	607	356	529	772	069	833	651	101	20
50	636	346	557	805	070	812	628	072	10
21° 00′	.3665	.9336	.3584	.3839	1.071	2.790	2.605	1.2043	69° 00′
10	694	325	611	872	072	769	583	1.2014	50
20	723	315	638	906	074	749	560	1.1985	40
30	752	304	665	939	075	729	539	956	30
40	782	293	692	.3973	076	709	517	926	20
50	811	283	719	.4006	077	689	496	897	10
22° 00′	.3840	.9272	.3746	.4040	1.079	2.669	2.475	1.1868	68° 00′
10	869	261	773	074	080	650	455	839	50
20	898	250	800	108	081	632	434	810	40
30	927	239	827	142	082	613	414	781	30
40	956	228	854	176	084	595	394	752	20
50	985	216	881	210	085	577	375	723	10
23° 00′	.4014	.9205	.3907	.4245	1.086	2.559	2.356	1.1694	67° 00′
10	043	194	934	279	088	542	337	665	50
20	072	182	961	314	089	525	318	636	40
30	102	171	.3987	348	090	508	300	606	30
40	131	159	.4014	383	092	491	282	577	20
50	160	147	041	417	093	475	264	548	10
24° 00′	.4189	.9135	.4067	.4452	1.095	2.459	2.246	1.1519	66° 00′

		sin θ	cos θ	cot θ	csc θ	sec θ	tan θ	Radians	Degrees
								Angle θ	

Angle θ Degrees	Radians	cos θ	sin θ	tan θ	sec θ	csc θ	cot θ		
24° 00′	.4189	.9135	.4067	.4452	1.095	2.459	2.246	1.1519	66° 00′
10	218	124	094	487	096	443	229	490	50
20	247	112	120	522	097	427	211	461	40
30	276	100	147	557	099	411	194	432	30
40	305	088	173	592	100	396	177	403	20
50	334	075	200	628	102	381	161	374	10
25° 00′	.4363	.9063	.4226	.4663	1.103	2.366	2.145	1.1345	65° 00′
10	392	051	253	699	105	352	128	316	50
20	422	038	279	734	106	337	112	286	40
30	451	026	305	770	108	323	097	257	30
40	480	013	331	806	109	309	081	228	20
50	509	.9001	358	841	111	295	066	199	10
26° 00′	.4538	.8988	.4384	.4877	1.113	2.281	2.050	1.1170	64° 00′
10	567	975	410	913	114	268	035	141	50
20	596	962	436	950	116	254	020	112	40
30	625	949	462	.4986	117	241	2.006	083	30
40	654	936	488	.5022	119	228	1.991	054	20
50	683	923	514	059	121	215	977	1.1025	10
27° 00′	.4712	.8910	.4540	.5095	1.122	2.203	1.963	1.0996	63° 00′
10	741	897	566	132	124	190	949	966	50
20	771	884	592	169	126	178	935	937	40
30	800	870	617	206	127	166	921	908	30
40	829	857	643	243	129	154	907	879	20
50	858	843	669	280	131	142	894	850	10
28° 00′	.4887	.8829	.4695	.5317	1.133	2.130	1.881	1.0821	62° 00′
10	916	816	720	354	134	118	868	792	50
20	945	802	746	392	136	107	855	763	40
30	.4974	788	772	430	138	096	842	734	30
40	.5003	774	797	467	140	085	829	705	20
50	032	760	823	505	142	074	816	676	10
29° 00′	.5061	.8746	.4848	.5543	1.143	2.063	1.804	1.0647	61° 00′
10	091	732	874	581	145	052	792	617	50
20	120	718	899	619	147	041	780	588	40
30	149	704	924	658	149	031	767	559	30
40	178	689	950	696	151	020	756	530	20
50	207	675	.4975	735	153	010	744	501	10
30° 00′	.5236	.8660	.5000	.5774	1.155	2.000	1.732	1.0472	60° 00′
10	265	646	025	812	157	1.990	720	443	50
20	294	631	050	851	159	980	709	414	40
30	323	616	075	890	161	970	698	385	30
40	352	601	100	930	163	961	686	356	20
50	381	587	125	.5969	165	951	675	327	10
31° 00′	.5411	.8572	.5150	.6009	1.167	1.942	1.664	1.0297	59° 00′
10	440	557	175	048	169	932	653	268	50
20	469	542	200	088	171	923	643	239	40
30	498	526	225	128	173	914	632	210	30
40	527	511	250	168	175	905	621	181	20
50	556	496	275	208	177	896	611	152	10
32° 00′	.5585	.8480	.5299	.6249	1.179	1.887	1.600	1.0123	58° 00′
		sin θ	cos θ	cot θ	csc θ	sec θ	tan θ	Radians	Degrees
								Angle θ	

Trigonometric functions (continued)

Angle θ Degrees	Radians	cos θ	sin θ	tan θ	sec θ	csc θ	cot θ		
32° 00′	.5585	.8480	.5299	.6249	1.179	1.887	1.600	1.0123	58° 00′
10	614	465	324	289	181	878	590	094	50
20	643	450	348	330	184	870	580	065	40
30	672	434	373	371	186	861	570	036	30
40	701	418	398	412	188	853	560	1.0007	20
50	730	403	422	453	190	844	550	.9977	10
33° 00′	.5760	.8387	.5446	.6494	1.192	1.836	1.540	.9948	57° 00′
10	789	371	471	536	195	828	530	919	50
20	818	355	495	577	197	820	520	890	40
30	847	339	519	619	199	812	511	861	30
40	876	323	544	661	202	804	501	832	20
50	905	307	568	703	204	796	492	803	10
34° 00′	.5934	.8290	.5592	.6745	1.206	1.788	1.483	.9774	56° 00′
10	963	274	616	787	209	781	473	745	50
20	.5992	258	640	830	211	773	464	716	40
30	.6021	241	664	873	213	766	455	687	30
40	050	225	688	916	216	758	446	657	20
50	080	208	712	.6959	218	751	437	628	10
35° 00′	.6109	.8192	.5736	.7002	1.221	1.743	1.428	.9599	55° 00′
10	138	175	760	046	223	736	419	570	50
20	167	158	783	089	226	729	411	541	40
30	196	141	807	133	228	722	402	512	30
40	225	124	831	177	231	715	393	483	20
50	254	107	854	221	233	708	385	454	10
36° 00′	.6283	.8090	.5878	.7265	1.236	1.701	1.376	.9425	54° 00′
10	312	073	901	310	239	695	368	396	50
20	341	056	925	355	241	688	360	367	40
30	370	039	948	400	244	681	351	338	30
40	400	021	972	445	247	675	343	308	20
50	429	.8004	.5995	490	249	668	335	279	10
37° 00′	.6458	.7986	.6018	.7536	1.252	1.662	1.327	.9250	53° 00′
10	487	966	041	581	255	655	319	221	50
20	516	951	065	627	258	649	311	192	40
30	545	934	088	673	260	643	303	163	30
40	574	916	111	720	263	636	295	134	20
50	603	898	134	766	266	630	288	105	10
38° 00′	.6632	.7880	.6157	.7813	1.269	1.624	1.280	.9076	52° 00′
10	661	862	180	860	272	618	272	047	50
20	690	844	202	907	275	612	265	.9018	40
30	720	826	225	.7954	278	606	257	.8988	30
40	749	808	248	.8002	281	601	250	959	20
50	778	790	271	050	284	595	242	930	10
39° 00′	.6807	.7771	.6293	.8098	1.287	1.589	1.235	.8901	51° 00′
10	836	753	316	146	290	583	228	872	50
20	865	735	338	195	293	578	220	843	40
30	894	716	361	243	296	572	213	814	30
40	923	698	383	292	299	567	206	785	20
50	952	679	406	342	302	561	199	756	10
40° 00′	.6981	.7660	.6428	.8391	1.305	1.556	1.192	.8727	50° 00′
		sin θ	cos θ	cot θ	csc θ	sec θ	tan θ	Radians	Degrees
								Angle θ	

Trigonometric functions (continued)

Angle θ Degrees	Angle θ Radians	$\cos \theta$	$\sin \theta$	$\tan \theta$	$\sec \theta$	$\csc \theta$	$\cot \theta$		
40° 00′	.6981	.7660	.6428	.8391	1.305	1.556	1.192	.8727	50° 00′
10	.7010	642	450	441	309	550	185	698	50
20	039	623	472	491	312	545	178	668	40
30	069	604	494	541	315	540	171	639	30
40	098	585	517	591	318	535	164	610	20
50	127	566	539	642	322	529	157	581	10
41° 00′	.7156	.7547	.6561	.8693	1.325	1.524	1.150	.8552	49° 00′
10	185	528	583	744	328	519	144	523	50
20	214	509	604	796	332	514	137	494	40
30	243	490	626	847	335	509	130	465	30
40	272	470	648	899	339	504	124	436	20
50	301	451	670	.8952	342	499	117	407	10
42° 00′	.7330	.7431	.6691	.9004	1.346	1.494	1.111	.8378	48° 00′
10	359	412	713	057	349	490	104	348	50
20	389	392	734	110	353	485	098	319	40
30	418	373	756	163	356	480	091	290	30
40	447	353	777	217	360	476	085	261	20
50	476	333	799	271	364	471	079	232	10
43° 00′	.7505	.7314	.6820	.9325	1.367	1.466	1.072	.8203	47° 00′
10	534	294	841	380	371	462	066	174	50
20	563	274	862	435	375	457	060	145	40
30	592	254	884	490	379	453	054	116	30
40	621	234	905	545	382	448	048	087	20
50	650	214	926	601	386	444	042	058	10
44° 00′	.7679	.7193	.6947	.9657	1.390	1.440	1.036	.8029	46° 00′
10	709	173	967	713	394	435	030	.7999	50
20	738	153	.6988	770	398	431	024	970	40
30	767	133	.7009	827	402	427	018	941	30
40	796	112	030	884	406	423	012	912	20
50	825	092	050	.9942	410	418	006	883	10
45° 00′	.7854	.7071	.7071	1.000	1.414	1.414	1.000	.7854	45° 00′

		$\sin \theta$	$\cos \theta$	$\cot \theta$	$\csc \theta$	$\sec \theta$	$\tan \theta$	Radians	Degrees
								Angle θ	

Abbreviations for engineering terms[1]

absolute .... abs
acre .... spell out
acre-foot .... acre-ft
air horsepower .... air hp
alternating-current (as adjective) .... a-c
ampere .... amp
ampere-hour .... amp-hr
amplitude, an elliptic function ...... am.
Angstrom unit .... Å
antilogarithm .... antilog
atmosphere .... atm
atomic weight .... at. wt
average .... avg
avoirdupois .... avdp
azimuth .... az or α

barometer .... bar.
barrel .... bbl
Baumé .... Bé
board feet (feet board measure) .... fbm
boiler pressure .... spell out
boiling point .... bp
brake horsepower .... bhp
brake horsepower-hour .... bhp-hr
Brinell hardness number .... Bhn
British thermal unit .... Btu or B
bushel .... bu

calorie .... cal
candle c
candle-hour .... c-hr
candlepower .... cp
cent .... c or ϕ
center to center .... c to c
centigram .... cg
centiliter cl
centimeter .... cm
centimeter-gram-second (system) .... cgs
chemical .... chem
chemically pure .... cp
circular .... cir
circular mils .... cir mils
coefficient .... coef
cologarithm .... colog
conductivity .... cond
constant .... const

cord .... cd
cosecant .... csc
cosine .... cos
cosine of the amplitude, an elliptic
    function .... cn
cotangent .... cot
coulomb .... spell out
cubic .... cu
cubic centimeter .... cu cm, cm^3
cubic feet per minute .... cfm or ft^3/min
cubic feet per second ...... cfs or ft^3/sec
cubic foot .... cu ft or ft^3
cubic inch .... cu in. or in.^{3}
cubic meter .... cu m or m^3
cubic micron ...... cu μ or cu mu or μ^3
cubic millimeter .... cu mm or mm^3
cubic yard .... cu yd or yd^3
cylinder .... cyl

decibel .... db
degree .... deg or °
degree Celsius C
degree Fahrenheit .... F
degree Kelvin .... K
degree Réaumur .... R
diameter .... diam
direct-current (as adjective) .... d-c
dollar .... $
dozen .... doz
dram .... dr
dyne .... spell out

efficiency .... eff
electric .... elec
electromotive force .... emf
elevation .... el
equation .... eq
external .... ext

farad .... spell out or f
feet board measure (board feet) .... fbm
feet per minute .... ft/min or fpm
feet per second .... ft/sec or fps
fluid .... fl
foot .... ft
foot-candle .... ft-c

[1] This list of abbreviations is revised from *Abbreviations for Scientific and Engineering Terms*, approved by the American Standards Association, and published by the American Society of Mechanical Engineers, New York City.

Abbreviations for engineering terms (continued)

foot-Lambert . . . . ft-L
foot-pound . . . . ft-lb
foot-second (see cubic feet per second)
freezing point . . . . fp
fusion point . . . . fnp

gallon . . . . gal
gallons per minute . . . . . . gal/min or gpm
gallons per second . . . . gal/sec or gps
gram . . . . g
gram-calorie . . . . g-cal

haversine . . . . hav
hectare . . . . ha
henry . . . . h
high-pressure (adjective) . . . . h-p
hogshead . . . . hhd
horsepower . . . . hp
horsepower-hour . . . . hp-hr
hour . . . . hr
hundred C
hundredweight (112 lb) . . . . cwt
hyperbolic cosine . . . . cosh
hyberbolic sine . . . . sinh
hyperbolic tangent . . . . tanh

inch . . . . in.
inch-pound . . . . in.-lb
inches per second . . . . in./sec or ips
indicated horsepower . . . . ihp
indicated horsepower-hour . . . . ihp-hr
inside diameter . . . . ID
internal . . . . int

joule . . . . j

kilocalorie . . . . kcal
kilogram . . . . kg
kilogram-calorie . . . . kg-cal
kilogram-meter . . . . kg-m
kilograms per cubic meter
. . . . kg per cu m or kg/m³
kilograms per second . . . . kg/sec or kgps
kiloliter . . . . kl
kilometer . . . . km
kilometers per second . . . . kmps
kilovolt . . . . kv
kilovolt-ampere . . . . kva
kilowatt . . . . kw
kilowatthour . . . . kwhr

latitude . . . . lat or ϕ
linear foot . . . . lin ft
liter l
logarithm (common) . . . . log
logarithm (natural) . . . . $\log_\varepsilon$ or ln
longitude . . . . long. or λ
low-pressure (as adjective) . . . . l-p
lumen l
lumen-hour . . . . l-hr
lumens per watt . . . . lpw

mass . . . . m or spell out
maximum . . . . max
mean effective pressure . . . . mep
melting point . . . . mp
meter . . . . m
meter-kilogram . . . . m-kg
microampere . . . . μa or mu a
microfarad . . . . μf
microinch . . . . μin.
micromicrofarad . . . . $\mu\mu$f
micromicron . . . . $\mu\mu$ or mu mu
micron . . . . μ or mu
microvolt . . . . μv
microwatt . . . . μw or mu w
mile . . . . mi or spell out
miles per hour . . . . mi/hr or mph
miles per hour per second
. . . . mi/hr/sec or mphps
milliampere . . . . ma
milligram . . . . mg
millihenry . . . . mh
millilambert . . . . mL
milliliter . . . . ml
millimeter . . . . mm
millimicron . . . . mμ or m mu
million . . . . spell out
million gallons per day . . . . mgd
millivolt . . . . mv
minute . . . . min
minute (angular measure) . . . . '
mole . . . . spell out
molecular weight . . . . mol. wt
month . . . . spell out

National Electrical Code . . . . NEC
newton . . . . n

ohm . . . . spell out or Ω
ohm-centimeter . . . . ohm-cm

ounce	oz
ounce-foot	oz-ft
ounce-inch	oz-in.
outside diameter	OD
parts per million	ppm
peck	pk
penny (pence)	d
pennyweight	dwt
pint	pt
pound	lb
pound-foot	lb-ft
pound-inch	lb-in.
pound sterling	£
pounds per brake horsepower-hour	lb/bph-hr or lb per bhp-hr
pounds per cubic foot	lb/ft³ or lb per cu ft
pounds per square foot	lb/ft² or psf
pounds per square inch	lb/in.² or psi
pounds per square inch absolute	lb/in. abs. or psia
power factor	spell out or pf
quart	qt
radian	rad or spell out
revolutions per minute	rev/min or rpm
revolutions per second	rev/sec or rps
rod	spell out
root mean square	rms
secant	sec
second	sec
second (angular measure)	″

shaft horsepower	shp
shilling	s
sine	sin
specific gravity	sp gr
specific heat	sp ht
square	sq
square centimeter	sq cm or cm²
square foot	ft² or sq ft
square inch	in.² or sq in.
square kilometer	sq km or km²
square meter	sq m or m²
square micron	sq μ or sq mu or μ²
square millimeter	sq mm or mm²
square root of mean square	rms
standard	std
tangent	tan
temperature	temp
thousand	M
thousand pound	kip
ton	spell out
versed sine	vers
volt	v
volt-ampere	va
volt-coulomb	spell out
watt	w
watthour	whr
watts per candle	wpc
week	spell out
weight	wt
yard	yd
year	yr

APPENDIX V

Code of ethics for engineers[1]

Preamble

The Engineer, to uphold and advance the honor and dignity of the engineering profession and in keeping with high standards of ethical conduct:

☐ Will be honest and impartial, and will serve with devotion his employer, his clients, and the public;

☐ Will strive to increase the competence and prestige of the engineering profession;

☐ Will use his knowledge and skill for the advancement of human welfare.

Section 1 The Engineer will be guided in all his professional relations by the highest standards of integrity, and will act in professional matters for each client or employer as a faithful agent or trustee.

a. He will be realistic and honest in all estimates, reports, statements, and testimony.

b. He will admit and accept his own errors when proven obviously wrong and refrain from distorting or altering the facts in an attempt to justify his decision.

c. He will advise his client or employer when he believes a project will not be successful.

d. He will not accept outside employment to the detriment of his regular work or interest, or without the consent of his employer.

e. He will not attempt to attract an engineer from another employer by unfair methods.

f. He will not actively participate in strikes, picket lines, or other collective coercive action.

[1] Adopted by the National Society of Professional Engineers.

600

Section 2 The Engineer will have proper regard for the safety, health, and welfare of the public in the performance of his professional duties. If his engineering judgment is overruled by nontechnical authority, he will clearly point out the consequences. He will notify the proper authority of any observed conditions which endanger public safety and health.

a. He will regard his duty to the public welfare as paramount.

b. He shall seek opportunities to be of constructive service in civic affairs and work for the advancement of the safety, health and well-being of his community.

c. He will not complete, sign, or seal plans and/or specifications that are not of a design safe to the public health and welfare and in conformity with accepted engineering standards. If the client or employer insists on such unprofessional conduct, he shall notify the proper authorities and withdraw from further service on the project.

Section 3 The Engineer will avoid all conduct or practice likely to discredit or unfavorably reflect upon the dignity or honor of the profession.

a. The Engineer shall not advertise his professional services but may utilize the following means of identification:

1. Professional cards and listings in recognized and dignified publications, provided they are consistent in size and are in a section of the publication regularly devoted to such professional cards and listings. The information displayed must be restricted to firm name, address, telephone number, appropriate symbol, name of principal participants and the fields of practice in which the firm is qualified.

2. Signs on equipment, offices and at the site of projects for which he renders services, limited to firm name, address, telephone number and type of services, as appropriate.

3. Brochures, business cards, letterheads and other factual representations of experience, facilities, personnel and capacity to render service, providing the same are not misleading relative to the extent of participation in the projects cited, and provided the same are not indiscriminately distributed.

4. Listings in the classified section of telephone directories, limited to name, address, telephone number and specialties in which the firm is qualified.

b. The Engineer may advertise for recruitment of personnel in appropriate publications or by special distribution. The information presented must be displayed in a dignified manner, restricted to firm name, address, telephone number, appropriate symbol, name of principal participants, the fields of practice in which the firm is qualified and factual descriptions of positions available, qualifications required and benefits available.

c. The Engineer may prepare articles for the lay or technical press which are factual, dignified and free from ostentations or laudatory implications. Such articles shall not imply other than his direct participation in the work described unless credit is given to others for their share of the work.

d. The Engineer may extend permission for his name to be used in commercial advertisements, such as may be published by manufacturers, contractors, material suppliers, etc., only by means of a modest dignified notation acknowledging his participation and the scope thereof in the project or product described. Such permission shall not include public endorsement of proprietary products.

e. The Engineer will not allow himself to be listed for employment using exaggerated statements of his qualifications.

Section 4 The Engineer will endeavor to extend public knowledge and appreciation of engineering and its achievements and to protect the engineering profession from misrepresentation and misunderstanding.

a. He shall not issue statements, criticisms, or arguments on matters connected with public policy which are inspired or paid for by private interests, unless he indicates on whose behalf he is making the statement.

Section 5 The Engineer will express an opinion of an engineering subject only when founded on adequate knowledge and honest conviction.

a. The Engineer will insist on the use of facts in reference to an engineering project in a group discussion, public forum or publication of articles.

Section 6 The Engineer will undertake engineering assigments for which he will be responsible only when qualified by training or experience; and he will engage, or advise engaging, experts and specialists whenever the client's or employer's interests are best served by such service.

Section 7 The Engineer will not disclose confidential information concerning the business affairs or technical processes of any present or former client or employer without his consent.

a. While in the employ of others, he will not enter promotional efforts or negotiations for work or make arrangements for other employment as a principal or to practice in connection with a specific project for which he has gained particular and specialized knowledge without the consent of all interested parties.

Section 8 The Engineer will endeavor to avoid a conflict of interest with his employer or client, but when unavoidable, the Engineer shall fully disclose the circumstances to his employer or client.

a. The Engineer will inform his client or employer of any business connections, interests, or circumstances which may be deemed as influencing his judgment or the quality of his services to his client or employer.

b. When in public service as a member, advisor, or employee of a governmental body or department, an engineer shall not participate in considerations or actions with respect to services provided by him or his organization in private engineering practice.

c. An engineer shall not solicit or accept an engineering contract from a governmental body on which a principal or officer of his organization serves as a member.

Section 9 The Engineer will uphold the principle of appropriate and adequate compensation for those engaged in engineering work.

a. He will not undertake or agree to perform any engineering service on a free basis, except for civic, charitable, religious, or eleemosynary nonprofit organizations when the professional services are advisory in nature.

b. He will not undertake work at a fee or salary below the accepted standards of the profession in the area.

c. He will not accept remuneration from either an employee or employment agency for giving employment.

d. When hiring other engineers, he shall offer a salary according to the engineer's qualifications and the recognized standards in the particular geographical area.

e. If, in sales employ, he will not offer, or give engineering consultation, or designs, or advice other than specifically applying to the equipment being sold.

Section 10 The Engineer will not accept compensation, financial or otherwise, from more than one interested party for the same service, or for services pertaining to the same work, unless there is full disclosure to and consent of all interested parties.

a. He will not accept financial or other considerations, including free engineering designs, from material or equipment suppliers for specifying their product.

b. He will not accept commissions or allowances, directly or indirectly, from contractors of other parties dealing with his clients or employer in connection with work for which he is responsible.

Section 11 The Engineer will not compete unfairly with another engineer by attempting to obtain employment or advancement or professional engagements by competitive bidding, by taking advantage of a salaried position, by criticizing other engineers, or by other improper or questionable methods.

a. The Engineer will not attempt to supplant another engineer in a particular employment after becoming aware that definite steps have been taken toward the other's employment.

b He will not offer to pay, either directly or indirectly, any commission, political contribution, or a gift, or other consideration in order to secure work, exclusive of securing salaried positions through employment agencies.

c. He shall not solicit or submit engineering proposals on the basis of competitive bidding. Competitive bidding for professional engineering services is defined as the formal or informal submission, or receipt, of verbal or written estimates of cost or proposals in terms of dollars, man days of work required, percentage of construction cost, or any other measure of compensation whereby the prospective client may compare engineering services on a price basis prior to the time that one engineer, or one engineering organization, has been selected for negotiations. The disclosure of recommended fee schedules prepared by various engineering societies is not considered to constitute competitive bidding. An engineer requested to submit a fee proposal or bid prior to the selection of an engineer or firm subject to the negotiation of a satisfactory contract, shall attempt to have the procedure changed to conform to ethical practices, but if not successful he shall withdraw from consideration for the proposed work. These principles shall be applied by the Engineer in obtaining the services of other professionals.

d. An Engineer shall not request, propose, or accept a professional commission on a contingent basis under circumstances in which his professional judgment may be comprised, or when a contingency provision is used as a device for promoting or securing a professional commission.

e. While in a salaried position, he will accept part-time engineering work only at a salary or fee not less than that recognized as standard in the area.

f. An engineer will not use equipment, supplies, laboratory, or office facilities of his employer to carry on outside private practice without consent.

Section 12 The Engineer will not attempt to injure, maliciously or falsely, directly or indirectly, the professional reputation, prospects, practice or employment of another engineer, nor will he indiscriminately criticize another engineer's work in public. If he believes that another engineer is guilty of unethical or illegal practice, he shall present such information to the proper authority for action.

a. An Engineer in private practice will not review the work of another engineer for the same client, except with the knowledge of such engineer, or unless the connection of such engineer with the work has been terminated.

b. An Engineer in governmental, industrial or educational employ is entitled to review and evaluate the work of other engineers when so required by his employment duties.

c. An Engineer in sales or industrial employ is entitled to make engineering comparisons of his products with products by other suppliers.

Section 13 The Engineer will not associate with or allow the use of his name by an enterprise of questionable character, nor will he become professionally associated with engineers who do not conform to ethical practices, or with persons not legally qualified to render the professional services for which the association is intended.

a. He will conform with registration laws in his practice of engineering.

b. He will not use association with a nonengineer, a corporation, or partnership, as a "cloak" for unethical acts, but must accept personal responsibility for his professional acts.

Section 14 The Engineer will give credit for engineering work to those to whom credit is due, and will recognize the proprietary interests of others.

a. Whenever possible, he will name the person or persons who may be individually responsible for designs, inventions, writings, or other accomplishments.

b. When an engineer uses designs supplied to him by a client, the designs remain the property of the client and should not be duplicated by the Engineer for others without express permission.

c. Before undertaking work for others in connection with which he may make improvements, plans, designs, inventions, or other records which may justify copyrights or patents, the Engineer should enter into a positive agreement regarding the ownership.

d. Designs, data, records, and notes made by an engineer and referring exclusively to his employer's work are his employer's property.

Section 15 The Engineer will cooperate in extending the effectiveness of the profession by interchanging information and experience with other engineers and students, and will endeavor to provide opportunity for the professional development and advancement of engineers under his supervision.

a. He will encourage his engineering employees' efforts to improve their education.

b. He will encourage engineering employees to attend and present papers at professional and technical society meetings.

c. He will urge his engineering employees to become registered at the earliest possible date.

d. He will assign a professional engineer duties of a nature to utilize his full training and experience, insofar as possible, and delegate lesser functions to subprofessionals or to technicians.

e. He will provide a prospective engineering employee with complete information on working conditions and his proposed status of employment, and after employment will keep him informed of any changes in them.

Answers to selected problems

Chapter 9

9-1. *e.* $x = 5$
  j. $x = -3$
  o. $x = 4$
  t. $x = 12$
9-2. *e.* 318.3
  j. 702.25
9-3. *e.* -8.961
  j. 0.805

9-4. *e.* $5.6856(10)^4$
  j. $-5.345(10)^2$
  o. $5.2(10)^1$
9-5. *e.* 1.55
  j. $-3.064(10)^{-6}$
  o. 1.6
9-6. *e.* $7(10)^{-2}\%$
  j. $1(10)^2\%$

9-7. *e.* $\pm2(10)^{-4}$
  j. $\pm10^{-1}$
9-10. *a.* 7.47 ft
  b. 1.89 ft
  c. 0.7% error

Chapter 10

10-1. *e.* 2.781
  j. 7.772
  o. 6.822
  t. 3.644
  y. 7.857
10-45. $8.51(10)^6$
10-50. $8.75(10)^1$
10-55. $3.79(10)^3$
10-60. $8.37(10)^5$
10-65. $4.35(10)^5$
10-70. $1.202(10)^6$
10-75. 1.095
10-80. $8.32(10)^3$
10-85. $6.06(10)^6$
10-90. $1.619(10)^6$

10-135. $2.53(10)^1$
10-140. $4.59(10)^{-1}$
10-145. $4.25(10)^4$
10-150. $5.91(10)^2$
10-155. $2.77(10)^{-1}$
10-160. $3.88(10)^{-3}$
10-165. $1.275(10)^8$
10-170. 1.278
10-175. $2.21(10)^3$
10-180. $5.96(10)^3$
10-225. $1.350(10)^1$
10-230. $1.524(10)^{-2}$
10-235. $9.54(10)^{-1}$
10-240. $1.099(10)^{-1}$
10-245. $2.87(10)^{-6}$

10-250. $1.437(10)^{-3}$
10-255. $2.93(10)^{-7}$
10-260. $2.96(10)^4$
10-265. $5.07(10)^{-1}$
10-270. 5.64
10-355. $1.430(10)^2$
10-360. $4.46(10)^{-3}$
10-365. $2.02(10)^9$
10-370. $9.98(10)^{-1}$
10-375. 1.772
10-380. $5.27(10)^{-1}$
10-385. $3.62(10)^3$
10-390. $2.53(10)^1$
10-445. $1.079(10)^5$
10-450. $1.357(10)^6$

10-455. $8.12(10)^{-7}$
10-460. 2.08
10-465. $3.26(10)^1$
10-470. $3.68(10)^2$
10-475. $5.36(10)^2$
10-480. $1.138(10)^7$
10-560. 0.978
10-565. 0.407
10-570. 0.669
10-575. 1.397
10-580. 1.028
10-585. 0.719
10-590. 1.034
10-595. 1.856
10-600. 1.061
10-605. $88.36°$
10-610. $7.25°$
10-615. 0.999
10-620. $31.8°$
10-625. $29.55°$
10-630. 0.602
10-635. 0.235
10-640. 0.897
10-645. 1.513
10-650. 1.569
10-655. 1.168
10-660. $b = 15.97$
$B = 23.5°$
10-665. $c = 4.09$
$B = 15°$

10-670. $a = 599$
$b = 1807$
10-675. $a = 677$
$a = 678$
10-730. $1.11(10)^2$
10-735. 1.331
10-740. 0.1048
10-745. 1.0352
10-750. $6.89(10)^{11}$
10-755. 0.492
10-760. 1.433
10-765. 1.0006
10-770. 0.386
10-775. 1.444
10-780. 0.044
10-785. 36
10-790. 3.89
10-795. 0.925
10-800. 1.018
10-805. -0.250
10-810. 3.51
10-815. -6.70
10-820. 4.495
10-825. -0.0026
10-830. $3.11(10)^1$
10-835. $2.73(10)^{-2}$
10-840. $3.97(10)^4$
10-845. $-1.230(10)^3$
10-850. $1.706(10)^5$
10-855. $8.53(10)^3$

10-860. $8.98(10)^7$
10-865. $9.41(10)^{-2}$
10-870. $5.62(10)^1$
10-875. $5.43(10)^3$
10-800. $2.75(10)^{-3}$
10-885. 1.776
10-890. $3.26(10)^3$
10-895. $2.45(10)^{12}$
10-900. $7.39(10)^4$
10-905. 1.049
10-910. $1.071(10)^{-1}$
10-915. $3.34(10)^1$
10-920. $3.24(10)^{-1}$
10-925. $1.071(10)^{-9}$
10-930. *a.* 1.039
b. 1.579
c. 3.69
d. 5.395
e. 17.61
f. 28.42
g. 74.21
10-935. *a.* $4.81 + j3.90$
b. $2.97 + j2.68$
c. $8.58 + j3.36$
d. $0.88 + j2.56$
10-940. *a.* $218 \, \underline{/317.4°}$
b. $100.5 \, \underline{/332.6°}$
c. $0.00803 \, \underline{/320.5°}$
d. $3.65 \, \underline{/327.4°}$

Chapter 11

11-5. $k = \dfrac{M^8 L^3}{F^4 \theta T}$

11-10. $k = \dfrac{F L^2}{Q^{1/2} M^3}$

11-15. 1.076 dynes/cm^2
11-20. $3.44(10)^8$ abhenries
11-25. $6.96(10)^4$ ft^3/hr
11-30. $2.06(10)^{-4}$
11-35. $6.4(10)^{-2}$ ft^4
11-40. Diagonal $= 1.274$ in.
11-45. $M = FL$
11-50. $r = L$

11-55. *a.* $\sigma = 1.160(10)^3$ lb/in.^{2}
b. $A = 9.48(10)^{-3}$ ft^2
c. $l = 4.12$ ft
d. $R = 9.96(10)^6$ lb/in.^{2}
11-60. *a.* $F = 49.15$ n
b. 5.01 kg
11-65. $F = 4.57(10)^9$ dynes
11-70. $m_1 = 5.97(10)^{24}$ kg
11-80. Guide was in error.
11-85. 0.278 meter/sec
11-90. $X_L = 7.11 \, \Omega$

Chapter 12

12-1. $X = 2.01913$ g
$s = \pm 0.0016$ g
$s_m = \pm 4.25(10)^{-4}$ g
Wt. $= 2.0191 \pm 0.0004$ g

12-4. $\bar{X} = 50.6$
Median $= 51$
Mode $= 55$
Graph $=$ Slight tendency to skew

Chapter 15

15-1. C.P. $= 1$–3–4–6–7–8–$9 = 21$ months

15-6. All paths are critical. No improvement is possible.

Chapter 18

18-5. $R = 6.8(10)^4$ lb
@ $10°15'$ from $4.5(10)^4$ F

18-10. $M_1 = 40.5$ lb
$M_2 = 66$ lb

18-15. $T_1 = 296$ lb
$T_2 = 296$ lb

18-20. $F_3 = 74.6$ lb
@ S $52°50'$ E

18-25. $R = 5.10$ lb
@ S $39°$ W

18-30. $M_A = 525$ lb$_f$ ft

18-35. $M_A = -3640$ lb-units
$M_D = -524$ lb-units

18-40. $R_R = 744$ lb$_f$
$R_L = 306$ lb$_f$

18-45. $R_R = 1.995(10)^4$ lb$_f$
$R_L = 1.355(10)^4$ lb$_f$

18-50. $P = 1.567(10)^3$ lb$_f$

18-55. $R = 153.1$ lb$_f$
$N = 235$ lb$_f$

18-60. $BC = 1597$ lb$_f$
$R = 1984$ lb
@ $75.5°$ above H

18-65. $R = 82.2$ lb$_f$
$F_{x \, \textcircled{A}} = 82.2$ lb$_f$
$F_{y \, \textcircled{A}} = 190$ lb$_f$

18-70. $V_2 = 9.85(10)^2$ ft/sec
$S = 3.03(10)^4$ ft

18-75. $V_2 = 1.18(10)^1$ mi/hr
$S = 3.36(10)^2$ ft

18-80. $a_1 = 2.67$ ft/sec^2
$a_2 = 2.14(10)^{-1}$ ft/sec^2
$S = 3.25$ mi

18-85. $S = 1.32(10)^2$ ft

18-90. $\theta = 16.2°$

18-95. $\omega_2 = 20.9$ rad/sec
$\omega_1 = 8.72$ rad/sec
$V = 13.08$ ft/sec

18-100. $\omega_2 = 1.690(10)^3$ rev/min
$\omega_2 = 177$ rad/sec
$\theta = 8.45(10)^1$ rev

18-105. $Wk = 990$ ft lb$_f$

18-110. $Wk = 623$ ft lb

18-115. $Wk = 2.14(10)^5$ ft lb$_f$

18-120. $V = 19.3$ mi/hr

18-125. $P = 18.65$ hp

18-130. $P = 0.61$ hp

18-135. $KE_1 = 38$ ft lb$_f$
$KE_2 = 153$ ft lb$_f$
$KE_3 = 342$ ft lb$_f$
$KE_{10} = 3810$ ft lb$_f$

18-140. $t = 1.97$ sec

18-145. 8.90 lb
9.98 lb

18-150. $Wk = 1.28(10)^5$ ft lb$_f$
$P = 10.35$ hp

18-155. $R = 300$ lb$_f$

18-160. $P = 334$ kw

18-165. B.F. $= 1310$ lb$_f$

18-175. $R_S = 370.2$ Ω
$RE = 40.1$ Ω

18-180. $V_1 = 11.2$ v
$V_2 = 21.0$ v
$V_3 = 21.0$ v
$V_4 = 18.78$ v
$I_2 = 3.05$ amp
$I_3 = 3.99$ amp
$I_4 = 7.03$ amp
$V_c = 50.9$ v

18-190. $V_B = 41.5$ v
$V_3 = 9.09$ v

18-195. $I = 13.62$ amp
$H_P = 4.02$ hp

18-200. $R_s = 4.964(10)^5$ Ω

Index